D1304120

INVERTEBRATE STRUCTURE AND FUNCTION

INVERTEBRATE

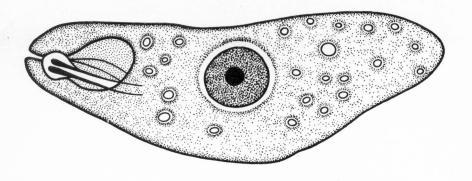

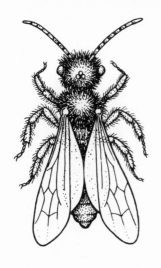

E. J. W. BARRINGTON FRS

Professor of Zoology Nottingham University

STRUCTURE AND FUNCTION

HOUGHTON MIFFLIN COMPANY · BOSTON

New York   Atlanta   Geneva, Ill.   Dallas   Palo Alto

CENTRAL METHODIST COLLEGE LIBRARY
FAYETTE, MISSOURI

Copyright © 1967 by E. J. W. Barrington

First published in Great Britain by Thomas Nelson and Sons Ltd.

Printed in Great Britain

Preface

The line traditionally drawn in zoological teaching between the vertebrates and the invertebrates is an unfortunate one: it obscures the fundamental unity that underlies the organization of living material. Of course it is possible to use the vertebrates for studying the working-out of biological principles within a compact system of closely interrelated groups. To this extent these animals are a convenient demonstration of unity in diversity; in consequence, they appeal to some students as an 'easy' group.

But the vertebrates are part of the Phylum Chordata, which contains truly invertebrate members. These in their turn are closely related to other invertebrate groups. Vertebrate studies by themselves, therefore, tell us little, if anything, of the origin of vertebrates, or of the origin of the principles of biological organization that have determined the course of their adaptive evolution. Indeed, the appeal that the vertebrates make to our anthropocentric tendencies can be dangerously deceptive. It can easily lead to over-optimistic generalization from limited data, obtained from some laboratory mammal that has nothing to recommend it for the purpose other than its convenience and its compliant behaviour.

If, therefore, we are to evaluate and exploit the dramatic advances of contemporary biology (those that are being made, for example, at the growing points of molecular and ultrastructural biology) we need as one essential condition the widest possible extension of our understanding of the principles of animal organization. This must come in large measure from invertebrate studies, and it is the purpose of this book to provide some help to students who wish to widen their viewpoint in this way. It is only too easy for them to become discouraged by the readiness with which the rich diversity of the animal kingdom can fragment into what Aldous Huxley has called, in another context, 'a quantity of mutually irrelevant happenings dotted, like so many unexplored and fantastic islands, on the face of a vast ocean of incomprehension'. I hope that this book may provide them with some protection against this occupational hazard of zoologists, and that it may make the invertebrates a little less 'difficult'.

My underlying theme is a self-evident one: that the business of animals is to stay alive until they have reproduced themselves, and that the business of zoologists is to try to understand how they do it. This understanding demands the recognition that structure and function are two indissociable aspects of animal organization, linked in patterns that have been determined by the course of events in the remote past. Those events, which can to some extent be reconstructed by deduction, and which are always worth speculating about, are reflected to the best of our ability in our schemes of animal classification.

These considerations have moulded the form of this book. In selecting its subject matter I have assumed that readers will already be using textbooks of descriptive and experimental zoology, of physiology, and of biochemistry. I have assumed also that they will be studying invertebrate structure and function at first hand in the laboratory and in the field. Detail has therefore been restricted to what seemed needed to set the scene, as it were, for a particular line of thought. What I have tried to do, in short, is to open up discussion of some of the problems and questions that force themselves on the attention of anyone who wishes to know why an animal is built in a particular way, and how it manages to survive in its characteristic habitat and community. As Wordsworth put it to the Leech Gatherer: 'How is it that you live, and what is it you do?'

It may seem illogical that a book taking unity as its theme does not include the vertebrates with the invertebrates. They are not, in fact, left without mention. But to have dealt with them in any detail would have made the book unwieldy, and I should in any case have deemed it presumptuous to suppose myself capable of writing such an account. For the same reasons the book is not a complete survey of invertebrate biology. But I hope that I have managed to select subjects that will at least serve as a guide and a stimulus to the achievement of some of that synthesis of knowledge that ought to flow from a biological education. I hope, in fact, that the book may serve as an accompaniment to the more general and reflective parts of a university zoology course; as a companion for the seminars, the tutorials, and the essay writing. Perhaps, too, it will illuminate the profound truth of Edith Sitwell's belief: that it is odious to regard oneself as 'superior' to any living being, human or animal.

I am grateful to Sir Gavin de Beer, F.R.S., who invited me to write this book; to Professor E. W. Knight-Jones, Professor O. E. Lowenstein, F.R.S., Dr Sidnie M. Manton, F.R.S., and Professor J. D. Robertson, who gave advice and encouragement during its preparation; and to my publishers, who have brought to its production more skill and patience than any author could reasonably have expected.

I am indebted also to Blackwell Scientific Publications Ltd for permission to quote two passages from *Larval Forms* by Walter Garstang; to Mrs George Bambridge, Macmillan & Co. Ltd, and Doubleday & Co. Inc for permission to quote from *Kim* by Rudyard Kipling; to the Clarendon Press for permission to quote from the *Oxford Translation of Aristotle*, 'Historia Animalium'; and to the American Association for the Advancement of Science for permission to quote from 'Are there any "Acellular Animals"?' by A. Boyden in *Science*, **125** (3239), 155–156 (1957), and from 'Concerning the "Cellularity" or Acellularity of the Protozoa' by S. H. Hutner and L. Provasoli in *Science*, **125** (3255), 989 (1957).

All illustrations in this book which have been taken from any other sources, with or without amendment, are used by permission of the publishers and, as far as possible, of the authors, to all of whom my grateful thanks are due. Full details of the sources are given underneath each illustration.

E.J.W.B.

Contents

6 MOVEMENT AND METAMERISM

7 MOVEMENT AND ARTHROPODIZATION

Part 3: Aspects of Metabolism

8 NUTRITION OF PROTOZOA

9 NUTRITION OF SOME LOWER METAZOA

10 FILTER FEEDING

11 RESPIRATION

12 EXCRETION

13 OSMOTIC AND IONIC REGULATION

Part 4: Information and Control

Part 5 : Reproduction

Part 6 : Associations

1
Living Systems

1–1 APPROACH TO ANIMAL LIFE

They say of Scandinavian furniture that 'good design is timeless—it is the product of evolution'. The student of other aspects of animal life would agree with this claim; adding that good design expresses aptness for function. Upon this point of view our survey of invertebrate biology is based.

It recognizes that animals are constructed upon patterns of organization that have been tested and proved through immense periods of competition and differential survival. It presupposes, therefore, that the way in which animals function can only be understood in the light of their past history. Further, it recognizes that the animals that share our life today are not imperfect creations that would fit better into their environment if they had some of our own advantages. The fact that they have survived at all (and mostly for very much longer than we have yet succeeded in doing) is a tribute to the fitness of their organization.

This organization is an expression of the properties of systems of carbon compounds, but this does not necessarily mean that life is no more than a fortuitous association of molecules, nor does it necessarily follow that the humanist is correct in supposing that 'man must rely only upon himself'. But it is at least certain that the activities of living organisms depend upon the operation of physical and chemical principles no different from those that govern the properties of non-living systems.

A fundamental characteristic of living systems is that they carry on a continuous exchange of energy and materials with their environment; we say that they are open systems, involved in exchanges that are the driving force of the complex systems of chemical reactions that we call metabolism. One result of their metabolic activity is that they are able to build up some of the products of metabolism into the substance of their bodies, thereby providing for the replacement of worn-out material and for growth. Indeed, no part of a living body escapes the consequences of this continuous flux. Studies with radioactive tracers have shown that even the molecules of apparently permanent, inert material, such as supporting skeletal structures, are steadily replaced by corresponding molecules taken into the body from outside. A further result of metabolic activity is the capacity for irritability and for adaptive response to stimulation, so that by movement of part or of the whole of the body the organism behaves in a way that makes possible a further consequence: the reproduction of the individual and hence the perpetuation of its species.

Reproduction depends upon the capacity of living systems for making copies of themselves—the process that we call replication. The perpetuation of the species, however, depends in the long run upon occasional imperfections in the replication, and as a result of these the copy may differ from the parental form in certain respects. These differences, which we call mutations, are likely either to aid or to impede the adjustments of a particular organism to its environment. But the resources of the environment are not limitless, so that the maintenance and growth of organisms involves competition between them for limited supplies of materials. Organisms tend by their own activities to extend the range of their distribution and thus to exploit their environment to the limits of their capacities. This tendency, as Hardy has argued, has probably been of immense evolutionary importance. Populations which develop mutations that aid such extension will probably be more successful in this competitive exploitation. They will tend to survive and reproduce at the expense of other populations, a consequence that is the basis of the process that we call natural selection. Thus we conceive the relations between living material and its environment to have been continuously moulded, with the resulting production of organisms that are ever more complex and ever more efficient in the exploitation of the environment. This is what we call evolution, which we see as a continuous sequence of change leading from the simplest forms of life to the most complex.

This concept of levels of complexity may seem self-evident to even the most superficial observer of animal life, yet it deserves some attention here, for it is not easy to translate it into more concrete terms. An early expression of it, and one that has powerfully influenced man's approach to other animals, is seen in Aristotle's *Scala Naturae* (Fig. 1-1), or Ladder of Nature. According to his interpretation:

> Nature proceeds little by little from things lifeless to animal life in such a way that it is impossible to determine the exact line of demarcation, nor on which side thereof an intermediate form should lie. Thus, next after lifeless things in the upward scale comes the plant, and of plants one will differ from another as to its amount of apparent vitality; and, in a word, the whole genus of plants, whilst it is devoid of life as compared with an animal, is endowed with life as compared with other corporeal entities. Indeed, as we have just remarked, there is observed in plants a continuous scale of ascent towards the animal. . . . In regard to sensibility, some animals give no indication whatsoever of it, whilst others indicate it but indistinctly. Further, the substance of some of these intermediate creatures is fleshlike, as is the case with the so-called tethya [ascidians] and the acalephae [sea-anemones]; but the sponge is in every respect like a vegetable. And so throughout the entire animal scale there is a graduated differentiation in amount of vitality and in capacity for motion.

Aristotle's interpretation was not an evolutionary one in our modern use of the term, but it does carry a clear implication of relative status. We have been accustomed to place at the top of the ladder the evil, flesh-eating beast that Sartre finds in us. Once we accept this position, however, there remains an implied corollary that other animals are in some sense 'lower', and that the 'lowest' are those at the bottom of the ladder. We do, in fact, regularly speak of 'lower' and 'higher' animals, and because of this it is necessary to consider exactly what we mean by these terms.

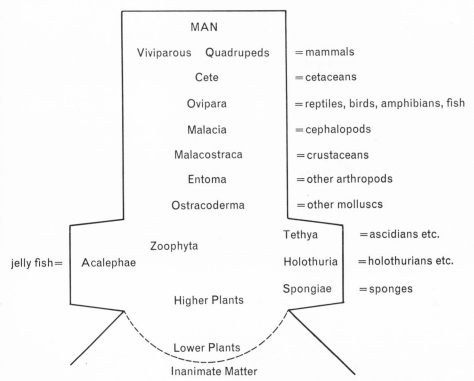

Fig. 1-1. The *Scala Naturae* or Ladder of Nature, according to the descriptions of Aristotle. From Singer, 1931. *A Short History of Biology.* Clarendon Press, Oxford.

We shall see that animals must be organized so as to function and behave in a manner best calculated to ensure survival and reproduction. From this point of view some environments are more 'difficult' than others. The littoral zone of the sea, particularly that part of it below the tide marks, is easier to occupy than either dry land or the air, for example, and we shall find some reasons later why this is so. Exploitation of these more difficult environments has required the development of new devices that are not needed by animals living in the easier habitats: waterproofing for land, and wings for the air, are obvious examples. From this point of view animals living in more difficult environments may be regarded as higher animals; the possession by them of new and specialized devices is an objective criterion by which their rightful place on the ladder may be defined.

But this analysis is not sufficient. Animals may inhabit very difficult environments, yet we may still feel that they are truly lower organisms. For example, life within the alimentary canal of another animal presents many problems. Few of us would expect to survive the experience of Jonah, but intestinal parasites regularly do so; yet this seems an inadequate reason for calling them higher animals. The important consideration here is that the possibilities of life on this planet may be exploited in many ways. One species may survive because it possesses a narrow and inflexible range of responses, allowing it to sample only a small fraction of the potential resources by which it is surrounded. Such an animal is *Peripatus*, which has reacted to the danger of desiccation on land by restricting itself to damp and concealed niches. Like the city financier in the garden, 'he looks importantly about him, while all the spring goes on without him'. Other animals may exploit their environment much more fully; perhaps because they possess devices that enable them to resist a wider range of stresses, or perhaps because they can sample a wider choice of food. These animals may be regarded as higher than those that lead more restricted lives.

Here we have another objective criterion, and an approach to an explanation of the biological significance of more complex organization. We have, too, an objective justification of the dominant status of man in the *Scala Naturae*. It can be justified by his ability to manipulate his environment to his own purpose. It can be justified also by the flexibility of his behaviour, and by the unique capacity of his nervous system, which results, among many other things, in making him the only animal that can scrutinize the rest of the animal kingdom in sufficient depth to be able to write books about it.

Two other concepts may conveniently be mentioned here, since they are closely associated with this matter of status. In our comparisons of animals we customarily refer to them, or to the groups to which they belong, as being either 'primitive' or 'specialized'. By specialized we mean that they possess characters that tend to debar them from further evolutionary change. Primitive groups or primitive animals, by contrast, possess many characters that are theoretically capable of further change. For example, we shall speak of the nerve net as a primitive type of nervous system, because we can conceive it as the forerunner of the polarized and centralized type of nervous system of higher animals.

Finally, it is our common habit to speak of animals or groups as being 'successful' or 'unsuccessful'. These terms, like 'higher' and 'lower', are relative, and can only be usefully employed if we provide ourselves with some objective standard. Since life is always a struggle, and the environment fundamentally hostile to its maintenance, it is fair to say that any group of animals that has survived at all is a successful one. But we may reasonably go further, and say that the more successful ones are those that have not merely survived, but have made the fullest use of the potentialities of the environment. In this sense the successful animals are what we have just defined as higher ones. But this is not all, for at any particular level of evolution there will be some groups that may be judged more successful than others. A useful objective criterion here is to consider relative abundance. Groups that have exploited most successfully a particular level of organization will tend to be more abundant than the less successful ones. This abundance will be reflected in the number of individuals representing the group at any given moment, and in the gross mass of their material (or biomass, as it is called).

Success will be reflected also in the number of species within the group, for diversification usually results when natural selection acts on a particular plan of organization to adapt it more closely to the environment. A number of subsidiary groups become established, each adapted to some particular mode of life. Within each of these the process continues until it has produced a range of species, each of which, by virtue of its own unique combination of characters, avoids competition with related species. This is the process that we call adaptive radiation. The more 'successful' the initial plan of organization, the greater the resultant diversification, and hence the greater the number of species to which it gives rise. The effect can be

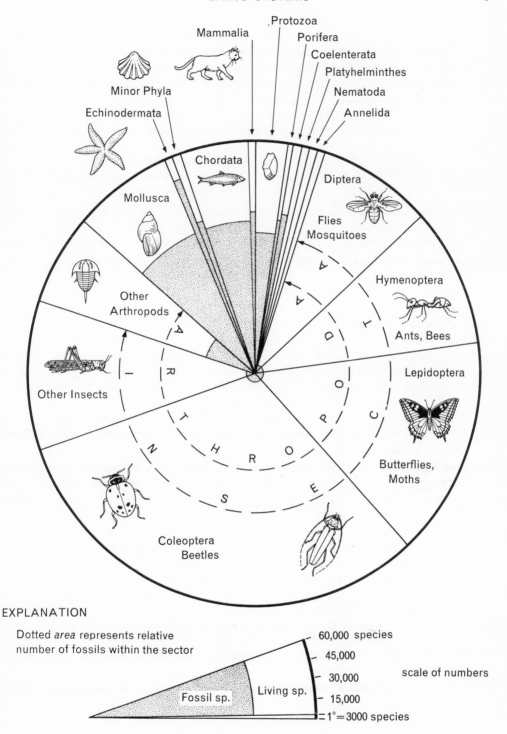

Fig. 1-2. Relative numbers of known species, living and fossil, of various animal phyla. From Muller and Campbell, 1954. *Syst. Zool.*, **3**, 168–170.

seen in Fig. 1–2, which shows the relative abundance of species in the major groups of animals. From this we can see, among other things, that the insects can be regarded as a highly successful group, in so far as they contain more species than all the rest of the animal kingdom put together. It is part of our present purpose to examine some of the reasons for these differing degrees of success. In doing so, we shall then see how success consolidated at one evolutionary level has provided a basis for fresh progress. Thus we shall come to appreciate the essential unity of living organisms, and our own dependence upon events that occurred early in the history of our planet.

1–2 ORIGIN OF LIVING SYSTEMS

The continuity of evolution is a fundamental element in the biologist's interpretation of the history of the earth. So much so, that he finds it logical to extend the concept to include also the origin of life from non-living material. At first sight it may seem formidably difficult to justify this extension. Living organisms are poised in such delicately balanced relationships with their environment that they are often said to present a highly improbable state of matter; a state of which it is therefore very difficult to conceive the origin. Until recently, indeed, the problem of the origin of life seemed to be beyond human understanding; but this was an over-pessimistic view, based, perhaps, upon the feeling that the facts of the situation were for ever beyond our reach.

Facts, however, are not the only tools of the scientist; a powerful element of creative thought is also involved in his activity. It is true that a scientist faced with a particular problem will need to deploy with the utmost efficiency his training and experience, and to bring into his consideration all relevant information. But given these, he will devise a hypothesis on which to base his further study of the problem. This is the creative aspect of his work. In everyday speech, he might claim to have 'had an idea', and he may not always find it easy to account for its emergence.

If the hypothesis is to be a useful one, however, it must be one that can be put to the test; it must, in fact, be tested to destruction. We cannot expect to be able to prove that our hypotheses are 'true'. Our sense organs, for example, and the instruments that extend their scope, can at best give us only a limited range of information. Moreover, in biological research we are dealing with such highly variable material that not until we have studied a wide range of species can we begin to feel confidence in the generalizations that we base upon the evidence available to us. In any case these generalizations have at best a limited validity. Their formulation is an exercise of the inductive method, in which universal statements are inferred from particular ones, and we should not forget Popper's fundamental criticism of this procedure. As he succinctly remarks, 'no matter how many instances of white swans we may have observed, this does not justify the conclusion that *all* swans are white'.

What we can do, however, is to apply the deductive method, and state certain consequences, or make certain predictions, that would be expected to follow from a particular hypothesis. By observation and experiment we can then determine whether or not these consequences materialize. If we find that they do not, then we say that our predictions have been falsified, and we begin to suspect that the hypothesis is ill founded. Continued falsification may then make it necessary to put the hypothesis away, and to make a fresh start. This is no disaster. As Popper has emphasized, an essential criterion for an empirical scientific system is that it must be possible to refute it by experience. However, we may be fortunate and find that our deductions are justified; we then say that we have verified them. Within these limits we have corroborated the hypothesis, in Popper's terminology. It may therefore be well founded, and at least we can go on to use it as a basis for further investigation and speculation. Additional corroboration will strengthen our confidence in it, but we can never afford to forget that one day it may need modification. Even the most cherished hypothesis is always open to eventual falsification; to forget this is to forget a fundamental principle of scientific procedure.

The problem of the origin of life can certainly be attacked in the way outlined above. We start with a belief in the existence of unifying principles in the organization of the universe. It is a belief derived from the work of Newton and Darwin, whose demonstration that unity can be found as well in the depths of the universe as in the life of this planet has permanently influenced our approach to the study of natural phenomena. At this stage in the history of human thought, therefore, we may reasonably accept, as a working hypothesis, that life may have originated during the early history of the earth as part of a continuous process of cosmic evolution. It is equally reasonable to suppose that its emergence was determined by the working-out of principles that are still demonstrable today, even though they operate in a very different context. In all of this we may be wrong. But this does not weaken the scientific validity of our procedure. What we are saying, in effect, is that living organisms of today are the products of evolution, and that therefore life itself may have originated out of non-living systems through an evolutionary process. Indeed, so confident are we of the validity of the principle of unity of plan in the cosmos that the possibility of life existing elsewhere in the solar system, and in other and remoter parts of the universe, has now become a matter for serious discussion.

If we are correct in this approach it follows that the history of animals and plants as we find it recorded in fossil form in the rocks must have been preceded by a much longer phase of evolution. This phase, in its earliest stages, would have been essentially chemical in character. During it there would have been laid down, under the influence of natural selection, the ground plan of the organization of living systems. The events of that remote period must therefore have had a profound influence upon the subsequent history of animals and plants, providing them with a common inheritance, which must have gone far towards determining the patterns of organization that they were later to achieve. It is because of this, and not only because of the intrinsic interest of the problem, that it becomes essential to attempt some interpretation of the possible course of this primeval phase of evolutionary history.

Our analysis may arbitrarily begin with the origin of the solar system. According to one view this event may have occurred, perhaps 4,500 million to 5,000 million years ago, through the condensation around the sun of a cloud of material similar to the dust and gas clouds that are known to exist in interstellar space, and which might have been the remains left after the earlier condensation of the sun. The predominant element in these interstellar clouds is hydrogen, and 80% of the substance of the sun is still composed of that element. It is likely, therefore, that the early atmosphere of the earth also contained large amounts of hydrogen. Other elements must have been present, however, for it is thought that many of them are formed from hydrogen by thermonuclear fusion in the centres of stars. There, it is supposed, temperatures of many millions of degrees are maintained by the energy released when lighter elements fuse to form heavier ones. From these celestial nuclear reactors the elements are then presumably discharged by the explosions of supernovae; indeed, the heavier elements may to some extent be a product of the stupendous release of energy that accompanies these violent events.

Thus we may suppose that the raw material of future terrestrial life was already available in interstellar space, segregated, perhaps, on the surface of interstellar dust grains. Darwin, in summarizing the arguments of *The Origin of Species*, remarks that 'there is a grandeur in this view of life, with its several powers, having been gradually breathed by the creator into a few forms or into one'. The grandeur has been powerfully and ironically enhanced by the extension of the principle of evolution into the field of cosmical physics. Thermonuclear reactions provide the elements out of which terrestrial life has been fashioned, and the radiant solar energy that drives it, while, in another context, they may yet provide the means by which it will eventually destroy itself.

Early in the history of the earth the prevailing high temperature would have promoted the combination of some of the available elements. In this way there could have arisen ammonia, methane, and water vapour, which are believed to have been the first constituents of the earth's atmosphere. This belief is supported by the identification of these same substances in the atmospheres of the larger and more distant planets, where conditions are believed to have changed less rapidly than on the earth. In the course of time the earth would have cooled sufficiently for water to condense on its surface. This would initially have been fresh water, but material swept from the land would have slowly accumulated in it; thus the salt-water oceans would have formed. According to one view, it is in these that the earliest forms of life may have arisen, their origin dependent upon the solvent properties of water, and its consequent facilitation of chemical reactions .

The periods of time that we are discussing are so vast that our minds cannot clearly grasp their scale. For example, the oldest rocks may have appeared around 3,000 million years ago; life began perhaps 1,000 million years later. What can be grasped, however, is an hypothesis that was first clearly formulated by Oparin, and that is in line with this analysis of the sequence of chemical events. This hypothesis proposes that life in that inconceivably remote period must have originated in reducing conditions: the abundant supply of oxygen, on which it now depends, could not at that time have been available. In accordance with the methodology outlined above, this deduction has been tested by laboratory experiments, and the results of these tests are found to support this general analysis. They have shown that organic material can actually be formed in such a reducing atmosphere, provided that an adequate supply of energy is available. In 1953–54 it was shown by Miller, in what have now become classical experiments, that the passage of electrical discharges through a mixture of hydrogen, ammonia, methane, and water vapour could lead to the formation of the fundamental substrates required by living organisms (e.g. formic acid, acetic acid, succinic acid) and also to amino acids (Fig. 1–3). Moreover, amino acids have been polymerized to form peptide-like structures, under conditions comparable with those that might have existed during the early history of the earth. The appearance of these substances, which are the essential structural units of living material, may, therefore, have been inevitable and predictable during those remote times. Electrical energy was probably available, resulting from lightning displays such as are recorded as taking place today on Jupiter. Ultraviolet light, however, would probably have been a more important energy source; it would not at that time have been reduced in intensity by the ozone layer that is formed now in our oxygen-rich atmosphere, and it would have been continuously available. Experiments similar to those of Miller, but using ultraviolet light as the energy source, regularly produce amino acids, provided that sufficient hydrogen is present to make the environment a reducing one.

Of course, the production of amino acids and peptide chains is a very long way indeed from the establishment, maintenance, and replication of the organized patterns of living systems; further assumptions are clearly needed to develop this interpretation. We must assume that subsequently there was a building-up of increasingly complex molecular chains and of the molecular associations known as coacervates. This might have taken place in ancient seas, perhaps by the adsorption of the molecules onto mineral particles. We must further assume that these molecular aggregations developed the power of self-replication.

This replication may have been achieved through the well-known capacity of

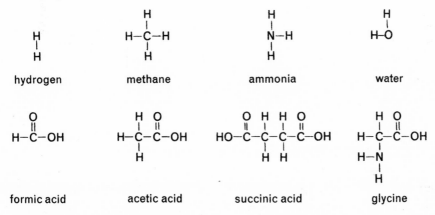

Fig. 1-3. The earliest molecules believed to have been present on the surface of the earth (*top row*), and molecules derived from them by electrical discharge or ultraviolet radiation (*bottom row*). After Urey.

complex organic molecules to undergo polymerization, for the reproduction of organisms today depends upon the properties of the polymeric molecules of deoxyribonucleic acid (DNA). These giant molecules, with molecular weights of the order of 10 million, are believed, according to the now well-known interpretation that was originally advanced by Watson and Crick, to be organized as a double helix, the two molecular chains of this being coiled around a common axis (Fig. 1-4). Each chain is thought to be composed of repeating units called nucleotides, which are formed of three constituents, a sugar (deoxyribose), a phosphate, and a nitrogenous base. The sugar and phosphate are always the same, but the base may be any one of four compounds, cytosine and thymine, which are pyrimidines, and adenine and guanine, which are purines. The association of the two chains into a double helix is interpreted as a consequence of hydrogen bonding between pairs of these bases (Fig. 1-5).

Current views suggest that the four bases effectively constitute a four-letter

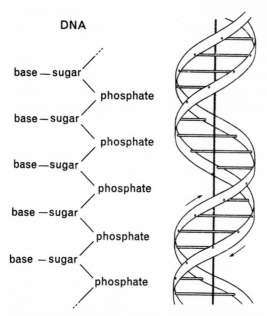

DNA

base — sugar

phosphate

base — sugar

phosphate

base — sugar

phosphate

base — sugar

phosphate

base — sugar

phosphate

Fig. 1-4. *Left,* chemical formula of a single chain of deoxyribonucleic acid. *Right,* a purely diagrammatic figure, in which the two ribbons symbolize the two phosphate sugar chains, and the horizontal rods the pairs of bases holding the chains together. The vertical line marks the fibre axis. Adapted from Watson and Crick, 1953. *Nature, Lond.,* **171,** 737–738.

alphabet by which information can be represented in a coded form, the code depending on the arrangement of particular sequences of nucleotides. There is evidence, for example, that each amino acid that has to be synthesized by an organism is coded as a characteristic sequence of three nucleotides; the order in which the triplets are arranged in the DNA molecule can then, on this hypothesis, determine the order in which the amino acids are built up into a particular protein. The code itself can be indefinitely replicated because each chain can synthesize another chain like itself (Fig. 1-6).

The assumption that the conditions obtaining during the phase of chemical evolution could have led to the establishment of a substance with such remarkable properties as those attributed to DNA is an immense one. Yet we are helped to accept it by the knowledge that ribose, deoxyribose, adenine, and guanine have been produced in the laboratory in experiments similar in principle to those of Miller, while nucleotides have been polymerized to yield nucleic acids containing at least 200 residues. This, too, can be said in favour of it: in the reducing conditions then pre-

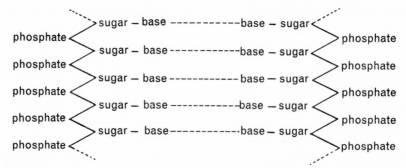

Fig. 1-5. Chemical formula of a pair of deoxyribonucleic acid (DNA) chains. The hydrogen bonding is symbolized by dotted lines. From Watson and Crick, 1953. *op. cit.*

Fig. 1-6. The Watson–Crick hypothesis for the replication of DNA. It is supposed that the two polynucleotide chains of a DNA molecule separate so as to expose their specific hydrogen-bonding surfaces. Each chain then serves as a template for the synthesis of its complement. Accordingly, each daughter molecule contains one of the parental chains paired with one newly synthesized chain. Throughout repetitions of this process, the single polynucleotide chains remain intact. Adapted from Meselson and Stahl, 1958. *Cold Spring Harb. Symp. quant. Biol.*, **23**, 9–12.

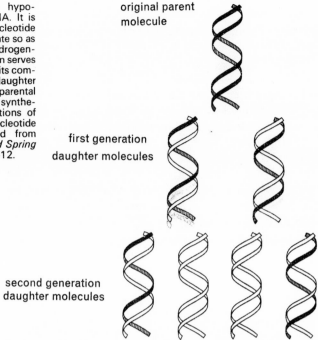

original parent molecule

first generation daughter molecules

second generation daughter molecules

vailing it would have been theoretically possible for organic molecules to accumulate and interact, whereas a similar accumulation could not occur today simply because the molecules would be oxidized by the atmosphere or broken down by living organisms. Moreover, the evolution of living material need not have been dependent upon entirely random processes. Calvin has suggested that simple inorganic compounds, or heavy metals, may have acted from an early stage as catalysts; they may thereby have served as driving forces that could have been favoured and canalized by natural selection.

1–3 EVOLUTION OF ENERGY RELATIONSHIPS

Whatever the means by which this organic complex evolved, its growth and replication would have required the supply of materials and energy that we have seen to be the foundation of living systems. We must assume, therefore, that in the primeval oceans there were other complex and energy-rich molecules that could be taken up into these systems, and that the latter could release and make use of the energy so obtained. This would have constituted the first appearance of metabolic processes.

The metabolism of organisms as we know them today depends upon a very peculiar way of storing and transferring energy, and of releasing it in a form that is immediately available for use in biological processes. In principle, a large proportion of the energy released by the metabolic breakdown of organic compounds is taken up by adenosine diphosphate (ADP), which is thus transformed into adenosine triphosphate (ATP). In due course this is broken down again by hydrolysis into ADP, the energy so released becoming available for some form or other of biological activity.

Within these two compounds the energy is held in association with phosphate bonds. These, which are known as high-energy bonds, constitute one of the unique features of living material; in formal equations they are represented symbolically by curved lines:

$$\text{adenosine} - \textcircled{P} \sim \textcircled{P} \sim \textcircled{P} \rightarrow \text{adenosine} - \textcircled{P} \sim \textcircled{P} + \text{HO} \textcircled{P} + \text{free-energy change}$$

It has often been stated that the energy associated with the terminal phosphate bond of ATP, with which we are particularly concerned, is 11–12 kcal/mole, but more recent estimates suggest that a value of 8 kcal/mole may be more accurate.

High-energy phosphate bonds permit the release of energy in a form which organisms can readily use. They are so central and uniform a feature of the organization of living systems that we may reasonably suppose that this energy-handling system evolved at an early stage of chemical evolution and that it thus became inseparable from life. There is good evidence to support this supposition. We have seen that adenine can be formed in the laboratory in conditions analogous to those that might have existed during the earliest stages of the chemical phase of evolution. It is thus all the more significant that high-energy phosphate linkages are generated when ferrous iron is oxidized by hydrogen peroxide in the presence of orthophosphate. These conditions could probably have existed from a very early stage of chemical evolution, and may well have promoted the incorporation of these linkages into living systems. Thus we may think of the earliest forms of life, according to this analysis, as precariously evolving in a reducing atmosphere, and dependent upon energy that was already stored in the complex molecules of their environment.

Organisms that now obtain their energy by breaking down complex and energy-rich carbon compounds taken in from their environment are known as heterotrophs. The earliest forms of anaerobic life that we have been postulating can therefore be termed primitive heterotrophs. Their emergence was a major achievement of chemical evolution, yet their future was not assured, for the reserves of energy stored in the molecules around them could not have lasted indefinitely. The molecules could not have been unlimited in abundance, and the supplies of them must sooner or later have been exhausted. It is supposed that this barrier to the maintenance and further evolution of living material was overcome by the emergence of the capacity for photosynthesis, the process in which (as we see it today) the electromagnetic energy of solar radiation is trapped by chlorophyll (Fig. 1–7) and transformed into potential chemical energy through the combination of carbon dioxide and water. Calvin has shown that the first stage in this process is the formation of phosphoglycerate, a three-carbon compound that is also formed during the glycolytic breakdown of glucose that we refer to later.

Chlorophyll is a magnesium–porphyrin complex. We shall see later that the production of porphyrins is so widespread in living organisms that we must suppose these substances to have appeared at a very early stage of evolution. Their use in photosynthesis would have provided a continuous supply of energy-rich carbon compounds, so that living organisms needed no longer to depend upon ready-made sources of these in the environment. No less important was the release of oxygen into the atmosphere as an end result of photosynthetic reactions. Because of this, and probably also because of some further release of the element through the dissociation of water vapour by solar radiation, the atmosphere changed from reducing to oxidizing conditions. This made possible a change in the metabolism of living systems from the primitive anaerobic type to the aerobic type that is so characteristic of living organisms today.

Organisms that obtain their energy through photosynthesis are termed photo-trophs. On the general hypothesis outlined above, the earliest phototrophs are to be regarded as having evolved from primitive heterotrophs. Their descendants today are the green plants, and presumably, the phototrophic bacteria, which similarly possess pigment (bacteriochlorophyll) enabling them to trap radiant energy. These organisms can build their organic molecules out of carbon dioxide and simple salts, so that their carbon needs can be met entirely from inorganic sources. For this reason they are said to be autotrophic as regards their carbon supplies.

Phototrophic bacteria use solar energy in more than one way. The green sulphur

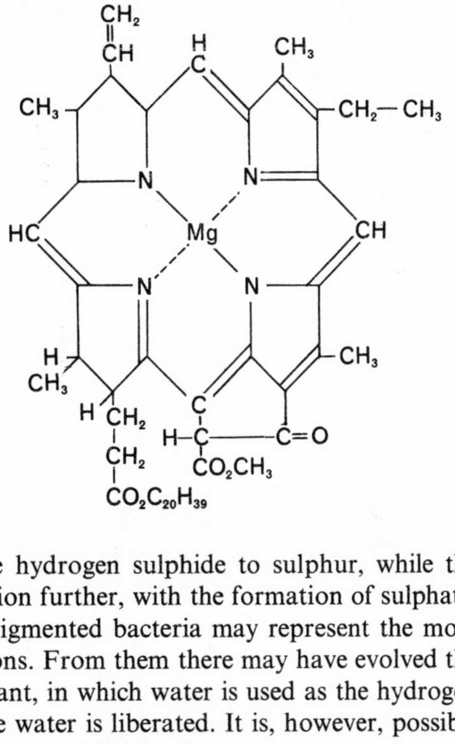

Fig. 1-7. Chlorophyll *a*. After Calvin.

bacteria, for example, use it to oxidize hydrogen sulphide to sulphur, while the purple sulphur bacteria carry the oxidation further, with the formation of sulphate. According to Oparin's analysis, these pigmented bacteria may represent the more primitive types of photosynthetic reactions. From them there may have evolved the photosynthetic reactions of the green plant, in which water is used as the hydrogen donor (see above) and the oxygen of the water is liberated. It is, however, possible that bacterial types of photosynthesis are secondary developments.

The establishment of photosynthesis was a major advance, but one further step was still needed to give the pattern of life that we find today. This was the emergence of secondary heterotrophs; organisms incapable of photosynthesis, and therefore dependent for their energy sources upon the oxidation of organic compounds formed by phototrophs. The primitive heterotrophs that we have earlier considered are visualized as a transient phase in the evolution of life, primitively dependent upon molecules formed in peculiar chemical conditions that soon passed away. Secondary heterotrophs are so called because they are visualized as having been derived from primitive phototrophs by the loss of the capacity for photosynthesis; a loss which, as we shall see later, can still occur in phototrophs at the present day. This step in

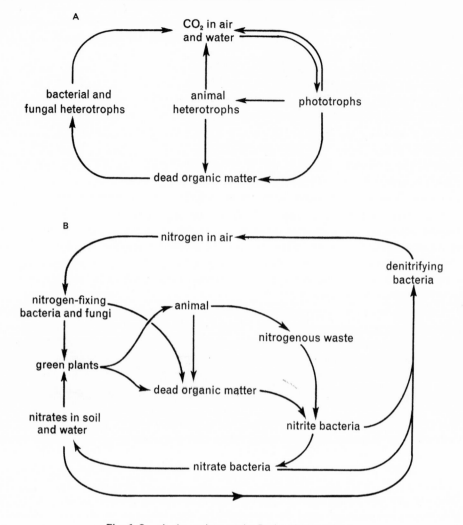

Fig. 1-8. A, the carbon cycle. B, the nitrogen cycle.

evolution was thus a regressive one. But it was a case of *reculer pour mieux sauter*: it provided not only the heterotrophic bacteria and the fungi, but also the whole of the animal world, with all its immensely diversified organization that we are about to study. If we need a simple definition of animals it may be said that they 'eat'; by which is meant that they take in (or ingest) complex carbon compounds as solid food. This process, which is called phagotrophy, is commonly associated with the active pursuit or trapping of food, and it is because of this that structure and function in animals have evolved along lines profoundly different from those that characterize plants. However, heterotrophy and phagotrophy do not always go together. Some animals (often those that live in the alimentary tract of others) take in energy-rich molecules through their body surface in dissolved form; they are said to be osmotrophs.

We have postulated a complex sequence of events. Whether or not it is correct, it is certain that in this or in some other way there were established the great cycles of flow of the chemical elements that are vital to the maintenance of life, and that involve living organisms in complex webs of nutritional interrelationships (Fig. 1–8). One of these is the carbon cycle, in which complex organic compounds are built up by the phototrophs and are ultimately decomposed by heterotrophic bacterial activity, with or without prior transformation by animals. Another is the cycle of nitrogen, the element upon which all organisms depend for the building-up of their proteins. Some organisms, including the green plants, are autotrophic as regards their nitrogen supply, taking it up in an inorganic form. Usually these organisms require nitrates, but some bacteria and fungi can utilize atmospheric nitrogen. From these resources are built up the organic nitrogenous compounds that are incorporated into the bodies of the autotrophs, and that in due course are ingested by the heterotrophic animals. The supply of nitrates is maintained by the heterotrophic bacteria that decompose the bodies and products of plants and animals; in so doing they are able to form nitrates out of ammonia and nitrites. Phosphorus and sulphur are other elements that are passed through comparable cycles in which an inorganic phase alternates with an organic one.

Finally, we must take account of another aspect of nutritional dependence which does not emerge from consideration of these simplified cycles. This is the dependence of many organisms upon the substances known as accessory growth factors, or vitamins. This dependence first became apparent from studies of human and mammalian nutrition, but its significance ranges much more extensively than that. A wide variety of vitamins are now known, classified by a conventional literal system. Some of them (those included within the A, C, and D groups) are primarily, and perhaps exclusively, vertebrate requirements. The B vitamins, on the contrary, are essential requirements for many organisms, and some are probably needed by all forms of life.

A widely accepted explanation for this is that during the chemical phase of evolution there were established metabolic patterns that were dependent upon the presence of certain enzymes and coenzymes. An example of these substances would be thiamine (vitamin B_1), which is believed to be a requirement of all living organisms. The explanation of this dependence is that thiamine gives rise to a substance called cocarboxylase (thiamine pyrophosphate). This functions as a coenzyme of carboxylase in the citric acid cycle, which we shall later see to be a sequence of reactions essential for the oxidative metabolism of living organisms. Dependence on vitamin B_1, therefore, is a consequence of the dependence of living organisms on the citric acid cycle.

What is at first sight surprising in this situation is that animals, and certain other organisms also, are unable to synthesize these essential substances for themselves, but must obtain them as part of their food. This, like the origin of animals, is believed to be a consequence of regressive chemical evolution. We know that in the mould *Neurospora*, for example, there can arise mutant strains that are deficient in certain biosynthetic capacities, and it is supposed that similar mutations have been a constant accompaniment of evolution. Certain of these mutations would have resulted in a loss of the ability to synthesize particular compounds, but these defects of metabolism (for that is what they are) have persisted because the organisms concerned were able to obtain the required substances from their external environment, where they were being synthesized by other organisms. Thiamine, for example, is synthesized by plants and many bacteria, and it is because of this that animals can obtain it from their environment or their food, without having to manufacture it themselves. For them it has become a vitamin. This we can define as an essential nutrient which a particular organism cannot synthesize for itself; which it requires in only very small amounts; and which contributes nothing either to its energy supplies or to its permanent structure.

The dependence of organisms upon these metabolites thus introduces a further complication into an analysis of their nutritional relationships. A particular species may be autotrophic as regards its carbon and nitrogen sources, and yet be heterotrophic in its dependence upon an exogenous source of certain vitamins. In fact, a species can only be said to be autotrophic in the complete sense of that term when it can secure chemical energy through photosynthesis, and when it can synthesize all other essential metabolites from inorganic sources in its environment. No animal, of course, is in this position. When we consider the nutrition of the Protozoa, however, we shall find that we still have with us today organisms that to some extent bridge the nutritional gap between animals and plants; this gap may well have been repeatedly bridged in the early stages of evolution.

Anaerobic release of energy from carbohydrate is widespread today in organisms, where it takes one of two forms. One of these is the process called fermentation, well known in yeast and bacteria. This involves a complex sequence of reactions which first provides for the activation of glucose by the incorporation of phosphate radicals into its molecule. One molecule of glucose forms one molecule of fructose diphosphate, the phosphate being donated by ATP; two molecules of the latter are thus converted at this stage into two molecules of ADP. The molecule of six-carbon fructose diphosphate is next split into two three-carbon molecules of triose phosphate, and each of these is then converted into a molecule of pyruvic acid. Four molecules of ATP are generated from ADP during these stages. Thus, allowing for the initial loss of two ATP molecules, the breakdown of one molecule has so far resulted in a net gain to the organism of two high-energy phosphate bonds. In yeast the pyruvic acid is then further broken down to alcohol, so that the overall equation can be written thus:

$$C_6H_{12}O_6 \rightarrow 2CH_3CH_2OH + 2CO_2 + \text{free-energy change of 50 kcal/mole}$$

It will be noted that the phosphate radicals, which are vital for the biological significance of the reaction, do not appear at all in this representation. The 50 kcal/mole shown in the equation is the total free-energy change of the reaction. Of this total, however, the organism only derives the energy associated with the two high-energy phosphate bonds that it has gained. Even at the higher of the two values stated earlier, therefore, the organism could only gain some 23 kcal/mole from the fermentation process, while at the lower value the gain would be 16 kcal/mole.

The anaerobic breakdown of carbohydrate in animal tissues differs from this process in two respects. It begins with glycogen, for which reason it is called glycolysis, and it ends with lactic acid. The intervening stages, however, from the phosphorylation of the glucose molecule to the production of pyruvic acid, are identical. This resemblance to fermentation is in itself a striking testimony to the essential unity of living organisms, and a powerful indication of their origin from a common ancestral pattern of metabolic organization. The overall equation for glycolysis can be written thus:

$$C_6H_{12}O_6 \rightarrow 2CH_3CH(OH)COOH + \text{free-energy change of 36 kcal/mole}$$

As with fermentation, the organism gains at most some 23 kcal/mole. It will be observed that once again the peculiar biological properties of the process are unrepresented; only a detailed analysis of the component steps can bring out the essential identity of glycolysis and fermentation.

The aerobic breakdown of carbohydrate, termed oxidation, may be represented by the following overall equation:

$$C_6H_{12}O_6 + 6O_2 \rightarrow 6CO_2 + 6H_2O + \text{free-energy change of 686 kcal/mole}$$

During this process pyruvic acid is formed as in the anaerobic breakdown, but the energy that is still present in its molecule is released through a sequential and self-renewing series of oxidative reactions that make up the Krebs or citric acid cycle. The pyruvic acid molecule is oxidatively decarboxylated by coenzyme A, and the remainder of the molecule then enters the citric acid cycle (Fig. 1-9) as a bound form of acetic acid, acetyl coenzyme A. The acetyl group condenses with oxaloacetate to give citrate; this is finally oxidized to carbon dioxide, oxaloacetate being regenerated during the process and thus becoming available for a further turn of the cycle. During the passage of one molecule through a complete cycle four pairs of hydrogen atoms are removed. These are combined with oxygen to form water, but only after they have been passed along a series of compounds called hydrogen acceptors. These form the systems called respiratory chains, in which the pigments known as cytochromes play a predominant part.

It will be apparent from the equations that oxidation has the immense advantage of providing for a much more complete release of energy than is secured by either fermentation or glycolysis. Through the action of the complex system of the metabolic pathways that we have outlined, a single molecule of glucose is made to yield nearly 40 energy-rich phosphate bonds, representing

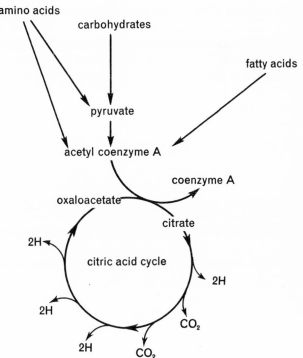

Fig. 1-9. Interrelationship of metabolic pathways with Kreb's citric acid cycle.

some 320 to 480 kcal/mole. Since the complete oxidation of a molecule of glucose yields 686 kcal/mole, this represents an efficiency of some 60–70 % at most. This value, however, is only a measure of the efficiency with which energy is captured by the organism. The efficiency with which this energy is used in performing biological work is very much lower, and is little different from the efficiency of engines made by man.

These metabolic pathways also have a further importance. The citric acid cycle is not confined to the oxidation of carbohydrate; it serves also to complete the oxidation of fat and of amino acids (Fig. 1–9). It functions, therefore, as a final common path for the catabolism of the three main categories of organic compounds, and for the efficient release of the energy locked within them. Finally, this release takes place at temperatures suitable for the maintenance of life, while the intervention of the high-energy phosphate bond ensures that this energy is available for chemical work, and is not uselessly dissipated as heat.

These, then, are some of the systems that emerged during the chemical phase of evolution, and that provided the raw material for all that followed in the evolution of living organisms. Their emergence would seem the more remarkable if we were not accustomed to view it from our earthbound standpoint. Here, in a cosmos in which hydrogen forms as much as 80 % of the material of the sun and stars, life manages to maintain itself in an atmosphere of which more than 20 % is free oxygen. It is able to do so because it is itself largely responsible for the presence of that element: photosynthetic activity can probably effect a complete renewal of our atmospheric oxygen in a mere 2,000 years.

2
Organization and Life

2–1 HOMOLOGY AND ANALOGY IN ORGANIZATION

Life depends upon more than the mere association of complex molecules; it depends
also upon the patterns in which these are arranged, for the coordinated functioning
of diverse metabolic pathways could not be secured without the orderly positioning
of their component parts. This has long been appreciated, and the existence of
structural patterns in protoplasm long suspected. The full scope and significance of the
concept, however, has only recently been unfolded with the disclosure by electron
microscopy of a new world of ultrastructure, strikingly similar in its fundamental
organization throughout the animal and plant kingdoms. This similarity inevitably
recalls the resemblances that we have already noted in the metabolic pathways by
which energy is transferred. These, we suggested, might have been established once
and for all during the chemical phase of evolution, and it is clear that structural
resemblances might be accounted for in the same way. This explanation is not one
that can ever be tested either by experiment or by direct observation. Yet it carries,
both in its biochemical and its structural contexts, important implications which are
bound to influence our interpretation of the history and relationships of living
organisms. For this reason it merits closer consideration.

Unity of pattern is a very familiar feature of the structure of animals at the level
of gross morphological analysis, and one of the aims of the comparative anatomist
must be to discover such unity. The same is no less true of the comparative biochemist
and the comparative physiologist, for it is a primary aim of all the sciences to expose
order in natural phenomena. The morphologist, in his analysis of unity and diversity,
discriminates between two different types of resemblance, known as homology and
analogy. This important distinction is a pre-Darwinian concept, and was, in fact, first
clearly enunciated by Richard Owen in connection with his analysis of vertebrate
organization. From this point of view an organ in one species is said to be homologous
with an organ in another species when the two organs are similar in their fundamental
structural plan, irrespective of the functions which they may carry out. Associated

with this structural similarity will be similarity of development and of relationships with adjacent structures. In contrast to this, the two organs would be termed analogous if they carried out similar functions, but were fundamentally different in their structure, development, and anatomical relationships.

The distinction, as Hertwig argued, is based in this classical formulation upon a concept that retains its validity, regardless of how it is explained. Nevertheless, the current explanation of the distinction is inevitably an evolutionary one. The possession of homologous organs by two species is attributed to the descent of these species from a common ancestral plan of structure; analogous organs are attributed to the independent evolution of similar functions in unrelated species, with different ancestries. However, the analysis has been complicated by the recognition that what animals inherit is genetic information coded in their DNA molecules, and not the structures that develop as a result of the exploitation of this information. It must therefore be accepted that species may possess organs that are homologous in their relationships, but that need not have been present in a common ancestral form. They may be possessed by the species concerned because these have inherited genetic systems with common potentialities for developing those organs. In other words, two related species, living in similar conditions, may, under the influence of natural selection, independently evolve similar adaptations because they have inherited from a common ancestor the potentiality for reacting in similar ways to similar demands. This type of resemblance is often termed latent homology, while the organs concerned are said to be homoplastic.

The question suggested in our present context by these considerations is whether the unity of pattern found in the fundamental biochemical and ultrastructural architecture of living systems is to be interpreted in terms of classical homology, latent homology, or analogy. Naturally we cannot feel sure of the answer. We can only repeat that the widespread distribution of such similarities throughout living organisms at least establishes some probability that they were evolved at an early stage of chemical evolution, and that they then became part of the common inheritance of all later forms of life. On the other hand, it must be remembered that life as we see it on this planet depends upon the unique properties of a limited range of complex molecules. Probably, therefore, there are relatively few ways in which these molecules can be brought together to form biochemical and ultrastructural systems, so that it is not impossible that similar systems might have arisen independently in more than one line of evolution, in a way which would fail to satisfy the classical concept of homology. The fact is that this concept, of such fundamental importance in comparative studies, has become increasingly difficult to define.

If this uncertainty of interpretation exists at the fundamental level of analysis that we are at present considering, it must become increasingly pronounced when we examine the complex and specialized systems that have been erected on these foundations during later evolution. It is a doubt that underlies Gray's warning concerning the uncertainties surrounding the evolutionary interpretation of comparative physiology. He suggested that in their physiological activities animals are so opportunistic that any attempt to approach the problems of phylogeny by the physiological pathway can only lead to confusion. This view may seem unduly pessimistic, but it is a valuable reminder of the need for an unceasingly critical approach to the interpretation of animal organization at all levels of analysis.

2–2 EUCELLULAR PLAN OF STRUCTURE

The best-known feature of biological organization, and one that does not rest on electron microscopy for its demonstration, is the nucleate plan of structure: the differentiation, that is, of a unit of protoplasm into cytoplasm and nucleus, the latter being demarcated by a nuclear membrane. We know that the special significance of this pattern is that the polymerized nucleotides of DNA are organized within the nucleus into the complex bodies called chromosomes. The establishment of these must have been the result of a long evolutionary process. It is probable that during the earlier phases of this process the DNA molecules existed in a less highly organized form, not yet enclosed by a nuclear membrane. This stage is still found today in the blue-green algae and the bacteria. The simplest arrangement is seen in certain sulphur bacteria, in which the DNA is present as randomly scattered granules, and in the blue-green algae, in which it is distributed as irregular strands. Division takes place by the ingrowth of a new cell boundary; the DNA is then distributed between the daughter cells in approximately equal parts, but without the precise division that we observe in fully-organized chromosomes. In other bacteria the DNA may be arranged as a tangled thread, with a duplex structure suggestive of a chromosome.

Apart from these supposedly primitive exceptions, the majority of living organisms, plant as well as animal, are composed of the units formed by nuclei and their associated masses of cytoplasm. These units are the structures that we call cells, a name that derives from the observations of seventeenth-century microscopists, notably Hooke, Grew, Malpighi, and Leeuwenhoek. It is well known that the term was initially applied to the thick-walled cavities that are readily visible in plant material; not until these observations were extended to animal material was increased emphasis placed upon the living contents of these units. To this extent the term has always been somewhat unsatisfactory, and today we find it so in another way also, for it is difficult to draw a sharp distinction between this plan of structure and that of bacteria. Both depend upon the differentiation established between the cytoplasm and the coded instructions in the DNA molecules, so that from this point of view they can be regarded as representing two grades of cellular organization. For this reason it may be helpful to follow the suggestion of Picken, and apply the term 'eucellular' to the second and more widespread grade. A eucell is thus defined as a cell in which the DNA molecules are carried as chromosomes within the nucleoplasm of a fully-differentiated nucleus that is separated from the cytoplasm by means of a nuclear membrane.

Nuclei with these characteristics, and with mitotic division of the chromosomes involving the development of spindle threads, are common both to animals and to seed-bearing plants. This establishes the strong probability that they were already evolved at the level of organization that was characteristic of their common ancestral stock. We shall later see more than one reason for regarding flagellate protozoans as being the closest to that stock of all Protozoa, and as antedating in their origin the other groups of living protozoans. Because of this we may reasonably expect to find in Protozoa a nuclear organization similar to that of plants and metazoans and derived, like theirs, from that same common origin. While, however, the Protozoa clearly do possess well-differentiated nuclei, the modes of division of these are so varied, and sometimes so unlike what is seen in a metazoan cell, that it was for long believed that nuclear division in Protozoa was predominantly amitotic; it was further

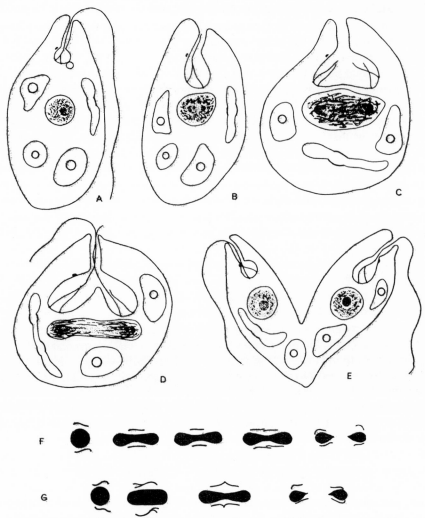

Fig. 2-1. Binary fission in *Euglena*. A–E, fission: semi-diagrammatic. Duplication of chromosomes, here shown at C (metaphase), is in some species first detectable earlier (at B, prophase) or later (at D, anaphase). F and G illustrate alternative theories of chromosome duplication and separation of chromatids. In F the chromosomes are split and their products slide one on the other towards opposite poles. In G, the chromatids are thought of as stripping apart in a widening 'V'. (A–E combined after various authors; F and G adapted from Leedale.) From MacKinnon and Hawes, 1961. *An Introduction to the Study of Protozoa*. Clarendon Press, Oxford.

supposed that in these organisms we see stages in the evolution of mitosis. This view, however, is certainly erroneous; mitosis is fully established in the Protozoa, although it admittedly varies greatly in its form.

In connection with this variation Belâr has suggested the recognition of two types of mitosis in Protozoa; these he has termed paramitosis and eumitosis. In paramitosis, which is found, for example, in euglenids, dinoflagellates, and radiolarians, the chromosomes remain elongated, and no typical equatorial plate is formed. In *Euglena* (Fig. 2–1) and allied forms the chromosomes appear around an intranuclear structure called the endosome; no spindle threads are formed, and the endosome itself seems to act as a centriolar apparatus. The chromosomes are drawn out and are finally broken into two, so that they eventually separate into a group at either pole. This is certainly suggestive of a possible stage in the evolution of the more typical mitosis found in many other protozoans, although it may be a result of secondary modification.

Eumitosis corresponds closely with the typical mitosis of the metazoan cell, for it involves the longitudinal division of the chromosomes and the appearance of an equatorial plate of compact chromosomes. In many protozoans with this form of division the nuclear membrane persists throughout the process, so that the achromatic spindle is confined within the nucleus. This happens, for example, in *Monocystis* and in the micronuclei of ciliates, where the spindle extends into polar caps that may contain centrioles. In other protozoans the mitotic figure may be entirely typical, arising in the cytoplasm, and being dependent upon the existence there of centrioles. The behaviour of the endosome, when present, is no less variable; in some instances it gives rise to the chromosomes, while in others it gives rise both to these and to the centrioles.

No clear evolutionary series can be discerned in these nuclear phenomena. Evidently the essential features of mitotic division are clearly established in the Protozoa, but it may be that the extensive variation in detail is a consequence of mitosis not being fully stabilized at this level of animal organization. A special case is found, however, in the differentiation of the nuclear material of the Ciliata into a micronucleus and a macronucleus. The latter is dense in appearance, because it is in a polyploid condition as a result of repeated mitosis occurring within the nuclear membrane. Presumably in correlation with this, it undergoes amitotic division, accomplished by simple elongation and constriction. This, however, only serves to emphasize the general rule of the dependence of protozoan organization upon mitosis, for it is the micronuclei of the Ciliata that transmit genetic material to the next generation, and these undergo mitotic division.

2–3 CELL THEORY

The interpretation of plants and animals as being composed of cells and their products is commonly referred to as the Cell Theory. Its enunciation in the early nineteenth century by Schleiden and Schwann constituted the formulation of one of the great generalizations of biological science. Baker, in his review of the history of the theory, points out that in the form in which it was first stated by Schwann, in 1839, it was primarily a theory of the embryological development of organic structure. Schwann believed this development to take place in two stages, the first being the differentiation of a structureless substance into structural units, and the second being the differentiation of these units, or cells, into the characteristic organization of the adult. A conversation with Schleiden led Schwann to believe that the first stage in the formation of a cell was the development of a nucleus within a structureless fluid; a limiting boundary, the cell membrane, was then secreted by the nucleus, and afterwards the body of the cell appeared within the membrane.

When, later in the century, this belief was shown to be quite incorrect, the Cell Theory in Schwann's original sense largely fell to the ground. By this time, however, it had become recognized that most organisms, both plant and animal, could certainly be regarded as formed of units, consisting of nucleus and cytoplasm. This, therefore, became the fundamental tenet of the Cell Theory. It was a different theory from that originally enunciated by Schwann, yet he had observed a fundamental truth, the understanding of which had progressed with advancing knowledge. In this there is nothing unusual. It is not only organisms that evolve; so also, if in a different sense, do our descriptions of their properties, and our attempts to explain them.

To speak of the Cell Theory as based upon a fundamental truth is not to say that the issues raised by it are straightforward and its implications universally acceptable. On the contrary, it has from time to time been the centre of vigorous, not to say passionate, controversy, which has been focused on two main matters of dispute. One of these concerns the nature of individuality in living organisms. It raises the question whether eucells are individual and isolated units, or whether they should be viewed solely as parts of an organism. The other matter is closely connected with this, and raises the question of the significance of our customary recognition of two main subkingdoms of the animal kingdom, the Protozoa and the Metazoa. The bodies of protozoans each contain (with some important exceptions) a single nucleus. The metazoan body, by contrast, is composed of many eucells. Is the protozoan, then, to be regarded as unicellular, comparable with a single cell of a metazoan? Or is it to be regarded as a non-cellular organism, comparable with the whole of the metazoan body? The issue has been argued with greater vigour in the past than is ever likely again. Yet it still deserves attention, for it has a bearing on the methodology of research into protozoan and cell biology, and on the interpretation of its results.

Dobell was responsible for one of the most powerful polemics in this field when, in 1911, he argued from the point of view of a protozoologist that a cell 'is part of an organism and not a whole organism'. He was strongly opposed to the idea that a protozoan (or protist) was homologous with a single cell in the body of a metazoan, a view that he considered to be an unfortunate product of the Cell Theory. He insisted instead that

> A protist is no more homologous with one cell in a metazoan than it is homologous with one organ (e.g. the brain or liver) of the latter. Only the cytologist blinded by what he sees through the microscope could ever believe in such a preposterous proposition. Fallopius, Wolff, von Baer, and the older biologists were prevented from falling into such an error owing to the imperfections of early microscopes.

His solution to the difficulties that he felt had been created by the over-rigid application of the Cell Theory was to define as Metazoa and Metaphyta all organisms possessing a cellular structure, and to define as Protista those possessing a non-cellular structure.

> The cell thus vanishes and can be replaced by facts as soon as we give a definite and objective meaning to the word 'cell'. That the Metazoa and Metaphyta are organisms composed of cells in much the same way that a house is built of bricks, is not a theory but a fact. Anybody who can use a microscope can easily convince himself that this is so.

In the context of the times Dobell's attack upon the tendency to dismiss the Protozoa as 'simple' organisms was valuable. Yet his assertion as a 'fact' that the use of a microscope would reveal a similarity between an organism with its cells and a house with its bricks was a dangerously over-simplified use of analogy, a hazard always faced by biologists in their search for models upon which to base their arguments.

Dobell was not alone in his views; they were supported by Minchin, a no less distinguished contemporary of his.

> The view generally held that the entire organism of a protozoan is truly homologous with a single body cell of a metazoan seems to me quite unassailable. . . . On the other hand, any protist, as an organism physiologically complete in itself, is clearly analogous to the entire individual in the Metazoa—a comparison, however, which leaves the question of genetic homology quite untouched.

We have said that this controversy is still alive. Dobell's view has been restated in different terms as recently as 1957. The effect of this restatement was to show that all passion had not yet been spent, for it led Boyden to reply that it was

> a contradiction of every valid demonstrable criterion of homology. . . . We say, on the contrary, that because of their essential structural correspondence part for part with the cells of Metazoa, Protozoa are undoubtedly cellular. Thus nuclei are the homologs of nuclei, cytosomes with their constituent parts are each homologs of the corresponding parts of the cells of Metazoa.

Boyden expressed his agreement with those who

> believe that cellular organization was a necessary step in the evolution of such systems and was early achieved and has been consistently maintained since. . . . The Cell Theory stands as one of the valid generalizations about the protoplasmic systems of animals.

This forthright statement aroused Hutner and Provasoli to reply that 'Boyden's strictures . . . are symptomatic of a malaise that is affecting research on the organization of cellular animals.' This malaise, they explained, is the neglect of the problem of the requisites for cellular existence, and a disregard of the differentiations and interdependencies of cells. 'Protozoa are organisms first, with some homologies to cells.' In amplification of this dictum, which illustrates the bearing of the controversy on the methodology of research, they argued that

> Protozoa are homologous in their general structure to the cells of Metazoa, but . . . they have the autonomy of the whole organism. We contend, therefore, that it is necessary to be clear about where the homology of cell to cell ends and where the homology of cell to organism starts.

It would take us too far afield to consider all the facets of these conflicting views, and of the terminology in which they are expressed, but our earlier discussion of the concepts of homology and analogy is clearly relevant, as also is our brief reference to the principles of scientific method. We have seen that the progress of science depends upon the formulation of hypotheses, which are then subjected to tests designed to disprove or corroborate them. Usually these hypotheses will be limited in scope, for this makes it easier to test them. If they range over too wide a field of thought, and include too extensive a range of possibilities, it may be difficult to find ways of disproving them. It is in this respect that the predictions of the Delphic oracle differed from the assertions of the twentieth-century scientist—or so we should wish to believe.

However, in our search for order in natural phenomena, and for the means of controlling them, we cannot afford to rest content with limited hypotheses. We prefer instead to systematize and extend our understanding by framing what are called theories. These are attempts to achieve a higher level of integration by grouping a series of statements into a system which is intended to provide a logical account or explanation of a range of natural phenomena. The individual statements may themselves be hypotheses, or they may be axioms (matters that are taken for granted). Or again they may be straightforward raw material of the kind called assertions or postulates, which are often just simple working ideas formulated as a basis for action. These various terms carry no sharply defined meanings. Indeed, the term 'theory' itself is sometimes used as synonymous with 'hypothesis', but the sense in which we are using it here is a common one, and it is in this sense that we can speak of the Cell Theory.

The content of this theory has been usefully analyzed by Baker into seven propositions, stated here in summary form:

1. Most organisms contain or consist of a large number of microscopical bodies called 'cells'.
2. Cells have certain definable characters which show that cells are all of essentially the same nature and are units of structure.
3. Cells arise from pre-existing cells.
4. Cells sometimes become transformed into bodies no longer possessing all the characters of cells.
5. Cells are to some extent individuals, so that in most organisms there are two grades of individuality, that of the cell and that of the organism as a whole.
6. Each cell of a metazoan corresponds in certain respects to the whole body of a simple protist.
7. Metazoa and Metaphyta probably originated by the adherence of protist individuals after division.

If these propositions are viewed as a whole, it becomes clear why there has been such disagreement regarding the validity of the Cell Theory. The last of them is a statement of a hypothesis; it cannot be tested by experiment, and it certainly would not be universally accepted; there is a strongly argued view (Sec. 18–4) that Metazoa arose by the subdivision of a multinucleate protozoan. This view implies, contrary to the sixth proposition, that it is the whole body of a metazoan that corresponds with the whole body of a protist. It is because of this disagreement that one writer can homologize the protozoan body with a single cell, and another deny this homology.

Proposition 5 also creates difficulties, for it raises the question of the nature and definition of individuality, while proposition 2 rests on an agreed selection of the 'definable characters' concerned, and leaves unresolved the question of what is meant by being of 'essentially the same nature'. Proposition 3 may seem unexceptionable, yet, curiously enough, Dobell found this to present a serious difficulty. By insisting that a cell must be part of a body, he was led by his own logic to the conclusion that a fertilized ovum was a whole organism and not a cell, but that cells arose from it during cleavage.

These difficulties, which could be pursued in much greater detail than is possible here, show that the Cell Theory in its entirety is too complex and far-ranging to provide an effective tool for an analytical approach to animal organization. The root of the problem has been clearly stated by Woodger. The classical definition of the cell as a mass of protoplasm with its associated nucleus is a highly abstract concept, and it is because of this that the concept can be so widely generalized. Not only is this concept of the cell an abstraction from the more complex reality that we perceive with the microscope, but even this more complex perceptual object is still an abstraction. This is necessarily so, because even the most perfect microscope preparation fails to reveal all the details of cell organization, and it inevitably omits the greater part of the functional relationships of the cell. Indeed, the concept of the individuality of the cell becomes progressively less meaningful as we learn more and more of the control of cells by neural and humoral processes, their dependence upon metabolites, and their regulation by internal and external feedback mechanisms.

There is much to be said for a suggestion put forward by Grimstone. Arguing from the abstract nature of the cell concept, he points out that our interpretation of cell problems, and specifically of the relationship of the cell to the protozoan body, must depend upon the context in which a particular problem is put. In some respects (and we shall see more of this below) it is undoubtedly possible and useful to compare the protozoan body with a single cell of a metazoan, and the conclusion is an empirical one (arising, that is, out of our experiment). This is a matter of fact. It may be regarded as a necessary consequence of the point that we have earlier made: that life is dependent upon certain patterns of molecular organization. Such a comparison is likely, therefore, to be helpful in furthering our understanding of cytological problems. In other respects, as in considerations of behaviour and life history, the individual protozoan must be compared with the whole metazoan organism, regardless of what view we may take of the way in which the Metazoa evolved from Protozoa.

Looked at in this way, there is no simple and final answer to the question whether the Protozoa are, in the classical sense, unicellular or non-cellular. The answer we give depends upon the form of the question that is being asked, and is not a complete and definitive statement. It is simply a recommendation to treat the facts in a particular way in that particular context. This flexibility of approach to problems of definition and interpretation in the biological sciences is a quality essential for the biologist to cultivate.

The need for this quality is well enough seen if we seek in a standard dictionary for a definition of 'organism'. It is, we learn, an 'organized body with connected interdependent parts sharing common life', and a 'whole with interdependent parts compared to living being'. On these definitions, the metazoan cell is clearly an organism, although it is also part of a larger organism that operates at a higher level of integration. Moreover, it is impossible to accept a lack of complete independence as an absolute and distinctive feature of a cell. The most superficial consideration of the living world shows that no organism, protozoan or metazoan, can live a life entirely independent of others, and we shall see in due course that the mechanisms by which members of communities are linked together and subjected to mutual control may be no different in fundamental principle from those that regulate the lives of cells within metazoan bodies.

2–4 MEMBRANES AND ORGANIZATION

The widespread distribution of the differentiated nucleus of the eucellular plan of structure is one aspect, and a familiar one, of uniformity in the organization of living material. Others have emerged in the more penetrating analysis made possible by electron microscopy.

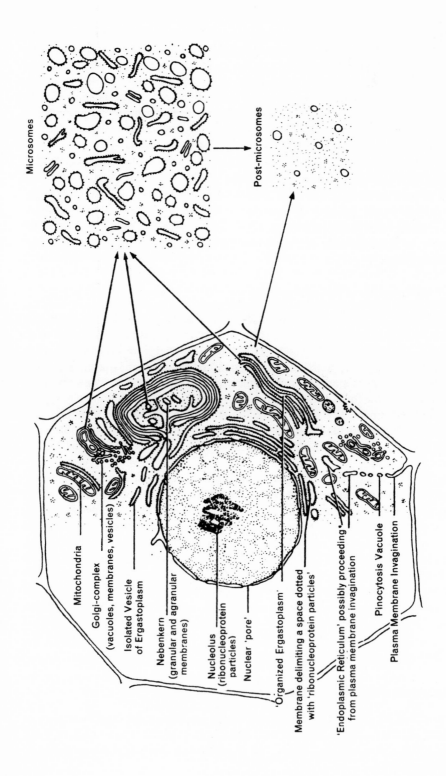

Microsomes

Post-microsomes

Mitochondria

Golgi-complex
(vacuoles, membranes, vesicles)

Isolated Vesicle
of Ergastoplasm

Nebenkern
(granular and agranular
membranes)

Nucleolus
(ribonucleoprotein
particles)

Nuclear 'pore'

'Organized Ergastoplasm'

Membrane delimiting a space dotted
with 'ribonucleoprotein particles'

'Endoplasmic Reticulum' possibly proceeding
from plasma membrane invagination

Pinocytosis Vacuole

Plasma Membrane Invagination

Fig. 2-2. Diagrammatic representation of cell ultrastructure. From Haguenau, 1958.
Int. Rev. Cytol., **7**, 425–483.

One example is the widespread development of membranes. We have already referred to the membrane of the nucleus; others are found both within the cell and over its surface (Fig. 2–2). The surface membrane (plasma membrane) has a tripartite structure, detectable with electron microscopy as a central light zone separating two dark ones; its total thickness is of the order of 75 Å, each zone having a thickness within the range of 20–30 Å. (An angstrom unit, Å, is 10^{-7} mm.) Consideration of the physico-chemical properties of such cell membranes (conveniently referred to as unit membranes) led Danielli to suggest, prior to the advent of electron microscopy, that each consisted (Figs. 2–3 and 2–4) of two layers of lipid molecules, the polar (electrically charged) surfaces of which faced outwards and bore a covering of adsorbed protein molecules. The lipid components would form unimolecular films, and the protein would increase the stability of these. Electron micrographs subsequently confirmed this interpretation in a striking way, for the central layer corresponds well with the lipid zone postulated by Danielli, and the outer layers with the protein component.

Fig. 2-3. *Right,* structure of cell membrane, according to Danielli. From Davson and Danielli, 1943. *The Permeability of Natural Membranes.* Cambridge University Press, London.

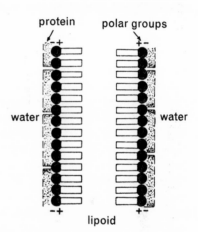

Fig. 2-4. *Below,* a detail of the structure of the cell membrane (cf. Fig. 2-3). The polar groups of the protein are in roughly the same plane as those of the fatty molecules, and the hydrocarbon parts of the protein extend into the fatty layer. From Davson and Danielli, 1943. *op. cit.*

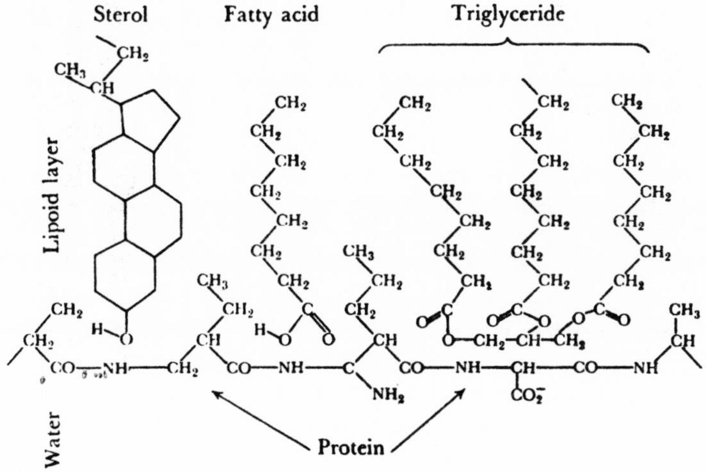

On this interpretation the unit membrane is an example of precisely orientated molecular structure, the biological significance of which lies in the opportunity that it provides for the controlled exchange of materials between the two media separated by such a membrane (the cytoplasm and the external environment, for example, if the membrane lies at the surface of a cell). The lipid component accounts for the ready passage of fat-soluble substances, while the protein gives elasticity and strength, and is responsible for the observed low surface tension. Pores are probably present in the plasma membrane, and these would explain to some extent why molecules of different sizes pass through with different degrees of ease. Other factors are also needed, however, to account for the complex relationships of cytoplasm with the external medium, and to explain why, for example, potassium accumulates much more readily within the cell than does sodium. It may be that the molecular orientation of the membrane structure provides for regional differences in electrical charge, for example, or in the distribution of adsorbed enzymes. Cells, by the expenditure of energy, can also cause substances to move across membranes in directions contrary to the trends of their concentration gradients. This is the phenomenon known as active transport, which we shall encounter in other contexts. In short, a plasma membrane is a semipermeable membrane of a remarkable type, involved in activities that are unpredictable in purely physical terms. Its properties, moreover, are continuously variable, and are subject to regulation both from within the cell and from agents acting upon it from the external medium.

Unit membranes are as much characteristic of the surface of the protozoan body as they are of the surface of the metazoan cell, so that here, as in other respects to be mentioned later, direct comparison of the two types of organism is both permissible and profitable. Since, however, a protozoan depends upon this membrane for the protection of its body surface, there are necessarily various modifications and elaborations of its structure. It is found in a relatively simple form as the surface membrane (plasmalemma) of the amoeboid Sarcodina (Rhizopoda), although even here it may be modified to bear a continuous covering of filamentous molecules, as in *Amoeba*, where the filaments are thought to be mucoproteins that possibly facilitate adhesion of the animal to the substratum.

In many other protozoans the body surface is much more complex than this. It may be thickened to form a highly differentiated layer like the longitudinally striated pellicle of *Euglena*; this is formed of two separate membranes, about 8 mμ apart (1 mμ = 10 Å), the outer one being a unit membrane of the general type just described. Still more complex is the body surface of the Ciliata. Light microscopy reveals that in *Paramecium*, for example, there is a cortex which is sculptured over its surface into a regular series of polygons, with a cilium (or sometimes a pair of cilia) arising from the middle of each (Fig. 2–5). The cortex as a whole is covered by a typical unit membrane which extends onto the cilia. The polygons are defined by a correspondingly regular series of cavities or alveoli, which form the alveolar layer that has also long been known from light microscopy. These alveoli are delimited by membranes, which are continuous from one alveolus to another. Thus in effect the body surface of *Paramecium* consists of a series of three membranes, the inner two of which are separated from each other at intervals to form the alveolar cavities.

We have seen that in the eucellular plan of structure the nucleus is separated from the cytoplasm by a nuclear membrane. This is significantly thicker than the

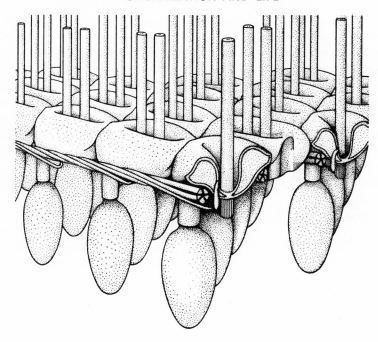

Fig. 2-5. Diagrammatic reconstruction of the cortex of *Paramecium*. Each pair of cilia emerges from the centre of a polygon; the pairs of inflated alveoli defining the polygons are shown in section at the right edge of the stereogram. Parasomal sacs are shown adjacent to the cilia in these polygons. Resting trichocysts alternate with the polygons in longitudinal rows. Kinetodesmal fibres form loose cables paralleling each kinety. (See also p. 49.) From Corliss, 1961. *The Ciliated Protozoa*. Pergamon Press, Oxford.

plasma membrane, for it commonly reaches a thickness of at least 20 mμ, and sometimes much more than this. In *Trichonympha*, for example, as studied by Grimstone, there are two membranes, each about 7 mμ thick, separated by a space about 23 mμ thick. The outer membrane is perforated by pores, which probably facilitate the passage of large molecules. It seems also to be common in Metazoa, and perhaps also in Protozoa, for this membrane to extend outwards at intervals and to become continuous with the system of membrane-lined cavities known as the endoplasmic reticulum (see below). It is reasonable to suppose that these extensions, like the pores, could provide pathways for the exchanges that must be continuously occurring between the nucleus and the cytoplasm.

The importance of membranes in protoplasmic organization is by no means confined to the surfaces of the cell and of its nucleus. It was suspected long before the introduction of electron microscopy that the coordinated functioning of the diverse metabolic pathways of the cell must depend on the separation of their components by some form of compartmental division of the cytoplasm. This belief has now received ample corroboration, one example being the elucidation of the structure of the cell organelles known as mitochondria (Figs. 2-2 and 2-6). The surface of these is formed of two unit membranes separated from each other by a space of about 10 mμ, but what is particularly characteristic of mitochondria is that the inner membrane gives rise to a number of inwardly directed projections. In the cells of metazoans (and also of land plants) these projections usually form flat plates called cristae. Sometimes, however, they extend into more complex and elongated structures called microtubules; these are particularly common in Protozoa, in which mitochondria are as readily identifiable as in metazoan cells.

It is well established that the mitochondria of metazoan cells are the site of the oxidative processes comprising the citric acid cycle, and that they carry the enzymes

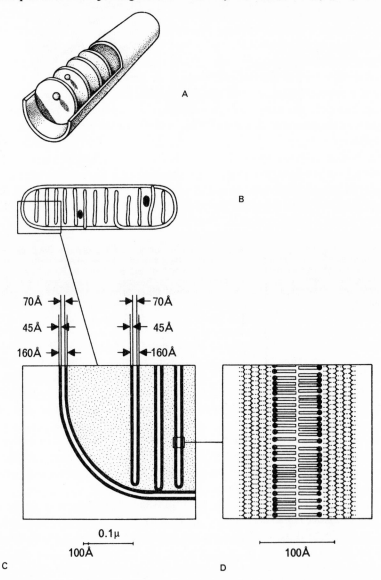

Fig. 2-6. Schematic three-dimensional presentation of the ultrastructural organization of the mitochondria of kidney tubules. A, mitochondrion. B, the mitochondrion as seen in a thin section. C, dimensions of the mitochondrion membranes. D, tentative interpretation of the observed pattern in terms of molecular organization, with two protein layers separated by a double layer of lipid molecules. From Sjostrand, 1956. *Int. Rev. Cytol.*, **5**, 455–533.

required for this cycle, together with its associated respiratory chains of cytochromes. Just as we have supposed that the properties of the cell membrane are in part attributable to the distribution in it of active molecules, so it is reasonably certain that the membranes and fluid-filled lumen of a mitochondrion provide for the orderly arrangement of the enzymes required for the oxidative metabolism of the cell. These enzymes, to quote Palade, may be thought of as 'built in, or woven into, the texture of the mitochondrial membranes in the same manner as repeated decorative patterns are woven into a sheet of damask'. A less colourful analogy is with a production belt, along which the complex molecules are passed as their energy is transformed into high-energy phosphate bonds. The significance of these analogies lies in the element of pattern that they emphasize, for this is what the evolution of protoplasmic membranes made possible. Mitochondria can be fragmented. When this has been done their component enzymes can still be identified, but they no longer interact in the orderly manner characteristic of the intact organelles, for the pattern of organization has been broken.

We have seen reasons for believing that aerobic oxidation must have been established early in chemical evolution. The existence of a common pattern of mitochondrion in Protozoa and Metazoa is in keeping with this view, for it suggests that both groups may well have inherited this type of organelle from a common ancestry. On the other hand, our discussion of homology has left open the possibility of the independent evolution of similar structures. It is thus conceivable that mitochondria might have evolved independently more than once, as the only feasible solution to the structural problem of isolating well-integrated enzyme systems. There can be no certainty of interpretation here. It should be added that conclusions regarding the functioning of mitochondria in Protozoa are to some extent inferential, for little direct evidence is available. There is, however, some indirect evidence that suggests their involvement in oxidative metabolism. For example, mitochondria are absent from *Trichonympha*, which lives within the alimentary tract of termites. This protozoan is an obligate anaerobe, presumably in adaptation to life in an environment in which the supply of oxygen is limited. In these conditions the animal is unlikely to be able to carry out the oxidative phosphorylation that is the end result of mitochondrial activity in the metazoan cell, so that the loss of mitochondria would be an understandable consequence of physiological adaptation to an entozoic mode of life.

Another feature of the metazoan cell is the presence of groups of unit membranes, usually arranged as stacks of flattened sacs or cisternae, with granules on their outer surfaces (Fig. 2-2). These structures constitute the ergastoplasm, which is chemically characterized by its granules, or ribosomes, which are composed of ribonucleic acid (RNA). RNA is chemically very similar to DNA, differing in that the deoxyribose sugar is replaced by ribose, and thymine by uracil. Current interpretations of the ergastoplasm are based upon the belief that some RNA is synthesized in the nucleus under the influence of the DNA of the chromosomes, and that in this way the coded instructions in the latter are transferred to the macromolecules of a particular fraction of the newly synthesized RNA. This, in the form of what is called messenger RNA, is then thought to pass into the cytoplasm (perhaps through the pores and channels already mentioned). Protein synthesis is believed to be the particular function of the ergastoplasm and its ribosomes. Amino acids are thought to become attached to the ribosomes through the activity of another form of RNA, called transfer RNA. The precise form of the protein molecules thus synthesized is then determined by the instructions delivered to the ergastoplasm by the messenger RNA. This sequence of events, if we are correct in interpreting the function of RNA in this way, must be central to the organized functioning of the cell, for its complex metabolic pathways are sequences of enzyme-mediated reactions. The enzymes, being themselves proteins, will (on this interpretation) be elaborated by the ergasto-plasm. Thus the pattern of metabolism within the cell will be determined by coded instructions derived from the nucleus.

It is to be expected that this mechanism of control would, like the other aspects of protoplasmic organization that we have mentioned, be a product of early chemical evolution. We might, therefore, expect to find it established in the Protozoa. Probably it is, for granule-studded membranes similar to those of the ergastoplasm are present in Protozoa, although typically in the form of single sacs rather than as aggregates. These may be equivalent to the ergastoplasm of Metazoa, although there is no certain evidence that this is so; moreover, some Protozoa may have granules that are un-attached to membranes, while in other species both granules and membranes may be missing.

Metazoan cells also contain unit membranes that are similar in general character to those of the ergastoplasm but which lack the granules. These membranes are known as smooth membranes. Some of them correspond in position with the organ-elles that were known in terms of classical light microscopy as the Golgi bodies. The very existence of these bodies was at one time a matter of dispute, but the evidence of electron microscopy has shown that they are indeed present, and that they are com-posed of piles of flattened membranous sacs. In many cells these may be diffusely distributed through the cytoplasm, but in the sperm of most animals, and in many other cells of invertebrates, they are localized to form disc-shaped bodies called dictyosomes. The Golgi bodies may participate in the secretory activity of the cell (e.g. Fig. 17-1), perhaps by concentrating and processing material that has been synthesized elsewhere under the influence of the ergastoplasm. Minute vesicles are often associated with the Golgi membranes. It is believed that secreted products are pinched off from the Golgi region in these, and so distributed to other parts of the cell, or eventually extruded from it.

That the Golgi bodies are concerned with some fundamental activity that is common to all organized protoplasm is suggested by the fact that similar structures have now been identified by electron microscopy in many Protozoa, including flagellates, gregarines, and ciliates. They are particularly well known in flagellates, where they take the form either of dictyosomes, like those of the Metazoa, or of para-basal bodies, which are essentially similar except that they are long and cylindrical in form, and are connected by a striated fibre to a centriole. Possibly these protozoan structures, too, are secretory, but there is no certainty that this is so.

Finally, in addition to the clearly defined types of membranous structures so far mentioned, there appears to be a complex system of membranous compartments or channels extending throughout the cytoplasm of the metazoan cell. These channels are thought to open externally at the plasma membrane and internally at the outer of the two nuclear membranes. According to one view they form, with the ergastoplasm and the Golgi membranes, a complex that provides a transport system linking all parts of the cell with each other and with the external medium. On this interpretation the various types of cytoplasmic membrane form a continuous system of communication, the endoplasmic reticulum. Through it could be passed the products of nuclear and cytoplasmic metabolism, while materials could also be taken into the cell and discharged from it by the same route. There is still doubt as to the correctness of this interpretation. It is not certain that the various membranes are continuous in this way, and there is little, if any, direct observational evidence that transport takes place through their channels. Moreover, it is possible that some of these membranes may be highly labile, disappearing and reforming in accordance with the demands established by the varying states of activity of the cell. In fact, the account given of them here, and the illustration of a cell shown in Fig. 2–2, are to be taken as no more than very generalized statements of cell organization. Each specialized type of cell may be expected to display its own variation upon this fundamental theme, closely adapted to the particular function for which it is responsible.

This brief review by no means exhausts the importance of the part played by unit membranes in protoplasmic organization. They are concerned, for example, in other and clearly defined functions in the Protozoa, and we shall deal with them later in connection with digestion and osmoregulation. We have seen enough, however, to suggest that the use made of these membranes in metazoan cells is very closely paralleled in protozoans. Some degree of parallelism could no doubt be acceptably explained as a consequence of independent evolution, but in these instances the parallelism seems to go beyond that limit. We are left rather with the impression that the complex metabolic pathways of living systems must from very early stages have been dependent for their orderly integration upon the physical properties of layers of orientated molecules. It seems very likely, therefore, that these properties were already being exploited in the early stages of chemical evolution, and that Protozoa and Metazoa have inherited their common plan of protoplasmic organization from the patterns that became stabilized at that time under the influence of natural selection.

3
Movement and Fibrils

3–1 MUSCLE FILAMENTS AND MYONEMES

The building of organic molecules into membranes is a principle of protoplasmic organization that has clearly lent itself to far-reaching exploitation. No less fertile has been another structural device, the polymerization of large protein molecules into fibrous threads. These have been widely used for effecting various types of movement in animals. Consideration of some examples will again show that living systems prove to be remarkably uniform when they are analyzed at the molecular level.

The most widely studied of these fibrillar structures are those that characterize the muscle fibres of mammals, and we refer first to these since the principles involved in their organization and functioning are thought to be of wide applicability. The fibres (Fig. 3–1) are formed of a modified cytoplasm, the sarcoplasm, surrounded by a membrane, the sarcolemma, the whole fibre consisting either of a single specialized cell or of a syncytium. The important property of a muscle fibre is its power of contraction, which, as we shall see later, can bring about movement when the fibre is associated with some form of skeletal structure. Contraction is an expression of the properties of protein molecules that are organized into threads called muscle filaments, or myofilaments (Fig. 3–2). These, which in mammalian muscle have a diameter within the range of 50 Å to 100 Å, may themselves be grouped into myofibrils. The best known of the muscle proteins are actin (with a molecular weight of 60,000) and myosin (a long molecule with a molecular weight of about 420,000). two proteins combine to form actomyosin, and it is this interaction that is the of the process of contraction. Current views of this process rest heavily upon uxley's work on the myofibril of the psoas muscle of the rabbit. This consists filaments of actin, 50 Å in diameter, and thick filaments of myosin, 100 Å in (Fig. 3–2). The myofibril is divided into units, or sarcomeres, by the so-called which the thin filaments appear to be attached. Between the thin filaments ck ones, the whole array forming a hexagonal pattern when seen in trans- on. The cross-striated appearance of the muscle results from the regular

36

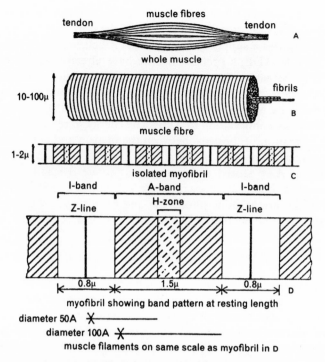

Fig. 3-1. The structure of striated muscle at different levels of organization; dimensions shown are those for rabbit psoas muscle. From Huxley, H. E., 1960. *The Cell*, vol. 4 (Brachet and Mirsky, eds.) Academic Press, New York.

alternation of strongly birefringent regions (the anisotropic bands, or A-bands) and weakly birefringent regions (the isotropic bands, or I-bands). A lighter H-zone is situated in the middle of the A-band. Of these several regions, the A-band is interpreted as being composed of overlapping thick and thin filaments, the I-band of thin filaments, and the H-zone of thick filaments. Contraction is thought to be a result of the thick and thin filaments being brought into combination by complex systems of cross-linkages formed of myosin; during the process the actin and myosin filaments

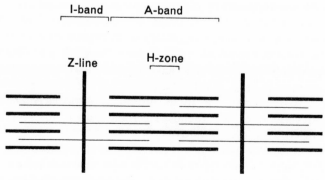

Fig. 3-2. Diagram of the relationships of actin filaments (thin) and myosin filaments (thick) of striated muscle.

are believed to slide past each other as a result of the actin filaments moving inwards, and it is this movement that causes a shortening of the fibre.

Contraction requires a supply of energy. This is believed to be released by the breakdown of ATP to ADP, a process that we have already seen to be of central importance in cell energetics. There is disagreement regarding the precise role of ATP in this connection, but it is probable that it depends upon myosin possessing what is termed ATP-ase activity. This means that myosin is able to react with ATP to bring about its dephosphorylation to ADP. The energy so released is then thought to promote the formation of 'bridges' between the myosin and actin filaments; this brings about contraction, perhaps by some form of direct traction.

The amount of ATP stored within muscular tissue is small, but reserves of energy-rich phosphate bonds are present in the substances called phosphagens, the best known of which are arginine phosphate and creatine phosphate. ADP reacts with these to form arginine or creatine as the case may be, according to the reversible equation:

$$\text{creatine phosphate} + \text{ADP} \rightleftharpoons \text{creatine} + \text{ATP}$$

These can be regenerated to high-energy phosphates by ATP. The phosphagens thus provide reserves of energy-rich phosphate bonds for the immediate regeneration of ATP from ADP, but the source of energy for continued muscular activity is the energy-rich phosphate bonds provided by glycolysis. These also provide for the regeneration of the phosphagens. The main phosphagen of invertebrates is arginine phosphate, whereas creatine phosphate is characteristic of vertebrates. However, the belief that this distinction is an absolute one, and that the echinoderms, hemichordates, and protochordates are something of a bridge in this respect between invertebrates and vertebrates, is now known to be an over-simplification. For example, various phosphagens, including creatine phosphate, have been identified in annelid worms.

This interpretation applies primarily to a striated muscle in a particular mammal; only the future will show how universal is the mechanism thus postulated. It is certain that muscular tissue of other groups shows much variation in histological structure and rates of contraction. For example, the myofibrils in the smooth locomotor muscles of annelids and cephalopods are arranged in a helical pattern, in contrast to the linear arrangement of classical smooth muscle. Such variations may well prove to be accompanied by differences in chemical composition and in the pattern of energy exchanges. Yet, although information here is very fragmentary, enough is known to indicate some uniformity in the organization of muscular tissue throughout the animal kingdom. That this is characterized by the possession of myofibrils is well known. These fibrils must have appeared early in metazoan evolution, and so also, we may assume, did their tendency for precise transverse alignment, expressed as cross-striations, for these, although particularly characteristic of arthropods and vertebrates, are found in certain muscle fibres of almost every phylum from the coelenterates upwards.

As for the proteins involved, actomyosin has been identified in the muscles of arthropods, although it is not always as readily separable into actin and myosin as it is in mammals. Other contractile proteins, however, are also known. Thus the muscles of annelids, arthropods, and molluscs contain tropomyosin, which is also present in the striated muscle of mammals, while molluscs have another protein, paramyosin, which closely resembles tropomyosin in its properties and is, perhaps, identical with it. The properties of these proteins, and, in particular, their capacity for reacting with ATP, can be studied by various procedures, one of which consists of treating the muscle with 50% glycerol. This extracts soluble materials, but leaves the fibrous proteins. Many kinds of muscle treated in this way respond to the presence of ATP by contraction, and by the development of tension. It is also possible to detect the ATP-ase activity of extracts of muscular tissue. This activity has been demonstrated in a wide range of contractile tissues, including those of sea-anemones, echiuroids, and crayfish. There is some reason, then, for supposing that the contractile mechanisms of these forms are similar in principle to the mammalian mechanism outlined above.

The use of muscular tissue for effecting movement is a specialized element of metazoan organization, demanding concomitant specialization in other tissues. It has not been evolved by sponges, and is necessarily absent from Protozoa. Obviously, then, the development of powers of movement in living systems preceded the evolution of muscle fibres. It is thus necessary to examine what other modes of movement have become available for animals, and, in so doing, to enquire whether the underlying biochemical mechanisms have anything in common with those of muscles. Bearing in mind what we have already learned of the widespread distribution of common metabolic pathways, we might well expect to find diverse modes of movement depending on very similar biochemical mechanisms. Again the evidence is fragmentary, yet there is some reason for believing this expectation to be well founded.

Fibrillar systems are particularly well developed within the bodies of Protozoa, and in some instances are associated with contractile properties, although in others they are possibly involved in support or conduction. An example is seen in the ciliate *Stentor*, one of the many protozoans that are able to change their shape very quickly. In the posterior region of its body there are fibrils called the endoplasmic myonemes, one corresponding to each row of cilia. These are revealed by the electron microscope as either structureless or formed of filaments, and it is generally assumed

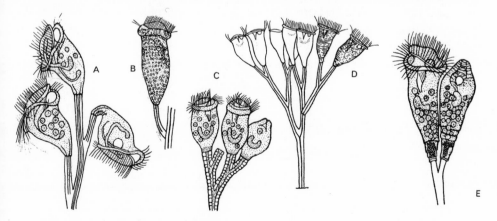

Fig. 3-3. A, *Carchesium polypinum*, ×200; B, *C. granulatum*, ×220; C, *Zoothamnium arbuscula*, ×200; D, *Z. adamis*, ×150; E, *Epistylis plicatilis*, ×200. From Kudo, 1960. *Protozoology* (4th ed.). Courtesy of Charles C. Thomas, Publisher, Springfield, Ill.

that they are contractile organelles, for they become markedly thickened when the animal contracts.

Similar myonemes occur in peritrichous ciliates (Fig. 3-3), and here there is a strong presumption that they are concerned in contraction, for in certain sessile forms, such as *Vorticella*, *Carchesium*, and *Zoothamnium*, they run together towards the base of the organism and continue into the stalk as a central structure called the spasmoneme, formed of bundles of filaments. In *Carchesium* each zooid contracts separately because it has a separate spasmoneme, but in *Zoothamnium* all the spasmonemes are continuous, so that stimulation of one individual results in contraction of the whole colony. It is of obvious significance that a spasmoneme is not found in certain other genera, such as *Epistylis* (Fig. 3-3), in which the stalk is not contractile. Myonemes are also present in gregarines, where they run longitudinally, transversely, and perhaps spirally. These organisms show a characteristic gliding movement, and it has generally been assumed that it is the myonemes that make this possible. However, our knowledge of these structures, here and in other Protozoa, is incomplete, and any interpretation of the facts must be largely inferential. Nevertheless, there is cytochemical evidence for the presence of ATP in the myonemes of vorticellids, so that there is at least some basis for supposing that the mode of functioning of these structures may have something in common with that of myofibrils.

3-2 FLAGELLA AND CILIA

More satisfactory evidence for a common plan of organization in the contractile systems of animals is to be found in the flagella and cilia which, with certain associated fibrillar systems, provide organelles of movement for many Protozoa, and which continue to function as important effector structures in most groups of animals. The exceptions are the Nematoda, from which they are entirely absent, and the Arthropoda, where they persist only in the excretory and reproductive systems of the Onychophora, in the sperms of some insects, and, in a modified form, in certain receptor organs.

Electron microscopy has shown that flagella and cilia have the same fundamental structure. The difference between them lies in their mode of beating, and in the type of movement that this produces. Both are adapted for action in a fluid medium. If they are attached to a fixed surface they set up motion in the medium relative to the

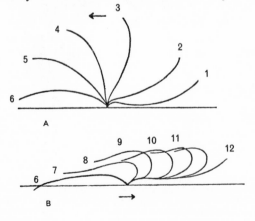

Fig. 3-4. A, forward effective stroke of frontal cilium of *Mytilus*. Note the rigid form during the whole stroke. B, backward preparatory stroke of frontal cilium of *Mytilus*. Note the flexible nature of the cilium. The flexure begins at the base and spreads to the tip. From Gray, 1928. *Ciliary Movement.* Cambridge University Press, London.

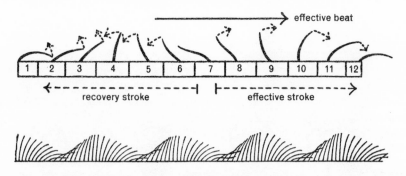

Fig. 3-5. *Above,* diagram to illustrate metachronal rhythm. Cilia *1* and *12* are at the end of the effective stroke; *2-7* indicate successive stages during the recovery stroke; *8-11* indicate stages during the effective stroke. All the cilia *1-12* are beating in sequence. *Below,* diagram illustrating the optical appearance given by a profile view of cilia beating in metachronal rhythm. From Gray, 1928. *op. cit.*

surface. If, however, they arise from a movable object then this is caused to move in relation to the medium. The difference between the results of flagellar and ciliary action arises from the beat of a flagellum (Fig. 3-12, p. 47) being often symmetrical, with several waves included in it at any one moment, whereas the beat of a cilium is asymmetrical and includes only one wave. In consequence, the flagellum is able to move the fluid medium continuously throughout its beat, and in such a way that the movement is at right angles to the surface of attachment. The cilium, by contrast, has an active phase, during which movement is brought about, and a recovery phase, which produces no significant movement (Fig. 3-4). The movement of the fluid is in this case parallel to the surface of attachment. Further, cilia are typically much more densely massed than flagella, and their beats are coordinated in the well-known pattern of metachronal rhythm (Fig. 3-5), conventionally compared to the passage of wind over a field of wheat.

In earlier days it was natural, but incorrect, to assume that the apparently simple amoeboid movement of sarcodine (rhizopod) Protozoa was the most primitive type of animal locomotion. We shall see reasons for supposing that the underlying mechanism of amoeboid movement may be similar in principle to that of flagellar and ciliary movement. The primitive status of flagellar movement, however, is clearly indicated by it being the characteristic mode of locomotion in the Mastigophora. This group undoubtedly occupies a basal position in protozoan phylogeny, as we shall see when we consider modes of nutrition in these animals. It is reasonable, therefore, to conclude that cilia were evolved from flagella. Pseudopodial movement must also have evolved in a stock with a flagellate ancestry, but here the structural basis can be detected only with the electron microscope, and even then with the greatest difficulty.

The close relationship of mastigophoran and sarcodine protozoans is better shown by the existence of flagellate reproductive stages in some of the latter— e.g. *Elphidium (Polystomella).* There are also adult forms that have both flagella and pseudopodia either simultaneously (Fig. 3-12, p. 47) or in two separate phases. Examples are seen in the phytomastigine order Chrysomonadina; many members of this group can assume an amoeboid form, and may even lose their flagella and chloro-

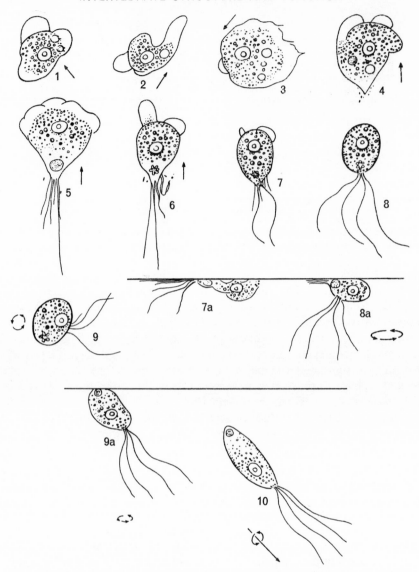

Fig. 3-6. Diagrammatic representation of the change of form of *Naegleria* when the organism is placed in distilled water. The arrows indicate the direction of motion. *1–3*, amoeboid form; *4*, 'polarized' form; *5, 6*, filiform pseudopodia present; *7–10*, acquisition of flagella. *7a–9a* are schematic of how events would appear if seen from the side when the amoeba leaves the surface of the coverslip. From Willmer, 1960. *Cytology and Evolution*. Academic Press, London.

plasts so that they then become virtually indistinguishable from typical sarcodinians. An example of the reverse transformation is seen in the sarcodine *Naegleria gruberi* (Fig. 3-6). This organism normally lives in the soil, where it ingests bacteria. Transformation to a flagellate phase takes place in laboratory cultures when the medium is diluted with pure water. At first the body becomes polarized in organization, with lobose pseudopodia at one end and filiform pseudopodia at the other; flagella then appear among the latter, and the organism passes into the flagellate phase. This phase, which is freely motile, is a transient one; it has been suggested by Willmer that it may be a response enabling the organism to obtain fresh food supplies or to reach an environment which is in other respects more suitable. In short, it can get the best of both worlds.

The forces set up by flagella and cilia are small, and are totally inadequate for the production of lively movement in larger animals. They do, nevertheless, serve some locomotor function in lower metazoans such as the smaller platyhelminths. In general, however, locomotion is provided for in Metazoa by the differentiation of muscle cells. It is these, acting in conjunction with skeletal structures, that have permitted the development of the large size of so many of these animals. Flagella and cilia often persist in them, but only to carry out limited functions. These can be understood in the light of the above-mentioned characteristics of their two modes of action.

Flagella create the feeding currents of sponges, and they provide for the movement of sperm in most animal groups. They serve also to propel fluid along slender tubes, notably in the protonephridia of the lower Metazoa. In contrast to this, the coordinated beat of cilia is used to effect the movement of fluid over surfaces. Examples are seen in the filter-feeding mechanisms of many Metazoa, and in the lining epithelium of alimentary canals. Cilia also provide, in a stiff and relatively immobile form, the sensory processes of certain receptor cells. They are found in the scolopale sense organ of the locust, which responds to movements of the tympanic membrane, and also on the antennae of the honey bee, but in these examples the ciliary nature of the processes can only be clearly established by considering the fine structure revealed by the electron microscope.

Apart from the flagella of bacteria, which have their own characteristic features, the fine structure of flagella and cilia shows a remarkable uniformity of pattern, not only within the Protozoa but also throughout the Metazoa; it is a pattern, therefore, that may well be another example of common inheritance from a very early stage of evolution. It had already been noted in the nineteenth century that the flagellate tails of metazoan sperm might fray out into fibrils, and it is a tribute to the acuity of the observations that were made with the light microscope at that time that Ballowitz was actually able to determine in chaffinch sperm the exact number of primary fibres (eleven) that are now known to be typical of flagella and sperm.

A flagellum or cilium (Fig. 3-7) consists of a matrix surrounded by a membrane that is continuous with the plasma membrane of the cell surface. Enclosed in the matrix are eleven fibres that run straight throughout the whole length of the organelle, two of them being single ones, and lying centrally, while the other nine are double fibres, forming a circle around the central pair. Additional features are the apparent presence of a sheath enclosing the central fibres, while in between the central and peripheral fibres are nine more very delicate fibres, which may sometimes be represented by spokes or radial lamellae. Finally, one of the two subfibres of each peripheral fibre bears a double row of short projections, or arms, which all point in the same direction. It is a remarkable measure of the constancy of structure in these organelles that in flagellates, a ciliate, a mollusc, an amphibian, and a mammal, these arms have been found to point always in the same (clockwise) direction.

Flagella and cilia take their origin in granules that are variously called basal granules, blepharoplasts, or kinetosomes (Figs. 3-7 and 3-8). It is well known that

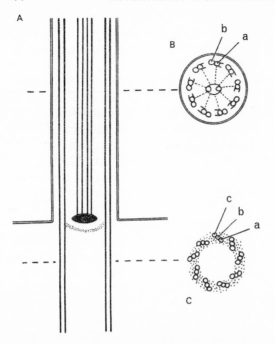

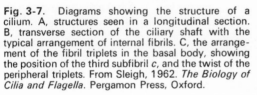

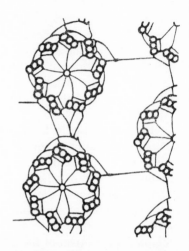

Fig. 3-7. Diagrams showing the structure of a cilium. A, structures seen in a longitudinal section. B, transverse section of the ciliary shaft with the typical arrangement of internal fibrils. C, the arrangement of the fibril triplets in the basal body, showing the position of the third subfibril *c*, and the twist of the peripheral triplets. From Sleigh, 1962. *The Biology of Cilia and Flagella*. Pergamon Press, Oxford.

Fig. 3-8. Diagram showing the fine structure of the basal bodies of *Trichonympha* in transverse section, and the delicate system of fibres present on some of the basal bodies in this organism. Note the 9 triplet outer fibres and the 'cartwheel', which occurs in the proximal region of the basal bodies. From Grimstone, 1961. *Biol. Rev.*, **36**, 97–150.

the granules called centrioles are active agents in cell division in animals (but not in plants). They are concerned in the process of fibrogenesis which produces the spindle fibres. Undoubtedly there is a close relationship between the centriole and the basal body of a flagellum or cilium. Not only are they both directly related to the formation of fibres, but in some instances a basal granule acts as a centriole during mitosis, dividing into two halves that move apart with only a strand connecting them. Alternatively, the centriole may be a separate granule connected with the blepharoplast by a fibril called the rhizoplast, while other bodies, such as the parabasal bodies mentioned earlier, may also be connected with it. The clearest evidence of this relationship between centrioles and basal bodies, however, is seen in their fine structure, for both contain an identical arrangement of peripheral fibres. Those of the basal body are continuous with the peripheral fibres of the flagellum or cilium associated with it, but differ from them in having a characteristic triplet pattern. We may expect that in due course the study of basal granules and centrioles, and of the relationship between these and flagella, cilia, and spindle fibres, will shed light on the means by which living systems can produce fibrous structures by the polymerization of protein molecules. For the present we can only note the important part that this capacity evidently plays in the organization of protoplasmic activity.

We must now consider briefly how far the mode of functioning of flagella and cilia depends upon properties that they share with the contractile myofibrils of muscle cells. To what extent, in other words, is muscular contraction a development of biochemical mechanisms that were already well established before the emergence of metazoan organization? The interpretation of the action of flagella and cilia presents problems that may be approached in more than one way. It is possible, for example, to analyze the form of their movement, and to examine how this brings about movement in the organisms that depend upon it. Alternatively, we can face the more difficult problems of the nature of the cellular mechanism that is responsible for the movement of these delicate threads, and of the ways in which the necessary supplies of energy are made available. These problems are, of course, related.

The movement of flagella commonly involves the generation of waves that are transmitted along it, either in a single plane, or in a corkscrew pattern. The effect of this upon the movement of a protozoan is well exemplified by *Euglena*, an organism that presents a comparatively simple case, although one that is by no means fully understood. The waves arise at the base of the flagellum, which in this organism seems to arise from the wall of the reservoir, apparently by two roots. This appearance, however, is illusory; such an arrangement would be difficult to reconcile with what is now known of the fine structure of flagella, and it is probable that there are actually two flagella in this organism, one main one and another short and vestigial one that is fused with it. The waves pass to the tip of the main flagellum, which beats at a rate of about 12 beats per second, and which also shows a movement of rotation. This rotation causes the tip of the organism to rotate (Fig. 3–9), while at the same time pushing it to one side (Fig. 3–10). Because of this, *Euglena* rotates as it swims (at a rate of about 1 turn per second), and it also follows a corkscrew course. The movement of its body is thus comparable with that of a propeller, for it sets up forces on the water that bring about forward displacement. It is not essential, therefore, for the flagellum itself to provide a forward component in such circumstances; it

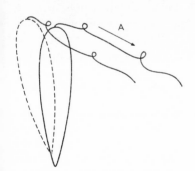

Fig. 3-9. *Left,* waves passing down the flagellum of *Euglena viridis* in the direction *A* produce a force in the opposite direction, causing the organism to take up the position indicated by the dotted figure. Adapted from Lowndes, 1941. *Proc. zool. Soc. Lond., A,* **111**, 111–134.

Fig. 3-10. *Below,* showing the varying positions taken up by *Euglena viridis* in swimming from A to B. From Lowndes, 1941. *op. cit.*

may well do so, however, in the particular case of *Euglena*, since in that organism the flagellum is directed backwards along the side of the body (one reason, incidentally, why students find it so difficult to observe).

While the flagellum is moving it must be dissipating energy as a result of work done against the surrounding water; this means that if it were solely dependent upon energy propagated along it from some source in the organism's body, its pulse would necessarily become diminished towards its free end. High-speed cinematography reveals that this does not happen. On the contrary, as the wave passes along the flagellum it actually develops an increase both in velocity and in amplitude (Figs. 3-11 and 3-12). From this we are bound to conclude that the flagellum must itself contribute energy to its movement. Understandably enough, we cannot yet give a complete explanation of how this contribution is contrived, but there is at least some evidence that the underlying biochemical mechanism is similar in principle to that of muscular contraction, in that ATP is the source of the required energy.

The evidence for this conclusion depends in part upon studies of the responses of intact cilia to the presence of ATP in the medium; cilia for this purpose being as relevant as flagella, in view of the similarity of their organization. Cilia from both the oyster and the frog show increased activity in the presence of ATP, the effect disappearing if the ATP is destroyed by hydrolysis. Such evidence has been supplemented by the use of the glycerol extraction procedures discussed earlier in connection with the analysis of muscular contraction. Frog cilia that have been extracted with glycerol for several days are inactive, but their activity can be restored if ATP is added to the medium; indeed, they will beat in such circumstances even if they have been separated from any protoplasmic connection. By analogy with myofibrils, it is necessary to suppose that the intact flagellum and cilium must contain an ATP-ase. Its presence in ciliated cells has, in fact, been demonstrated both by direct enzymatic studies and by histochemical procedures. There is some evidence that it may be localized within the cilia themselves in the ciliate protozoan *Tetrahymena*, and it is known also to be present in the tails of sperm. Finally, ciliary activity can be arrested by the use of reagents such as sodium fluoride, sodium azide, and sodium cyanide, which selectively inhibit specific stages in the metabolic pathways of anaerobic glycolysis, the citric acid cycle, and the cytochrome system respectively. We may suppose, then, that flagellar and ciliary activity, like muscular contraction, depends upon a pattern of biochemical organization that we have already judged to play a fundamentally important part in the energetics of living systems.

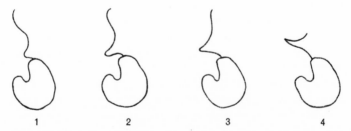

    1   2   3   4

Fig. 3-11. *Peranema trichophora*, drawn from four consecutive frames of a film. The wave of movement of the flagellum is passing from the base to the tip. From Lowndes, 1941. *op. cit.*

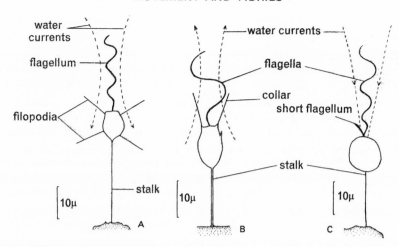

Fig. 3-12. *Actinomonas*, showing body form and the water currents caused by flagellar beating. B, *Codonosiga*. C, *Monas*. From Sleigh, 1964. *Q. Jl. microsc. Sci.*, **105**, 405–414.

The study of animal morphology at the macroscopic level readily convinces the observer that the design of moving parts is precisely and delicately adapted to the functions that they have to perform; we shall see examples of this in due course. It cannot be doubted, therefore, that the same must be true of the ultrastructure of flagella and cilia, provided we are justified in our assumption that all levels of animal organization have been built up under the influence of natural selection. At present, however, our information is too limited to enable us to link satisfactorily the fine structure of these organelles with our conclusions regarding their biochemical mechanisms. Analyses of isolated flagella and sperm show that protein predominates in them. This suggests that the nine peripheral fibres may well be protein macromolecules, and that movement results from contractile changes in these. Their position is ideal for this action, for they are well placed to exert a bending moment around the axis of the organelle. It has been suggested that the two central fibrils might act as compression elements in the system, providing mechanical resistance to the bending couple, but calculations indicate that they are unlikely to be strong enough to carry out this function. Possibly, therefore, the rigidity of flagella and cilia depends upon internal turgor, a situation that would present a striking analogy with the use of hydrostatic skeletons by Metazoa. Sleigh has pointed out that a cylinder in which peripheral contractile structures are antagonized by internal turgor would be transformed into a close spiral by contraction, a response that is certainly seen in the contractile stalks of peritrichous ciliates but that is not characteristic of flagella or cilia. He has suggested, therefore, that the central fibrils, and the radial strands that link them with the peripheral ones, may prevent this spiralization by restricting the effects of contraction to the sites at which it is taking place at any particular moment.

Indications of adaptive specialization are no less apparent at the level of light microscopy, as may be judged from a comparison of the three forms illustrated (Fig. 3-12). All are sessile, using their flagella to set up feeding currents in the surrounding water. *Actinomonas* is a fresh-water protozoan with a spherical body and contractile stalk. It provides an example of the situation mentioned earlier: the coexistence of a flagellum with pseudopodia, which in this case comprise a group of filopodia (see later). The wave motion of the beating flagellum passes upwards from the base, but the currents that are set up in the surrounding water pass downwards. As a result, food particles are carried towards the filopodia which catch and engulf them.

Codonosiga is one of the fresh-water choanoflagellates, organisms that resemble the choanocytes of sponges in having a flagellum surrounded by a protoplasmic collar. Here again the waves of the flagellum travel distally, but in this instance they draw water currents towards the collar from below. Food particles are trapped on the outside of the collar, which, like that of choanocytes, is composed of microvilli; these strain the water, and the trapped particles are carried downwards by a flow of proto-plasm to the base of the collar, where they are ingested into food vacuoles.

Monas is another fresh-water form with two flagella. The larger one sends waves from its base to its tip, their amplitude increasing as they pass distally. As with *Actinomonas*, the water currents pass downwards, but, in contrast to what happens in the latter organism, the food particles are here brought to a focus at the base of the flagellum, the small one, with its flickering movement, perhaps helping to trap them. The broadly dispersed pattern of currents in *Actinomonas* is elegantly adapted to the trapping of food particles by the wide-ranging filopodia; in *Monas* they must be ingested at the tip of the body, near to the origin of the flagella, and the concentra-tion of the currents provides for this.

It will be noted in these examples (and others would show the same pheno-menon) that the direction of passage of the waves of the flagellum is no guide to the direction of the water currents that they produce. There is a somewhat analogous situation in free-swimming polychaete worms and fish. The eel is propelled by sinu-soidal waves of the body that pass backwards, whereas *Nereis* is propelled by waves that pass forwards. We shall see later that this difference is a result of the polychaete worm having projections of its body surface in the form of parapodia, whereas no such structures disturb the smooth outline of the eel. Sleigh, in discussing this situation, has suggested that a similar explanation might conceivably account for the differing effects of the wave motion of flagella. It has been shown by electron microscopy that these organelles sometimes have filamentous projections of their surface, termed mastigonemes. Possibly, then, these may be orientated in such a way as to influence the direction of the water currents; but at the present time this suggestion, like those made above in connection with the internal structure of

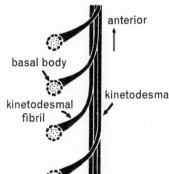

anterior

basal body

kinetodesma

kinetodesmal
fibril

Fig. 3-13. Diagram showing the formation of the ciliate kinetodesma from overlapping fibrils arising from each basal body. From Grimstone, 1961. *op. cit.*

flagella, can be no more than speculation. These speculations indicate, however, that concepts derived from macromorphological studies may have some relevance at the micromorphological level of analysis, and they indicate paths along which these problems of protoplasmic organization may be solved in the future.

One special problem, closely associated with the functioning of fibre systems, is presented by the existence in ciliate Protozoa of patterns of fibres, called kineto-desmata, which lie in the ectoplasm and which are closely associated with the basal bodies of the cilia. The cilia of these animals (Fig. 2–5, p. 31) are arranged in rows, each row, or kinety, consisting of a complex which comprises the cilia themselves, their basal granules, and the kinetodesma, which lies just to the right of each row (Fig. 3–13). The kinetodesma is visible as a fibre with the light microscope, and can be well demonstrated by silver impregnation, but electron microscopy is needed to elucidate fully its complex relationships. A single kinetodesma in *Paramecium* is composed of a number of overlapping fibrils, each of which arises from a basal body. The thickness of the whole fibre in any animal depends upon the length of the con-stituent fibrils; in *Stentor*, for example, they are long, extending for about half the length of the row of some 1,000 cilia, so that at any one point of its length the kineto-desma is composed of about 500 fibrils. These fibrils often show a spiral surface structure, with a periodicity of about 400 Å. Other types of fibre are also demon-strable, but little is known of the significance of their variations. Beneath the pellicle of *Paramecium*, for example, there are many very fine fibres, with no surface striation. These link together the basal bodies, or run towards the body surface, or pass in-wards to meet in the motorium, a conspicuous body lying near the cytopharynx.

There is evidence that the motorium, together with the associated fibres, is a conducting and coordinating mechanism comparable to some extent with the nervous system of Metazoa. The best evidence for this comes from the studies of Taylor on *Euplotes*. This is a ciliate in which the ventral surface of the body bears locomotor organelles called cirri, formed by the fusion of cilia. The movement of these is well coordinated, but the coordination is lost, and locomotion correspondingly disturbed, if fibres that run from the motorium to the five anal cirri are transected. It is far from certain, however, that kinetodesmata and associated fibre systems can all be ac-counted for in this way. It has been supposed that they might be responsible for the coordination that provides for metachronal rhythms, but it is doubtful whether such a system could possibly account for the wide range of patterns of movement that are actually observed.

Advances in knowledge since Taylor's work have opened up other lines of explanation of flagellar and ciliary coordination. It has been plausibly argued, for example, that coordination of ciliary beat in *Opalina* could be accounted for in terms of orderly depolarization of the surface membrane. Another important factor may be viscous interaction between them in the fluid medium in which they operate. There may also be some form of transmission through the cytoplasm that is indepen-dent of any visible fibres. In fact, some at least of these fibres may have nothing at all to do with conduction. They may equally well have supporting functions, or they may be concerned, like the basal bodies, with the morphogenesis of the constituent fibrils of flagella and cilia. We have accepted the existence of these latter structures without considering how they are laid down in their orderly patterns, for this again is a problem for the future to resolve.

3–3   AMOEBOID MOVEMENT

It remains now to consider amoeboid movement, which, as we have earlier seen, must have arisen later than flagellar movement. It is a form of locomotion particularly characteristic of many of the sarcodine Protozoa, but it is found also in a wide variety of metazoan cells, ranging from the oocytes of sponges to the white blood corpuscles of vertebrates. The familiar accounts of it are based largely upon studies of the lobose pseudopodia of *Amoeba* and its relatives; it is thus easy to lose sight of the range of variety within this type of movement. In *Amoeba* itself, as observed with the light microscope, amoeboid movement involves the well-known streaming movement of the protoplasm, associated with the outgrowth of pseudopodia and the progressive displacement of the organism. But as Bovee emphasizes, amoebae are not shapeless organisms, moving at random and with erratic alteration of their course. On the contrary, they are closely adapted to their particular environment, responding to it by their own characteristic patterns of reactions, as with *Subulamoeba* (Fig. 3-14). Different species, in fact, may have pseudopodia which, although lobose, are yet morphologically distinct; their differences probably reflect differences in protein composition, for they can be shown by immunological studies to be antigenically distinct from each other.

Contrasting with the typically lobose forms are the Foraminifera, which have a net-like system of branching and fusing pseudopodia, thread-like in form, and termed filopodia. These have a mechanical rigidity that has been shown by electron microscopy to depend upon the presence of loose bundles of fibrils, each bundle being a protoplasmic unit containing mitochondria. It is important also not to overlook the highly specialized types of pseudopodia found in the Heliozoa and Radiolaria, groups that are sometimes separated from the other amoeboid protozoans as a distinct class. Thus in the Heliozoa, such as *Actinophrys sol*, there are radiating pseudopodia called axopodia. These have central axial rods that are rooted within the body, and that are composed of parallel fibres running into the nuclear membrane. The activity of these axopodia is particularly shown by the projection of lobes and processes from their bases.

These latter types of pseudopodia have been little studied, so that theories of the nature of amoeboid movement are largely based upon observations of the lobose pseudopodia of amoebae. This is understandable and acceptable, provided that these theories can eventually take account of the conditions in other types of pseudopodia; a particularly difficult problem, for example, is presented by the occurrence of bidirectional streaming in filopodia, with an outward and an inward flow taking place along each pseudopodium.

As de Bruyn has shown, the theories have varied from time to time in obvious conformity with the prevailing interpretation of cytoplasmic structure, but this situation is by no means peculiar to this particular problem. Scientific theories must inevitably be moulded by the climate of opinion in which they are developed, and it is precisely because of this, if for no other reason, that they need periodic re-examination.

The early belief that protozoans contained organs like those of higher animals led at one time to the supposition that a pseudopodium was a hernia-like protrusion developed at a point of weakness of the body surface. Later recognition of the cell-like character of the protozoan body led to views of amoeboid movement that were

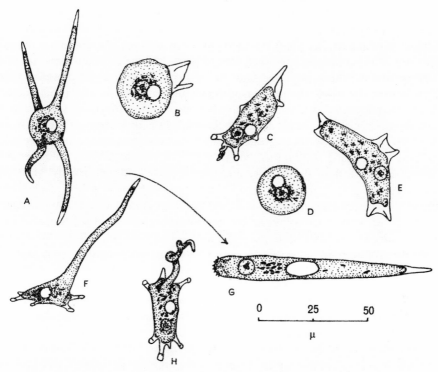

Fig. 3-14. *Subulamoeba saphirina.* A, radiate and afloat. B, beginning locomotion. C, in moderate progress, showing conical, mayorellid, determinate pseudopods. D, at rest, spherical. E, changing direction, with a new pair of pseudopods formed near the nucleus indicative of the new route. F, with a long tubular pseudopod thrown forwards, to become G, the rapidly locomotive organism. H, dorsal view of the organism, with the elongate pseudopod. From Bovee, 1964. *Primitive Motile Systems in Cell Biology* (Allen and Kamiya, eds.). Academic Press, New York.

based upon somewhat more realistic interpretations of cytoplasmic structure. Such was Heitzmann's advocacy of a living three-dimensional network of contractile fibres which he supposed to be embedded in a non-living and non-contractile fluid. On this view amoeboid movement was ascribed to contraction of the reticulum, the substance of the fibres being transferred during contraction to the nodes of the reticulum, where it accumulated in the form of granules.

In due course, by the end of the nineteenth century, this reticular theory of cytoplasmic structure was replaced by other views, according to which the fundamental structural elements were thought to be droplets, filaments, or granules, dispersed in a structureless fluid. These views made it difficult to account for amoeboid movement in purely structural terms. Instead, it was suggested that it might depend upon local changes in surface tension; a view that acquired a certain plausibility from Bütschli's success in constructing a physical model of it. Acting on the assumption that cytoplasm had a foam-like structure, he prepared emulsions of water, olive oil, and potassium carbonate, and placed drops of these in water or in dilute glycerol. In these media the drops proceeded to move in a superficially amoeba-like way, with a streaming movement of their contents. The model was an ingenious one, no better and no worse, perhaps, than some of the others that biologists have delighted to invent in other fields of speculation, but it stands remote from the contemporary approach to the problem.

This approach derives from the recognition of the colloidal character of cytoplasm, and of the differences between the properties of the ectoplasm and those of the endoplasm. It is now suggested that the former is a colloidal gel, the plasmagel, and the endoplasm a sol, the plasmasol. Amoeboid movement, from this point of view, can be interpreted as a result of coordinated gelation and solation, the contraction of the superficial layer of gel directing the streaming movements of the plasmasol (Fig. 3–15), and perhaps forcing out a pseudopodium at some point where local conditions are evoking solation at the surface. This interpretation, which remains in principle the most favoured one, has been especially developed by Mast and Pantin. According to their views, *Amoeba* can be thought of as a tube of plasmagel containing the more fluid plasmasol. At the end that is posterior at any particular moment the gel undergoes solation; contraction forces the fluid sol forwards, and there is a transformation of sol to gel at the anterior end, so that solation is balanced by gelation. It has been suggested, however, that this interpretation may be oversimple. Allen argues that the endoplasm is not uniformly solated, so that its properties are not those of a Newtonian fluid. He thus supposes that contraction of gel at the posterior end cannot by itself account for the forward flow. Instead, he believes that contraction occurs at the anterior end, in a 'fountain zone', and that this process actively pulls the axial endoplasm forwards.

Not the least of the difficulties in these interpretation is that the role of the surface membrane in amoeboid movement remains obscure; yet we cannot feel that any interpretation of amoeboid movement is satisfactory if it does not take account of the existence of the membrane, and of its elastic properties. One suggestion is that its function is essentially a physico-chemical one, changes in membrane potential perhaps initiating the outgrowth of a new pseudopodium. Another view is that it is closely associated with the plasmagel, contributing to the contractile force exerted by it, and undergoing continuous renewal from the interior. A third suggestion is that it flows freely and independently over the surface of the amoeba, and that it serves to aid adhesion between the organism and the substratum.

Whatever interpretation of amoeboid movement may eventually win general acceptance, it must account for the force that must necessarily determine the forward streaming of the plasmasol. In this connection there has been an interesting reversion to earlier views that it may depend upon the contractility of the cytoplasm. Indeed, Heitzmann might well feel that his reticular theory had been translated in the mid-twentieth century into molecular terms. In these terms the structure of cytoplasm, apart from its membranes and fibrils, is commonly visualized as based upon the cross-linking of polypeptide chains, with water and metabolites present in the interstices of the meshwork. Within this system contraction could occur either by the development of additional cross-linkages, which would reduce the size of the mesh, or by the folding of the polypeptide chains, which would have a similar effect. Such contraction would seem to provide some theoretical basis for amoeboid movement, for it would result in the elimination of fluid from the contracting meshwork; this fluid might then be taken up elsewhere, to produce solation, with forward displacement of the protoplasm. The sites of these changes would doubtless be determined by a combination of internal and external influences, and in *Amoeba limax*, which moves steadily in one direction, the internal ones must presumably be particularly well established.

This type of interpretation is clearly based upon analogy with the part played by fibrillar structures in muscular contraction. As far as flagellar and ciliary movements are concerned we have seen some justification for drawing such an analogy, but it must be admitted that the justification is less clear for amoeboid movement. Current views on the organization of cytoplasm, with their emphasis on the significance of

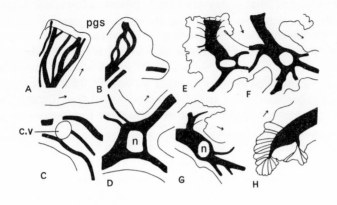

Fig. 3-15. *Above*, drawings showing position of plasmasol-stream network (black) and plasmagel network (white) in *Amoeba*. Note how the nucleus (*n*) is held back in D, E, F, and G, and the contractile vacuole (*c.v.*) in C, by the narrower channels in front. *Below*, composite drawing showing distribution of plasmagel (white) and plasmasol (black), based on photographs, cine films, and on direct observation. The smallest plasmasol streams are omitted for clarity. This distribution of plasmagel explains why the nucleus and the contractile vacuole maintain respectively a central and a posterior position. From Goldacre, 1964. *Primitive Motile Systems in Cell Biology* (Allen and Kamiya, eds.). Academic Press, New York.

membranes and fibrils, are certainly helpful in this respect, but the principal difficulty is the failure to demonstrate convincingly any filamentous ultrastructure that could be compared with muscle filaments. Negative results cannot, of course, close the issue at this early stage of electron microscopic exploration. Indeed, there is evidence that a fibrillar structure may exist in slime moulds. Nevertheless, there is an undoubted simplicity of organization in the protoplasm of *Amoeba*, judged, that is, against the complexity of its behaviour. There seems to be no clearly defined ultrastructural difference between the ectoplasm and the endoplasm, nor can the distribution of visible structures be readily related to any particular phase of amoeboid movement. Mitochondria are identifiable, which confirms our estimate of the fundamental importance of these structures and of the enzyme systems that they bear, but there is no evidence of more continuous membrane systems. Instead, there is a great abundance of vacuoles, large and small; many contain food or its digestive products, while others are empty or contain particles of unidentified nature. It is not surprising, therefore, that some of the earlier investigators based their views upon the supposedly foam-like structure of cytoplasm. Indeed, it would be fair to recognize that, within the limits of the facilities available to them, this type of interpretation was not ill founded, at least as regards the structure of the cytoplasm of *Amoeba*.

It may be, of course, that highly organized systems of fibrils and membranes are not reconcilable with demands for flowing movements to develop in all parts of a unit mass of protoplasm. Whether the organization of the body of *Amoeba* is primitive or specialized in this regard it is impossible to say, but at least there is some evidence that the biochemical mechanisms underlying its activity have something in common with those involved in other forms of movement. This evidence comes from studies of extracts prepared from amoebae by controlled centrifugation and homogenization. In the presence of ATP these extracts show four significant properties: gelation, a streaming of particles, a capacity for contraction and for the transmission of tension, and an extrusion of water. Moreover, it can be shown by electron microscopy that oriented fibres develop in the gel phase. These properties could, in theory, provide at least part of the physical basis for amoeboid movement. Certainly their manifestation in the presence of ATP suggests that this movement must depend ultimately on energy exchanges similar in principle to those operating in muscular contraction and in the movement of flagella and cilia. At this stage, however, we should clearly be unjustified in pressing these comparisons any further.

4
Movement and Hydrostatics

4–1 PRINCIPLE OF THE HYDROSTATIC SKELETON

The differentiation of muscular tissue was one of the consequences of the establishment of metazoan organization, but it was not sufficient in itself to bring about effective movement of the body. The reason for this is that the contraction of muscle fibres is an active process whereas their relaxation is not. If the form of the body is to be maintained the contracted fibres must be restored to their original length, and this can only be achieved by applying an external force to them. In many higher animals this force is applied through a jointed skeleton. The muscles are attached to the movable parts of this in such a way that the contraction of one muscle brings about the relaxation of another; the two are then said to be antagonists, or to antagonize each other. This, of course, is not the only significance of a jointed skeleton; by providing a system of levers it secures the economical application of energy, while it also contributes to the general support and protection of the body.

Rigid skeletons made a comparatively late appearance in the history of animal evolution, and there are still many metazoan organisms today that do not possess them. We have suggested that life may have appeared some 2,000 million years ago. But the first remains of calcareous skeletal structures are not found until the beginning of the Cambrian period, perhaps 600 million years ago. These remains include parts of the skeletons of trilobites and echinoderms, and of the shells of molluscs and brachiopods. A great deal of evolutionary history must have preceded the emergence of these groups, but unfortunately we know tantalizingly little of that history. That there are remains of living organisms in pre-Cambrian strata is agreed, but their nature is obscure (Fig. 4–1). Stromatolites represent the primitive algae, but there is some evidence also of coelenterates and annelids, and perhaps of worm burrows. There is, however, a remarkable absence of skeletal structures, which seem to have been evolved relatively suddenly at about the onset of Cambrian times. Glaessner suggests that this is to be regarded as a new step in chemical evolution, resulting, perhaps, from animals having at last achieved a level of complexity at which the

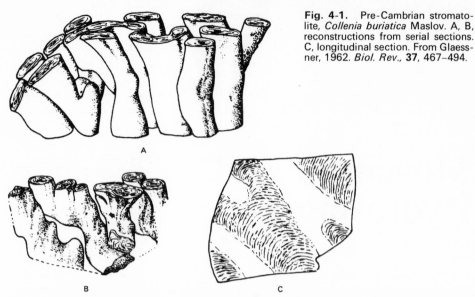

Fig. 4-1. Pre-Cambrian stromato-lite, *Collenia buriatica* Maslov. A, B, reconstructions from serial sections. C, longitudinal section. From Glaessner, 1962. *Biol. Rev.,* **37**, 467–494.

metabolism and excretion of calcium and phosphate could be adapted, under the influence of natural selection, to the strengthening and protection of the body.

Whatever may be the truth of this interpretation, it seems clear that in animals of the remote past, as in many at the present time, movement must have depended upon something other than jointed skeletons for providing antagonistic relationships in muscular systems. The need must have been met, as it is today, by the ready availability of water. This shares with other fluids two properties that are of crucial importance in this connection: incompressibility, and the capacity for transmitting pressure changes equally in all directions. Add to this that the low viscosity of water allows it to be readily deformed, and we have the physical basis of a type of skeletal system known as the hydrostatic skeleton. The functioning of such a system depends upon the musculature being so arranged that it surrounds an enclosed volume of fluid. In these circumstances the contraction of any one part of the muscular system sets up a pressure in the fluid which is then transmitted in all directions to the rest of the body.

The consequences of this can be considered by reference to a hypothetical and highly simplified organism (Fig. 4–2A). This has the form of a continuous tube, closed at both ends, and containing a fluid which is enclosed by a body wall; the latter possesses a layer of circular muscle, but no longitudinal muscle and no elasticity. Contraction of the circular muscles at the right-hand end of the tube produces an increase of pressure in the fluid; this increase is transmitted throughout the length of the tube, the result of this depending upon whether or not the organism is free to elongate. If it is (Fig. 4–2B), the body can lengthen to the left, the diameter remaining the same at this end. If the organism is not free to elongate, the left-hand end will respond to the increase of pressure by increasing in diameter (Fig. 4–2C). There is an important difference between these two possibilities. In Fig. 4–2C the body can be restored to its original shape by contraction of the muscles of the left-hand end, for this will restore the original pressure distribution and will promote relaxation of the muscles of the right-hand end. In Fig. 4–2B the original form cannot be restored, for

Fig. 4-2. Diagram to illustrate the action of a hypothetical animal with circular muscles only. In A all the muscles are relaxed. In B the muscles of the right-hand end have contracted but the length of this end has remained the same; the original length of the right-hand muscles cannot be restored by contraction of the left-hand muscles. In C the muscles of the right-hand end have contracted, but the muscles of the left-hand end have relaxed, and there has been no change in length; the right-hand muscles can be restored to their original length by contraction of the left-hand ones. From Chapman, 1950. *J. exp. Biol.*, **27**, 29–39.

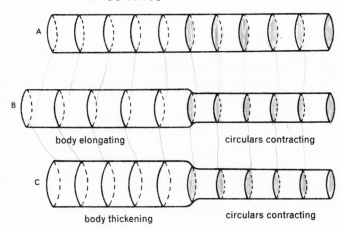

body elongating   circulars contracting

body thickening   circulars contracting

no change in pressure distribution can bring about shortening of the body to its original length.

This limitation can be overcome by the addition of a layer of longitudinal muscle to the body wall (Fig. 4-3A). Some of the consequent possible results are shown in the other illustrations. In Fig. 4-3B the circular muscles to the right have contracted and have brought about elongation of that end. In Fig. 4-3C they have contracted but the body has remained the same length; the left-hand end has consequently thickened. In Fig. 4-3D the circular muscles to the right have contracted; this end has again remained the same length, but now the left end has lengthened, without any change in diameter. From all of these positions the original form of the body can be restored. This restoration can be effected in Fig. 4-3C by contraction of the circular muscles at the left-hand end, exactly as in Fig. 4-2C. In Figs. 4-3B and 4-3D, however, it is only possible because longitudinal muscles are present. Their contraction can establish the pressure needed to bring about relaxation of the circular muscles and the restoration of their original shape. Thus the presence of the hydrostatic skeleton enables the two sets of muscles to act antagonistically to each other. Moreover, it makes locomotion possible. If, in Fig. 4-3D, there is adequate friction between the organism and the substratum, the left-hand end may remain stationary while contraction of the longitudinal muscles draws the right-hand end towards it. Thus the

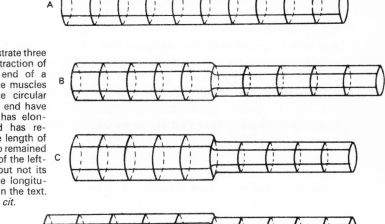

Fig. 4-3. Diagram to illustrate three possible results of the contraction of circular muscles at one end of a cylindrical animal. In A the muscles are all relaxed. In B the circular muscles of the right-hand end have contracted and this end has elongated; the left-hand end has remained unaltered. In C the length of the right-hand end has also remained the same; in D the length of the left-hand end has increased, but not its diameter. The effect of the longitudinal muscle is explained in the text. From Chapman, 1950. *op. cit.*

organism could become displaced to the left, in comparison with its original position in Fig. 4-3A.

These highly simplified examples show that antagonistic muscles, operating in conjunction with a hydrostatic skeleton, can bring about changes in shape and can also effect locomotion. The system has serious disadvantages, however, in comparison with those using jointed skeletons. Firstly, contraction at one point affects the pressure throughout the body and so influences all of the other muscles. Contraction of the latter will now demand more work than usual, for it has to be carried out against an increased pressure. This may result in a wasteful distribution of energy, and it makes it very difficult for one part of the body to respond independently of other parts. Further, contraction of any part of the body demands great change in length of the muscles concerned; indeed, they may have to contract to an extent little, if at all, less than the contraction of the part of the body that they are moving. Because of this the reactions must be slow ones, for there is bound to be great waste of energy if such extensive deformations are carried out quickly.

All of these difficulties are overcome when muscle can be attached in antagonistic sets to parts of jointed skeletons. The application of force is localized, and can be quite independent of what is happening in other parts of the body. Moreover, the development of systems of levers allows very small contractions to bring about large degrees of movement; reactions can thus be rapid, and can be effected with economy of energy. Nevertheless, hydrostatic skeletons are widespread in animals, and the groups making use of them have achieved considerable success in the exploitation of their environment. For this there are two main reasons. In the simpler organisms the muscle fibres are arranged in two main layers, one circular and the other longitudinal; this facilitates reactions which, while limited in variety, can yet be of great adaptive value. In more complex organisms the relationship of the hydrostatic skeleton to the associated muscles and nerves has been elaborated in such a way as to increase both localization and complexity of response. We shall consider here only a few illustrations of these principles, but they will be sufficient to show how structural and physiological limitations have been overcome, or even turned to positive advantage.

4-2 COELENTERATE ORGANIZATION AND THE HYDROSTATIC SKELETON

The characteristic feature of coelenterate* organization is that the body is composed of two membranes, or cell layers, to which Allman, in 1853, gave the names of ectoderm and endoderm (Fig. 4-4). Between these layers lies a form of connective tissue, the mesogloea, with a matrix containing mucopolysaccharides. Cells are not necessarily present in the mesogloea, and even when they are their functions are in doubt. On the other hand, nineteenth-century references to this substance as a 'structureless lamella' are certainly incorrect; if they were not, it would be difficult to account for the movements carried out by the coelenterate body.

The structurally significant aspect of the mesogloea is the extensive development in it of collagenous fibres that are systematically arranged to form a lattice. In the anemone *Calliactis parasitica*, for example, there are inner and outer sheets in which the fibres run mainly parallel with the epithelia and at 45° to the long axis of the body, while other fibres run across the thickness of the mesogloea from one layer of fibres to the other (Fig. 4-5). Thus the system as a whole has the form of a three-dimensional

*This term is used here as being equivalent to *cnidarian* (*see* Classification).

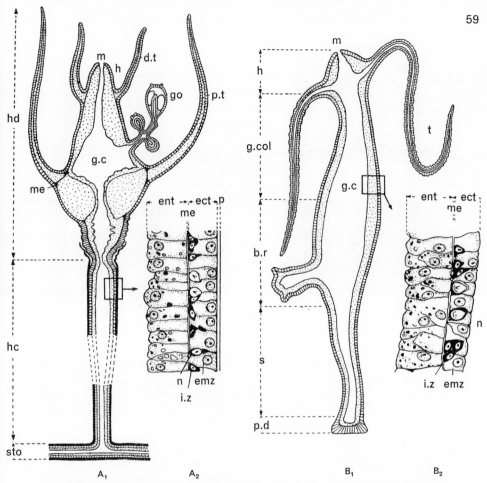

Fig. 4-4. Anatomy of two hydrozoa. A_1, *Tubularia larynx*; A_2, section through its body wall. B_1, B_2, *Hydra vulgaris*. *b.r*, budding region; *d.t*, distal tentacles; *ect*, ecto-derm; *emz*, musculo-epithelial cells; *ent*, endoderm; *g.c*, gastric cavity; *g.col*, gastric column; *go*, gonophores; *h*, hypostome, peristomium; *hc*, hydrocaulus; *hd*, hydranth; *i.z*, interstitial cells; *m*, mouth; *me*, mesogloea; *n*, nematocytes; *p*, perisarc; *p.d*, pedal disc; *p.t*, proximal tentacles; *s*, stalk; *sto*, stolon; *t*, tentacle. From Tardent, 1963. *Biol. Rev.*, **38**, 293–333.

lattice. The source of these fibres is unknown, as also is the origin of their regular arrangement. There is no clear evidence that they are secreted by the cells of the mesogloea, and it seems unlikely that their orientation is a consequence of the organ-ized activity of any secretory tissue. We shall see that mechanical forces are imposed on the mesogloea by the activities of the animal, and possibly these forces determine the arrangement of the fibres. In any event, it is certain that the adaptive efficiency of the movements of coelenterates depends upon the properties of the mesogloea and its relationships with the specialized contractile tissue of these animals.

As the brothers Hertwig showed in 1879, the coelenterates possess a peculiar type of musculo-epithelial cell, highly characteristic of the group, and virtually restricted to it. The free surface of each of these cells may bear a single flagellum, which, with its associated basal granule, has the typical ultrastructure that we have already discussed. The musculo-epithelial cells of the mesenteries of *Metridium*, as described by Robson,

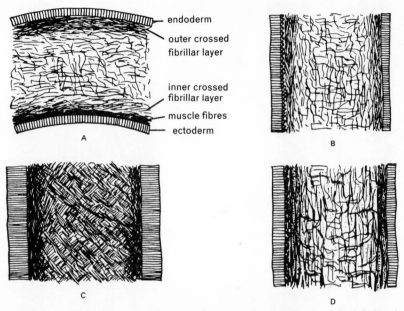

A

B

C

D

Fig. 4-5. Diagrams illustrating the general appearance of the body wall of *Calliactis* as seen in A, horizontal section, B, radial section, C, tangential section, and D, section at 45° to the long axis. Note in A and B the similar appearance of the inner and outer crossed fibrillar layers and the middle, less highly orientated region. Note in C the outer crossed fibrillar layer showing warp and weft arrangement, and in D the crossed fibrillar arrangement in which the fibres are cut either along their length or in transverse section, and are represented by dots. From Chapman, 1953. *Q. Jl. microsc. Sci.*, **94**, 155–176.

possess cell bodies arranged as a closely knit mosaic to form the endodermal epithelium, while the base of each cell extends into a contractile fibre (Fig. 4–6). These fibres, which constitute the muscular tissue of the body, form a lattice work which is thus connected with the cell bodies by protoplasmic strands. The interstices of these strands contain fluid, which, it is thought, may have hydrostatic properties that facilitate the movements of the cell bodies during contraction, and protect them from excessive local strain. No doubt it also aids in the diffusion of metabolites.

The physiological organization of the muscle fibres is probably similar to that found in other groups of animals, and is not affected by the association of the fibres with epithelial cell bodies. The electron microscope shows them to contain a dense mass of filaments, while actomyosin-like proteins have been extracted from actinians,

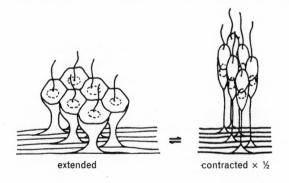

extended   contracted × ½

Fig. 4-6. Diagram representing movements of the musculo-epithelium (not to scale). From Robson, 1957. *Q. Jl microsc. Sci.*, **98**, 265–278.

Fig. 4-7. Changes of shape of *Metridium senile*. All drawings are of the same individual on different occasions, and all are to the same scale. From Clark, 1964. *Dynamics in Metazoan Evolution*. Clarendon Press, Oxford.

and have been shown to contract in the presence of ATP. These facts, taken in conjunction with the identification of mitochondria in the cytoplasmic extension of the fibres, suggest that their mode of functioning may be on the same general lines as those already discussed. We may feel sure, however, that there are differences in details of organization. The filaments are not as regularly arranged as they are, for example, in some smooth muscle of worms, nor has electron microscopy given any evidence of the presence of two types of filaments that might correspond to the actin and myosin fibres of higher forms. The filaments are, however, interconnected by bridges that may be composed of a different material.

The way in which these features of coelenterate organization are translated into movement have been closely analyzed by Pantin and his colleagues. According to Pantin's interpretation, the functional significance of cnidarian structure is seen at its simplest in the Anthozoa, allowing for the fact that the familiar *Hydra* almost certainly shows a secondary simplification of the more complex organization of the Hydrozoa. We may take as an example the sea-anemone *Metridium senile* (Fig. 4-7). To the uninstructed eye this animal, like other anemones, seems to show little movement except when it is directly stimulated, but careful and prolonged observation of

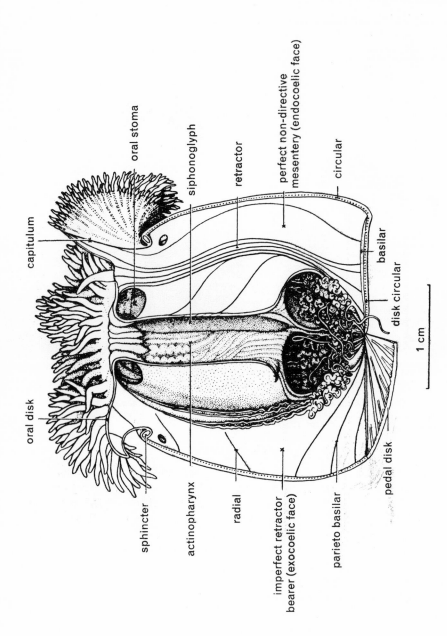

oral stoma

siphonoglyph

retractor

perfect non-directive
mesentery (endocoelic face)

circular

capitulum

basilar

disk circular

1 cm

oral disk

sphincter

actinopharynx

radial

imperfect retractor
bearer (exocoelic face)

parieto basilar

pedal disk

Fig. 4-8. General muscular organization and anatomical nomenclature of *Metridium*. From Batham and Pantin, 1951. *Q. Jl microsc. Sci.*, **92**, 27–54.

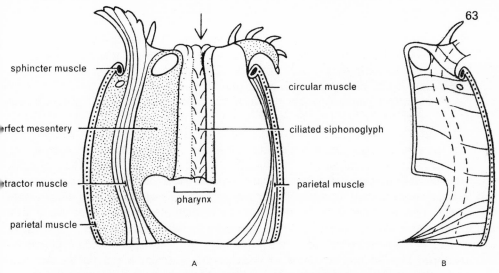

Fig. 4-9. Diagrams of the chief musculature of the column of *Metridium*. A, section through whole specimen, showing endocoelic faces of a non-directive perfect mesentery on left, of a young imperfect mesentery on right. B, exocoelic face of a non-directive perfect mesentery, showing direction of radial muscles. Broken lines indicate position of retractor muscle on opposite face. From Batham and Pantin, 1950. *J. exp. Biol.*, **27**, 264–288.

individual specimens, combined with the use of time-lapse cinematography, reveals a slow and continuous activity, with marked changes of shape. This activity seems to be inherent and spontaneous, in the sense that it does not arise as a consequence of external stimulation.

To understand how these movements are effected, and how the animal is able to respond adaptively to stimulation, we must consider the arrangement of the muscular system in some detail. Its essential features are shown in Fig. 4-8. Three main regions of the body can be distinguished. These are functionally differentiated, and they are to some extent able to act independently of each other. The first of these regions comprises the tentacles, capitulum, and oral disc, which are primarily concerned with feeding. The second region is the pedal disc, concerned with adhesion and with the effecting of a slow, creeping locomotion. The third region is the column, which is responsible for the main changes in shape of the body, and for its defensive contraction. The first two regions, however, are also involved in the movements of the column, for they close over, above and below, the central body cavity or coelenteron. This cavity contains a fluid, the coelenteric fluid. Because this can be completely enclosed the animal is able to build up in it a level of pressure that makes possible the translation of muscular contraction into movement. The relationship of coelenteric fluid with the surrounding layers of ectodermal and endodermal muscle fibres constitutes, in fact, a simple form of hydrostatic skeleton.

The arrangement of muscles in *Metridium* is more complex than a simple antagonism of circular and longitudinal muscles layers (Fig. 4-9), for the effector systems of anemones are elaborated in part by folding of the layers of muscle fibres, and in part by separation of the fibres so that they become embedded in the mesoglea. The endoderm in *Metridium* provides circular muscle fibres, which do, in fact, run as an almost continuous layer around the body, passing underneath the radial mesenteries which extend across from the body wall and partially subdivide the coelenteron.

In more primitive anemones the longitudinal musculature is supplied by the ectoderm. So it is also in the tentacles of *Metridium*, but in the trunk of this animal they are borne on the mesenteries as bands of fibres called the parietal and retractor muscles, an example of the folding to which we have referred.

The parietal muscles, which run from the column to the pedal disc, are best developed in the youngest cycles (sets) of imperfect mesenteries (mesenteries, that is, which do not reach the stomodaeum). The larger and older imperfect mesenteries, and the perfect ones (those which do reach the stomodaeum) bear very strong retractor muscles, running from the oral disc to the pedal disc. All of these muscles aid in the maintenance of the form of the polyp, but the retractor muscles are also able to bring about the withdrawal of the oral disc and the rapid contraction of the whole animal. They are aided in this by the way in which their fibres radiate at each end so as to provide a broad insertion. These powerful longitudinal muscles, which have evolved as a specialization within the Anthozoa, show how specialized effects can be developed even within the limits of coelenterate muscular organization. Another illustration of this is the development of radial muscles in the perfect mesenteries. These enlarge the stomodaeum when they contract, and thus regulate the loss of fluid from the coelenteron.

The muscle fibres are exceedingly slender, being about 0.5μ thick, but they can reach a length of over 1 mm. In this they surpass the maximum recorded length of mammalian smooth muscle fibres, which may extend to 500μ in the uterus of the pregnant female. Even so, the fibres are short in relation to the total length of the muscles. These are therefore composed of slender fibres which are placed end to end and side by side, and which form what are called muscle fields. The fibres, like all smooth muscle fibres, have a great capacity for deformation, much greater than that of striated muscle. Thus smooth muscle generally may contract by as much as 400% to 500%, whereas a corresponding figure for striated muscle fibres would be 20% or less. This property contributes to the substantial changes of shape that are so marked a feature of coelenterate responses, but these depend also upon the support given to the muscles by the mesogloea, with which they are closely associated (Fig. 4–10). This association becomes apparent when the column contracts. As the body then shortens, much of the mesogloea thickens, its capacity for this marked deformation being presumably dependent upon the lattice structure to which we have referred. The layer of the mesogloea that immediately adjoins the muscle fibres is intimately bound to these, and virtually forms part of the muscle layer. Because of this, the shortening of the muscle causes a buckling of this region of the mesogloea, the muscle layer being thereby thrown into the folds that are so familiar in sections of the contracted coelenterate body (Figs. 4–10C and D). Further contraction eventually throws the body wall itself into folds; these constitute a second stage of buckling (Fig. 4–10F), which marks the maximum degree of contraction that can be attained. Thus the close association of muscle fibres and mesoglea imposes limits on the degree of deformation that the body can undergo.

We have already noted that one of the consequences of possessing this type of hydrostatic skeleton is a great waste of energy if a contraction is performed quickly. This is doubtless one reason why coelenterates are characteristically slow-moving in their sessile phase, and it explains why the movements of *Metridium* are sluggish and imperceptible. A corollary of this is that maximum efficiency of muscular action, by

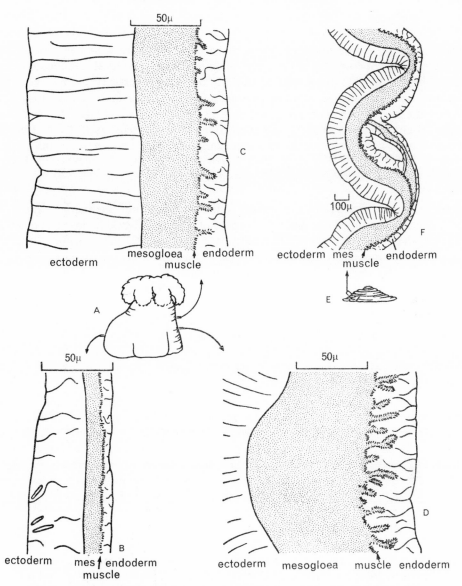

Fig. 4-10. Buckling in *Metridium*. A, animal fixed in shape assumed during loco-motion. Arrows indicate regions whence sections B, C, and D were taken. B, C, D, vertical sections of body wall showing circular muscle layer unbuckled in complete expansion (B); and in increasing states of contraction, partially buckled (C) and highly buckled (D). Note great thickening of mesogloea. E, maximally contracted animal, showing in the low-power vertical section (F) the appearance of buckling of the second order in the whole body wall. From Batham and Pantin, 1951. *op. cit.*

which is meant in this context the least waste of energy, requires that the pressure in the coelenteron shall be kept as low as is consonant with the prevention of the collapse of the body. This condition seems to be achieved in *Metridium*, for in the unstimu-lated animal the pressure is of the order of only 2 mm to 3 mm of water. This value is naturally influenced by the condition of the musculature of the body wall; it increases to a value of 6 mm to 7 mm when the animal contracts to some 30 % of its body length.

An inescapable point of weakness in the coelenterate hydrostatic skeleton is that the coelenteron is open to the outside at the mouth, so that there must necessarily be some exchange of fluid with the external medium. To some extent this is countered in anemones by the pharynx projecting down into the coelenteron (Figs. 4-8 and 4-9) and functioning as a valve, which helps to retain the fluid in the body cavity. However, in extreme cases, often at certain intervals after feeding, the animal may collapse and empty itself of coelenteric fluid, and thereafter proceed to refill itself. Even at other times it must have some means of replenishing the fluid. The agent for this is the ciliated siphonoglyph (Fig. 4-9), which provides a channel down which a gentle stream of water can be continuously passed into the coelenteron. The pressure that it can build up is necessarily a small one, but, as we have seen, this is all that the animal needs, and the siphonoglyph is evidently well adapted to meet this requirement.

Pantin has pointed out that the existence of a hydrostatic skeleton is responsible for introducing an element of bilaterality into actinian organization, for when the pharynx collapses under lateral pressure it will establish an axis of bilateral symmetry; this may well have influenced the situation of the siphonoglyph. It is common to think of bilateral symmetry as a consequence of a free-moving mode of life, and of radial symmetry as associated with sessile habits; the combination of both types of symmetry in the coelenterates is thus an interesting feature of their organization, and one to which some phylogenetic importance has been attached. Pantin's suggestion reminds us, however, that a particular plan of symmetry may arise in more than one way, and that its significance needs to be carefully assessed in relation to all aspects of the mode of life of a group.

We have mentioned that there is considerable functional differentiation between the column, the foot, and the tentacles and oral disc. In some anemones waves of muscular contraction pass across the foot and provide for a slow creeping that is probably similar in principle to that seen in flatworms and gastropods, although it has not been closely analyzed. The tentacles and disc, however, are concerned with feeding, and here we find a particularly good illustration of the relationship between form and function in the actinian body. This region differs from the column in retaining what is presumably a more primitive arrangement of the muscular system (Fig. 4-11). The circular muscles are provided by the endoderm, as in the column, but the longitudinal and radial muscles are provided by the ectoderm. One advantage of this concerns the bending of the tentacles that is involved in the ingestion of food; this is carried out by local contraction of the ectodermal longitudinal muscles, and is thus functionally isolated from the contractions of the column. This ectodermal relationship is also of mechanical advantage, for it enables the longitudinal muscles of the tentacles to exert a greater bending moment than they could if they lay internally to the mesogloea. Moreover, in the latter position their efficiency would be diminished by the resistance of the mesogloea, which would antagonize their action.

It is noticeable that in the tentacles the longitudinal muscles are much better developed than are the circular ones (Fig. 4-11). This feature, too, is of functional significance. The longitudinal muscles are responsible for transporting food to the mouth, and they must be able to carry out massive contractions, which may involve them shortening to an extent similar in magnitude to the actual movement of the tentacle. By contrast, the circular muscles are concerned only with maintaining the

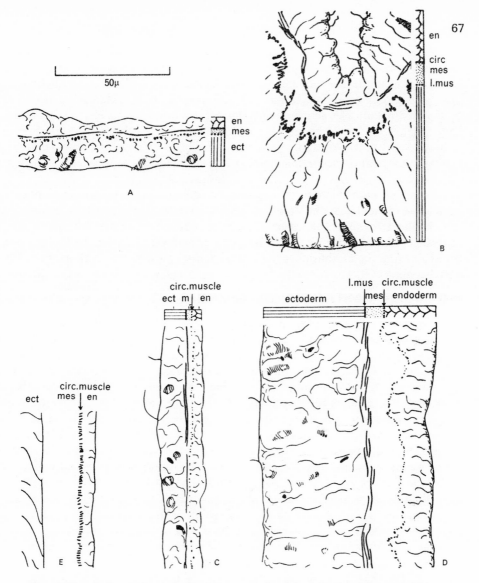

Fig. 4-11. A–D, sections of *Metridium* tentacles. Mesogloea is left unstippled. A and B, transverse to tentacular axis, A extended, B contracted. Note simple buckling of ectodermal (longitudinal) muscle field. C and D, longitudinal sections, C extended, D contracted. Note relatively weak circular muscle field, and simple buckling on contraction. A and C are from the same tentacle from one of the outer cycles. B and D are from the same tentacle from the innermost cycle. E, longitudinal section of extended body wall on same scale. Compare this more uniform and compact muscle layer with tentacle musculature. *circ*, circular muscle; *en*, endoderm; *ect*, ectoderm; *mes*, meso-gloea; *l.mus*, longitudinal muscle. From Batham and Pantin, 1951. *op. cit.*

shape of the tentacles, and with ensuring that when they are fully extended their internal pressure is not uselessly dissipated in local bulging and deformation. As we have seen, the pressure changes that are actually transmitted through the coelenteric fluid are very small; a comparatively slight tonic action of the circular muscles will thus be sufficient to control the distribution of these changes through the length of the tentacle.

Paradoxically, the significance of these circular muscles can readily be judged from the condition in many of the hydrozoan polyps, where they are absent. In *Obelia*, for example, the endoderm is transformed into a flexible supporting rod that is somewhat reminiscent of a notochord; the movements of the tentacles are effected by longitudinal muscles acting directly against this rod, which is effectively a flexible endoskeleton. Such coelenterates are exploiting a mechanical system that is different in principle from that operating in the tentacles of *Metridium*, and that is curiously similar to the relation between muscles and an endoskeleton. It is because of this that circular muscles are not developed in the tentacles of such forms.

Finally, it is worth noting that, despite the generally primitive arrangement of the muscles of the tentacles and oral disc, we find here an example of the separation of muscle fibres, for they sink inwards, carrying reduced cell bodies with them, while separate epithelial cells provide the outer covering layer. This may be thought of as foreshadowing the establishment of a mesodermal musculature such as that of the platyhelminths.

4–3   SOME LIMITATIONS OF SPONGES

The Coelenterata are not the only diploblastic animals, for ctenophores and sponges also have bodies composed of two main layers of cells. Ctenophores, distinguished by well-defined characters, including the complete absence of nematocysts, may yet have some phylogenetic relationship with coelenterates. The organization of sponges, however, is so different from that of coelenterates, or of any other Metazoa, that it provides good grounds for suspecting that the Porifera may have originated from protozoan ancestors quite independently of the main metazoan line. Indeed, even the animal nature of the sponges was in doubt for a long time, although the water currents that they produce had been recognized in the eighteenth century. The doubt lasted well into the nineteenth century; when Fyfe reported in 1819 that iodine was present in their bodies, he held this to confirm the view that they must be plants.

What is of particular interest about sponges is that their plan of structure constitutes one of the major blind alleys of evolution, and has evidently not lent itself to further elaboration. This suggests that there must be serious weaknesses or limitations in it, and it is instructive to enquire what these may be. In part the limitations certainly arise from the lack of either differentiated muscular tissue or a hydrostatic skeleton. The outer layer of the body (Fig. 4–12), the dermal epithelium or pinacoderm, consists of flattened, non-ciliated cells called pinacocytes. These are highly contractile, as is the sponge body as a whole, but the movements of these cells are amoeboid in character rather than muscular. The inner layer of the body is formed of peculiar cells called choanocytes, each possessing a single flagellum which is surrounded at its base by a protoplasmic collar (cf. p. 48). Each of the two layers is thus highly characteristic of the group, and certainly very different from the ectoderm and endoderm of the coelenterates.

Between them lies a gelatinous mesogloea which contains many free-moving amoeboid cells. The existence of these is one indication of the low level of differentiation in the sponge body, for they play a part in a diversity of functions that in higher animals would be assigned to specific tissues. Some of them, with lobose pseudopodia and large nuclei, are called archaeocytes, for they seem to be a reserve from which other types of cell can be differentiated. Others, called scleroblasts, are responsible

Fig. 4-12. Diagram of the simplest type of sponge, the asconid type. *1*, osculum; *2*, layer of choanocytres; *3*, spongocoel; *4*, epidermis; *5*, pore through porocyte; *6*, porocyte; *7*, mesenchyme; *8*, amoebocyte; *9*, spicule. From Hyman, 1940. *The Invertebrata*, vol. 1. McGraw-Hill, New York. Used by permission.

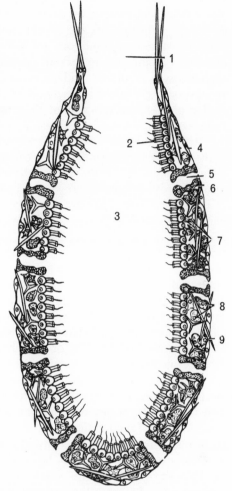

for secreting the skeleton, which consists either of spicules, fibres of spongin, or of both these. Others again give rise to the reproductive cells, or may be concerned with transport of sperm (Sec. 18-4), or with the transport, digestion, and storage of food material. There is an impression of loose diversification of function in this aspect of sponge organization; yet order can also be discerned in it. For example, sponge skeletons have specific forms, depending on the pattern of the spicules, on the extent to which they are scattered or associated in in structural patterns, and on the degree to which spongin contributes to the support of the body. Order is seen also in the mode of secretion of the spicules, for the production of a single spicule may require the integrated activity of several cells. The result can be the development of a complex and beautiful supporting framework, yet its function is limited to the strengthening of the delicate body. It is an unjointed skeleton, lacking the locomotor potentialities of the skeletons of higher animals, and unable to establish functional relationships in this respect with the contractile cells.

Pinacocytes are not the only contractile elements in the sponge body. Some species have stellate connective tissue cells, called collencytes, which extend across the spaces through which the water passes, and which serve to reduce the size of these spaces when the need for this arises. Spindle-shaped cells called myocytes are also often present. These resemble the smooth muscle cells of higher animals in their general form, and they have been thought in consequence to represent specialized contractile tissue; it seems probable, however, that they may often be supporting or secretory in function.

What these various types of contractile cell can do effectively enough is to provide for a protective contraction of the sponge body and closure of the canal system through which the water passes. What they cannot do is to effect either locomotion of the whole body or controlled movements of individual parts of it. We have seen already that such movements demand well-differentiated muscles that can antagonize each other, and that can exert force either on a jointed skeleton or on an enclosed fluid. The necessary conditions are totally lacking in sponges. Quite apart from the absence of an integrating nervous system (Sec. 14–1) and of a jointed skeleton, contractile tissue is diffuse and unspecialized. No less important, the water in the spongocoel is contained in a network of channels open at many points to the outside, so that pressure changes cannot be transmitted in the manner required of a hydrostatic skeleton.

These limitations impose on sponges an immobility that must be a major factor in the evolutionary sterility of their organization. Paradoxically, it has been said that littoral sponges are 'continually on the move', but the movement is partly an illusion resulting from differential growth, and partly a consequence of the amoeboid activity of the pinacocytes. They are certainly not motile in the way that we find in most metazoans, and their behaviour is consequently of the most extreme simplicity. There are no well-differentiated defence responses. The animals depend for protection upon the spicules in the body wall, or the tough spongin; upon the force of the exhalent jet of water; and upon their capacity to contract the inhalent openings and thereby keep out intruders. Locomotion is confined for practical purposes to the flagellated larvae. The adult sponge is a sessile animal, unable to move in search of food, and dependent for its nutrition, as we shall see, upon the feebly organized hydraulic systems of its canals and its flagellated chambers. These it is unable to supplement by such devices as the extension of the body or the movement of tentacles which are so familiar in other sessile invertebrates, notably the coelenterates.

One may ask what advantages were gained by cells aggregating at such a low level of integration, for many of the Protozoa exemplify the high degree of differentiation that can be achieved within the limits of a uninucleate body. The answer is doubtless to be found in the larger size of the resulting structure, which must increase the capacity for resisting the physical stresses of the environment. Moreover, cell differentiation, combined with the organization of the different cell types into tissues, increases the efficiency with which functions can be discharged, so that already in sponges we find a protective external dermal epithelium, and an internal epithelium which is concerned, with other cells, in digestion. Complex reproductive processes are also favoured by multicellular organization, not only because the cells concerned can be set apart from the others (a complete segregation of this sort is not, in fact, found in sponges, but also because the maturation and safeguarding of the gametes is very much more easily achieved.

4–4   TRIPLOBLASTIC STRUCTURE: FLATWORMS

The coelenterates provide an illustration of the hydrostatic skeleton functioning within the limits of a comparatively simple organization of body structure. In other invertebrate groups, at more advanced levels of morphological and histological differentiation, the fundamental principles of the hydrostatic skeleton continue to operate, although they are expressed in different and more elaborate patterns of structure. This is already apparent in the Platyhelminthes and the Nemertina. The relationships of these two groups to the Coelenterata are matters for interesting speculation (Sec. 18–4), but regardless of these phylogenetic issues it is clear that the organization of the platyhelminth and nemertine body is more complex than that of the coelenterate one, and that this makes possible the exploitation of a greater range of action and of habitat. Differentiation in coelenterates, as in sponges, is a differentiation of tissues. In the flatworms these have become further elaborated and integrated to form compact organs, between which there is a division of labour far more extensive than is possible between one tissue and another.

Closely associated with the development of organs, and probably an essential factor in the promotion of this, is the appearance during development of a mesoderm, an extensive mass of cells which separates the ectoderm from the endoderm, and which is derived from one or other of those two germ layers. It largely arises from the endoderm, and is then known as endomesoderm; ectomesoderm, however, derived from the ectoderm, also has an important part to play in many animals. But whatever its origin, the mesoderm as a whole is regarded as constituting a third germ layer. Those animals possessing it are therefore referred to as triploblastic, in contrast to the diploblastic sponges and coelenterates. No doubt the evolution of the mesoderm is foreshadowed in both of those groups in the wandering cells that move through the mesogloea, particularly in sponges, and in the increasing differentiation of muscle layers that we have noted in actinians. Never in those groups, however, does this trend in development reach as far as in the platyhelminths, where for the first time we find a true mesodermal parenchyma. The structure of this is somewhat obscure, although it is commonly regarded as a syncytium with interstices that are filled with fluid. Whatever its structure, however, its presence greatly aids the morphological and functional differentiation of the organs that we have noted as a new feature of the group. It relieves the ectoderm and endoderm of some of their primitive and generalized functions, gives them space in which to extend, and provides a measure of transport and communication between them by diffusion and by the passage of fluid.

Free-living flatworms have a ciliated epidermis, and the smaller ones can swim by ciliary action. This can also serve for creeping over a solid substratum, with the cilia exerting their propulsive force by beating in a mucous secretion. With increase in size this mode of locomotion becomes inadequate, and is replaced by muscular contraction, which can generate much greater forces. The muscles operate in conjunction with a hydrostatic skeleton, but there is an important difference from the situation in coelenterates in that the mesenchymatous parenchyma replaces the coelenteric fluid as the deformable mass. Associated with this is a different arrangement of the musculature. As Pantin remarks, these worms present us with a new invention: the development of muscle fibres freely, and in depth, at any point in the parenchyma, instead of their restriction to the ectodermal and endodermal epithelia. We have seen, however, that this invention is already foreshadowed in the coelenterates.

It is true that some Acoela, for example, possess musculo-epithelial cells in the ectoderm, a feature that is suggestive of close relationship with coelenterates, although it might have been independently evolved. The very active movements of the Turbellaria, however, depend upon an effector system that is more complex than that of coelenterates, and that is arranged according to a fundamentally different plan (Fig. 4–13). Immediately beneath the epidermis lies a well-developed basement membrane containing inextensible fibres. These form alternately left- and right-handed spirals around the body, in such a way that the angle at which the fibres cross each other can change as the length of the body changes. They form, therefore, a flexible lattice structure; this can extend and retract in essentially the same way as 'lazy tongs' (p. 74), yet it is able to limit the extensibility of the body. A layer of longitudinal muscle and another of circular muscle are present beneath the basement membrane; both layers are separate from the epidermis, and both are several or many fibres thick. Between these layers lie diagonal muscle fibres, while dorso-ventral fibres run vertically between the dorsal and ventral surfaces of the body.

The functioning of the muscles depends upon the circular and longitudinal layers, with their associated diagonal fibres, being situated immediately beneath the

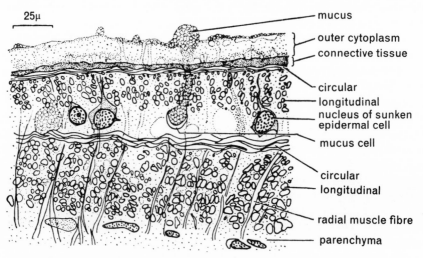

Fig. 4-13. Drawing of part of a transverse section of *Prorhynchus putealis* Haswell, to show position of surface layers. From Robson, 1957. *op. cit.*

basement membrane. The significance of this position is that all of these effector structures thus lie externally to the deformable parenchyma. In coelenterates, by contrast, one muscle layer is external to the mesogloea and the other typically internal. The difference is correlated with the use of the parenchyma as the deformable hydrostatic skeleton. Only because the two antagonistic systems of circular and longitudinal musculature lie externally to that skeleton can they bring direct pressure to bear upon it. Exactly what contribution the diagonal muscle fibres make is not clear, although it has been suggested that they may contribute to the total strength of the body musculature and assist also in the maintenance of internal turgor. The dorso-ventral muscles are presumably of particular importance in these animals in ensuring the maintenance of the flattened body form.

The total effect of this arrangement of musculature and hydrostatic skeleton is that flatworms can reversibly deform their bodies by twisting and flattening to an extent that cannot be achieved by coelenterates. This makes possible the three modes of progression (additional to ciliary movement) that will be familiar to all who have observed flatworms and nemertines. One of these is a looping movement, that is even more characteristic of leeches than it is of these groups. Another is a gliding movement, produced by the transmission of waves down the length of the body. These waves, which may involve the whole surface, or may be confined to the edges of the body, are produced by localized contraction of the longitudinal muscles. They result in localized swelling of the body, which becomes temporarily adherent to the substratum by mucus secreted from the body surface. This provides the friction that we have earlier mentioned as essential for progression. Displacement of the body here results from its extension anterior to the point of contact, an extension that is brought about by contraction of the circular muscles, with coordinated relaxation of the longitudinal ones. Coordination, indeed, is an essential factor; transmission of pressure changes through the parenchyma is a fundamental requirement, but the activity of these animals must depend also upon control of the musculature exerted through the nervous system. The third method of locomotion, found in nemertines but not in platyhelminths, is essentially a variant of these delicate waves; it involves the transmission down the body of conspicuous and irregular waves of peristalsis.

The possibilities of a parenchymatous hydrostatic skeleton are thus considerable, although there are also limitations. These will become apparent when we consider the factors that have influenced evolution of the annelid worms. One limitation that is immediately obvious, however, is that a parenchyma is likely to be less easily deformable than a fluid enclosed in a cavity. In this connection it is interesting that the nemertines do, in fact, make use of a fluid hydrostatic skeleton in the functioning of their proboscis. This structure, in its resting position, is invaginated within the body in a fluid-filled cavity called the rhynchocoel. The walls of this cavity are provided with longitudinal and circular muscle, contractions of which bring about pressure changes in the fluid, with consequent eversion of the proboscis to a length that may greatly exceed that of the worm itself. This organ is used both for feeding and for burrowing. The latter function depends on the proboscis being inserted into the sand of the substratum, and then dilated at its tip. Contraction of its retractor muscles will now draw the rest of the body after it, the dilated tip serving as the anchorage during this movement. The speed, precision, and power of the movements of this organ are a good testimony to the efficiency of a completely fluid hydrostatic skeleton, in association with fully differentiated muscle layers. This is the device that has been so fully exploited in annelid worms and many other invertebrates, but the exploitation was only possible after further advances in body organization. Before considering these, however, we must first examine the peculiar and unique organization of the nematode worms.

4–5 TRIPLOBLASTIC STRUCTURE: ROUNDWORMS

The principles of the hydrostatic skeleton are fundamentally so simple that they can operate within more than one type of structural organization. This is sufficiently evident from a comparison of coelenterates with platyhelminths, but it is illustrated no less well by the Nematoda. These animals form a very isolated assemblage, sharing a combination of features so characteristic of the group that it is difficult to determine either its relationships or its evolutionary background, although there are reasons for linking nematodes with a number of smaller acoelomate groups in the Phylum Aschelminthes. At present we are concerned particularly with the structure of the body wall. This is covered by a cuticle, secreted by a non-cellular epidermis, and consisting of protein, not of chitin. Underneath the epidermis is a single layer of

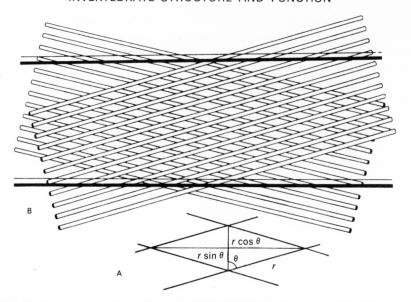

Fig. 4-14. A schematic representation of the basketwork structure of fibrils in the cuticle of *Ascaris*. A, general diagram illustrating the orientation of two of the fibril layers in relation to two of the transverse external annulations. B, the equivalent unit parallelogram. From Harris and Crofton, 1957. *J. exp. Biol.*, **34**, 116–130.

peculiar muscle cells, which have an outer contractile portion and an inner core of unmodified and non-contractile protoplasm. These cells are arranged as a layer of longitudinal muscle, circular muscle being entirely absent from the body wall. Between this muscle layer and the alimentary canal lie highly vacuolated cells, the vacuoles running together to form what is in effect a perivisceral cavity, filled with fluid. This particular feature is similar in principle to the arrangement of the paren-chyma of platyhelminths. Like the latter animals, the nematodes are acoelomate; but the important difference here is that there is no antagonism between longitudinal and circular muscles. Instead, the longitudinal muscles are antagonized by the force exerted upon the cuticle by the pressure of the body fluid.

This is a unique type of hydrostatic skeletal system, depending for its operation upon the highly specialized structure of the cuticle. In *Ascaris* (and this is probably true of most nematodes) the cuticle contains sets of diagonally-crossed fibres, which are sufficiently thick to be seen in fixed material (Fig. 4–14). There are three layers of these fibres, creating a spiral basketwork. The fibres in each layer form two sets that cross each other so that they enclose minute parallelograms. The diagonals that make up the walls of these parallelograms have been compared by Harris and Crofton to sets of 'lazy tongs', for they can move with reference to each other in such a way that the worm can become either shorter and thicker, or longer and thinner. Because of this the cuticle, in association with the longitudinal musculature, forms a system capable both of distortion, and of exerting tension against the internal pressure. The fibres themselves are probably inextensible; it is supposed, therefore, that the cuticle must also contain an elastic component.

The internal hydrostatic pressure of *Ascaris* is considerable (Fig. 4–15), although it shows a wide range of variation, from 16 to 125 mm of mercury, with a mean value of 70 mm of mercury (equivalent to 95 cm of water). This pressure, acting in conjunction with the tension exercised by the body wall, and with some degree of muscular tone, accounts for the constant shape, cross-section, and length which is so characteristic of the nematode body. It provides also for the simple undulating movement of these animals; a type of movement that, by fitting them so well for life in viscous media, is one factor that pre-adapts them for the parasitic habit (Sec. 23–4). It depends on the fact that when muscular contraction at one point produces local shortening, this is compensated for by lengthening elsewhere, because the displaced body fluid exerts pressure against the elastic force maintained by the body wall.

It is possible, as Harris and Crofton show, to carry this analysis even further. Commenting on the constant form of these animals, they remark that 'the elementary student may be forgiven at times for thinking that there is only one nematode but that the model comes in different sizes and with a great variety of life histories.' This constant form, they suggest, may well be determined by limitations inherent in the plan of structure that we have outlined.

For example, transfer of fluid from point to point within the body provides for an essentially mechanical coordination of movement that eliminates the need for local reflex pathways. Hence the simplicity of the nematode nervous system, which has anterior and posterior groups of nerve cells linked by nerve cords that contain few if any cells. The high internal pressure would cause collapse of the lumen of the alimentary tract if it were not antagonized in some way. This antagonism is ensured by the existence of a muscular pumping pharynx, which, incidentally, is another pre-adaptation for parasitic life. The absence of cilia is a feature of nematodes, and it is probably significant that ciliary action would be quite inadequate for maintaining sufficient pressure within the intestine of these worms. Maintenance of this pressure

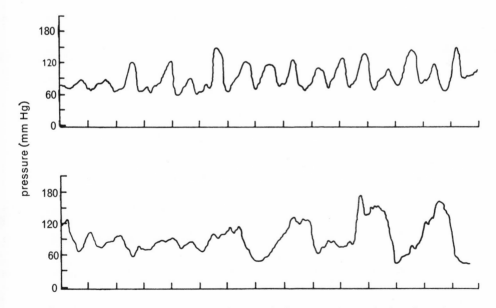

Fig. 4-15. Tracing from a photographic record of pressure changes in *Ascaris*, made with a glass helix pressure gauge. The two halves of the record are consecutive. Time marks are at 30-second intervals. From Harris and Crofton, 1957. *op. cit.*

is aided by the 'self-sealing' of the anus, defaecation being provided for by the action of dilator muscles of the hind gut. Then, to give one further example, it is characteristic of nematodes that the excretory canals are embedded in lateral thickenings called the lateral lines. This may well be an adaptation for ensuring that these canals are not closed by the internal pressure.

This interpretation of the form of nematodes as being determined by mechanical factors is somewhat theoretical, yet very plausible. No less plausible is the interpretation of the form of platyhelminths as being determined partly by the factors that we have discussed earlier, and partly by considerations of transport and diffusion (Sec. 11-1). In animals, as in the structures that we design ourselves, external appearance reflects functional requirements, and is often all the more satisfying the more closely that it does so.

5

Movement, Hydrostatics, and the Coelom

5–1 SIGNIFICANCE OF THE COELOM

An advance in animal organization, no less important than the development of a mesoderm and internal musculature, is the appearance within the mesoderm of the cavity known as the coelom. This can be defined as a cavity that arises within the endomesoderm, and that is therefore covered on its outer surface by the somatic mesoderm and on its inner surface by the splanchnic mesoderm. It contains a fluid, the coelomic fluid, and is lined by an epithelium, the coelomic epithelium or peritoneum.

It is usually referred to as the secondary body cavity, because it is preceded in development by the primary body cavity or blastocoel, which is the cavity of the blastula. This cavity is usually obliterated by the development of the archenteron, the primitive digestive cavity. The archenteron persists in coelenterates as the only cavity, but since its lumen is strictly part of the outside world it is not regarded as a body cavity *in sensu stricto*. It also persists as the only cavity in the platyhelminths, for in them, too, the blastocoel is obliterated and the coelom has not yet appeared. This group is triploblastic but acoelomate. Sometimes the blastocoel persists to form in the adult a body cavity that is superficially like a coelom in that it contains a fluid, but differs from a typical coelomic cavity in lacking a lining epithelium. This is the situation in the Nematoda. It is found also in those groups that may be related to the nematodes, including the Nematomorpha, Rotifera, Gastrotricha, and Echinoderida, and in some other groups of uncertain relationships, including the Acanthocephala and the Entoprocta. It is possible that the body cavity of the Priapulida is also of this nature.

The question of the evolutionary origin of the coelom has been much debated, but inevitably there is a lack of definite information, and conclusions can only be reached by inference. Four main theories have been proposed: that it originates from outgrowths of the alimentary canal (enterocoel theory), from the enlarged cavities

77

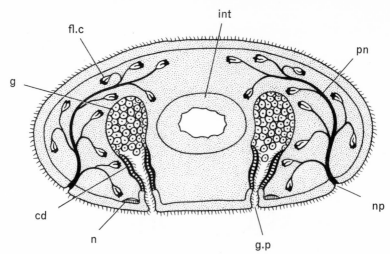

Fig. 5-1. Diagrams of transverse sections illustrating the gonocoel theory of the origin of the coelom. A, the platyhelminth stage; B, *top right*, the nemertine stage; C, *lower right*, the annelid stage. *b.v*, lateral blood vessel; *c*, coelom; *cd*, coelomoduct; *d.v*, dorsal longitudinal blood vessel; *fl.c*, flame-cell; *g*, gonad; *g.p*, genital pore; *int*, intestine; *l.n*, lateral nerve; *l.n.c*, longitudinal nephridial canal; *mtn*, metanephridium; *n* and *nc*, ventral longitudinal nerve; *np*, nephridiopore; *nst*, nephridiostome; *p*, proboscis; *pn*, protonephridium; *sol*, solenocyte. Adapted from Goodrich, 1945. *Q. Jl microsc. Sci.*, **86**, 113–392.

of nephridia (nephrocoel theory), from splits in the mesoderm (schizocoel theory), or from the enlarged cavities of gonads (gonocoel theory).

As Hyman points out in her analysis of these several theories, none is wholly free from difficulties. The nephrocoel theory is only of historical interest. It was first proposed by Lankester in 1874 at a time when the relationships of the coelom with nephridia and coelomoducts (Sec. 12–1) had still to be clarified; it has since found few supporters. The schizocoel and enterocoel theories derive from the two methods of development of the coelom, which may arise either by splitting of the mesoderm, in which case the cavity is called a schizocoel, or by the evagination of pouches from the wall of the archenteron, in which case it is called an enterocoel. A schizocoel is found in the Annelida, Arthropoda, and Mollusca—groups that are believed on good grounds to be closely related and that can be placed, with the Platyhelminthes and Nemertina, in a group called the Protostomia (Sec. 18–5). An enterocoel is found in the Echinodermata, Pogonophora, Hemichordata, Cephalochordata, and perhaps in the Urochordata—groups that are believed to have close relationships with the Vertebrata and that can be placed, with them, in the Deuterostomia.

This may seem to suggest that the mode of development of the coelom is of phylogenetic importance, but in fact it is by no means certain that this is so. Even within the echinoderms and hemichordates, for example, there is marked variation in this development. Moreover, the vertebrates have a schizocoel, whereas the cephalochordates, to which they are undoubtedly very closely related, have an enterocoel. We see here an illustration of a fact that cannot be over emphasized: the pathways of early development are greatly subject to evolutionary modification, and therefore form an insecure basis for phylogenetic speculation unless they are carefully considered in relation to other aspects of organization.

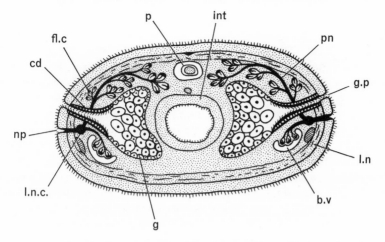

B

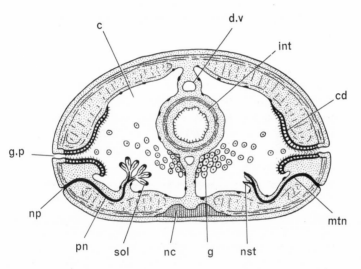

C

The enterocoel theory was associated by Sedgwick in 1884 with a specific aspect of coelenterate organization, for he suggested that the coelom might have been derived from the coelenteric pouches enclosed by the mesenteries in the Scyphozoa and Anthozoa. This version of the theory, however, demands the derivation of triploblastic animals from forms that are already so highly specialized that they would seem unlikely to have been the starting points of a major evolutionary advance. Nor, as Clark points out, is it easy to explain the selective advantage of such a step. These coelenteric pouches serve to increase digestive efficiency through the enlarged surface area that they provide, and through the specialization of the cells along their free edges (Sec. 9–5), while their mesenteries help to regulate the water content of the hydrostatic skeleton. These advantages would be lost if the pouches separated off as separate coelomic cavities.

The schizocoel theory is at first sight more plausible than either of the preceding theories, yet it has received little support. This is probably because of its essentially indefinite character, and particularly because of its inability to account for the clear-cut morphological difference between the coelom and the spaces of the blood vascular system.

The most favoured theory of the four has certainly been the gonocoel theory, illustrated in diagrammatic form in Fig. 5-1. Among the points in its favour is the fact that some acoelomate nemertines pass through a stage in which they possess a series of gonads with large and sometimes empty cavities; it is possible to visualize the further enlargement of these into the spacious coelomic cavities of annelids. Moreover, this particular theory would account for gonads commonly developing from the coelomic wall. In this respect, however, it fails to explain why the germ cells often make their first appearance in regions other than the coelomic wall, and only reach this after considerable passage through the body. Nor is this the only difficulty presented by the gonocoel theory. To derive the coelom from serially repeated gonads is to imply that its origin was closely connected with the establishment of metamerism. Clearly this entirely fails to account for the existence of many unsegmented coelomate groups, for these cannot be dismissed with the assumption that they have lost their segmentation after derivation from a metamerically segmented ancestor. We shall return to this point when we deal with the origin of metamerism, although theories relating to this do little, if anything, to clarify the present question. It is wiser, in fact, not to seek a formal answer to it.

The difficulties outlined above—and they could be pursued in much greater detail—suggest that a discussion of the origin of the coelom couched in terms of classical morphology is bound to be sterile. Rather, we should examine the uses to which the coelom can be put, so gaining a deeper understanding of the conditions that may have favoured its appearance and early evolution. We shall see that it must have proved so manifestly advantageous that it might conceivably have arisen independently on more than one occasion.

One obvious advantage derived from a coelomic cavity is that it establishes a cavity around the alimentary tract, which is now surrounded by the peritoneum and, in many animals, suspended in the cavity by a double fold of peritoneum called a mesentery. This, together with the development of a visceral musculature from the associated mesoderm, permits free movement of the tract, an advantage conferred also upon the heart and other mobile organs. As regards the alimentary canal, this freedom improves efficiency in the handling of the food material. In microphagous animals, which tend to rely largely upon cilia for the handling of the food particles, this is less important, but it must have been a crucial factor in promoting the development of macrophagy, with the consequent need to break up food and to mix it with the enzymes of the alimentary lumen.

Another advantage is concerned with transport. We have noted that the presence of fluid in the interstices of the parenchyma of the acoelomate platyhelminths must also help in the transmission of metabolites. For this purpose the coelomic fluid is altogether more efficient, as is apparent from the way in which excretory organs, whether nephridia or coelomoducts, open into the cavity and abstract dissolved nitrogenous waste from it. At the same time, and through the same pathway, the coelomic fluid has an important part to play in osmoregulation. We shall be considering both of these aspects later, and we shall see then how the development of a blood vascular system has become involved in their execution.

In addition, and arising from what we have said above regarding the origin of the germ cells, the coelom is an important factor in reproduction, for the germ cells mature in it, either in the cavity as a whole or in restricted parts of it, and are eventually discharged through the coelomoducts. These ducts were very probably genital in their initial function, and only later became concerned with excretion and osmoregulation, displacing in consequence the nephridia, which, in their closed protonephridial form, are the most primitive excretory organs (Sec. 12–1).

Lastly, but perhaps most important of all, the coelom with its contained fluid provides the structural basis for a hydrostatic skeleton more highly organized than that of coelenterates and platyhelminths. In this respect it probably played a major part in ensuring the successful survival of the lower coelomates during the period when calcium and phosphorus metabolism had not been elaborated to a point at which rigid and jointed skeletons could be constructed. The movements of annelid worms, echinoderms, and many of the smaller groups, are based upon hydrostatic principles in essentially the same way as are the movements of coelenterates, but they show a greatly increased flexibility and speed of response. This is partly, of course, because of the more highly differentiated structure of the body as a whole, and in particular because of the much greater elaboration of the nervous system. A major contribution to this improvement, however, is certainly attributable to the presence of the coelom, and it may well be that this aspect of the function of the coelom was the most important single factor determining its appearance. This possibility will be more readily appreciated if we examine some examples of its functioning as a hydrostatic skeleton.

5–2 SIPUNCULIDS AND POLYZOA

The Sipunculoidea provide an example of the operation of a coelomic hydrostatic skeleton at a simple level of organization. *Sipunculus* carries out three types of movement: swimming, burrowing, and defence reactions. Burrowing depends upon the eversion of a proboscis or introvert; during this process a hump forms in the middle of the body, and there is a considerable increase in pressure in the coelomic fluid. The resting value of this pressure is of the order of 2 cm to 3 cm of water, but it may rise during burrowing to as much as 25 cm, although eversion of the proboscis can take place at much lower pressures than this. Even higher values are found during defence movements, which depend upon the establishment by the body musculature of a very high turgor; pressure as high as 108 cm has been recorded in these conditions in another sipunculid, *Phascolosoma gouldi*. Part of the defence reaction is a flexure of the body. This is seen also when *Sipunculus* burrows rapidly, the flexure anchoring the animal in its burrow and enabling it to direct the full thrust of its hydrostatic skeleton upon the proboscis.

In animals such as these, in which the coelomic cavity is continuous, the full force of the whole body musculature can be brought to bear upon one point. We shall consider this aspect of the functioning of the coelom from another point of view when we examine the situation in annelid worms. Meantime, we can appreciate that it must be of the greatest mechanical advantage in enabling burrowing animals to penetrate the substratum. Since the burrowing habit makes available a rich source of nutriment, as well as providing for protection, we can easily understand the advantages obtained by those early metazoans that developed their hydrostatic

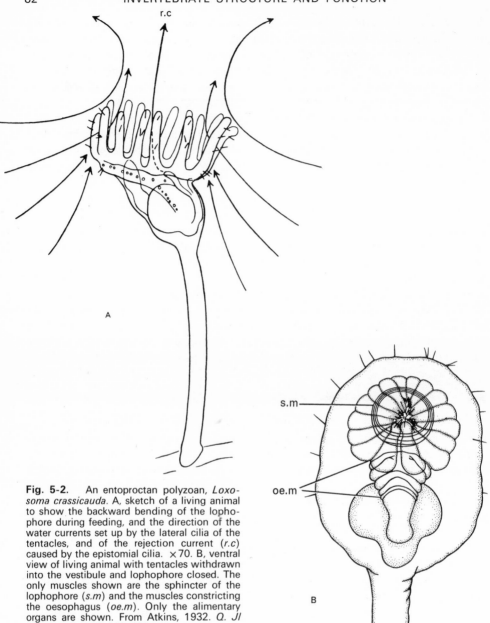

Fig. 5-2. An entoproctan polyzoan, *Loxo-soma crassicauda*. A, sketch of a living animal to show the backward bending of the lopho-phore during feeding, and the direction of the water currents set up by the lateral cilia of the tentacles, and of the rejection current (*r.c*) caused by the epistomial cilia. × 70. B, ventral view of living animal with tentacles withdrawn into the vestibule and lophophore closed. The only muscles shown are the sphincter of the lophophore (*s.m*) and the muscles constricting the oesophagus (*oe.m*). Only the alimentary organs are shown. From Atkins, 1932. *Q. Jl microsc. Sci.*, **75**, 393–423.

skeleton in this way. Sessile animals would also have benefited, however, as can be well seen in the Polyzoa.

We have already mentioned the Entoprocta as an example of a group in which the blastocoel persists as the permanent body cavity or pseudocoel. These animals (Fig. 5–2) are microphagous feeders and use for this purpose a circlet of tentacles, which can be withdrawn for protection within a vestibule formed by an extension of the body wall. The opening of the vestibule to the exterior can be closed by a sphincter

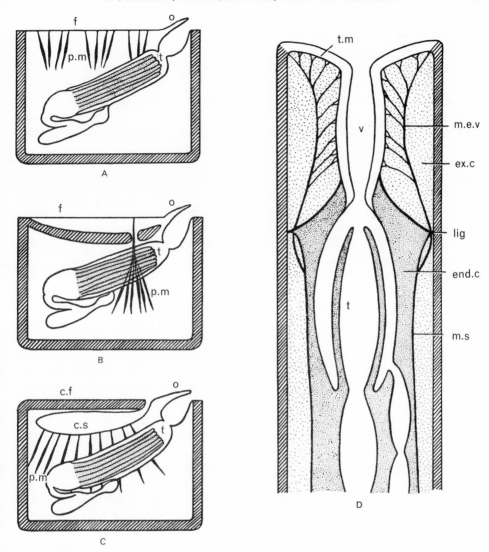

Fig. 5-3. Diagrams to illustrate the mechanism of protrusion of the tentacles in various types of polyzoan. A, *Membranipora.* B, *Micropora.* C, the Ascophora. D, a cyclostomous polyzoan. *c.f,* calcified frontal wall; *c.s,* compensation sac; *end.c,* endo-saccal coelom; *ex.c,* exosaccal coelom; *f,* frontal wall of zooecium; *lig,* ligament of membranous sac; *m.e.v,* extensor muscles of the vestibule; *m.s,* membranous sac; *o,* operculum; *p.m,* parietal muscles; *t,* tentacles; *t.m,* terminal membrane; *v,* vestibule. After Harmer. From Chapman, 1958. *Biol. Rev.,* **33,** 338–371.

muscle; when this muscle is relaxed the tentacles spread outwards, presumably under the influence of the hydrostatic pressure of the fluid of the pseudocoel.

The Entoprocta have no close relationship with the Polyzoa Ectoprocta. They, too, are microphagous, with feeding tentacles, but they are coelomate and extrusion is here brought about by the hydrostatic pressure of the coelomic fluid. Quite apart from this difference, the mechanics of extrusion in many ectoproctans are much more complex than in the Entoprocta, for the body wall develops a degree of rigidity that does not seem likely at first sight to permit the establishment of hydraulically mediated movements. In correlation with this the tentacles are not simply folded inwards and enclosed by the body wall, but are withdrawn into a space formed by the introversion of the anterior part of the body. This introvert, which is termed the tentacle sheath, is everted when the tentacles are to be exposed, and takes a considerable part of the body contents with it. Introversion, by contrast, is a simpler proposition, since it merely depends upon the contraction of specialized retractor muscles which run from the body wall to their insertions on the polypide.

The organization of the fresh-water forms (such as *Plumatella* and *Cristatella*), which constitutes the Class Phylactolaemata, does not present any special difficulty. Their body wall is flexible, and is well provided with circular and longitudinal muscle, so that contraction of the musculature is sufficient, in cooperation with the coelomic fluid, to bring about extrusion or withdrawal of the polypide and its tentacles. In the remaining Ectoprocta (the typically marine Class Gymnolaemata) the situation is more complicated. In these the body wall develops a varying degree of rigidity, and it is in connection with this that hydrostatic devices of exceptional elegance have been evolved (Fig. 5–3).

The difficulty here lies in varying the pressure in the coelomic body cavity when this is surrounded by a body wall that is not flexible. *Membranipora* exemplifies one of the solutions of this problem that have been evolved. In this animal, as in many other members of the Order Cheilostomata, the individuals are associated in an encrusting colony. The basal part of each body, the zooecium, is largely a rigid box, with its base attached to the substratum, and with four sides attached to neighbouring zooecia. The remaining wall, which is exposed to the outside of the colony, is flexible, and it is upon this, the frontal membrane, that the solution of the hydrostatic problem depends. Muscles, termed the parietal muscles, are inserted upon the membrane, their origins being on the rigid lateral walls. Contraction of these muscles pulls the membrane inwards, causing an increase of pressure that is sufficient to evert the polypide.

In other genera, such as members of the group Ascophora, the exposed wall of the zooecium is calcified, so that it loses its flexibility. This modification, which increases the protective value of the zooecium, may seem to destroy the possibility of increasing internal pressure, yet the difficulty is overcome by the development of a separate internal cavity, the compensation sac. The parietal muscles are here attached to the floor of this sac in such a way that when they contract they enlarge the lumen of the sac, and thus produce the required change of pressure in the coelomic fluid. Actually, the difference between this arrangement and the preceding one is probably less than it may seem, for it is likely that the floor of the compensation sac represents the original frontal membrane, which we can regard as having become arched over by an external secondary wall.

One other example of these elegant devices may be illustrated by *Micropora*. Here the frontal membrane remains flexible, but an internal calcified wall called the cryptocyst becomes deposited under the membrane; as with the previous example, this probably gives some protective advantage. The parietal muscles extend through the cryptocyst to reach the frontal membrane; their contraction depresses the membrane and thereby increases the coelomic pressure.

5–3   ECHINODERMS

Our next example of the operation of a coelomic hydrostatic skeleton is taken from the Echinodermata, a group that provides good illustrations of the way in which the coelomic fluid can provide both for locomotion and for feeding in large and highly organized animals. The coelom of echinoderms is highly specialized in its subdivision into several distinct systems; these include the main perivisceral coelom, the perihaemal system, the aboral sinus system, and the water-vascular system. The complex form of the coelom of the adult is derived from a comparatively simple plan of organization in the larvae (cf. Fig. 18–15), in which the coelomic cavity is divided into three main regions, anterior, median, and posterior. This arrangement is seen not only in larval echinoderms, but also in the developmental stages of the Pogonophora and Hemichordata. In the latter two groups it is associated with a corresponding tripartite division of the body into prosoma, mesosoma, and metasoma. This tripartite organization of the coelom is, in fact, one of the characteristic features of the echinoderm/chordate line, or Deuterostomia, but it has been lost in the Urochordata. Here the coelom has been greatly reduced, and perhaps even lost, although it may be represented by the paired epicardia, which grow out from the alimentary tract and come to surround the heart. The tripartite structure has also been obscured in the cephalochordates and vertebrates, in this instance because of the development of metamerism, although traces of the pattern may be discernible in the development of the coelomic pouches of amphioxus.

It is difficult now to judge the extent of the hydrostatic functions of the coelom in the earliest deuterostomes, not least because the origin of the group remains obscure. It is possible that they were initially creeping forms, so that a hydrostatic skeleton might at one time have contributed to their movement. What is reasonably certain, however, is that at an early stage of their history they became sessile microphagous forms, using ciliated tentacles for their feeding. Probably the pterobranch hemichordates (Fig. 10–16) offer us the best idea today of this stage in their evolution. In these animals the tentacles are hollow outgrowths of the mesosoma and contain extensions of the mesosomatic coelom. In the Pogonophora the tentacles similarly contain coelomic spaces, but in this group they are outgrowths of the prosoma. One early function of the deuterostome coelom, then, was probably to facilitate extension of the tentacles, just as occurs today in the Ectoprocta, although without the complication of introversion that we find in that group.

The hydrostatic function of the deuterostome coelom has been most closely studied in the echinoderms, for the development of locomotion in the Eleutherozoa has depended very heavily upon that function. It is seen in a simple form in the holothurians, which are in some respects very worm-like in their mechanism of movement. The metasomatic coelom here forms a spacious and fluid-filled body cavity which, in conjunction with the musculature of the body wall, permits these animals to carry out peristaltic movements. Some of them have thus successfully developed burrowing habits. The main coelomic body cavity is equally well developed in the echinoids (sea-urchins) and asteroids (starfish), but in these animals the body wall is so firm that peristaltic movements are impossible; it seems doubtful, therefore, whether this region of the coelom can be of much hydrostatic significance. Their locomotion depends upon the transformation of the ancestral ciliary feeding mechanism, with its tentacles and contained coelomic spaces, into the tube-feet and water-

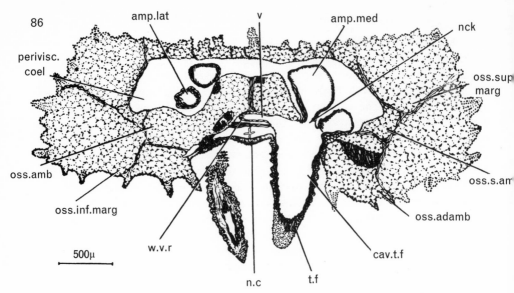

Fig. 5-4. Transverse section through the arm of *Astropecten irregularis. amp.lat,* lateral lobe of the ampulla; *amp.med,* medial lobe of the ampulla; *cav.t.f,* tube-foot cavity; *nck,* neck of the ampulla; *n.c,* radial nerve cord; *oss.adamb,* adambulacral ossicle; *oss.amb,* ambulacral ossicle; *oss.inf.marg,* infra-marginal ossicle; *oss.s.amb,* supra-ambulacral ossicle; *oss.sup.marg,* supra-marginal ossicle; *perivisc.coel,* peri-visceral coelom; *t.f,* tube foot; *v,* valve. *w.v.r,* radial water vessel. From Smith, 1946. *Phil. Trans. R. Soc. B,* **232,** 279–310.

vascular system. Indeed, these are also of importance in holothurians, except in those specialized burrowers in which the tube-feet have been lost.

The general principles of locomotion in these animals can be illustrated by a consideration of starfish. Along each arm of these animals extends an open ambulacral groove, from which arises a series of tube-feet (podia). These are arranged in two rows, and usually have suckers at their tips. Each tube-foot (Fig. 5-4) has a coelomic cavity which communicates by a narrow neck with an ampulla lying in the main perivisceral coelom. This ampulla, which may be divided into a median lobe and two lateral lobes, forms with the tube-foot a functional unit. The coelomic cavity of this unit is connected by a lateral water vessel with the main radial water vessel that extends along the length of each arm, and that connects with a circumoral ring vessel in the central disc of the body. From this the stone canal runs upwards to open to the outside at the madreporite, which is perforated by ciliated pores.

The functioning of the system depends upon differences between the musculature of the ampulla and the tube-foot (Fig. 5-5). In the ampulla the muscles consist mainly of rings of smooth muscle fibres which are set vertically and which lie parallel to the long axis of the arm. Protraction of the tube-foot is brought about by the contraction of these muscles, the effect of this being to drive fluid out of the ampulla into the foot. The increase in pressure is wholly translated into elongation of the foot, any wasteful lateral bulging of this organ being prevented by a collagenous sheath of connective tissue in its wall. This sheath allows extension but resists lateral pressure, so that it may be compared, from a functional point of view, with the circular muscle fibres in the tentacles of anemones. The musculature of the tube-foot (Fig. 5-6), in contrast to that of the ampulla, consists of longitudinal muscles, which are bounded on the inside by the ciliated epithelium of the coelom and on the outside by the collagenous

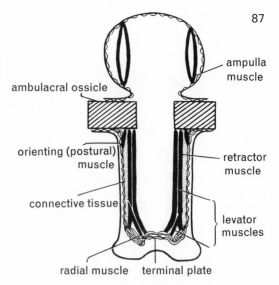

Fig. 5-5. Diagram of a longitudinal section through a foot and ampulla of *Asterias rubens*, showing the arrangement of the chief muscle systems. From Smith, 1947. *Q. Jl microsc. Sci.*, **88**, 1–14.

ampulla muscle

ambulacral ossicle

orienting (postural) muscle

retractor muscle

connective tissue

levator muscles

radial muscle   terminal plate

connective tissue, by the ectoderm, and by the cuticle. The hydrostatic pressure of protrusion brings about relaxation of these muscles (Fig. 5-7). Withdrawal of the foot is accomplished by their contraction, the connective tissue fibres becoming pushed together into layers during this process. Bending of the foot is achieved by localized contraction of the longitudinal muscles, while postural muscles provide for its orientation. This makes possible the highly organized stepping movements by which these animals pull themselves along. The whole system is a striking example of the complexity of behaviour that can be mediated by a hydrostatic skeleton, given adequate specialization of the muscles and nervous system.

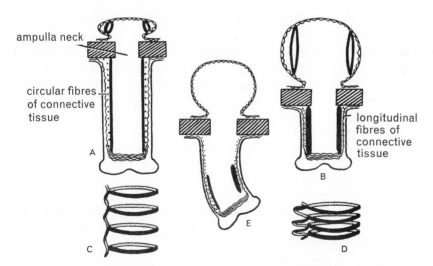

ampulla neck

circular fibres of connective tissue

longitudinal fibres of connective tissue

Fig. 5-6. A, B, E, diagrams showing the conditions of contraction and relaxation of the ampulla muscles and the retractor fibres of the foot of *Asterias rubens* during A, protraction, B, retraction, and E, localized bending of the podium. Muscles in contraction are represented by the thicker, and relaxed muscles by the thinner, of the black bands. C and D show how the longitudinal and circular fibres of the connective tissue sheath within the column of the foot are arranged when the foot is C, protracted, and D, retracted. From Smith, 1947. *op. cit.*

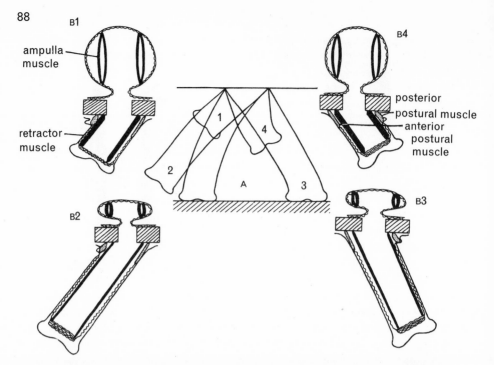

Fig. 5-7. *A1–4.* The successive phases of the ambulatory step. *B1–4* show the conditions of contraction and relaxation of the protractor, retractor, and postural muscles of the foot during the successive phases of static posture of the 'ideal' step; the protractor and retractor muscles are shown in black, the orienting (postural) fibres are stippled. The anterior postural fibres orientate the foot in the forward direction, the posterior fibres in the backward direction of the step. From Smith, 1947. *op. cit.*

Protrusion is an entirely passive process, as far as the foot is concerned; thus in *Asterias rubens* the volume of the ampulla (which in this genus is undivided) is about the same as the maximum extension attained by the foot. In this situation there must be no serious loss of fluid during protrusion and withdrawal, for the effect would be as disastrous as having a leaking hydraulic brake system. Loss is prevented by a valve at the junction of the tube-foot with the lateral vessel. This valve is essentially an extension of the lateral water vessel, arranged to permit fluid to pass from the vessel into the tube but not in the reverse direction. Its importance may be judged from the fact that the total volume of fluid in the stone canal, circumoral vessel, and radial vessels amounts to only 1 % to 2 % of the estimated volume of the contents of the tube-feet and ampullae; it would thus be quite impossible for the latter organs to be replenished at all rapidly from the fluid in the vessels. What those vessels do is to provide a trickle of fluid, through the ciliated madreporite; in this respect they are functionally comparable, although at a much higher level of structural complexity, with the siphonoglyph of anemones.

5–4 MOLLUSCS

The ground plan of the molluscs (Fig. 5–8) is a body divided into two functionally distinct regions. One of these, the upper part, comprises the visceral hump and mantle; it functions largely through mucus secretion and ciliary action. The other, the lower part, comprises the head and foot, and is largely muscular, although it too is provided with cilia and mucus cells. This plan of structure is not easily relatable to that of any other phylum; one idea is that it might have evolved from a platyhelminth-like stock in which enlargement of the alimentary system led to the development of the characteristic molluscan visceral hump.

Whatever the truth of this, it is certainly very difficult to interpret the history of the coelom (Fig. 12-6). This is typically small in molluscs, and it is usually described as consisting of a pericardial coelom around the heart, a gonadal coelom, and paired coelomic ducts which, together with the pericardial wall, serve as excretory organs. This interpretation is based, by implication, upon the gonocoel theory of the origin of the coelom. If we reject this theory, it is difficult to see how anything more than the pericardial cavity can be regarded as coelomic. The complication here is that there are good developmental grounds for considering that the molluscs are closely associated with the Annelida and the Arthropoda; indeed, we have seen that all three groups are thought of as included within the Protostomia. Has the small coelom of molluscs been directly derived from a stage of evolution preceding the appearance of the spacious coelom of annelids, or has it been secondarily reduced from a more exten-sively developed condition? If the former, the appearance of the coelom would have antedated the establishment of its hydrostatic functions, which, in any case, are often of minor importance in molluscs. It then becomes difficult to see what advantage could have promoted its early evolution in these animals, apart, perhaps, from the facilita-tion of the heart beat. If the molluscan coelom has been secondarily reduced it is surprising that there is no trace of this in the development of present-day forms, for the undoubted reduction of the coelom of arthropods has left clear embryological

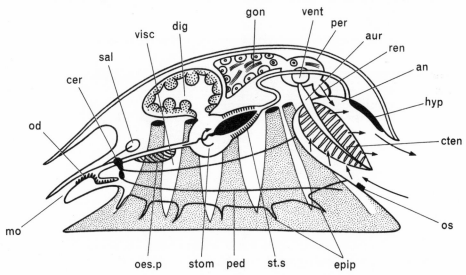

Fig. 5-8. Schematic view of an early mollusc. *an*, anus; *aur*, auricle; *cer*, cerebral ganglion; *cten*, ctenidium; *dig*, digestive gland; *epip*, epipodium; *gon*, gonad; *hyp*, hypobranchial gland; *mo*, mouth; *od*, odontophore; *oes. p*, oesophageal pouches; *os*, osphradium; *ped*, pedal cord; *per*, pericardium; *ren*, renal organ; *sal*, salivary gland; *stom*, stomach; *st.s*, style sac; *vent*, ventricle; *visc*, visceral loop. Certain structures, such as the organs of the head and nerve cords, are turned so as to appear slightly in dorsal view, and the digestive diverticula have been displaced from their respective left and right positions. Adapted from Morton, 1958. *Molluscs*. Hutchinson, London.

evidence of the process, at least in *Peripatus*. Yet it must be noted that there is no comparable evidence in the embryology of the Urochordata, although reduction of the coelom must certainly have taken place in this group. Moreover, the archaic mollusc *Neopilina*, recently discovered in deep-sea dredgings from the Pacific Ocean, contains two extensive dorsal coeloms (Fig. 5-9). The fact is that the origin and evolutionary relationships of the molluscan coelom are another example of a biological problem that eludes our understanding because of the lack of adequate evidence. The possibility that it may have evolved independently of the annelidan coelom certainly cannot be excluded.

Movement in molluscs, while primarily dependent upon the foot, takes place in more than one way. Indeed, the whole body plan of the group has proved to be extraordinarily fertile in the range of adaptive specializations that have been deve-

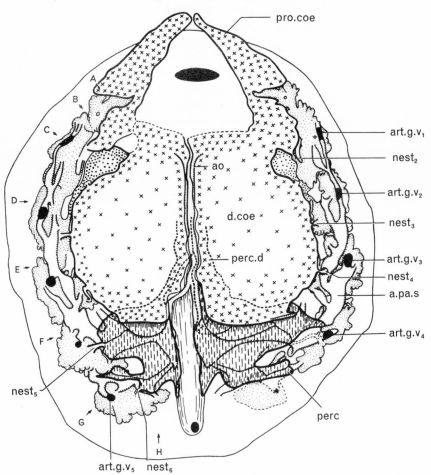

Fig. 5-9. Graphic reconstruction of *Neopilina*, showing the urogenital system, vessels, and coelomic cavities. A–H, positions of pedal retractors (not drawn); *a.pa.s,* arterial pallial sinus; *ao,* aorta; *art.g.v$_{1-5}$,* entrance of arterial vessels from 1st to 5th gill; *d.coe,* dorsal coelom (with crosses); *nest$_{2-6}$,* communications between coelom and kidneys; *perc,* pericardium; *perc.d,* pericardial diverticula along the aorta; *pro.coe,* preoral diverticula of dorsal coelom. From Lemche and Wingstrand, 1959. *Galathea Rep.,* vol. 3. Danish Science Press, Copenhagen.

loped from it. The foot is always a very muscular organ, and to some extent its musculature operates in conjunction with the hydrostatic properties of the blood system. This is because the blood of molluscs, although conveyed from the heart in a system of arteries, passes eventually into a haemocoel, a complex of rather indefinite vascular cavities lying in a spongy meshwork. The relative degree of development of haemocoel and of well-defined vessels varies a good deal, but in principle possession of a haemocoelic body cavity is characteristic of the whole phylum. To this extent it resembles the Phylum Arthropoda, but it does not follow that the haemocoel has arisen in the same way in the two groups. It is clear from the embryology of *Peripatus* that in the arthropods the haemocoel has evolved by the encroachment of the blood system upon an originally well-developed and metamerically segmented coelom. No comparable information is available for the molluscs, and the earlier history of their haemocoel is as unknown as is that of their coelom.

It is impossible to do more here than refer briefly to some of the potentialities latent in the organization of the molluscan foot. The hydrostatic properties of its haemocoel are not always greatly used. Indeed, at one extreme its haemocoelic spaces are little developed, and the foot is essentially a solid and muscular organ. This is the situation in the chitons and limpets, where the foot is used as a powerful adhesive sucker, bound to the substratum by a layer of mucus. *Patella* is able, by virtue of this adhesive power, and aided by the conical shape of the shell, to resist wave action on open shores, to avoid dessication when the tides leave it exposed, and yet to move around for grazing when the tide is in. This type of adaptation is clearly profitable, for a limpet-like form has been developed independently several times in the gastropod molluscs.

Small molluscs can glide by means of the cilia on the ventral surface of the foot, very much as do the platyhelminths, but this becomes impracticable in larger forms. Many of these have a more flexible foot, and employ waves of muscular contraction; these can be readily observed in *Helix*, where they pass anteriorly over the sole of the foot in a steady rhythm. According to Lissmann's analysis, a given point on the ventral surface is lifted from the substratum as the wave reaches it, and is then thrust forwards, presumably by the combined force of muscular contraction and hydrostatic pressure. The hinder part of the body is then drawn forwards, while the relaxed parts of the ventral surface remain adhering to the ground. This pattern of thrust and traction can be demonstrated as an animal crawls over a movable bridge that is weighted in order to counterbalance the forces exerted through the foot (Fig. 5–10). A model of the sequence of events is illustrated in Fig. 5–11. It must be accepted as a highly simplified one, for during the whole process the foot is necessarily acting as a unit.

In other gastropods the foot is used more vigorously than this. Such is the case in *Aplysia* (Fig. 5–12), in which the anterior and posterior ends of the foot are lifted away from the ground in alternation, with the remainder of the body arching between them. This must presumably depend upon turgor being maintained by the haemocoelic fluid, and even in the quieter locomotion of *Helix* this turgor must be important in extending the anterior end of the foot. Indeed, turgor is presumably the basis upon which the burrowing habits of certain gastropods have developed. This mode of life is seen in both prosobranchs and opisthobranchs, the important feature being the formation of a mucus-covered plough. A head-shield develops from the anterior

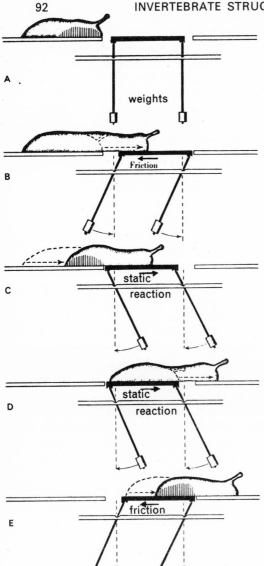

Fig. 5-10. Diagram illustrating the recording of the movement of *Helix pomatia*. The displacing force which is applied to the movable bridge reaches a position of equilibrium when the applied force is equal and opposite to the restoring couple of the weights which tend to return the bridge to the position shown in A. From Lissmann, 1946. *J. exp. Biol.*, **22**, 37–50.

end of the foot in prosobranchs, or from the head itself in opisthobranchs, while in both groups the sides of the foot grow up as parapodia, the general result being to create a measure of streamlining.

The application of muscles and a hydrostatic skeleton to burrowing has been most fully exploited in the Lamellibranchia, a group that is comparatively sedentary in habit and that relies largely upon filter feeding for its nutrition. Here the interaction of muscles and haemocoel is responsible for the protrusion of the foot from between the two valves of the shell, and for the extensive changes in shape that underlie its use in locomotion.

In the primitive protobranchiate *Nucula* the foot has a flat ventral surface not unlike that of a gastropod, although it differs in its mode of operation. It is thrust into the mud, and expanded into a plug or holdfast; the body is then drawn after it by contraction of the pedal retractor muscles, which in lamellibranchs run from the shell into the muscular tissue of the foot. In more advanced forms, such as the fresh-water mussel *Anodonta*, the foot has become a narrow wedge or tongue, which is forced forwards by contraction of its transverse muscle fibres. When these relax, the foot swells under the pressure of the haemocoelic blood, the pressure being increased by the adduction of the valves of the shell, which forces blood from the body into the

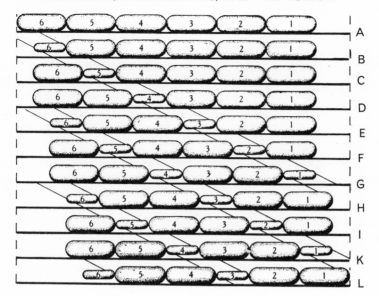

Fig. 5-11. Model illustrating the mechanism of locomotion in the snail. Beginning from the posterior end the balloons are successively deflated and re-inflated as shown in the figure. Deflation corresponds to longitudinal contraction, inflation to elongation. The oblique lines indicate the passage of waves of activity. From Lissmann, 1946. *op. cit.*

vascular meshwork of the foot. Contraction of the longitudinal muscles then draws the body forwards while the foot remains fixed. This type of progression has been developed into a highly effective boring mechanism, as in the piddock (*Pholas*), which bores into rock, and the shipworm (*Teredo*), which bores into wood. In both instances the edges of the shell valves form the boring tools, the motive power arising from the interaction of the muscles and the adhesive power of the foot.

Lastly, the molluscan foot has lent itself to the evolution of very active pelagic forms, and both prosobranch and opisthobranch gastropods provide examples of this. In the heteropod prosobranchs the foot is drawn out into a highly mobile fin, which in *Carinaria*, for example, is held upwards, the animal swimming upside down. In the opisthobranchs the tendency to streamlining, already noted in connection with burrowing, has found an application to pelagic life. *Aplysia* can lift itself wholly away from the substratum by flapping its parapodia, and *Pleurobranchus* swims in this way (Fig. 5-13). The extreme development of this trend occurs in the pteropods

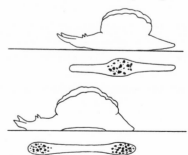

Fig. 5-12. Locomotory movements of *Aplysia californica*, lateral and ventral views. From Parker, 1917. *J. exp. Zool.,* **24**, 141, fig. 1.

(sea butterflies); these move by the steady beat of the lateral epipodia (Fig. 5–14), which are presumably derived from the parapodia of less modified forms. The extent of the locomotor adaptation involved is well seen in *Clione* (Fig. 5–15); here the paired 'wings' have only a narrow base of attachment, and are twisted at that point during both upward and downward beats so as to increase the power of their stroke in both directions.

However, the Cephalopoda are the most remarkable among the molluscs for the high level of adaptive efficiency that they have achieved in locomotion as well as in other respects. They differ from the rest of the phylum in possessing a design that is primarily related to efficient swimming, achieved in most of them by jet propulsion. Actually, this method of movement is also found elsewhere in the molluscs. It is seen

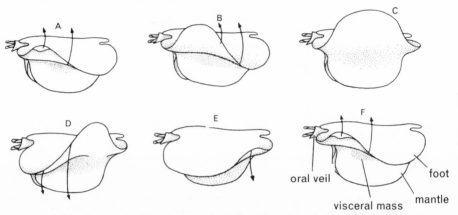

Fig. 5-13. The swimming mechanism of *Pleurobranchus*; the animals are shown as viewed from the morphological right side, but the gill is not illustrated. The swimming lobe of the left side is here shown, for simplicity, to be stationary in a relaxed position. The visceral mass is visible through the body wall. From Thompson and Slinn, 1959. *J. mar. biol. Ass. U.K.*, **38**, 507–524.

in the scallops, where, against the whole evolutionary trend of the lamellibranchs, we find pelagic animals that derive their motive force by expelling water from between the clapping valves of their shell. The device, however, is not one that can be used for long periods, and the cephalopods have achieved an altogether more efficient variant of it.

The principle is seen in a primitive form in *Nautilus*. This animal was believed at one time to use its external chambered shell as a boat, its tentacles as oars, and its hood as a sail (Fig. 5–16 shows it with sail set!). In fact, it draws water into its mantle cavity and expels it through a muscular funnel that is formed from the foot. The funnel in this animal is still bilobed, while the mantle wall cannot itself contract since it is still bound to the shell. Expulsion of the water is therefore effected by the muscles of the funnel, and by the adductor muscles which retract the body. In all other recent cephalopods the device is improved by the funnel becoming a complete tube, and by the reduction of the shell, which allows the mantle to contract under the action of its circular muscles. The result is a great increase in the force of the jet of water, while other adaptive improvements include the development of stabilizing fins, streamlining of the body, and the use of stud and socket fasteners to hold the mantle to the head so as to prevent the egress of water at this point.

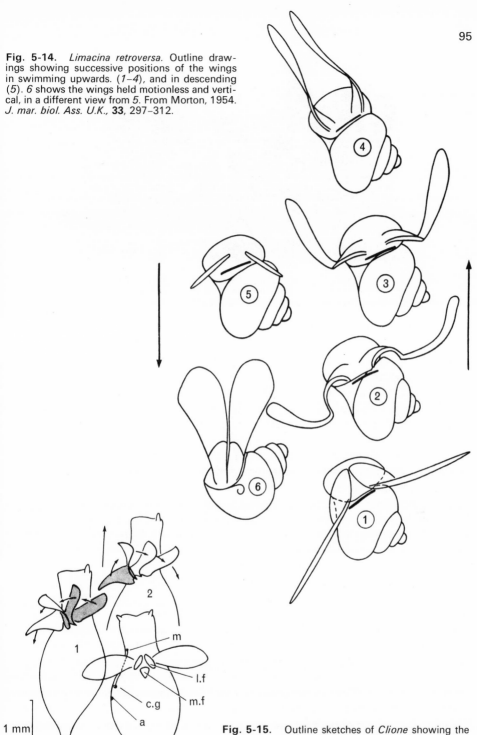

Fig. 5-14. *Limacina retroversa.* Outline drawings showing successive positions of the wings in swimming upwards. (*1–4*), and in descending (*5*). *6* shows the wings held motionless and vertical, in a different view from *5*. From Morton, 1954. *J. mar. biol. Ass. U.K.,* **33**, 297–312.

Fig. 5-15. Outline sketches of *Clione* showing the successive positions of the wing in downward (*1*) and upward (*2*) strokes (left-side view), and (*3*) ventral view. *a*, anus; *c.g*, common genital aperture; *l.f*, lateral lobe of the vestigial foot; *m*, male aperture; *m.f*, median lobe of the foot. From Morton, 1958. *J. mar. biol. Ass. U.K.,* **37**, 287–297.

1 mm

Fig. 5-16. The Paper Nautilus, *Argonauta argo*, from Belon (1551). The animal is incorrectly drawn using its arms as oars and its membrane as a sail. From Singer, 1931. *A Short History of Biology*. Clarendon Press, Oxford.

The cephalopods take us into the field of hydrodynamics with this use of sea water, but other molluscs have found ways of using it as part of a hydrostatic system. A good example is the protrusibile siphons of lamellibranchs. Consider *Mya arenaria* (Fig. 5-17) which is characteristically found in the tidal mud of estuaries, living as a suspension feeder at a depth of 6 in to 8 in, with the openings of its siphons lying level with the surface of the mud. Into these it draws currents of water which bear suspended debris and micro-organisms, the subsequent fate of which we consider elsewhere. The siphons are extended by water pressure, contractions of the adductor muscles of the shell forcing water into them from the mantle cavity. During extension the siphon apertures and the foot opening remain closed, forming a watertight system in which pressure can be built up. This process has to proceed in stages, elongation taking place about 1 cm at a time. Between each successive elongation more water is taken into the mantle cavity so that an increased volume of water can be provided to match the increasing volume of the siphons. In this way a degree of extension can be secured that would be unattainable if the animal had to rely upon pressure increases in a body cavity containing only a restricted volume of fluid.

An interesting contrast to *Mya*, and one that well illustrates the elegant way in which hydrostatic mechanisms can be adapted to the requirements of different modes of life, is provided by *Scrobicularia plana* (Fig. 5-18), another bivalve which lives in mud between the tide marks, where there is some lowering of salinity by a flow of fresh water. It differs from *Mya* in being a deposit feeder, with siphons that are separate from each other; an arrangement that permits the inhalent siphon to extend over the surface of the mud flat and thus to draw in the rich organic matter that accumulates there. These siphons may elongate to a length of 10 cm or more, and they do so in a manner that is noticeably different from that found in *Mya*, for the movement is a steady and smooth one, unrelated to any pumping action of the valves of the shell. This indicates that extension cannot depend upon the forcing of water into the siphons, as occurs in *Mya*. Indeed, it can proceed even after one valve has been completely removed.

The structures actually involved in extension are the intrinsic muscles of the

Fig. 5.-17. *Mya arenaria*, with siphons and foot fully extended. Half natural size. From Yonge, 1949. *The Sea Shore.* Collins, London.

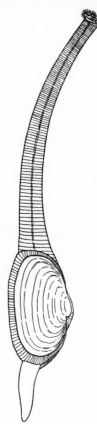

Fig. 5-18. *Scrobicularia plana*, showing mode of feeding. The animal normally lives much deeper, up to 6 or 8 inches below the surface. (From Hesse, Allee, and Schmidt, 1951. *Ecological Animal Geography* (2nd ed.). Wiley, New York.) From Yonge, 1949. *op. cit.*

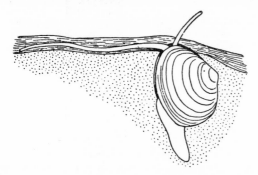

siphons, with the blood acting in this instance as the fluid component of the system. Elongation of the siphons is brought about by the contraction of strands of radial muscle, this making the walls thinner and displacing some of the blood they contain. The fluid acts as an antagonist of the muscles, while collagen fibres resist deformation, their lattice-like arrangement allowing the siphon wall to become thinner and longer, but resisting outward bulging. Because of these fibres the total cross-sectional area of the siphons remains unaltered during extension, while the walls become thinner; an arrangement that has the great advantage of ensuring that the passage of in-current water is not hindered. The withdrawal of the siphons is a consequence of muscular action alone, the structures here concerned being longitudinal muscles that take their origin from the shell.

6

Movement and
Metamerism

6–1 SIGNIFICANCE OF METAMERISM

Important though the evolution of the coelom has proved, there is another innovation, closely associated with it, that has had no less profound an influence upon the history of many of the invertebrates, and of the whole of the vertebrates. This is the development of metamerism, the plan of structure in which the body is differentiated along its longitudinal axis into a series of units or segments, each of which contains elements of some of the chief systems of organs. The characteristics of a typical segment have been usefully defined by Goodrich. In invertebrates each segment is demarcated externally by an anterior and a posterior groove. This, however, applies primarily to those animals in which the primitive pattern of segmentation remains unmodified and unobscured. In arthropods, particularly in the head and thorax, grooves may have a functional significance unrelated to segmentation. Ideally, each such segment will contain a pair of mesodermal somites with coelomic cavities, and a pair of coelomoducts leading from these to the outside. In addition, there will be a pair of nephridia (in those species that have retained this particular system), a pair of nerve ganglia born on the paired ventral nerve cord, and often a pair of appendages.

In principle a similar situation exists in the vertebrates, but with variations imposed by certain fundamental differences in the organization of this group as compared with invertebrates. For example, the muscles of the body wall of fish are associated with an internal axial skeleton, so that a hydrostatic skeleton plays no part in movement. Here the criteria of a segment are the presence of paired mesodermal somites and coelomic cavities, units of striated muscle (myomeres) derived from the somites, paired coelomic cavities, paired coelomoducts in the form of kidney tubules, and paired dorsal and ventral nerve roots. In these animals the paired limbs are not metamerically repeated, a difference that sheds some light on the circumstances that have influenced the origin of metameric organization (see below).

Metamerism, as we have here defined it, is a characteristic of the Annelida, the

Arthropoda, and the Vertebrata (together with the protochordate amphioxus). This means that it must certainly have evolved independently at least twice, for the vertebrates probably share a common origin with the echinoderms within the Deuterostomia, and certainly show no close relationship with the metameric invertebrates. Moreover, the protochordates include the unsegmented Urochordata, which in itself indicates that metamerism must have appeared within the vertebrate line quite independently of the metamerism of annelids and arthropods. In addition to these major expressions of metamerism, however, a division of the body, with repetition of parts, is also found in the tapeworms. One can thus argue—as does Hyman, for example—that these acoelomate animals should also be regarded as metamerically segmented. Nevertheless, many zoologists have been unwilling to accept this interpretation, preferring to consider the annelids, arthropods, and vertebrates as the only truly metameric animals. For this attitude there is good justification, if we consider the functional significance of metamerism.

We shall see that this significance is undoubtedly to be found in the modes of locomotion of metameric animals, and especially of the more primitive ones, which illustrate something of the circumstances in which metamerism first became established. In tapeworms the repetition of the body structure is a parasitic and not a locomotor specialization; it serves primarily for the construction of a reproductive machine, each proglottid containing a complete set of hermaphroditic reproductive organs. Locomotion is merely a matter of movement of individual proglottids after they have broken off from the main body. One feature which is often emphasized is that the new segments of a worm or arthropod appear at the hind end of the body, while in vertebrates the centre of growth is also posterior, situated at the junction of body and tail. In tapeworms, on the other hand, the growth zone is at the anterior end, immediately behind the scolex. This has led some supporters of the metameric interpretation of the structure of these animals to argue that the scolex is, in fact, posterior, so that the worm is attached to its host back to front. Such an argument is perhaps more revealing of the mental processes of its devisor than of the evolution of the cestodes; it illustrates the danger of placing undue emphasis upon form to the exclusion of functional considerations. Bearing in mind, then, the close relationship of annelids and arthropods, we may take it that metameric segmentation must have appeared twice, once in the annelidan–arthropodan stock and once in the chordate stock.

The problem of the origin of metamerism is no less obscure than is the similar problem of the origin of the coelom. It may be relevant that the lower groups of animals show a marked tendency for repeating certain organ systems. The platyhelminths are clearly unsegmented animals (Fig. 6-1), but some have multiple gonads alternating with pouches of the alimentary canal, and this is seen also in nemertines (Fig. 6-2). In the echinoderm–chordate line a well-known example is the repetition of gill slits, gonads, and alimentary pouches in the hemichordates. The advantage of such repetition probably lies in the resultant increase in surface area of the organs concerned. It is likely to be of particular significance in the acoelomate invertebrates, where the absence both of a coelom and often of a vascular system must limit the efficiency of transport of metabolites. This type of repetition, sometimes termed pseudometamerism, is, therefore, an understandable phase of the evolution of animal organization, but whether it was a determining factor in the evolution of

CENTRAL METHODIST COLLEGE LIBRARY
FAYETTE, MISSOURI

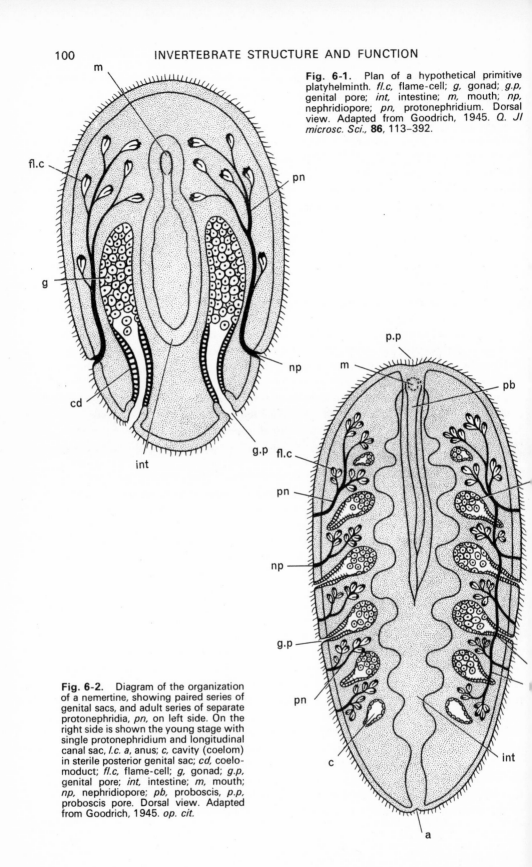

Fig. 6-1. Plan of a hypothetical primitive platyhelminth. *fl.c,* flame-cell; *g,* gonad; *g.p,* genital pore; *int,* intestine; *m,* mouth; *np,* nephridiopore; *pn,* protonephridium. Dorsal view. Adapted from Goodrich, 1945. *Q. Jl microsc. Sci.,* **86,** 113–392.

Fig. 6-2. Diagram of the organization of a nemertine, showing paired series of genital sacs, and adult series of separate protonephridia, *pn,* on left side. On the right side is shown the young stage with single protonephridium and longitudinal canal sac, *l.c. a,* anus; *c,* cavity (coelom) in sterile posterior genital sac; *cd,* coelomoduct; *fl.c,* flame-cell; *g,* gonad; *g.p,* genital pore; *int,* intestine; *m,* mouth; *np,* nephridiopore; *pb,* proboscis, *p.p,* proboscis pore. Dorsal view. Adapted from Goodrich, 1945. *op. cit.*

metamerism is more doubtful. Certainly a much more important one must have been locomotion.

We shall be considering below how far the movement of annelids and arthropods depends upon the segmentation of the musculature, coelom, and nervous system. So important is the subdivision of the musculature in annelids and vertebrates, and of the coelom in annelids, that it becomes highly probable that metamerism in these animals was determined primarily by these structures, the repetition of other systems becoming arranged in conformity with them. Some of these systems may already have been subdivided for reasons just indicated, while some may have become subdivided later as a matter of structural convenience. The interrelationship of form and function is here somewhat involved, but it should become easier to grasp if we examine some aspects of the organization of locomotion in the metameric invertebrates, and the contribution made to it by the metamerism of the body.

6–2 LOCOMOTION OF OLIGOCHAETES

Annelid worms are essentially creeping and burrowing animals, and it is reasonable to accept their present-day modes of life as being those that influenced the origin and early evolution of their metamerism. The lower vertebrates, by contrast, are characteristically free-swimming and often pelagic animals, and this, in conjunction with the early development of an axial skeleton, must have determined the form that metamerism took in them and in their protochordate ancestors. Vertebrate limbs seem to have arisen, probably on more than one line of advance, as lateral folds. These met certain hydrodynamic requirements, involving the stability of a body moving in a fluid medium, and in doing so they became restricted to two pairs of appendages. It was therefore swimming that laid the foundations for the eventual emergence of tetrapod vertebrates, and of human beings with two hands and two feet. In complete contrast to this, it was probably the creeping and burrowing of unknown worm-like ancestors, exploiting the rich food resources of bottom deposits, that determined the subsequent evolution of arthropods, with their serially repeated and remarkably versatile limbs, and their feeding methods which have drawn heavily upon this versatility.

It will be convenient to look to the oligochaetes for our first example of annelidan locomotion. They are by no means the most primitive of living annelids in their habits, but the earthworm possesses a plan of structure that conforms very closely in some respects with the idealized type of hydrostatic skeleton we considered earlier. The body wall is composed of continuous layers of longitudinal muscles (on the outside) and circular muscles (on the inside), these being placed so that they can exert pressure upon the coelomic fluid which they surround. The longitudinal muscle is often said to be segmented in conformity with the external annulation, but this is not strictly correct. The longitudinal muscle fibres are long enough to extend through two or three segments, so that in this respect the segments are linked in small groups. Each segment, however, has its own complement of segmental nerves, so that precise and localized control of muscular contraction can certainly be exercized by the central nervous system.

There is, however, another factor that makes an essential contribution to the localization of muscular activity: the subdivision of the coelomic cavity by the

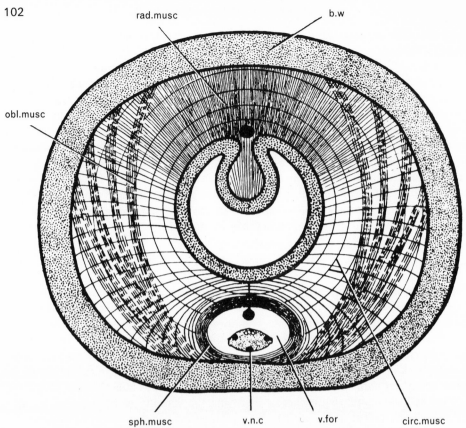

Fig. 6-3. Diagram to show the arrangement of the septal muscles in the earthworm. *b.w*, body wall; *circ. musc*, circular muscle; *obl. musc*, oblique muscles; *rad. musc*, radial muscles; *sph. musc*, sphincter of ventral foramen; *v. for*, ventral foramen; *v.n.c*, ventral nerve cord. From Newell, 1950. *J. exp. Biol.*, **27**, 110–121.

transverse septa, which are developed uniformly throughout the greater part of the body. It is in this respect that the hydrostatic skeleton of the earthworm differs in a very important way from that of the unsegmented animals (and of the idealized model) that we have previously considered. We saw that in these the pressure changes set up at one point are distributed throughout the body, with a consequent dissipation of energy. It seems inevitable that this must impose limits upon the speed and efficiency of the locomotor responses of unsegmented animals. In the earthworm, by contrast, the septa damp down the pressure changes and tend to limit them to particular regions of the body. This they are the better able to do because they are well provided with intrinsic muscle fibres which enable them to resist stress. Nevertheless, they cannot provide complete barriers. They are necessarily penetrated by the ventral cord, and a foramen at this point (Fig. 6-3) provides for continuity of coelomic fluid from one segment to the next. In actively moving worms, however, these foramina are closed by sphincter muscles; because of this, and because of the intrinsic musculature of the septa, increase of pressure in the fluid of one segment is substantially isolated from adjacent segments.

Metameric segmentation, as we find it in the earthworm, therefore provides an escape from an important limitation inherent in unsegmented hydrostatic skeletal systems. The influence of this becomes apparent when we examine how the animal moves. According to the analysis of Gray and Lissmann, locomotion begins with a contraction of the circular muscles in a limited region of the anterior end of the body (Fig. 6-4). This contraction passes backwards down the body as a peristaltic wave, each wave being followed by a wave of contraction of the longitudinal muscle; this continues in regular alternation. At those regions where the longitudinal muscle is contracting, the body surface bulges outwards and the chaetae are protruded; here the worm can exert a thrust against the substratum. Where the circular muscle is contracting the body becomes thinner, and the chaetae are withdrawn. Here the segments extend forwards, aided by the thrust from the swollen regions. Thus the extension of the thinner parts of the body can be translated into forward movement. It is a method of locomotion particularly well suited for a burrowing animal, since the swollen parts of the body press against the whole circumference of the burrow. In those earthworms, such as *Lumbricus* and *Allolobophora*, where the four pairs of chaetae are situated in the ventral half of the segments, an effective thrust can also be exerted against the substratum when the animal is moving over the surface. Its dependence upon this thrust is demonstrated when it is placed on a polished surface such as a sheet of glass; friction between the body and the substratum is now negligible, and the worm is powerless to move.

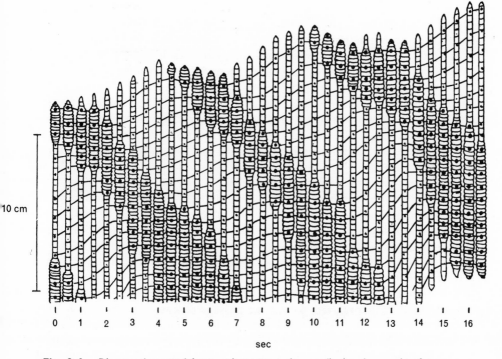

Fig. 6-4. Diagram (prepared from a cinematograph record) showing mode of progression of an earthworm. Regions of the body showing longitudinal contraction are drawn twice as wide as those undergoing circular contraction and are also marked by larger dots. As long as a segment is longitudinally contracted it remains at rest relative to the ground; it moves forwards during all other phases of the cycle. The track of individual points on the worm's body and their movements relative to each other are shown by the lines running obliquely forwards from left to right of the diagram. From Gray and Lissmann, 1938. *J. exp. Biol.*, **15**, 506–517.

Peristaltic waves of the body wall are not confined to segmented animals. We have noted their occurrence in flatworms, and more particularly in nemertines. But in these animals the waves are irregular, and the movement that they produce is comparatively sluggish and is rarely prolonged. The locomotion of earthworms is based upon a much more advanced physiological organization. It depends upon a refinement of integration, which is exerted through the metamerically segmented nervous system and acts upon correspondingly segmented effectors. We shall see later something of the importance in this connection of the organization of patterns of activity within the nervous system. The locomotion depends equally upon the segmental partitioning of the coelomic fluid, which results in force being exerted sequentially at restricted points of the body surface, and which allows one part of the body to act in this respect independently of other parts. One indication of the efficiency of the mechanism is given by measurements of the degree of force that is thereby exerted. It has been shown that the earthworm can apply pressures of up to 8.5 g/cm^2 to its first septum. This force is exerted upon the soil during burrowing by the prostomium, which has a diameter of 1.0 mm. By exploiting the principle of the wedge, the anterior tip of the body can exert a pressure of no less than 1,060 g/cm^2.

6–3 LOCOMOTION OF POLYCHAETES

We have dealt first with oligochaete worms because they illustrate in a comparatively simple way the interaction between metameric segmentation and the functioning of a hydrostatic skeleton. Polychaete worms are generally held to be more primitive than the earthworms, and are clearly so if they are judged by their modes of life, for creeping and burrowing in a marine environment must have preceded the fresh-water and terrestrial habits that characterize the oligochaetes. Yet polychaetes are certainly highly specialized animals within the limits of their general plan of organization, and their mode of locomotion introduces certain features that are lacking in the oligochaetes. These we shall illustrate mainly by a consideration of *Nereis*, although it must not be forgotten that this animal provides only one example of the widely diversified modes of life of polychaete worms.

Two structural elements are especially important in the locomotion of *Nereis*: the longitudinal muscles of the body wall, and the parapodia (Fig. 6–5). As in the earthworm, the segmentation of the muscles and of their nerve supply facilitates the passage of waves of contraction down the body. An important difference, however, is that in *Nereis* the longitudinal muscle does not form a continuous layer. Instead, it is broken up into two pairs of blocks, one pair dorsal and the other ventral. Because of this the muscles of the two sides of a segment can be in opposite phases, one contracted and the other relaxed, so that the passage of waves of contraction along the body can throw it into lateral undulations. These are a characteristic feature of the locomotion of *Nereis*, and contrast markedly with the peristaltic waves of the earthworm. Another point of difference from the latter animal is that in *Nereis* the waves of contraction pass forwards; we shall see later the explanation of this.

So far in our consideration of hydrostatic skeletons we have found that the musculature of body walls is commonly arranged so that circular muscle can be opposed to longitudinal muscle. The nematodes provided an exception to this, and the principle is also somewhat departed from in *Nereis*. In this animal the circular

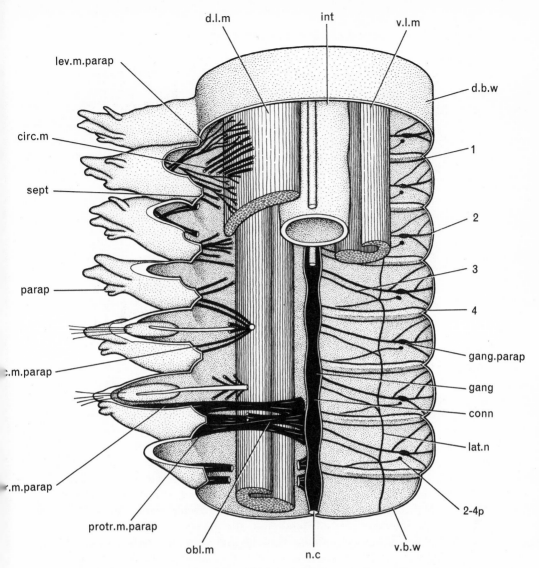

Fig. 6-5. Stereogram of seven body segments of *Nereis virens* dissected at various levels to show the nerve cord and segmental nerves and the muscles of the body wall and parapodia. The anterior end is at the top of the figure. *1–4*, the segmental nerves in antero-posterior succession; *2–4p*, peripheral connexion between nerves *2* and *4*; *acic.m.parap*, acicular muscle of the parapodium; *circ.m*, circular muscles of the body wall. *conn*, nerve cord connective; *d.b.w*, dorsal body wall; *d.l.m*, dorsal longitudinal muscle; *gang*, nerve cord ganglion; *gang.parap*, ganglion of the parapodial nerve (II); *int*, intestine; *lat.n*, lateral nerve; *lev.m.parap*, levator muscle of the parapodium; *n.c*, nerve cord; *obl.m*, oblique muscle; *parap*, parapodium; *protr.m.parap*, protractor muscle of the parapodium; *retr.m.parap*, retractor muscle of the parapodium; *sept*, intersegmental septum; *v.b.w*, ventral body wall; *v.l.m*, ventral longitudinal muscle. From Smith, 1957. *Phil. Trans. R. Soc. B.*, **240**, 135–196.

muscle layer is relatively weak, more particularly because it is interrupted laterally where muscles derived from the circular layer run into the parapodia. This means that the body wall itself is weaker than that of the earthworm. Some support is probably given by fibres that are present in it, and a contribution is also made by the oblique muscles that run upwards and outwards from the region of the ventral nerve cord. Despite this supplementary strengthening, however, the body is clearly ill

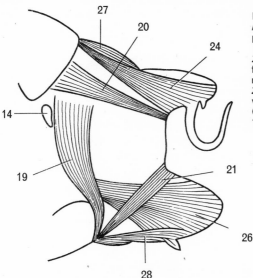

Fig. 6-6. Intrinsic parapodial musculature of *Nephtys.* Muscles on the posterior wall of the parapodium. *14,* insertion of dorsal extensor; *19,* distal posterior dorso-ventral muscle; *20, 21,* muscles to inter-ramal region; *24,* muscle from dorsal body wall to notopodium; *26,* muscle from dorsal body wall to neuropodium; *27, 28,* muscles from body wall to dorsal and ventral parts of parapodium. Adapted from Clark and Clark, 1960. *Q. Jl microsc. Sci.,* **101,** 149–176.

adapted for the peristaltic movements that are so well provided for in earthworms. It is the lateral undulations that are important in the locomotion of *Nereis,* together with the parapodia that translate these into forward displacement of the body. We see here a form of movement different from that of the earthworm, and one that anticipates the locomotory mechanisms of arthropods.

A parapodium is a hollow extension of the body, typically divided into dorsal and ventral components called the notopodium and neuropodium (cf. Fig. 6–5, 6–6). Each lobe carries a bundle of bristles, or chaetae, strengthened by a supporting aciculum. The parapodium can be moved forwards and backwards, its point of attachment to the body wall acting as a hinge, while it is sufficiently flexible to undergo a considerable measure of protrusion and withdrawal. Protrusion takes place as a result of hydrostatic pressure exerted through the coelomic fluid, this being possible because the coelomic cavity extends into the parapodium. Retraction is brought about by the contraction of oblique muscles that have their origin in the mid-ventral line of the body wall, and are inserted dorsally and ventrally onto the parapodium. Typically, there are two pairs of these muscles in each segment, one pair anterior and one posterior; these are so arranged that they also effect the anterior and posterior beat of the parapodium. They constitute its extrinsic muscles. In addition, there are intrinsic protractor and retractor muscles which are responsible for the protrusion and withdrawal of the chaetae bundles and their supporting acicula.

The parapodium in *Nereis* is clearly quite versatile in its mode of action. It also contains potentialities susceptible to much further exploitation; in particular, the development of an intrinsic musculature (Fig. 6–6). In many polychaetes the intrinsic muscles of the parapodium are concerned in modifying the shape of the organ, or in moving the chaetae bundles, and make no direct contribution to the locomotory forces. But in others, of which *Nephtys* is an example, the acicular muscles can swing the chaetae bundles forwards and backwards, and can produce the power stroke of the parapodium without the cooperation of the extrinsic muscles. These animals remain dependent upon the hydrostatic skeleton to provide a firm basis for muscular action. Nevertheless, as Clark points out, this development foreshadows a type of movement in which, as in arthropods, a balanced system of antagonistic muscles operates upon a jointed skeleton.

The properties of the musculature and parapodia of *Nereis* interact to provide for several different types of movement. One of these is a slow creeping, which depends almost entirely upon the use of the parapodia as a series of levers. Initially a parapodium moves forwards, with its tip lifted from the ground and with the aciculum withdrawn, this phase of the movement constituting the preparatory stroke. At the end of this stroke the parapodium makes contact with the substratum, the aciculum is protruded, and the oblique muscles contract so that the body is pulled forwards. The parapodium, which comes to be directed backwards during this phase, is now exerting its power stroke. The movements of the parapodia are integrated so that the two members of any one segmental pair alternate with each other in phase. Moreover, the movement of any one parapodium begins slightly after that of the one next behind it. The actions are thus seen as waves of movement that travel forwards over the length of the body.

Slow creeping readily passes into rapid creeping. This involves a similar rhythmic pattern of waves, but with the difference that the longitudinal muscles of the body wall are now of primary importance. They contract serially in parallel with the movements of the parapodia. The oblique muscles of the latter are now probably of much less importance than in slow creeping, for rapid creeping is mainly effected by the longitudinal muscles pulling against points of friction established between the parapodia and the substratum. The contractions of the longitudinal muscle throw the body into lateral sinusoidal waves that pass anteriorly along its length (Fig. 6-7). At any given moment a parapodium on the crest of a wave, where the longitudinal muscles are relaxed, will be stationary with respect to the substratum. Its partner on the opposite side of the segment is in the trough of the wave, having moved there as the longitudinal muscles contract (Fig. 6-7). During this contraction the muscles exert a thrust on the substratum, but this is transmitted through the stationary parapodium on the opposite side. The parapodia on the crests are not entirely inactive, for they exert their own power stroke through their adductor muscles. The

Fig. 6-7. Diagrams showing (A, B, C) forward ambulatory movement (to the left) of *Nereis* relative to the ground. Note that the two sides of a segment (black) move forward alternately, one side pivoting on the other. Each parapodium on the crest of a wave is lifted from the ground as it completes its effective stroke, and is carried forwards and inwards as the underlying longitudinal muscles contract. It is then carried forwards and outwards as these muscles relax, the early part of this phase constituting the preparatory stroke. The motive power is derived almost entirely from the longitudinal muscles pulling against *points d'appui* established on the opposite sides of the body by the bases of the parapodia at the crests of the waves. Adapted from Gray, 1939. *J. exp. Biol.*, **16**, 9–17.

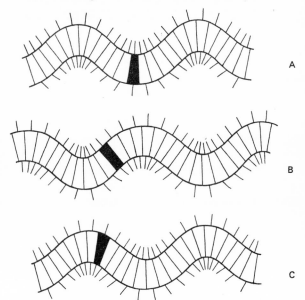

A

B

C

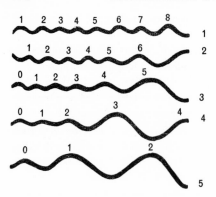

Fig. 6-8. Diagram showing the transition from ambulatory pattern of movement of *Nereis* to that of swimming. From Gray, 1939. *op. cit.*

force of this stroke is thus added to that generated by the contraction of the longitudinal muscles of the opposite side; yet it is the latter muscles that make the major contribution, and that permit the rapid creeping type of locomotion.

It is because of this relationship of muscles and parapodia that the sinusoidal locomotory waves of *Nereis* pass forwards over the body, in the opposite direction to the peristaltic locomotory waves of the earthworm. Were they to travel backwards the worm would also move backwards. This consideration applies equally in the third type of movement displayed by *Nereis*, which occurs in the free-swimming phase. The pattern of movement is essentially the same as that of rapid creeping; sinusoidal waves of the body interact with parapodial movement, but there is a marked increase in the length of the waves, and also in their amplitude and frequency (Fig. 6-8). Here again the worm is propelled forwards by body waves that also pass forwards; a situation that presents a striking contrast with fish, which swim forwards through the agency of waves that pass backwards. The difference is again a result of the presence of the parapodia. These move backwards during their active stroke, and so, by creating a backward flow of water, give a forward thrust to the body. The efficiency of their action is probably very low; indeed, the progress of the animal is slow as compared with the frequency and speed of the waves of propulsion. Nevertheless, without this parapodial action the worm would swim backwards.

We have so far considered *Nereis* as a representative burrowing and swimming worm, but these modes of locomotion by no means exhaust the versatility of the locomotor mechanisms of polychaetes. *Nereis* is an example of the groups of polychaetes referred to as 'errant' forms, so called because their mode of life is typically free-moving, and contrasts with the burrowing of the 'sedentary' forms. However, the errant forms can also burrow. Indeed, this mode of life is so advantageous, both in the protection that it provides and in the rich supplies of organic deposits that are thus made available as food, that it may well have been a major factor in stimulating the evolution of metamerism with its associated improvements in locomotor mechanisms. We have already seen that these improvements powerfully contribute to the efficiency of the earthworm's burrowing, and it is likely that they also did so during the evolution of polychaete locomotor mechanisms.

The burrowing of an errant polychaete such as *Nereis* depends greatly upon the thrust exerted by the proboscis, which comprises essentially the buccal cavity and pharynx. The protrusion of the proboscis is a result of pressure exerted by the muscular body wall and transmitted through the coelomic fluid; a simple application of the operation of the hydrostatic skeleton. The same principle is even better seen in *Nephtys*, an errant form that is a particularly active burrower. As described by Clark, the animal makes an opening in the sand by vigorously everting its proboscis, meanwhile anchoring its body at its widest region, which lies between segments 15 and 45. After this the proboscis is withdrawn into the body and the worm crawls forwards into the space thereby exposed, using for its locomotion lateral undulations of the same general type as those described above. These undulations are elegantly adapted to the variation in width of the body at different points of its length. The anterior segments are particularly narrow, and here the undulations are large enough to bring the sides of the body into contact with the wall of the burrow. Farther back their amplitude is reduced, in correlation with the greater width of the body.

It is thought that in some circumstances burrowing polychaetes make use of thixotropy, a property of colloidal systems that allows an increased rate of shear to produce a reduction in resistance in the system. This is seen in certain types of sand, particularly when clay is present. It has been observed, for example, that when *Nephtys* begins to burrow in such a medium it may hold its head against the sand and set this into vibration by lateral waves of movement of the body. Because of its thixotropic property the sand becomes semi-fluid, permitting the entry of the head; thereafter the worm continues to burrow by the method just outlined.

In the sedentary polychaetes we commonly find a marked reduction of the parapodia and of their associated musculature. This is correlated with an improved development of the longitudinal and circular muscles, which come to form much more complete layers than in *Nereis*, and which permit a peristaltic type of movement similar in some respects to that of the earthworm. As always, there is scope for much variation in the degree of specialization. *Sabella*, for example, is capable of peristalsis but can also move forwards or backwards in its tube through the activity of its parapodia. More commonly, movement by peristaltic waves seems to be incompatible with the exertion of positive thrust through the parapodia.

Another adaptive modification in the locomotor mechanism of polychaetes, closely associated (but not exclusively so) with a burrowing habit, is the reduction of the transverse septa. This is a particular example of a phenomenon that is widespread in those groups of animals that are metameric: the reduction or complete loss of the metameric repetition of certain of their organ systems. Presumably those particular facets of metamerism lost their functional advantage in the particular modes of life adopted by these animals. By considering this phenomenon we should therefore learn more about the advantages that were initially gained by a metameric organization. From this point of view a study of the habits of lugworms has proved to be particularly illuminating.

The burrowing of *Arenicola* has something in common with that of *Nephtys*, referred to above, although it proceeds more slowly. Trueman finds that the hydrostatic pressure in the coelom of a non-burrowing worm is equivalent to about 2 cm of water. Burrowing is initiated by a scraping action of the proboscis, which continues until some 4 chaetigerous segments have been inserted into the sand. Intra-coelomic pressure has remained small up to this stage, but from now on the anterior end can act as an anchor, and pressure is built up to about 110 cm of water by cyclical contractions of the circular and longitudinal muscles. The head can now be forced forwards, while the hinder segments are drawn after it. Trueman calculates that the

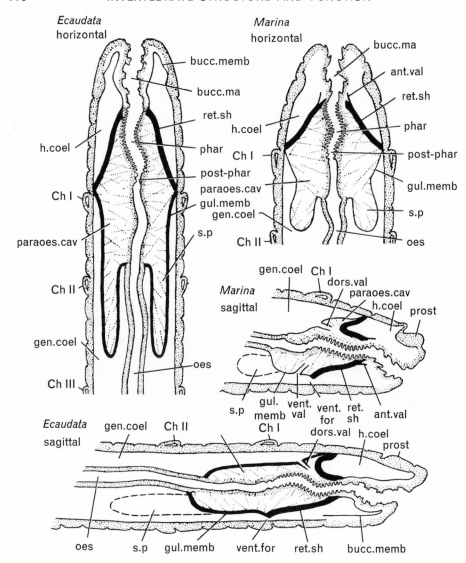

Fig. 6-9. Diagrams of the structure of the proboscis apparatus of *Arenicola ecaudata left* and *A. marina right. ant.val,* anterior valve; *bucc.ma,* buccal mass; *bucc.memb,* buccal membrane; *Ch,* chaetigerous annulus; *dors.val,* dorsal valve; *gen.coel,* general coelom; *gul.memb,* gular membrane; *oes,* oesophagus; *h.coel,* head coelom; *paraoes. cav,* paraoesophageal cavity; *phar,* pharynx; *post-phar,* post-pharynx; *prost,* prostomium; *ret.sh,* retractor sheath; *s.p,* septal sheath; *vent.val,* ventral valve. From Wells, 1954. *Q. Jl microsc. Sci.,* **95**, 251–270.

thrust exerted upon the sand through the tip of the proboscis is of the order of 100 g/cm². But a human being standing upon the sand may exert a pressure of 150 g/cm² without sinking, so that at first sight it is remarkable that the worm can penetrate at such a low pressure. The explanation seems to be that it makes use of alternate extrusion and retraction of the proboscis to effect thixotropic softening of the sand, much as does *Nephtys.*

Arenicola is thus dependent upon its hydrostatic skeleton, but the successful exploitation of this depends, in contrast to the superficially similar mode of life of earthworms, upon the reduction of the transverse septa. These have largely been lost from the trunk region, the only ones remaining being the three anterior ones, usually termed diaphragms. Lugworms are thus no longer able to confine pressure changes to those regions of the trunk in which localized muscular contraction is taking place. Against this, however, they have gained the advantage of being able to generate a large thrust through the combined action of a substantial length of trunk musculature. The gain is specifically of advantage in burrowing, provided always that the internal pressure remains below the danger limit. Outside the burrow it becomes apparent that this loss of septa sets limits on the versatility of movement of the animal. Lugworms have little capacity for swimming, or even for crawling on the substratum; in this latter respect the advantage lies with the earthworm, and its capacity for localized application of thrust.

Some of the hydrostatic adaptations of lugworms show a degree of interspecific variation (Fig. 6–9). In *Arenicola ecaudata*, for example, the anterior or head coelom is substantially isolated from the rest of the coelom, apart from the existence of a dorsal valve and ventral foramen, which are probably closed during the extrusion of the pharynx. The pressure for this extrusion is exerted through the contraction of the first diaphragm (differentiated into a retractor sheath and gular membrane), so that the process is independent of pressure changes in the main coelom. In *A. marina*, on the other hand, the first diaphragm is less well differentiated, and here the general coelomic pressure is of greater importance in extrusion, for the second and third diaphragms are incomplete and exert little restraining effect upon movements of the fluid. The structure of the tail, however, shows that the animal makes use of the advantages of metameric septa. They are well developed in this region, perhaps because they help to control the extrusion of faeces. The supposition is that they isolate the tail from the effect of changes of pressure in the continuous trunk coelom, and aid localized increases of pressure when discharge of the faeces is to take place. There could be no better illustration of the versatility of action of hydrostatic skeletons than the adaptive variations of organization that have thus become established within the limits of the body of a single polychaete worm.

7

Movement and Arthropodization

7–1 SKELETON OF ARTHROPODS

By the standards that we have discussed earlier, the outstanding success of the Arthropoda cannot be doubted. They have adapted themselves to water, land, and air, sometimes under most extreme conditions, in a way that bears comparison with the achievements of vertebrates, while the Class Insecta alone, with some 700,000 species, contains more species than all the rest of the animal kingdom (Fig. 1–2, p. 5). Their success is due to a process that is sometimes called 'arthropodization'. This is essentially the exploitation within the group of the far-reaching potentialities that are latent in the plan of structure exemplified in annelid worms. To say this is not necessarily to mean that the arthropods must have evolved from primitive annelids. Their origins are, in fact, unknown, for they must lie far back in pre-Cambrian times, but we are justified in assuming that the group arose from some worm-like stock. A comparison of them with modern annelids is thus a useful basis for assessing the significance of the features to which they owe their success.

One of the most important of those features, and the key to all their subsequent history, is the development of a firm exoskeleton which can resist deformation, and which is suitable for the construction of systems of levers. The movements of worms are restricted in scope and wasteful of energy, being dependent upon contractions of a muscular body wall and the distribution of the resultant pressure changes. Often they involve the development of lateral undulations, which represent an expenditure of considerable effort in return for a comparatively slow rate of forward progression. With a firm exoskeleton, and with the jointed appendages that this allows, the muscular body wall can be broken down into separate muscles, arranged so as to ensure that their contractions bring about responses that are localized both in time and space.

Arthropods, like annelids, are metamerically segmented, and so their appendages, like parapodia, form a metamerically repeated series. Within this series there has evolved a regional specialization and division of labour, leading to an increased complexity of reaction and greater efficiency of performance. A contributing factor is the extensive development of cross-striations in the muscle fibres. Except in the Onychophora, the muscles are almost entirely striated, a feature that is believed to secure increased speed of contraction and hence of response.

Two other features are also very characteristic of the arthropod group. One is the almost complete loss of cilia, presumably a result of the increased development of cuticle over the external surfaces and to some extent over the internal ones also. The other is the loss of the coelom as the main body cavity, and its restriction to vestigial spaces in the gonads and excretory organs. Consideration of the development of *Peripatus* (Fig. 12–5) suggests that this loss is closely connected with the breakdown of the blood vessels to form a continuous blood-filled cavity called the haemocoel, the heart coming to lie in this and taking in blood through openings called ostia. The haemocoel provides for a hydrostatic skeleton that maintains turgor in animals in which the cuticle remains flexible, as it does, for example, in the Branchiopoda, and in centipedes. It is also of particular importance during the moulting of animals with rigid exoskeletons, for it contributes to the distension of the body, which ensures that the newly formed skeletal covering is adapted to the shape of the growing animal. It has been suggested that in this respect the haemocoel has some advantage over a segmented coelom in that its fluid can be driven through it by the force of the heart beat, and without obstruction by metameric septa.

However this may be, it is clear that arthropods have lost much of the internal metamerism that we assume was present in their annelid-like ancestors. We have earlier suggested that the hydrostatic function of the coelomic fluid was an important factor influencing the initial establishment of metamerism. The evolution of arthropod locomotor mechanisms seems to have brought about a decreased dependence on hydrostatic properties. We may think of the haemocoel as being adaptively correlated with other factors of arthropodan organization. It has certainly evolved quite independently of the similar cavity of molluscs.

It is common to find that the body surface of invertebrates is protected by an epidermal secretion (the cuticle). This is true of arthropods, but the secretory process in these animals is of exceptional complexity, while their epidermis shows an impressive range of potentialities. Typically there is a firm basement membrane to which muscles can be attached, and which is strengthened by being linked through intracellular fibrils to the cuticle. The muscle attachments may consist of thickenings of the membrane, or of outgrowths of it that take the form of fibrillar bars. Further, the ectoderm may give rise to subepithelial connective tissue fibrils, while striated muscle may sometimes arise from it.

Fundamentally the arthropodan cuticle is a complex of protein and chitin (see below), but lipids also play an important part in its composition, as do the polyphenols and phenolases (polyphenol oxidases) that are involved in the tanning process to be described later. These various substances are distributed in two zones, an inner chitinous procuticle and an outer non-chitinous epicuticle. In general the significance of the differentiation of an epicuticle in arthropods is that it both protects the underlying procuticle and also provides an important physiological barrier between the animals and their external environment. Undoubtedly the epicuticle has been of the utmost value in supporting their exploitation of life on dry land. It is already recognizable in the very primitive cuticle of the Onychophora, where electron microscopy reveals an epicuticle of four distinct layers. Its chemical composition in this particular group is uncertain, but it is probable that it contains both protein and lipid components, and it is likely that the molecular arrangement of these components contributes to the markedly hydrofuge (or 'unwettable') properties of the body surface of *Peripatus*—which do not, however, make it waterproof, so that the Onychophora cannot resist desiccation.

In other groups the epicuticle provides more complete protection. Its composition is best understood in insects (Fig. 7–1), but enough is known of the crustacean cuticle to show that in that group its organization is very similar (Fig. 7–2). The proteins of the insectan epicuticle form a cuticulin layer, with which are associated the polyphenols and phenolases. According to Wigglesworth's analysis of events preceding the moult in the bug *Rhodnius*, the cuticulin is the first layer of the epicuticle to be secreted. It is then penetrated by processes of the epidermal cells which secrete the polyphenol layer. Later, just before the moulting of the old cuticle, lipids are deposited as a waterproof wax layer, perhaps secreted by the same epidermal cell processes. Finally, just after moulting, a protective cement layer is secreted by dermal glands. This layer, which probably consists of lipoprotein, forms a protective outer covering. Thus the innermost layer of the epicuticle is the first to be formed, and the outermost layer the last, a mode of development that clearly depends upon the epidermal cells having channels of communication with the outside. This applies also in principle to the crustacean epicuticle, for here the cuticle is penetrated by pore canals communicating with the epidermis, and by ducts arising from tegumental

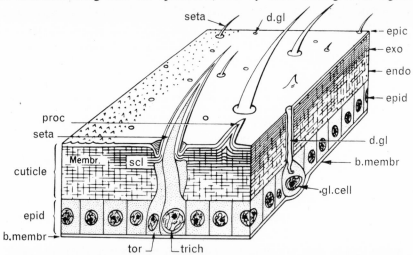

Fig. 7-1. Diagrammatic reconstruction of a block of the integument of an insect to show the general organization, drawn at boundary between a sclerite and membrane to show the fundamental similarity of soft and hard cuticles. *b.membr*, basement membrane; *d.gl*, duct of unicellular gland; *endo*, endocuticle or soft inner portion of procuticle; *epic*, epicuticle (subdivisions not indicated); *epid*, epidermal cell layer; *exo*, exocuticle or hard and usually darkened outer portion of procuticle; *gl.cell*, gland cell; *membr*, membrane; *proc*, a type of immovable non-cellular process; *scl*, sclerite or hardened and darkened area of cuticle; *seta*, the commonest type of movable (tactile) projection; *tor*, tormogen or socket-forming cell; *trich*, trichogen or seta-forming cell. From Richards, 1951. *The Integument of Arthropods*. University of Minnesota Press, Minneapolis. Copyright 1951 by the University of Minnesota, University of Minnesota Press.

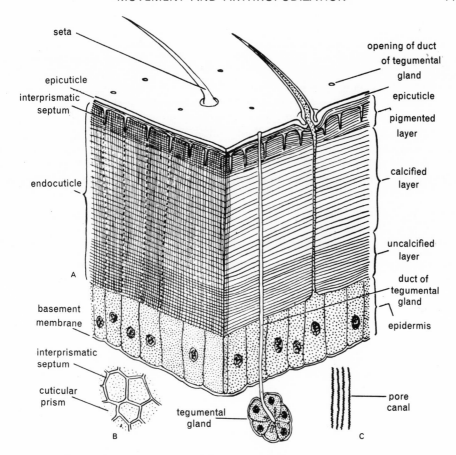

seta

opening of duct
of tegumental
gland

epicuticle

interprismatic
septum

epicuticle

pigmented
layer

calcified
layer

endocuticle

uncalcified
layer

duct of
tegumental
gland

A

basement
membrane

epidermis

interprismatic
septum

cuticular
prism

tegumental
gland

pore
canal

B

C

Fig. 7-2. A, diagram to illustrate the structure of the decapod cuticle as seen in vertical section. B, horizontal section through pigmented layer of endocuticle. C, pore canals as they appear in vertical sections of the epicuticle under higher magnification than (A) and (B). From Waterman (ed.), 1960. *The Physiology of Crustacea,* vol. 1. Academic Press, New York.

glands that lie below the epidermis. The precise contribution that these make to the development of the cuticle is not, however, clearly understood. In the Onychophora there are no such communications. Here the layers of the epicuticle are presumably laid down in the order that they occupy, an illustration of its more primitive organization.

The remainder of the cuticle, underlying the epicuticle, is the procuticle, which consists of a complex of protein and chitin. Chitin (Fig. 7–3) is a polysaccharide which was first discovered in 1811 in fungi, and which, at that time, was named fungine. It can be chemically defined as a polymer of high molecular weight, consisting of acetyl-glucosamine residues which are linked together by 1,4–β–glycosidic bonds to form long and unbranched molecules. Like cellulose, which it resembles in some of its properties, chitin is a 'structural' polysaccharide, well suited by the aggregation of its linear chains to contribute to the protection and support of the body. Its value can be measured by the prodigious quantities in which it is secreted. According to Tracey, copepods alone are estimated to produce several times 10^9 tons per year, whereas the world production of natural cellulose amounts to 10^{11} tons per year.

The term chitin has in the past been used very loosely, to refer to various types of hard cuticle which, regardless of their chemical constitution, have been described as 'chitinized'. This is a misleading terminology, for the hardening of the arthropod cuticle does not primarily involve chitin at all, nor is this substance confined to the arthropods. Its presence, in a precise chemical sense, can be established by specific procedures such as colour tests and X-ray diffraction studies. From such studies it is known to be widely distributed in the animal kingdom, although it does not always have the same crystallographic properties. One form, referred to as β-chitin, occurs in association with collagen, as, for example, in the chaetae of polychaetes and in the reduced shell (pen) of *Loligo*. The other form, α-chitin, is characteristic of arthropods, and is found also in fungi.

It is possible that chitin is present in Protozoa and Porifera, but it seems to be absent from Platyhelminthes and Echinodermata. It is absent also from the Chordata, but is found amongst the Deuterostomia in the Pogonophora. The position in some of the other groups of animals is uncertain. Chitin does seem to be present in the

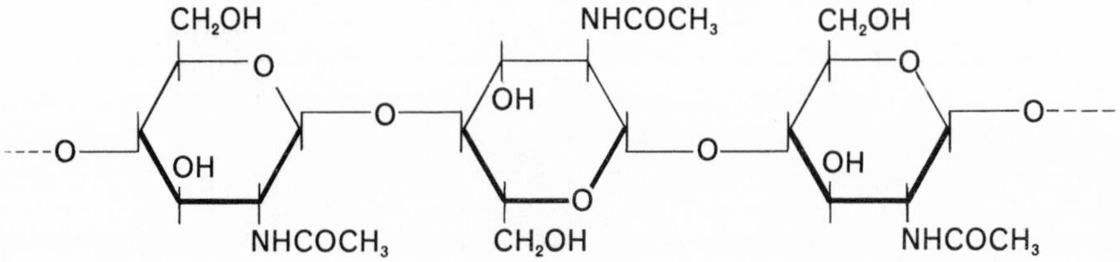

Fig. 7-3. Chitin

perisarc of hydroid coelenterates, and in the radula of snails, while it is also said to be present in some Ectoprocta. It has not been identified in the cuticle of annelids, despite its presence in their chaetae and jaws. The contrast between annelids and arthropods is in this respect clear-cut, for in the latter group it is universally present as a continuous layer. This advance in chemical complexity of the protective covering of the body is thus an important difference between the two groups. Evidently chitin is not an invention peculiar to arthropods. Rather is it another illustration of the way in which well characterized compounds have been evolved independently in many different groups of animals.

The cuticle may remain a soft and flexible material, with a protein component, termed arthropodin, that is predominantly soluble. This is seen, for example, in the Onychophora and centipedes, in the cuticle of larvae, in many branchiopod crustaceans, and in the intersegmental membranes that form the mobile junctions between the hard parts of toughened exoskeletons. Cuticle of this type is very flexible and non-elastic, and it is these properties that enable it to provide for freedom of movement. Normally, however, most of the cuticle, particularly that of adults, undergoes hardening. This is a progressive process, upon which, and upon the varying extent to which it is developed, the mechanical properties of the exoskeleton necessarily depend.

Hardening may be brought about in two ways. One of these is by the deposition of calcium carbonate, mainly as calcite but to some extent also in an amorphous form. The process is well known in the decapod crustaceans, where calcification starts in the epicuticle and then extends inwards through the procuticle (or endocuticle, as it is often called in the crustaceans). Resorption of the calcium salts takes place in these animals prior to the moult, so that this method of hardening involves a regular cycle in calcium metabolism. Calcification is also characteristic of diplopods, in which its development in the outer procuticle confers upon their exoskeleton a rigidity and inflexibility that is functionally correlated with their burrowing habits. Its adaptive significance is emphasized by its absence in *Polyxenus*, a diplopod that is not a burrower, but that exploits instead the roofs of crevices.

The other method of hardening, called sclerotization, involves a change in the molecular organization of the protein component of the cuticle, accompanied by a characteristic darkening in colour. This process, when maximally developed, produces an exoskeletal material that differs from unmodified chitin in being highly elastic and essentially non-plastic, so that it returns to its original shape when deforming forces are removed. Sclerotization, like the calcification of the decapod cuticle, begins in the epicuticle and is a progressive process. Local differences in the degree of hardening often reflect different mechanical requirements at specific regions of the body.

In *Peripatus*, where the exoskeleton remains very flexible, sclerotization is only weakly developed; over the body as a whole it is restricted to the epicuticle, where it may help to prevent the non-elastic cuticle from being pulled out of shape. It does, however, extend inwards to toughen the procuticle of the hard jaws and claws, and we shall see that its restriction elsewhere is adaptively correlated with the mode of life of the Onychophora. In insects this inward extension is more fully developed. As a result it is customary to regard the fully differentiated procuticle of these animals as composed of an external dark sclerotized region, the exocuticle, and an inner light endocuticle, the latter being unsclerotized and thus more or less transparent (Fig. 7-1). A similar extension takes place in many crustaceans, but full uniformity of nomenclature of insectan and crustacean cuticles has not yet been generally agreed, nor is it certain that it could be justified by the actual composition of the two types of exoskeleton. Considerable sclerotization is also found in chilopods. The exoskeleton of these myriapods thus has an elasticity that contrasts with the rigidity of the calcified exoskeleton of the diplopods. We shall later consider the adaptive significance of this contrast.

To understand the nature of sclerotization it is necessary to appreciate its structural consequences. The unhardened procuticle already has certain valuable properties, for the highly polymerized molecular chains of the chitin and protein complex are very strong, and provide a covering which is both firm and flexible. These latter properties would be adequate for an animal that still relied upon hydrostatic forces for its movements, and we shall shortly see these forces operating in *Peripatus* and to some extent also in centipedes. The strength of the procuticle results from the molecular chains being grouped in lamellae that have been compared to the veneers of plywood. Within each lamella the chains are parallel with each other, but those of one lamella lie at an angle with those of adjacent ones. The flexibility of this complex of lamellae is a result of there being little bonding between adjacent molecules, and still less between adjacent lamellae, so that the cuticle can be readily bent. Stiffness can

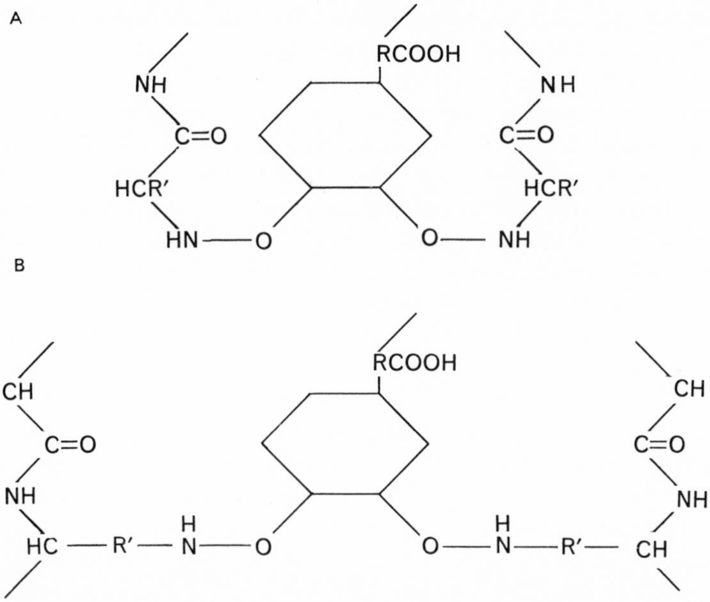

Fig. 7-4. Quinone-tanning reactions. A, quinone tanning by reaction with imino group of the main protein chain. B, quinone tanning by reaction with amino group of basic side chains.

only be secured by the insertion of appropriate bonds, and it is this bonding that is effected by sclerotization. The result is the production of a highly resistant and insoluble protein called sclerotin.

The stabilization of proteins by the introduction of cross-linkages between their molecules has been achieved by animals in two distinct ways. One of these, characteristic of the vertebrates, consists in the establishment of disulphide bonds between the cysteine residues of the molecules. This method, which is comparable with the vulcanization of rubber, yields the product called keratin. This was perhaps first evolved as a waterproofing device, although its mechanical properties have been well utilized by the vertebrates in such skeletal products as beaks, feathers, and claws.

The other method, which is particularly characteristic of arthropods, involves the use of orthoquinones to form cross-linkages between the free imino or amino groups of the protein molecules (Fig. 7–4). This process, which yields sclerotin, may be compared with the commercial tanning of collagen by benzoquinone. Under natural conditions the quinone may be formed by dehydrogenation of an *ortho*-dihydroxyphenol, the reaction being catalyzed by a phenolase (or polyphenol oxidase) (Fig. 7–5). One example of this is the formation of the egg case (ootheca) of the cockroach. The two colleterial glands secrete the several components that are needed. Included in the secretion of the left gland are three substances: a protein, a phenolase, and a glucoside of protocatechuic acid. The secretion of the right gland is a clear fluid containing a glucosidase. The two secretions are mixed when they are discharged, and the glucosidase hydrolyzes the glucoside, with the release of protocatechuic acid, which is an *ortho*-dihydroxyphenol. The protocatechuic acid is oxidized to an orthoquinone by the phenolase, and the orthoquinone then reacts with the protein molecules, binding them together to form the tough sclerotin of the fully formed ootheca. The ootheca of *Locusta migratoria* is formed by a similar mechanism, with 3,4-dihydroxyphenylacetic acid (Fig. 7-5) taking the place of protocatechuic acid.

It has been thought that reactions similar to these occur in all insects during the sclerotization of the cuticle. However, the difficulties of analysis and interpretation are here greater than in the case of the cockroach because the secretions are produced in such small quantities, and it is not surprising that many features of the process are still obscure. It is certain that the pattern of events has become much diversified in its details, but it must be sufficient here to describe one other example as an illustration of this. At the end of the last larval instar of the blowfly, *Calliphora erythrocephala*, the larval cuticle becomes hardened to form the characteristic puparium. Prior to this stage the tyrosine metabolism mainly takes the form of deamination (Fig. 7-6A). Puparium formation is believed to be initiated by a metabolic change evoked by the secretion of the moulting hormone, ecdysone (Sec. 17-4). Tyrosine is now metabolized along a pathway (Fig. 7-6B) that leads to the formation of N-acetyldopamine quinone. Phenolase is active, because it can catalyze the *ortho*-hydroxylation of monophenols as well as the dehydrogenation of *o*-dihydroxyphenols; dopa decarboxylase and acetylcoenzyme A are the other enzymes involved. The quinone is believed to act as the tanning agent in the formation of the puparium; a conclusion that is confirmed by the demonstration that if isotopically labelled N–acetyldopamine is injected into the larva towards the end of the last larval instar, it is incorporated into the puparium.

Quite apart from the variation found within the insects themselves, it is probable that different groups of animals differ in their tanning mechanisms. There is certainly scope for such differences, for there is good evidence that sclerotization, in the general sense of tanning through the agency of aromatic cross-linkages, is by no means restricted to arthropods. It is not found in echinoderms or chordates, but it has been reported in the central capsule of the radiolarian *Thalassicola*, in the cysts of the

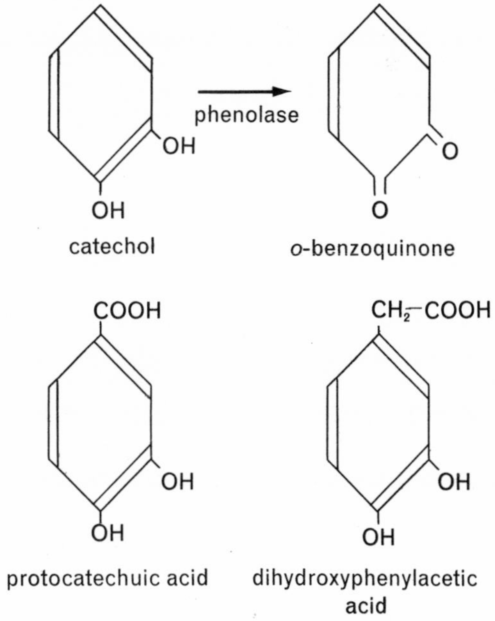

catechol   *o*-benzoquinone

Fig. 7-5. A quinone and some polyphenols.

protocatechuic acid   dihydroxyphenylacetic acid

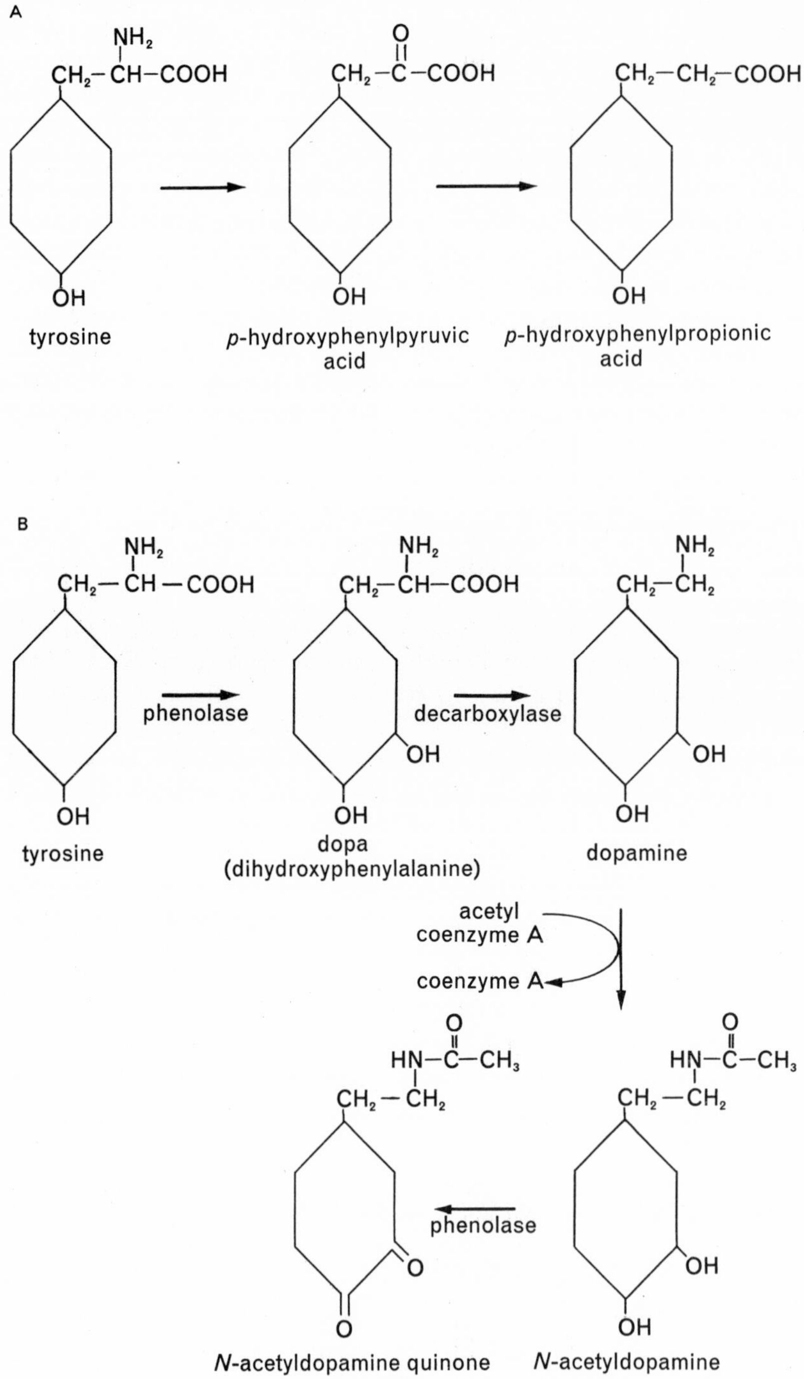

Fig. 7-6. Pathways for the metabolism of tyrosine.

eelworm *Heterodera*, in the egg capsules of the liver-fluke *Fasciola*, and in the chaetae of polychaete and oligochaete worms. It is probably widespread also in molluscs, for the byssus of *Mytilus*, the hinges of lamellibranch shells, and the radulae of gastropods, are all thought to be hardened by sclerotization.

It must be emphasized that the tests used to justify these conclusions are not specific in the sense of demonstrating that the products are identical with arthropod sclerotin; nor is the evidence sufficient to justify any firm conclusion regarding the distribution of the process in the various groups. We probably see here yet another example of the way in which a highly advantageous biochemical feature is based upon materials of common occurrence, which in this instance are proteins containing phenolic amino acids, and the enzymes capable of oxidizing them. It is to be expected that sclerotization could arise in many different evolutionary lines, and it is all the more interesting that in the annelids the process has been restricted to isolated structures like the chaetae. The lack of any extension of it into the general cuticle is correlated with a locomotor mechanism that depends upon hydrostatic pressure and a contractile body wall.

7–2 TAGMATA AND THE HEAD

The metamerism of arthropod limbs has introduced the possibility of division of labour among them, and this has led to a great diversity of specialization. This adaptive diversification is associated with a grouping of the appendages so that those carrying out similar functions lie on adjacent segments, for this ensures efficiency of operation. The resulting regional differentiation is reflected not only in the limbs themselves, but also in the form of the segments, which is necessarily influenced by functional demands. Because of this the arthropod body becomes demarcated into clearly defined regions called tagmata. In general there is a well-defined head, where the appendages are predominantly concerned with sensory and alimentary functions, while over the rest of the body the appendages, where present, are primarily loco-motory and often also respiratory. This broad subdivision of functions is by no means invariable or absolute, for there is much overlap of function between the several tagmata. Each major group, however, has its characteristic pattern of 'tagmosis', and retains this with remarkable constancy during its adaptive radiation. The composi-tion of the insect head, for example, has remained unchanged since Devonian times. Because of this we might expect the various patterns to provide a helpful guide to the mutual affinities of the arthropod classes. To some extent they do this, but the evi-dence, not only from tagmosis but also from other aspects of their organization, is far from being clear-cut and conclusive.

Heads are characteristic of free-living animals that are bilaterally symmetrical. It is in this region that new stimuli are usually first encountered, so that paired receptor systems tend to become concentrated here, together with the associated regulatory centres, both neural and neurosecretory.

Something I owe to the soil that grew—
More to the life that fed—
But most to Allah who gave me two
Separate sides to my head.

Here, too, the food will be ingested, so that the mouth is located in this region, often in association with structures used in seizing and manipulating the food. The resultant specializations are expressed in the process called cephalization, or head formation. This leads in metameric animals, both vertebrate and invertebrate, to fusion and modification of originally separate and uniform segments, as a result of which the segmental composition of the head becomes increasingly difficult to determine. We may thus expect (p. 98) a segment to comprise a pair of mesodermal somites (often with coelomic cavities), a pair of coelomoducts, and a pair of nerve ganglia, while externally it should bear a pair of appendages and be delimited anteriorly and posteriorly by a transverse groove. Nevertheless, one or other of these features may be unrecognizable in the specialized body form of the adult; grooves, moreover, may be deceptive, for they sometimes have a functional explanation that is unrelated to any history of segmentation. It is thus commonly necessary to seek evidence for segmental composition in early stages of development.

Signs of cephalization are already apparent in the Platyhelminthes, where nerve ganglia (often called cerebral ganglia), eyes, and tentacles are localized at the anterior end. As might be expected, the process is still at a very early stage in these animals, and in the Acoela the cerebral ganglia are represented by no more than thickenings of the nerve plexus. In annelids the process has advanced further. In an errant polychaete such as *Nereis* a morphologically recognizable head region is formed by two regions called the prostomium and peristomium, the former lying anterior to the mouth while the peristomium surrounds it.

The prostomium, which primitively contains the cerebral ganglion ('brain'), lies in front of the first true segment. In polychaetes it develops directly from the anterior (upper) region of the trochophore larva. The interpretation of the peristomium is less clear, although it has commonly been assumed that it is composed of one or more cephalized segments. In *Nereis*, for example, it bears four pairs of cirri, which are probably the remains of two pairs of parapodia belonging to two cephalized segments. It is possible, however, that more than two may be present in some polychaetes. In certain ariciid polychaetes no less than three pairs of mesodermal somites have been identified in the mouth region during early development, although no ganglia are differentiated in relation to them nor is there a corresponding annulation of the ectoderm. We can conclude that cephalization is well established in polychaetes, but that there is variation within the group, so that a final interpretation of the structure of their head is not yet possible.

The head of arthropods, which is very much more complex than that of annelids, has evolved along several lines, each characteristic of one of the major groupings within the phylum. We can expect, therefore, that analysis of the structure of the head in this phylum will provide important clues to an understanding of the relationships of those groupings. On the whole, this expectation is justified, but, as in other aspects of arthropod organization, it is essential to take careful account of the possibility of parallel and convergent evolution having occurred.

It is characteristic of the phylum that the segmentation of the anterior end of the embryonic head is restricted to the ventral and ventro-lateral regions, where developmental stages of somites, limbs, and ganglia are recognizable to varying degrees. The dorsal region is thus formed only of unsegmented tissue, which is sometimes termed the acron. Another characteristic is that the most anterior of the true segments have come to lie in front of the mouth. This is often expressed in the statement that the mouth appears to have moved backwards in the course of evolution. Tiegs and Manton have shown, however, that this situation is actually a consequence of morphogenetic movements that carry the anterior head segments forwards, while at the same time there is a backgrowth of the labrum and prostomium relative to the somite region. This brings the antennae into a position in which they can function as pre-oral sense organs, which is a highly advantageous adaptation in active animals. The pre-oral region formed in this way may be called the procephalon.

Behind the procephalon there is commonly a post-oral region, also belonging to the head. This region may be called the gnathocephalon, for here the appendages are primarily concerned with feeding. Usually it comprises three segments, so that the head is then composed altogether of six segments. There are, however, exceptions to this plan. Moreover, even when the same plan is found in different animals, this cannot be taken as necessarily establishing common ancestry. The difficulty is well illustrated by Manton's analysis of the functional morphology of the mandibles, which are commonly developed in arthropods out of a pair of appendages associated with the mouth.

Two types of mandible can be distinguished from the developmental point of view. In one of these (type A of Manton's analysis) the biting jaw is formed from the base of the appendage, while the distal part is reduced in the adult to a biramous or uniramous palp (cf. Fig. 7-10, p. 127). The biting region develops out of the proximal part of the coxa (coxopodite), together with the proximal endite, a component that may be enlarged on other crustacean appendages to form a gnathobase (Fig. 10-23, p. 203). Mandibles of this type are found in Crustacea and, in a somewhat different form, in Chelicerata. In the second type of mandible (type B), the jaw is formed from the whole of the embryonic limb, and not merely from its base (cf. Fig. 7-11, p. 127). This type is found in the Onychophora, and also in the myriapods (where it is usually jointed), and in Insecta (where it is unjointed).

Analysis of the functioning of the arthropod mandible discloses a further complication, for it exposes a second dichotomy that cuts across the dichotomy of development. In the Onychophora the two mandibles carry out a backward slicing movement that is essentially like the movement of the walking limbs. The mandibles of other groups are more complex in their movements than this, and present two modes of action, referred to by Manton as types I and II. Type I is a rotatory and counter-rotatory movement; it is carried out around a dorso-ventral axis, and is similar in principle to the movement of a coxa on a locomotor appendage of the trunk, from which movement it is doubtless derived. This type is found in the Branchiopoda and less specialized Malacostraca, and in *Petrobius*, for example, among the insects.

Type II is a stronger movement. It is carried out transversely (at right angles, that is, to the roll of type I), and is more effective for crushing, gripping, and cutting. The achievement of the type II movement must have presented mechanical difficulties, for it is necessary to secure abduction of the mandible by muscles, and this is not easily contrived when the appendage already lies at the side of the head. The problem appears to have been solved in two ways. The myriapods and Chelicerata have derived this transverse movement directly from a transversely gripping movement of the trunk limbs, whereas in Crustacea and Insecta it has been secondarily developed by independent modification of the rolling movement of type I.

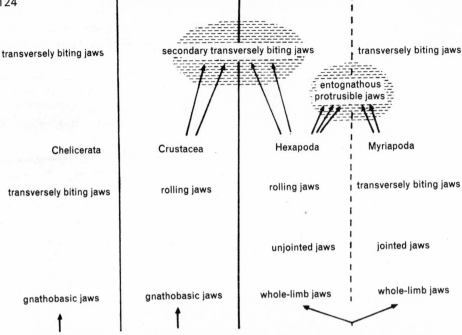

transversely biting jaws

secondary transversely biting jaws

transversely biting jaws

entognathous protrusible jaws

Chelicerata   Crustacea   Hexapoda   Myriapoda

transversely biting jaws

rolling jaws

rolling jaws

transversely biting jaws

unjointed jaws   jointed jaws

gnathobasic jaws   gnathobasic jaws   whole-limb jaws   whole-limb jaws

Fig. 7-7. Diagrams showing the conclusions reached by Manton concerning the distribution of the principle types of mandibles or jaws. The heavy vertical lines indicate an entire absence of common ancestry between the jaws referred to on either side; an interrupted vertical line indicates separate evolutions of the jaw mechanisms of Hexapoda (Insecta) and Myriapoda which probably had a common origin; and the shaded areas indicate mandibular mechanisms showing convergent similarities derived from unlike origins. From Manton, 1964. *Phil. Trans. R. Soc. B*, **247**, 1–183.

We have seen that the structure of the crustacean mandible differs so fundamentally from that of insects that the jaws of these two groups (respectively belonging to type A and type B) must have been independently evolved. It follows that the establishment in these same two groups of the type II movement must also have been achieved independently. The situation is illustrated in Fig. 7–7. This shows that four types of mandible must have been evolved independently in the arthropods, and that convergent similarities have developed between crustaceans and insects (as regards direction of bite) and between certain insects and myriapods (as regards the evolution of protrusible jaws). This is a good illustration of parallel and convergent evolution in operation, and well worth noting, for in later discussion we shall find reasons for supposing that similar considerations operate in the analysis of other aspects of arthropodan evolution.

We can now consider the arrangement of the segments of the head in the main classes of Arthropoda, as shown in Table 7–1. With living forms, cephalization has clearly advanced least in the Onychophora (Fig. 7–8), for in these animals the head consists only of the procephalon, comprising three segments. This is in accord with the generally primitive level of organization of this group, which we shall see illustrated further when we examine its locomotor mechanisms. Nevertheless, the onychophoran head has its own unique features. These include the differentiation of jaws on the second segment, the persistence of the appendages (pre-antennae) of the first segment, and the oral (slime) papillae, which are a specialized and characteristic

Table 7–1   Appendages of the first seven segments of arthropods

	ONYCHOPHORA	TRILOBITA	CRUSTACEA (Malacostraca)	MYRIAPODA (Scolopendra)	INSECTA	ARACHNIDA
1	Preantennae	?	Embryonic	Embryonic	Embryonic	Embryonic
2	Mandibles	Antennae	Antennules	Antennae	Antennae	Chelicerae
3	Oral papillae	Biramous limbs	Antennae	Embryonic	Embryonic	Pedipalpi
4	Legs	Biramous limbs	Mandibles	Mandibles	Mandibles	Legs
5	Legs	Biramous limbs	Maxillae (1st)	Maxillae (1st)	Maxillae (1st)	Legs
6	Legs	Biramous limbs	Maxillae (2nd)	Maxillae (2nd)	Maxillae (2nd)	Legs
7	Legs	Biramous limbs	Maxillipeds	Maxillipeds	Legs	Legs

feature of the group. The pre-antennae may be regarded as a primitive character, as also is the form of the mandibles, which bear some resemblance to the claws of the trunk limbs in biting at the tip instead of at the sides. The leg-like movement of these appendages, to which we have earlier referred, may also be primitive, but is adaptively correlated with the onychophoran habit of squeezing through narrow crevices.

A primitive form of head might also be expected in the Trilobita (Fig. 7-9), marine forms that were dominant in the early Palaeozoic but finally became extinct in the Permian. The expectation is justified, although the data give little help in determining the affinities of the group. One pair of antenna-like pre-oral appendages is present, probably associated with the second segment. The remaining appendages of the body are biramous, and differ very little from each other, so that they afford no clear basis for establishing the posterior limit of the head. Certain external features, however, including a facial suture and genal spines, make it possible to delimit a presumed head from a trunk, and on this basis four pairs of post-antennary appendages are regarded as cephalic ones. They pass into the series of trunk appendages without interruption or sudden change of form, so that from the functional aspect the head of these animals is very imperfectly defined.

Those who favour associating the trilobites with the crustaceans see some resemblance in the head structure of the two groups. The evidence for this association, however, is by no means convincing, as we shall see later, and in any case the head

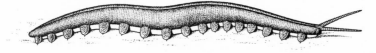

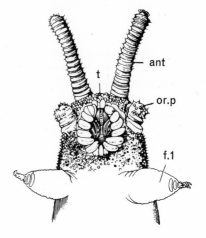

Fig. 7-8. *Above, Peripatus capensis,* enlarged very slightly. Adapted from Shipley and MacBride, 1904. *Zoology.* Cambridge University Press. *Right,* ventral view of the head of *P. capensis. ant,* pre-antenna; *or.p,* oral papilla; *f.l,* first leg; *t,* tongue. From Sedgwick, 1922. *Cambridge Natural History,* vol. 5. Macmillan, London.

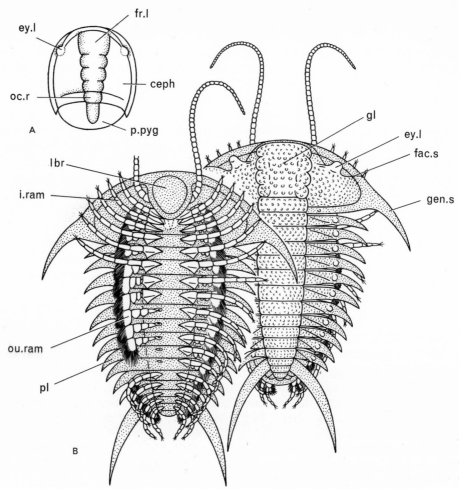

Fig. 7-9. A, diagram of protaspis larva after Whittington, 1957. B, reconstruction of the trilobite *Ceraurus pleurexanthemus* Green, Ordovician, 27 mm, after Størmer, 1951. *ceph*, cephalon; *ey.l*, eye lobe; *fac.s*, facial suture; *fr.l*, frontal lobe; *gen.s*, genal spine; *gl*, glabella; *i.ram*, inner ramus of leg; *lbr*, hypostome (labrum); *oc.r*, occipital ring; *ou.ram*, outer ramus of leg; *pl*, pleural fold; *p.pyg*, protopygidium. Adapted from Tiegs and Manton, 1958. *Biol. Rev.*, **33**, 255–337. Used by courtesy of the Cambridge Philosophical Society.

has evolved very much further in crustaceans. In these animals it includes a procephalon of three pre-oral segments, the first of which, the pre-antennary segment, has no appendages; its coelomic sacs, however, have been detected during development. The remaining two pre-oral segments bear sensory appendages: the antennules (first antennae) and the antennae (second antennae). This procephalon may be thought of as the primitive head of crustaceans, with which other segments become associated to form a gnathocephalon of variable constitution. This variability suggests a certain parallel with vertebrates; in both groups the progress of cephalization has tended to shift the posterior limit of the head backwards.

A well-defined feature of crustaceans is the development of mandibles on the fourth segment. This is the first segment of the gnathocephalon, which is typically completed by two more segments, bearing the maxillules (first maxillae) and the maxillae (second maxillae). The form of these appendages varies in relation to the feeding habits of the group concerned, but they are commonly somewhat lobate. In some crustaceans (e.g. *Mysis*) there is a distinct mandibular groove immediately behind the mandible; this has been thought to suggest that the primitive crustacean head may at one stage have ended at this level, but in fact the groove is a mechanical necessity correlated with the mandibular musculature. In other forms (e.g. amphipods, isopods) the first thoracic segment fuses with the head, a situation that is functionally associated with the use of the appendages of this segment (maxillipeds) in feeding (Fig. 7-10). In the Eucarida there are as many as three pairs of maxillipeds, all associated in some way with the feeding activities of the head appendages. Since the carapace of these animals arises from the maxillary (sixth) segment it is generally accepted that this segment marks the true morphological limit of the head region. However, there is some uncertainty because the division of labour among the appendages of crustaceans has not established a sharp functional differentiation between the head and the anterior segments of the remainder of the body. This will become even more apparent later when we consider the filter-feeding mechanisms of these animals.

Myriapods and insects have a plan of head structure that in certain respects resembles that of crustaceans. Here again there is a procephalon formed of three pre-oral segments. The pre-antennary segment is represented by a pair of mesodermal somites but bears no appendages; the second segment bears antennae, but the third, in contrast to that of crustaceans, bears none. The head is completed by a gnathocephalon of three segments (Fig. 7-11), bearing, respectively, the mandibles, the first maxillae, and the second maxillae (fused in insects to form the labium). It is possible, despite the diversity of specialization in myriapods and insects, to discern a common plan of structure in their three pairs of gnathocephalic appendages. As we shall see later, other grounds also justify associating these groups together. There are also resemblances between them and crustaceans, but these are less fundamental. In addition to the lack of pre-antennary appendages, the presence of mandibles on the fourth segment is certainly a point of resemblance, but we have seen that the jaws of these groups must have evolved independently. It is thus no longer possible to sustain

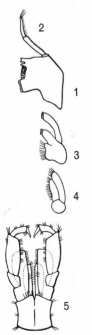

Fig. 7-10. *Left,* The mouth appendages of *Gammarus.* *1,* left mandible; *2,* palp; *3,* 1st maxilla of left side; *4,* 2nd maxilla of left side; *5,* maxilliped of each side together forming an underlip. From Shipley and MacBride, 1904. *op. cit.*

Fig. 7-11. *Below,* Mouth appendages of *Blatta.* A, mandible. B, first maxilla; *1,* cardo; *2,* stipes; *3,* lacinia; *4,* galea; *5,* palp. C, right and left second maxillae fused to form the labium; *1,* submentum; *2,* mentum; *3,* ligula, corresponding to the lacinia; *4,* paraglossa, corresponding to the galea; *5,* palp. From Shipley and MacBride, 1904. *op. cit.*

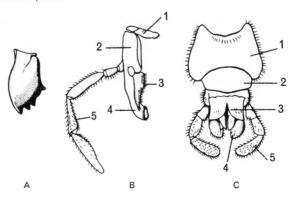

the view that crustaceans, myriapods, and insects should be classified together as the 'Mandibulata'. In any case, the remainder of the crustacean gnathocephalon is not closely comparable with the myriapod and insectan type, from which it differs in the form of its appendages and in the degree of its variability. The head appendages of isopods and amphipods admittedly show a superficial resemblance to those of insects, particularly in the form of the maxillipeds, which recalls that of the insect labium (Fig. 7–11). These appendages, however, arise in the crustaceans from the seventh segment, and it is certain that this particular resemblance must be another result of convergence. It has been attributed to the influence of a bottom-dwelling mode of life upon the feeding mechanism.

Finally, the organization of the head region of the Chelicerata is so anomalous as to suggest that these animals form a natural group with no obvious affinity with any of the others. There is no clearly defined head in the sense in which we have so far described it. Instead, the head region is incorporated into an anterior tagma, called the prosoma, which comprises eight segments. No appendages are found on the first segment, but there is some evidence for coelomic sacs in the embryo. Prehensile chelicerae are developed on the second segment, taking the place of the antennae that are found here in all other arthropods except the Onychophora.

A distinctive peculiarity of the Chelicerata, although one that is seen also at a more primitive level of organization in the trilobites, is the absence of mandibles. In the chelicerates these are replaced functionally by gnathobases, borne on the anterior appendages. A gnathobase may be defined, following Lankester, as a jaw process that has the function of assisting, by apposition to its fellow on the opposite side, in seizing and moving particles that may be introduced into the mouth. Most chelicerates are fluid feeders, and in some of them the crushing action of the gnathobases is used to extract juices from the prey. An exception to this is *Limulus* (Fig. 7–12), the only living member of the Subclass Xiphosura; it ingests solid food, and, through the agency of the gnathobases, can make use of either soft or hard material. Soft food is held by this animal in a ventral depression of the body; there it is chewed by the gnathobases (borne on all of the walking limbs), and the shredded material is passed forwards to the mouth. Hard material is

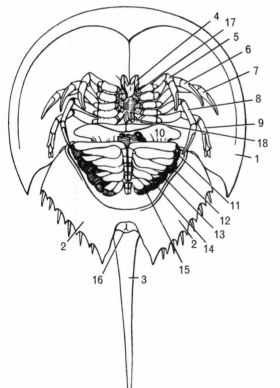

Fig. 7-12. Ventral view of the King-crab, *Limulus polyphemus*, $\times \frac{1}{2}$. *1*, carapace covering prosoma; *2*, mesosoma and metasoma; *3*, telson; *4*, chelicera; *5*, pedipalp; *6, 7, 8, 9*, 3rd to 6th appendages, ambulatory limbs; *10*, genital operculum turned forward to show the genital aperture; *11, 12, 13, 14, 15*, appendages bearing gill-books; *16*, anus; *17*, mouth; *18*, chilaria. From Shipley and MacBride, 1904. *op. cit.*

gripped between the chilaria, pressed forwards by the genital operculum, and cracked by the gnathobases.

Manton, in her account of *Limulus*, emphasizes the unusual features of this method of feeding. Contrary to the general tendency of arthropods to develop mandibles adjacent to the mouth, it is the more posterior gnathobases of *Limulus* that are the strongest and most jaw-like. Further, as we have noted, the feeding movements are directed transversely, at right angles to the antero-posterior swing that provides for locomotion, so that feeding and locomotor movements are mutually exclusive. The feeding methods of *Limulus*, like so much else in its organization, may be regarded as an adaptation to burrowing into the upper layers of the substratum. Their efficiency may be judged from the report that when a single animal, only 3 in. wide, was placed on a limited area of substratum with 100 $\frac{1}{2}$-in. clams, it removed 99 of them in 72 hours.

The third segment of chelicerates, which lies behind the mouth, bears appendages called pedipalps. In *Limulus* these are sensory or prehensile in function, while in spiders they are also involved in reproductive activity. They are followed by four pairs of limbs which are primarily ambulatory, although, as we have just seen, they are important also in feeding. The eighth segment of the prosoma is visible only in the embryo, but it is represented in the adult by the chilaria.

7–3   LOCOMOTION AND THE CRUSTACEAN LIMB

Tagmosis in the post-cephalic region of the arthropod body is closely related to modes of locomotion. Its interpretation raises complex issues, not only of phylogenetic history but also of the factors that influence the functioning of locomotor appendages as individual units and in relationship to each other. These factors are best considered in the predominantly terrestrial groups, which have been analyzed in depth by Manton. It will be convenient first, however, to refer to the Crustacea, which have mostly retained the aquatic mode of life that must have characterized the first arthropods. Within this habitat they have attained nonetheless a remarkable degree of diversity, and their limbs show the versatility with which metameric structures can respond to the demands of feeding and locomotion.

Many smaller crustaceans are filter feeders. We shall see later that this type of activity depends upon the simultaneous use of limbs for swimming and for filtering water. These limbs, which move like paddles, are typically of the kind called phyllopodia (Fig. 10–21, p. 201), with an axis that bears foliaceous outgrowths, arranged as a row of endites on the medial side, and one or more exites on the outer side. Often the cuticle of these limbs is thin, and their shape is largely maintained by blood turgor. The movement of these delicate structures is integrated in a metachronal rhythm, and it is partly because of this that the filter-feeding crustaceans are small, for the locomotor efficiency of this type of limb is at its highest in small organisms. Phyllopodia bear a certain resemblance to parapodia in their lobate form and delicate structure, and because of this, and also because of their presence in the primitive Branchiopoda, it has been argued that they represent the primitive type of crustacean limb. This view may well be sound in principle, but it is unlikely that the ancestral type would have closely resembled such highly foliaceous limbs as those of modern branchiopods. Filter-feeding crustaceans show a great diversity of specialized feeding mechanisms,

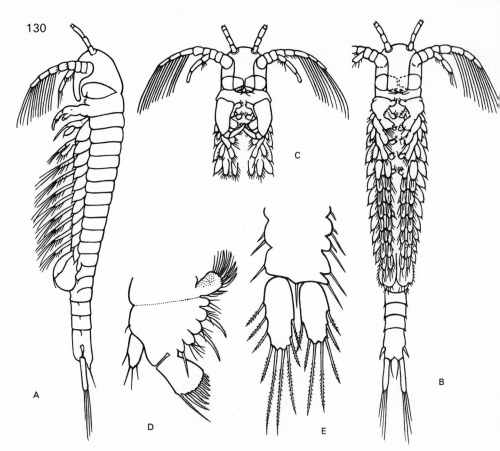

Fig. 7-13. Reconstructions of the crustacean *Lepidocaris rhyniensis* Scourfield, 3 mm, Devonian. A, female from the side; B, female from below; C, head of male, ventral view; D, one of the first pair of trunk limbs; E, one of the posterior (7th? to 11th) pairs. After Scourfield, from Tiegs and Manton, 1958. *op. cit.* Used by courtesy of the Cambridge Philosophical Society.

dependent upon corresponding diversity in details of limb structure and function. The ancestral limb is thus more likely to have been of a generalized and simple type, upon which the adaptive radiation of feeding habits could have been founded. It is significant that such a limb is seen in the Devonian fossil *Lepidocaris* (Fig. 7–13). This had simple biramous appendages which, in the anterior thoracic region, bore gnathobases. These, as we have already noted, develop in phyllopodia out of the proximal endite. In many living crustaceans they make an important contribution to filter feeding, and Cannon, in his analysis of the well-preserved material of *Lepidocaris*, was able to show that they may have done so also in that animal.

Filter feeding is typically associated with a small size of body. The attainment of larger size, such as is found in many Malacostraca, seems likely to have emerged from a pattern of adaptation associated with a bottom-dwelling habit, and with the utilization of bulky food material (macrophagy, p. 162). Weapons have been acquired by the development of powerful chelipeds, and the protective value of the cuticle has been increased by heavy calcification. Also associated with this mode of life is the evolution of walking by means of legs, which are found in crustaceans as slender, biramous, non-foliaceous appendages called stenopodia. It has been suggested that limbs of this general type may be more primitive than phyllopodia, one reason for this idea being that they occur in the nauplius larva (Fig. 19-7). This consideration, however, cannot carry much weight, for, as we shall see later, larval organization is a very uncertain basis for phylogenetic speculation.

Another reason is that the stenopodial type of appendage is present in trilobites, but this, too, needs to be regarded with caution. Our analysis of the head has already shown that the argument for a close relationship between the trilobites and crustaceans is far from convincing. But trilobites do not only differ from crustaceans in their lack of mandibles. Both groups admittedly have biramous limbs, but those of trilobites differ from those of crustaceans in consisting of an internal walking ramus and an outer branchial one, but the latter with a fringe of respiratory filaments (Fig. 7-9, p. 126). Furthermore, there is no good evidence that trilobite limbs bore gnathobases, while the outer ramus is said to differ from that of the crustacean limb in its origin. Nevertheless, there are certain Cambrian fossils that combine a generally crustacean appearance with a trilobite type of limb. Because of this the possibility of some remote relationship between the two groups cannot be wholly dismissed, although there is no positive evidence to support it.

One other aspect of crustacean tagmosis that merits attention is the establishment in the Malacostraca of the plan of organization called the caridoid facies. This is the body form in which the head is followed by a thorax of eight segments, with limbs that are used for walking, and that also bear natatory exopodites and respiratory epipodites. The body is completed by a third tagma, the abdomen. This is composed of six abdominal segments, five of which bear swimming pleopods, used as paddles, while the sixth bears uropods that form, with the post-segmental telson, the tail fan.

The origin of the caridoid facies is unknown. We shall see later, however, that certain functional considerations operative in terrestrial arthropods may lead to a reduction in the number of walking legs as these become longer. Because of this, reduction has taken place in chelicerates, insects, and in certain myriapods, and the malacostracans probably provide another example. This interpretation implies that the caridoid facies first evolved as an adaptation to the bottom-dwelling life and ambulatory movement that we have already envisaged, but evidently it did not restrict the group to that habitat. Mysids and euphausiids, in which the caridoid facies is well defined, are free-swimming and filter-feeding forms. Probably, then, there was a divergence of habit at an early stage of malacostracan evolution, with some lines perfecting the bottom-dwelling mode of life while others exploited the possibilities of pelagic life and filter feeding. In the later stages of this divergence the abdomen of bottom dwellers, with its natatory appendages, became less important, as is shown by the great reduction that it has undergone in crabs.

Crustaceans, although well able to develop walking legs, have shown remarkably little facility for the exploitation of the land. At least four independent attempts have been made from the littoral zone, originating in the isopods, amphipods, anomurans, and brachyurans. The mechanical practicability of the adventure is sufficiently illustrated by the amphibious isopod *Ligia*, which is the common shore slater that lives just above the tidal zone. This animal uses essentially the same walking mechanism on land as in the sea, so that the mode of functioning of the appendages of the aquatic members of the group is presumably pre-adapted to terrestrial life. There is here a parallel with the evolutionary history of the vertebrates, for it is well established that the structure of the rhipidistian fin showed the essential pattern of the pentadactyl limb before the emergence of the Amphibia.

We shall see later that the terrestrial limitations of crustaceans are essentially physiological ones, involving, for example, failure to achieve adequate modification of nitrogen excretion or of water balance. Any explanation of this can only be hypothetical, but it may be significant that these various terrestrial lines all originated in specialized shore-dwelling groups. Perhaps the very success of crustaceans as aquatic animals has militated against the establishment in the group of any alternative mode of life; probably those that did attempt life on land were already too specialized to develop an adequate range of new adaptations. Another possibility is that limitations in their gene complexes resulted in a lack of suitable mutations, but this is difficult to reconcile with the widespread occurence of parallel and convergent evolution in the phylum.

7–4 LOCOMOTION IN TERRESTRIAL ARTHROPODS

Our understanding of the functioning of the locomotor mechanisms of terrestrial arthropods reveals *Peripatus* to be an animal of key importance, showing potentialities that were to be realized more fully as the 'arthropodization' of the phylum advanced further. Sclerotization is only feebly developed over much of the cuticle of this animal. As we have shown, this is not due to any inability to develop the necessary biochemical mechanism, for a tough and well-sclerotized endocuticle is present in the jaws and claws. In fact, the retention of a soft and flexible cuticle over the general body surface is part of an adaptive complex that includes also the retention of smooth muscle, with its capacity for extensive deformation. Because of this the cuticle is highly permeable, and the animal is consequently unable to resist desiccation. In one sense this permeability, like that of Amphibia, is a serious limitation in a terrestrial animal. It undoubtedly restricts the range of habitats that are open to the Onychophora, yet within their chosen range they nonetheless show a high level of adaptive organization. A much-favoured habitat of *Peripatus* is the deeper parts of decaying logs. Here it profits from its soft cuticle and the deformability of its smooth muscle, for these features enable it to penetrate through narrow passages into concealed cavities where it is protected both from loss of water and also from the pursuit of predatory arthropods. Surprisingly, it can pass through holes as small as one-ninth of the area of its resting cross-section. We have seen in other invertebrates how deformability is associated with some form of fibrous mesoglea. This is true also of *Peripatus*, which has as one of its characteristic specializations a well-developed connective tissue layer underlying the ectoderm, and providing for the insertions of the muscles. A similar adaptation is also found in myriapods.

The Onychophora are sometimes thought of as a primitive group that has managed to survive 'in spite of' its primitive features, as though they were an example of 'Mir war auf dieser Welt das Glück nicht hold'. But to think in this way is to raise a difficult question: why has selection pressure not led to the replacement of primitive features by more advanced and less limiting ones? The fact is that this point of view, as Manton has emphasized, is a mistaken one. It is self-evident that *Peripatus* represents an early stage of arthropodization, yet its life is not a struggle against structural and physiological limitations. We may rather say that these have been accepted, and

that the animal is successfully exploiting them through the agency of a highly specialized behaviour pattern. After all, 'if a man does not keep pace with his companions,
perhaps it is because he hears a different drummer'.

The relationships of the Onychophora are by no means clear, but it seems
reasonable to regard the group as having arisen from worm-like animals (perhaps
primitive annelidans, although, as we have emphasized, this is not certain), in which
parapodia-like limbs became directed more ventrally instead of laterally. We know
little of the circumstances in which this change could have occurred, but there is
a middle Cambrian fossil, *Aysheaia* (Fig. 7-14), which closely resembles *Peripatus* in
the form of its body and limbs. It was marine in habit, so that it may very well represent a stock, possibly ancestral to the Onychophora, in which the limbs had already
become pre-adapted for terrestrial locomotion, just as in the isopods.

There are polychaetes that are able, in a sense, to walk upon ventrally directed
parapodia, but in worms the propulsive force is mainly provided by the longitudinal

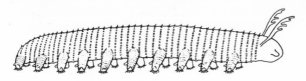

Fig. 7-14. *Aysheaia pedunculata* Walcott, 50 mm. Middle Cambrian, conjectural
restoration, after Hutchinson. From Tiegs and Manton, 1958. *op. cit.* Used by courtesy
of the Cambridge Philosophical Society.

muscles of the body wall. In *Peripatus* the forward and backward strokes of the limbs
are effected by their own extrinsic muscles. The main function of the longitudinal
muscles is now to maintain, in conjunction with the haemocoelic fluid, a rigid body
wall upon which the extrinsic muscles of the limbs are inserted. This change in function of the muscles must have been of crucial importance in the transformation of
worm-like forms into arthropods, and we may assume that increased sclerotization
and hardening of the exoskeleton would have improved the efficiency of action of the
limb muscles. The use of extrinsic limb muscles instead of the musculature of the body
wall results in the elimination of body undulations, which are so wasteful of energy
in the locomotion of polychaetes. A further advantage gained by *Peripatus* is that the
length of the limbs can be regulated by their intrinsic muscles. This regulation is
essential for the securing of efficient walking, since during the forward and backward
stroke of a limb the distance between its base and its tip must be shortest at mid-stroke.
In other arthropods, the jointing of the walking limbs provides another way of securing this regulation.

Evidently the locomotion of an arthropod, even at this relatively primitive level
of organization, involves a remarkable refinement of adaptation and control. Nor is
this all. For example, the animal is able to use a variety of gaits. These differ in several
respects, including the duration of the pace, the relative duration of the forward and
backward strokes, and the angle of swing. These differences determine the number of
legs that are actually propelling the animal at a given moment, and hence the driving
force that they are able to apply. On this basis Manton distinguishes three main gaits
in *Peripatus*: bottom gear, middle gear, and top gear (Fig. 7-15).

In bottom gear there is a small swing of the legs, and a backward stroke of

'Bottom Gear' for Starting Up and Gaining Speed

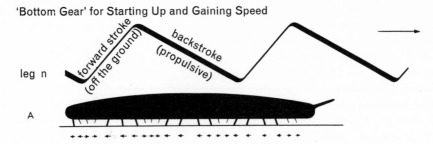

'Middle Gear' for Faster Walking after Some Momentum has been Acquired

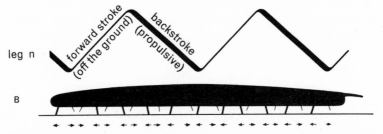

'Top Gear' for Fast Easy Walking

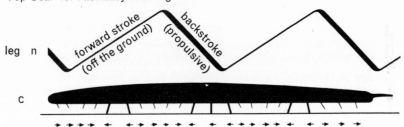

Fig. 7-15. Diagrams showing the three 'gears' of *Peripatus*. Adapted from Manton, 1950. *J. Linn. Soc. (Zool.)*, **41**, 529–570. Reproduced with permission.

relatively long duration, so that more than half of the legs are simultaneously in contact with the ground. Thus a powerful driving force is exerted, so that this gait is used for starting and for gaining speed. In middle gear the forward and backward strokes are of equal duration, but half of the legs are still propelling at the same time. This gait is for walking when some momentum has been achieved. In top gear the backward stroke is of shorter duration, and less than half of the legs are in contact with the ground at once. This is for fast walking, when speed has been established and a powerful drive is less needed. The readiness with which *Peripatus* can change from one of these gaits to another reflects the flexibility of its still comparatively primitive level of organization. In the more advanced terrestrial arthropods, with their more rigid skeleton, new problems are presented. To some extent these animals tend to specialize upon one particular gait, suited for a particular mode of life. Yet this is not the only solution; flexibility can still be secured provided that the number and interrelationship of the limbs is suitably modified. These aspects of locomotor adaptation are well illustrated in the myriapods and Insecta.

Sedgwick, in a discussion of myriapods, suggested in 1909 that the Onychophora, Myriapoda, and Insecta might be the survivors of a once great and continuous group of land arthropods, a large number of which had become extinct. This is still an acceptable view. The affinities of *Peripatus* must surely be with the myriapods rather than with the crustaceans. Among the onychophoran characters forcing us to this conclusion are the terrestrial habit, the mode of formation of the mandible, the restriction of tagmosis to the head, the development of tracheae throughout the body, and the presence in certain species of eversible sacs that absorb moisture, and that resemble comparable structures in the Symphyla. Significant also is the presence, in the embryos of certain myriapods, of large coelomic vesicles recalling those of the onychophoran embryo. In both groups the mid-gut lacks the digestive gland found in crustaceans and chelicerates, while other features in common are the absence of any trace of biramous limbs or of a suppressed nauplius stage. The absence of Malpighian tubules from *Peripatus* results in the intestine of this animal secreting uric acid crystals throughout its length, in physiological adaptation to terrestrial life. This intestinal activity does not occur in myriapods to the same extent, for these animals do possess Malpighian tubules; nevertheless there is some particulate excretion from the intestine in certain species.

Evidence for a relationship between the myriapods and insects is no less convincing. Especially striking, in addition to the fundamentally terrestrial mode of life, is the uniform structure of the head, with a similar distribution of appendages and with the same mode of development of the mandible. Other features shared by the two groups are the absence of a digestive gland, the presence of tracheae throughout the body and of a well-developed fat body in the haemocoel, and considerable similarity in the structure and development of the heart and aorta.

It is now possible to see, from Manton's studies, that this interpretation of the relationship between the three groups conforms well with the organization of their locomotor mechanisms. What seems to have happened, in general principle, is that the myriapods, in adaptation to contrasting modes of life, have specialized in one or other of the several gaits seen in the more generalized Onychophora, and have to some extent reduced the number of their legs, while in insects a high degree of flexibility of movement is correlated with a reduction in the number of the legs to three pairs. A full illustration of this interpretation demands a closer attention to complex detail than is practicable here, but the argument can be illustrated by contrasting the Diplopoda with the Chilopoda. These two groups are differentiated from each other by very marked differences in mode of life. The differences are reflected in many details of structural organization, yet not so profoundly as to preclude the possibility of a common ancestry. This is the justification for continuing to give centipedes and millipedes the common designation of myriapods.

Diplopods are burrowers, which push head foremost into loose soil and crevices, or underneath stones; they have also developed the protective reaction of coiling their body. We have seen that the structure of their cuticle is influenced by the burrowing habit; no less characteristic is the effect of this habit upon the mode of locomotion. This depends upon a specialization of the low-gear type of gait. The back stroke is of relatively long duration, which makes possible a strong and slow movement of the legs. Further, the legs are very numerous; thus a large number can be included in each metachronal wave, so that at any one moment many legs are exerting the driving stroke, and a correspondingly large force is transmitted to the anterior end of the body.

Burrowing requires the elimination of unnecessary projections. Thus the integument of diplopods is smooth as well as hard, the contours of the head are rounded, and the antennae can be folded flat. The walking limbs also make an important contribution to this aspect of adaptation. They are of moderate length, yet not so long as to form obstructions to movement within the burrow; moreover, they arise mid-ventrally, so that they project little, if at all, from the general body surface. Associated with this is the peculiar form of the individual segments. These are unusually wide and deep, aiding the covering over of the legs from above. In addition, they are fused together in pairs to form what are termed diplosegments. Manton has shown that this fusion is an adaptation that can be explained in terms of the functional demands of diplopod movement and mode of life. The individual segments are very short, presumably because if they were of more normal length the body, with its large number of limbs, would be too long for effective transmission of force for head-on burrowing. A large number of short segments, however, would also create problems. The body would now be unnecessarily flexible, and this flexibility would have to be regulated by muscles. Further, it would be difficult to provide an adequate area for the insertion of the segmental muscles. These difficulties are overcome by the formation of diplosegments, without losing the advantage of the propulsive force derived from the large number of appendages. Moreover, the provision of muscle insertions is facilitated, and the body is more rigid. This rigidity is further secured by the development of ball and socket joints between the individual rings; these discourage longitudinal telescoping and contraction of the body.

Millipedes eat as they push their way through decaying vegetable matter. Centipedes, by contrast, are active carnivores, searching widely for their food, which they pursue in the open and in crevices. Manton remarks that in consequence of this difference of habit, chilopods are nearly always hungry when they are caught, while diplopods are seldom in need of a meal. Chilopods, as we have seen, possess an elastic cuticle in contrast to the rigid one of diplopods, and, in correlation with this, they have not exploited the mechanical principles involved in the association of muscles with systems of rigid fulcra and levers. Large trunk sclerites are present, so that chilopods are clearly more advanced in arthropodization than are the Onychophora, but these sclerites do not articulate. Thus the hydrostatic pressure of the haemocoel assumes great importance in these animals, and the muscles tend to act indirectly on the sclerites through the mediation of this fluid system. The result of all this is that the chilopod body is highly deformable, and is capable of much dorso-ventral flattening, and of shortening and extension. Because of this, the animals can readily insert themselves into crevices, but by a method quite different from the burrowing action of the rigid diplopod body; thus, the head is flattened, the antennae are inserted anteriorly instead of dorsally, while the poison claws and second maxillae can move horizontally, so that they can manipulate prey in shallow spaces.

The legs of chilopods, in association with the free-running mode of life, may be long, and, in contrast to the diplopod legs, they exploit the top-gear type of gait. Longer legs make greater speed possible, for the stride can now be longer and speed will be correspondingly increased, always provided that the duration of pace is not increased. Exploitation of top gear will also contribute to greater speed, for in this type of gait the back stroke is relatively shorter than in bottom gear, so that the duration of pace can actually be decreased.

The effective use of long legs, however, presents one important functional difficulty. When many of them are present, there is a danger that they may get in each other's way. In order to avoid this difficulty, and the stumbling that would result from it, the animal must execute its locomotor movements with very great precision, which means a corresponding loss in flexibility of movement. The situation can be eased, however, by two structural adaptations, which are well shown in *Scutigera*. This is the fleetest of centipedes, feeding predominantly on insects in open spaces. It is worth noting that, because of this habit, its head has not become flattened in adaptation for life in crevices; instead, it preserves a primitive dome-shaped outline, with dorsally inserted antennae. For the same reason, the mouth parts and poison claw are less well adapted for operating in dorso-ventrally confined spaces. These characteristics have led to a suggestion that the Scutigeromorpha are the most primitive of chilopods, but this merely emphasizes the importance of considering functional organization. As Manton points out, functional analysis of the trunk region shows that this group is, in fact, 'the last word in centipede advancement and specialization'; it is not surprising to find that it is only in these most agile of centipedes that compound eyes have developed.

The first of the structural adaptations to which we have referred is that the legs differ in length. They are so arranged that each is longer than the one in front; each can, therefore, be put down just outside the tip of the preceding one (Fig. 7–16), and in this way a maximum stride is ensured without the mechanical interference of one leg with another. This device, however, can only operate with success if there are relatively few legs. This is because there is a limit to which the legs can vary in length, since at any one speed their stride must be the same. It would be impossible to achieve this with a large number of legs, all different in length, and consequently in *Scutigera*, as in other chilopods such as *Lithobius*, they have been reduced in number. This reduction is the second device to which we alluded. With it there goes another requirement. It is essential that undulation of the body should be reduced as much as possible under conditions of normal locomotion, for excessive lateral displacement would result in the legs overlapping once again, thus causing stumbling. This requirement is achieved in chilopods by a reduction in number and increase in size of the tergites, an adaptation that gives some measure of axial stiffening.

We have stated the principles of chilopod locomotor organization in very general terms, but within the group there has been much adaptive divergence in matters of detail. One example illustrates the application of the principles within a somewhat different pattern of life than the one that we have been discussing. *Geophilus* is a burrowing chilopod, but it burrows like an earthworm and certainly not like a diplopod. We have noted the importance of the hydrostatic functions of the haemocoel in chilopods, and they are well exploited by *Geophilus*, which makes use during burrowing of the deformability of its hydrostatic skeleton. The legs are necessarily short. During burrowing they serve for anchorage, while when the animal is walking it uses a large angle of swing to compensate for their shortness. The burrowing habit is here associated with a comparatively long body. The body wall is elastic, as usual in chilopods, and the dorsal and ventral sclerites are able to slide over each other, with intercalary sclerites increasing the capacity for telescoping. Further, much lateral

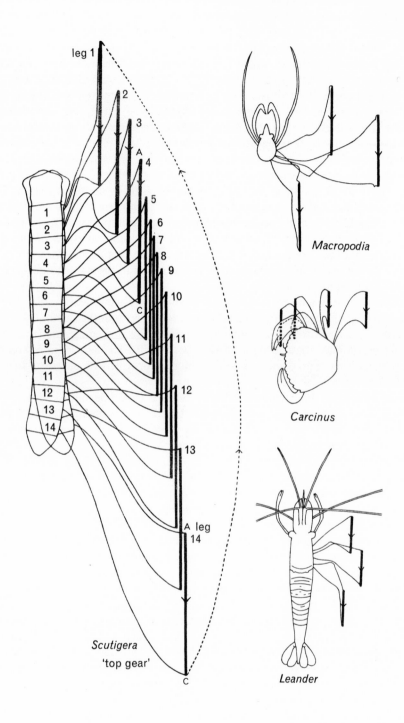

Macropodia

Carcinus

Leander

Scutigera
'top gear'

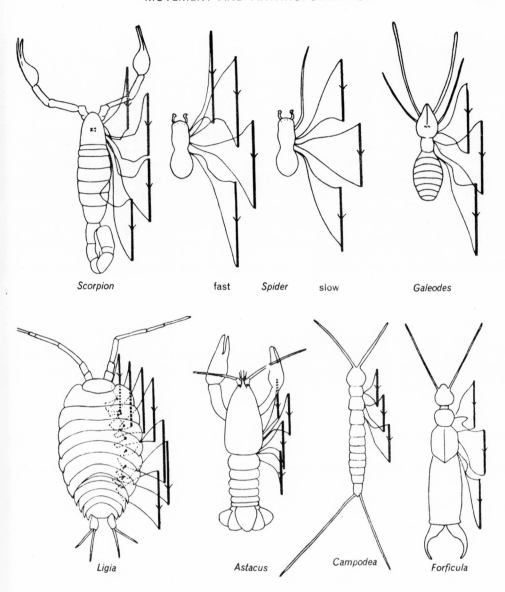

Scorpion   fast   *Spider*   slow   *Galeodes*

Ligia   Astacus   *Campodea*   *Forficula*

Fig. 7-16. The field of movement of the legs of a series of Arthropoda. The heavy vertical lines represent the movements of the tip of the leg relative to the body during the propulsive backstroke. In *Scutigera* the limb-tips are swung forwards approximately on the common dotted line, and the forward stroke for the other animals is not shown. The other animals shown are the spider-crab *Macropodia rostratus*, the prawn (*Palaemon*) *Leander serratus*, the shore-crab *Carcinus maenas*, the scorpion *Bluthus australis*, a British lycosid spider progressing at 36 and 250 mm per sec in the two diagrams, *Galeodes arabs*, *Ligia oceanica*, *Astacus fluviatilis*, a British species of *Campodea*, and the earwig *Forficula auricularia*. From Manton, 1952. *J. Linn. Soc. (Zool.)*, **42**, 93–117.

expansion is made possible by the elasticity of the pleural region, which possesses only isolated sclerites. The contrast with diplopods is fundamental, and illustrates well the consequences that flow from the adoption of two entirely different approaches to a burrowing habit.

The principles that we have outlined can reasonably be applied to the history of insect locomotion as well. The myriapodan class Symphyla has often been regarded as particularly close to insects, and, as far as locomotory mechanisms are concerned, it would be possible to justify this view, for symphylans lack the locomotor specializations of other myriapods and retain the full range of the gaits that are also found in insects. Manton's analysis of the mandibular mechanism, however, has thrown new light on this matter, for, as we have seen, it has shown that the transverse movement of the mandibles must have evolved along two independent lines. Because of this it seems no longer possible to derive insects from the Symphyla. We can only assume that they evolved from some unknown group of terrestrial arthropods that may well have been ancestral also to the myriapods.

The characteristic tagma of insects is the three-segmented thorax, with its three pairs of elongated legs (Fig. 7-16) that are often longer than those of myriapods. This reduction in the number of appendages carries to an extreme the principle outlined earlier. Mutual interference of the legs is avoided, while their very small number leaves the animals free to use a flexibility of gait without stumbling. The localization of these three segments immediately behind the head illustrates another consideration. The action of the legs, when they are so few in number, will be more effective if the leg-bearing segments are adjacent to each other, for this abolishes any tendency to the lateral undulations that we have seen to be so wasteful of energy and confusing to movement. It is thus not surprising to find these appendages borne close together on one tagma. Further, the localization of this tagma directly behind the head aids in the support and manipulation of that region.

The insectan thorax is of special importance in the history of arthropodan locomotor mechanisms, because it eventually gave rise, by the development of wings, to a new mode of locomotion. Before we consider this, however, we may note that the principles operating in the evolution of ambulatory movement in the Onychophora, myriapods, and Insecta can also be applied to an understanding of the ambulatory locomotion of crustaceans and chelicerates. Thus it becomes easier to understand the origin of the caridoid facies of malacostracans, provided that we accept, as suggested earlier, that this arose in association with a bottom-dwelling habit. The development behind the head of these animals of an eight-segmented thorax, with some of the segments bearing long walking limbs, can be interpreted as illustrating the same principles as are thought to have governed the origin of the insect thorax, although the principles have not been carried to quite such an extreme conclusion here.

As for the Chelicerata, this group is so different in organization from other living arthropods that, as we have seen in considering the head region, it must have followed an independent path. It has been suggested that the class may have had some remote relationship with the Trilobita, but there is a substantial gap between the two groups which we are unable to bridge with any assurance. The Chelicerata began their history as an aquatic group, the Merostomata, represented today by *Limulus*; the scorpions are terrestrial derivatives of these, and are found as early as the Upper Silurian, when the vertebrates had not yet passed beyond the agnathan phase of their evolution. The characteristic tagmata of the scorpion (Fig. 7-16) are the prosoma, bearing chelicerae, pedipalps, and walking legs, and the opisthosoma, the latter divided into a mesosoma and a metasoma.

As in crustaceans, the concentration of locomotion in a few pairs of walking legs leaves no ambulatory function for the more posterior appendages, but the evolution of the latter has taken a manifestly different course in the two groups. Characteristic of the Chelicerata is the distinction between prosomatic locomotor appendages and mesosomatic respiratory ones, a characteristic that is already becoming apparent in the aquatic fossil forms. Some of these were active swimmers, while others were crawling forms, but from a very early stage there was a tendency for the adaptive evolution of relatively few locomotor limbs. The eventual establishment of four pairs of long walking legs in the terrestrial forms is in accord with the general principles suggested earlier. The mesosoma of scorpions includes four pairs of respiratory appendages, forming the lung books which are peculiar to the Arachnida. The six-segmented metasoma is reduced, serving primarily in scorpions for manipulation of the terminal sting.

7–5 FLIGHT IN INSECTS

In the course of evolution there have been a number of attempts to exploit the possibilities of flight, outstanding success having been achieved by insects, birds, and man. The human solution has depended upon the use of wings as aerofoils, power being applied through a moving airscrew (propeller), or by the use of jet propulsion. The latter device has been extensively applied by other animals to secure movement in water, but has not been used for flight. Instead, movement through the air has been achieved by applying power to mobile wings in order to establish a flow of air over them; they thereby serve both as airscrews and aerofoils. In birds the mechanics of the system are remarkably uniform, but in insects the situation is otherwise. Here the existence of an exoskeleton has allowed a diversity in the relationships between the wings and muscles that drive them; this diversity is readily apparent in the variety of wing movement found in these animals. The complexity of these movements becomes evident when the path traversed by the wing of an insect is analyzed. A wing has to translate the energy derived from the muscles into a force that will provide for movement in the required direction, and that will at the same time counteract the effect of gravity. Failure to appreciate this complexity of operation has led to misunderstanding of the mode of operation of the wings. In an extreme case, as Chadwick points out, it has even been concluded that it is mathematically impossible for the bee to fly!

In practice, of course, the insect wing does not move exactly like an airscrew. (The wheel and axle is one of the very few human inventions that have not been anticipated in earlier stages of evolution.) The wing actually moves in a continuous sweep, and, if the insect is held stationary, the tip of the wing describes a figure of eight (Fig. 7-17). During forward horizontal flight, the wing vibrates in a plane that lies obliquely to the long axis of the body. The main propulsive force is exerted during the downward stroke, the anterior edge of the wing being lower and the posterior edge higher. During the upward stroke this relationship is reversed, the wing being so pulled that its anterior edge lies higher than the posterior one. The effect of this pattern of movement, which is naturally subject to much variation in detail, is to create a zone of increased pressure behind and below the animal, and a zone of decreased pressure in front of and above it. Along this gradient of pressure the insect moves.

One consequence of this mode of flight illustrates the way in which structure becomes adapted to the physical conditions in which it operates. In so far as the wing functions as an aerofoil, it can do so with efficiency if the air stream flowing towards it is free of turbulence. This condition can operate for the anterior pair of wings, but the movement of these creates a state of turbulence that may impede the functioning of the posterior pair. In some insects (in the Hymenoptera, for example, and in the Lepidoptera), this difficulty has been overcome by coupling the anterior and posterior

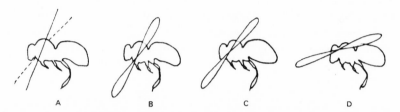

Fig. 7-17.   Flight in the honey-bee *Apis* (after Stellwaag). A, a bee turning; the lines show the plane of vibration of the wings on the two sides. B, plane of vibration during forward flight. C, during hovering. D, during backward flight. From Wigglesworth, 1947. *The Principles of Insect Physiology* (3rd ed.). Methuen, London.

wings together so that they function as a single unit. In some other insects only one of the two pairs of wings is functional in flight. This is the situation in the Coleoptera, where the anterior wings, the elytra, are stiffened and held at an acute angle during flight, the posterior ones being solely responsible for locomotion. In the Diptera, by contrast, propulsion is effected by the anterior wings, the posterior ones being reduced to halteres. These structures, which vibrate in flight at the same frequency as the wings, have groups of campaniform sensillae (Sec. 14–3) at their bases; information provided by these sensillae enables the insect to maintain its equilbrium during flight. Finally, a type of adaptation different from all of these is found in the dragonflies. Here both pairs of wings are functionally equivalent in their contribution to flight, but they beat out of phase with each other. The effect of this is that the posterior pair meets the backward stream of air before the latter has been disturbed by the anterior pair.

Following Boettiger, we can analyze the machinery of insect flight into four components. The first of these comprises the wings, which we have already briefly described. The second component is the complex of parts that articulates the wings to the thorax; included here are the base of the wing and the structures relating it to the thorax, together with the direct flight muscles. The latter are so called because they run from the pleural and sternal regions of the thorax to be inserted directly on the sclerites at the base of the wing; they thus control the setting of these parts. The third component comprises the well-developed and powerful indirect (or driving) flight muscles (Fig. 7–18). One group of these runs dorsally and longitudinally between the mesothorax and the metathorax. The other group runs dorso-ventrally between the tergum and the sternum. These muscles are termed indirect because they do not run direct to insertions on the wings. They are, however, coupled functionally to the wings by parts of the thorax; the latter constitute the fourth component of the flight machinery.

These four components are not always used. In the more primitive insects (for example, the dragonflies) power is applied to the wings through the direct muscles, each of the four wings of a dragonfly possessing elevator and depressor muscles. These are called lamellar muscles, because the protofibrils of the muscle cells are grouped together to form sheets or lamellae, with sarcoplasm and mitochondria lying between them. Lamellar muscles are found also in cockroaches and mantises. Little is known of the physiology of this muscular tissue, but it may be a primitive type of flight muscle. Its important characteristic is that each contraction of the

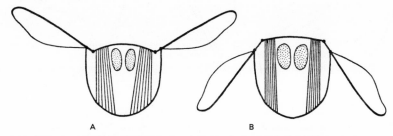

A   B

Fig. 7-18. Diagrams illustrating the traditional theory of the mode of action of the indirect flight muscles of insects. From Imms, 1959. *Outlines of Entomology* (5th ed.). Methuen, London.

muscle is the result of stimulation by a single nerve impulse; in this respect the muscle behaves like the general body musculature of insects. This type of flight mechanism has been called the synchronous type, because the stroke of the wings is synchronous with the stimulation of their musculature by the nervous system.

In many insects, including the Ephemeroptera, Locustidae, and Lepidoptera, the protofibrils are grouped to form delicate fibrils with a diameter of about 1.5 μ. Muscles of this type, called microfibrillar muscles, are characteristic of insects with comparatively soft bodies. Those with harder cuticles, such as Hymenoptera, Coleoptera, and Diptera, have fibrillar muscles in which the fibrils are larger, with a diameter of 3.0 μ. These are the insects with the most highly developed powers of flight; powers that are believed to depend in part upon the complexity of the wing articulation, and in part upon the physiological properties of the fibrillar muscular tissue that forms the indirect flight muscles. In such insects important parts are played by all four of the components that we have mentioned. Their mode of operation, however, is very complex, and it will be impossible to do more here than describe it in brief outline.

One important characteristic of this second type of flight mechanism is that it is asynchronous, by which is meant that the wing stroke is not synchronous with the nervous stimulation of the muscles. The rate of stimulation can be determined by direct recording of the action potentials in the muscles, and it can thus be shown that it bears no relation to the rate of beat of the wings. Instead, it appears that each nerve impulse sets up in the muscle an active state, during the maintenance of which a variable number of contractions can occur. It is because of this that insects possessing an asynchronous flight mechanism can maintain such a remarkably high frequency

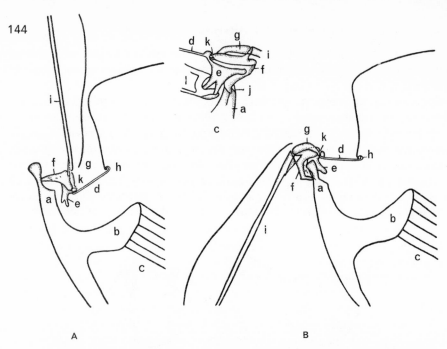

Fig. 7-19. Cross-sectional view of thorax of *Sarcophaga bullata*, showing details of the articulation of the right wing. A, wing in up position, anterior view. B, wing in the down position, anterior view. C, posterior view of the axillary sclerites of right wing showing their relation to the mesopleural process, the lever arm, and the anterior parascutum. *a*, mesopleural process; *b*, pleural apophysis; *c*, anterior pleurosternal muscle; *d*, anterior parascutum; *e*, first axillary sclerite; *f*, second axillary sclerite; *g*, base of radial vein; *h*, hinge; *i*, radial vein; *j*, hook articulation; *k*, point of articulation of anterior notal process, first axillary sclerite, base of radial vein and second axillary sclerite; *1*, end of the lever arm. From Boettiger and Furshpan, 1952. *Biol. Bull. mar. biol. Lab., Woods Hole,* **102,** 200–211.

of wing beat. Whereas the wings of a butterfly may beat at a frequency of 9 per second, and those of a dragonfly at 28, the frequency in the housefly may be 180–200 per second, and in the mosquito 1024.

The mode of operation of an asynchronous flight mechanism has been closely analyzed in the fly, *Sarcophaga bullata*, by Boettiger. His analysis was rendered possible by the fortunate circumstance that when the fly is exposed to fumes of carbon tetrachloride its wings become set in either an up or a down position corresponding to the positions during the normal flight movements. Study of these positions, and pushing of the wings from one position to another, thus made possible the elucidation of the normal functioning of the relevant parts of the skeleton. Previously it had been supposed that the downstroke was produced by a lateral expansion of the notum brought about by contraction of the longitudinal indirect muscles; then, it was thought, contraction of the vertical indirect muscles would draw the notum inwards and bring about the upstroke (Fig. 7-18). Boettiger's analysis showed that this cannot be so, and that in fact contraction of both longitudinal and vertical muscles will tend to produce lateral expansion of the notum. The true course of events is complex, and reference must be made to his account for a full description. In principle, however, tension in the indirect muscles produces an outward thrust at the point *f* (Fig. 7-19), the effect of this being to force apart the mesopleural process (*a*) and the hinge (*h*) which connects the parascutum to the lateral border of the tergum. This thrust strains the tergum and the mesopleural process and results in the building-up of a store of potential energy. The relationships of adjacent parts of the skeleton are such that the point k is moved. A critical stage is reached in this movement when k moves past the line running from the hinge (h) to the point of articulation of the second axillary sclerite (f) to the mesopleural process. At this stage the point k is forced towards its extreme position, either upwards or downwards, because there is a recoil of the skeletal elements that are under strain. The stored potential energy is thus released, and is manifested in wing movement. The whole process is referred to as the click (or snap) mechanism, because the wing 'clicks' from one position to another when the parts are subjected to appropriate pressure in flies that are under the influence of carbon tetrachloride.

The result of this sequence of events is that changes in length of the indirect flight muscles are magnified some 400 to 600 times in wing movement. Thus these muscles can operate almost isometrically, with minimum change of length. No less important is the peculiar physiological property of fibrillar muscles which, as we have noted earlier, permits them to respond to nervous excitation by the maintenance of prolonged tension. It would further appear that they are able to contract as a direct response to the stimulus of being stretched; contractions can thus occur without the tissue being dependent upon a corresponding inflow of nerve impulses. The operation of the 'click' mechanism depends upon muscular tension being applied to the wing articulation. Movement of the wing into one position (up or down, as the case may be) produces a quick release of the particular muscles concerned in that movement. This causes an immediate stretching of the antagonistic muscles, which then contract and bring about, through the resulting tension, the opposite wing movement.

8
Nutrition of Protozoa

8–1 FEEDING

The conclusions drawn from our theoretical discussion of the course of biochemical evolution, and of the origins of green plants and animals, are in accord with the diversity of nutritional mechanisms that are seen in the flagellate Protozoa. Many flagellates are phototrophs, and because of this it is impossible to separate sharply the Class Mastigophora (Flagellata) from the unicellular algae. At one time it was suggested that a flagellate could be regarded as an animal if it lacked a cellulose cell wall and sexual reproduction, and if it divided by longitudinal and not by transverse fission, but these criteria have now been abandoned. Modes of nutrition provide a more useful guide. On this basis algae can be defined as a heterogeneous group of unicellular and multicellular phototrophs, comprising many evolutionary lines, but never reaching the level of differentiation of archegoniate plants. The flagellate Protozoa thus comprise unicellular forms that are clearly animal-like in their nutrition, but it is necessary to include with them certain phototrophic forms that are closely related to them. Difficulties of demarcation cannot, therefore, be wholly removed, nor is this surprising, for it is precisely here that we stand very close indeed to the common stock from which both plants and animals have diverged. Thus there is a marked tendency for the appearance of the animal mode of nutrition in primarily phototrophic groups.

Several species of *Euglena* provide good examples of this. The genus is typically phototrophic, but *E. gracilis* can survive and grow in the dark, in conditions in which it cannot possibly be deriving energy from photosynthesis. Its survival is due to osmotrophic heterotrophy: in the absence of solar radiation it can obtain energy by oxidizing acetic acid. Indeed, many flagellates flourish in the presence of this substance. They seem to have little capacity for utilizing carbohydrate, and the acetate provides them with what is probably their sole source of carbon.

The osmotrophy of *E. gracilis* provides the organism with a source of energy,

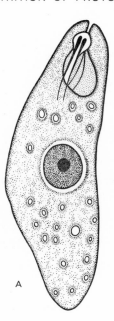
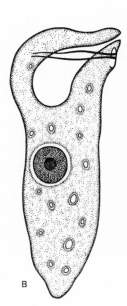

Fig. 8-1. *Peranema.* A, viewed from ventral surface; B, twisted, and viewed from the side. From Chen, 1950. *Q. Jl. microsc. Sci.,* **91**, 279–308.

but it also meets other needs, for euglenids, despite being phototrophic, have certain specific vitamin demands. This was first demonstrated for *E. pisciformis*, which cannot grow without an exogenous supply of thiamine. This dependence seems to be a common situation in euglenids, nor is thiamine the only substance so required, for *E. gracilis* and *E. viridis*, together with many other phytoflagellates, need an exogenous supply of vitamin B_{12}, although closely-related cobalt compounds can sometimes be substituted for this.

We have already suggested that vitamin requirements may be a result of regressive biochemical evolution. Another example of such regression is the tendency for certain phytoflagellates to lose their chlorophyll. *E. deses* does so after prolonged culture in the dark, while *E. gracilis* may give rise spontaneously to colourless forms; these are identical with a flagellate that was known at one time as *Astasia longa*. The appearance of colourless forms can also be induced by treatment with streptomycin, *E. gracilis* being a species that responds in this way. Not all euglenid species, however, can abandon photosynthesis; *E. pisciformis*, for example, will die if it is maintained in the dark. It is thus an obligatory phototroph, whereas *E. gracilis* is a facultative one.

The species that can survive without chlorophyll depend, of course, upon their capacity for osmotrophy, but we might expect that during evolution the establishment of colourless forms through mutation would be followed by the development of phagotrophy. This must surely account for the presence in the phytomastigine Order Euglenoidina of truly animal-like forms, colourless and phagotrophic, of which *Peranema* is an example. This organism, like other euglenoids, possesses a reservoir and a contractile vacuole, but in addition there is a rod organ which lies beside them, but which is not connected with them (Fig. 8–1). This organ consists of two parallel rods attached at their anterior ends to a zone of hyaline cytoplasm that is probably an ingestive opening, or cytostome. *Peranema* readily attacks other euglenids, provided that they are stationary. When it touches the anterior end of a *Euglena* the

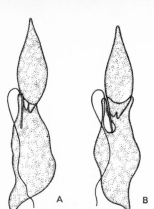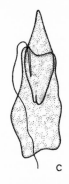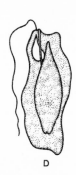

Fig. 8-2. Successive stages (A–D) of *Peranema* swallowing a *Euglena viridis*. The wide extension of the anterior end is seen, and also the independence of the food entrance from the reservoir. From Chen, 1950. *op. cit.*

rod organ protrudes and becomes attached to the surface of the prey (Fig. 8–2). The anterior end of the *Peranema* then dilates, its body moves around the prey, and the rod organ begins to push the latter through the cytostome. Through continual detachment and re-attachment of the organ, combined with forward movement of the *Peranema*, the prey is gradually swallowed, the process being completed within an average time of eight minutes.

We shall see that suctorial feeding has evolved in the Metazoa as a specialized process, often dependent upon the possession of piercing structures, and it is thus of particular interest to find the same development occurring here. Sometimes the rod organ rasps at the surface of the attacked *Euglena* until this has been cut open. The cytoplasm and chromatophores then flow into the body of the *Peranema*, and accumulate there in food vacuoles. As with other euglenoids, paramylon is a reserve product of this organism, and so also is oil. Observations of the fate of starch, oil, and casein taken into the food vacuoles show that it can digest all three types of material, and that it is able to convert them into those reserve substances.

The ease with which colourless flagellates arise today suggests that there may in the past have been repeated evolution of heterotrophic flagellates from phototrophic ones. Certainly the coexistence of phagotrophy and phototrophy within the same order is not peculiar to the Euglenoidina, for we find this situation also in another group of Phytomastigina, the Order Dinoflagellata. Members of this group often have an external covering of cellulose plates, and are further characterized by the possession of two flagella arranged in grooves in a clearly defined way; one lies transversely to the main axis of the body, in a groove called the cingulum, while the other is trailed along that axis in another groove, the sulculus. The group includes both fresh-water and marine organisms, but it is particularly prevalent in the open sea, where its members are among the most plentiful of micro-organisms.

Chloroplasts are present in dinoflagellates, which are a typically phototrophic

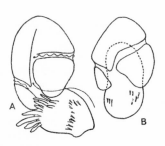

Fig. 8-3. *Gyrodinium pavillardi* capturing (A) and ingesting (B) a specimen of *Strombidium*. The ciliate is held in the region of the frontal membranellae, and ingested in the ventral part of the sulcus, the lips of which are distended. From MacKinnon and Hawes, 1961. *An Introduction to the Study of Protozoa.* Clarendon Press, Oxford.

group, but their photosynthetic activity is sometimes combined with the capacity for ingesting small organisms. One example of this is the brackish-water form *Gyrodinium*, which is able to immobilize large ciliates and to engulf them through the posterior end of the sulculus (Fig. 8–3). Another example is *Ceratium hirundinella*, some of which are colourless while others possess chromatophores. Such colourless individuals can feed on solid prey, which they seize either in a fine network of cytoplasm extended over the body surface, or in a single pseudopodium. Whether individuals with chromatophores also feed in this way is uncertain, but it is at least likely that they do so. Dinoflagellates certainly occur in the sea at depths too great to permit photosynthesis, and they may play a significant part as heterotrophs in the cycle of marine nutrients.

The complete abandonment of phototrophy, analogous to the situation in *Peranema*, is seen in *Noctiluca*. This is an aberrant dinoflagellate, often present near the surface of the sea in enormous numbers, and especially conspicuous because of its bioluminescence. *Noctiluca*, which lacks chromatophores, is exclusively phagotrophic, and, although itself only about 1.5 mm in diameter, is able to feed on animals as large as copepod larvae. These are drawn in through a permanent mouth (cytostome), after having become attached to a movable adhesive structure called the tentacle, which is found also in some other dinoflagellates. The longitudinal and transverse flagella of the latter may be represented in *Noctiluca* by structures called, respectively, the cilium and the tooth. Their function is not clear, but they probably play some part in manipulating the food material. Clearly, then, the development of phagotrophy has involved considerable specialization of the feeding mechanism in dinoflagellates, as it has in *Peranema*.

The remaining groups of Protozoa completely lack the power of photosynthesis, so that they can be regarded without equivocation as true animals, Protozoa *in sensu stricto*. We have no direct evidence regarding their origin, but bearing in mind the many lines of evolution that are discernible in the algae and phytoflagellates, there is certainly no reason to suppose that they are monophyletic. The Subclass Zoomastigina of the Class Mastigophora includes genera that lack chloroplasts and have no very close relationships with plant-like forms. Simpler members, such as *Bodo* and *Trypanosoma*, are placed in the Order Protomonadina, a group of small

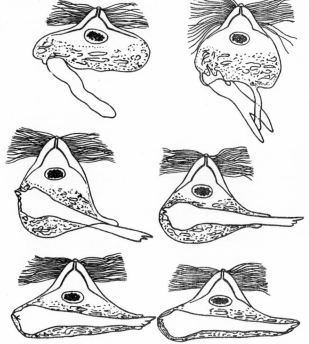

Fig. 8-4. *Trichonympha* sp. from the gut of a termite showing mode of ingesting fragments of wood. From Baer, 1951. *Ecology of Animal Parasites*. University of Illinois Press, Urbana, Ill.

organisms, with one or two flagella. They include many free-living forms, but show a marked tendency towards entozoic habits, leading in the case of the trypanosomes both to harmless commensals and to highly important pathogenic forms, parasites of man and his domestic animals (Sec. 23-4). Thus *Bodo*, which is both free-living and entozoic, contains food vacuoles and is phagotrophic, whereas *Trypanosoma* is osmotrophic. In many other zooflagellates an entozoic mode of life is combined with an exceedingly complex body form which involves the development of an elaborate system of flagella, ranging in number from a score or so to many thousands. These animals may be phagotrophic (Fig. 8-4) or osmotrophic. Within the hind-gut of the cockroach, for example, are found *Lophomonas striata* and *L. blattarum*. The former is osmotrophic, but the latter ingests bacteria through the soft posterior region of the body wall. We shall be returning later to the habits and significance of some of these remarkable organisms.

The Class Sarcodina (Rhizopoda) comprises organisms that are characterized, during at least part of their life cycle, by the use of pseudopodia for movement and feeding. They are typically phagotrophic, the food being surrounded with cytoplasm so that it becomes enclosed in a food vacuole. We have earlier noted the close relationship of these animals with the Mastigophora. The facts are fully in accord with the view that the rhizopods have been derived from flagellate ancestors, with the complete abandonment of phototrophy. In the light of our earlier arguments, we may assume further that they are likely to be the products of more than one line of evolution.

The origin of the Class Ciliata is more difficult to determine, for the ciliation of these animals, their remarkable nuclear specialization, and the phenomenon of conjugation, set them very much apart from the two preceding classes. However, we have seen that there is no fundamental distinction to be made between flagella and cilia. Moreover, since some of the most specialized flagellates have developed a complete covering of flagella, the ciliation of the Ciliata does not preclude them from being derived from some unknown flagellate type. This view becomes even easier to accept if we adopt the suggestion that the aberrant genus *Opalina*, with its unique arrangement of nuclei, belongs in the Mastigophora rather than in the Ciliata.

The more elaborate organization of ciliates in comparison with the Sarcodina is seen in the way they secure their food. The members of the Order Suctoria, generally considered to be an aberrant group of ciliates, have an exceptional method of feeding in that they capture their food by tentacles and suck material down these into the body. The means by which this is accomplished is not understood, although electron microscope studies have shown that sometimes the tentacles possess internal canals.

The remaining ciliates typically ingest food through a mouth, but they use this in two distinct ways that foreshadow the distinction between microphagy and macrophagy which we shall encounter in the Metazoa. Some seize and ingest large animals, often other ciliates, with the mouth (cytostome). This may be set on a proboscis, as it is in *Didinium*, which can eat ciliates several times larger than itself. The cytostome leads into a cytopharynx, which may be strengthened by rods in a manner closely paralleling the arrangement that we have noted in *Peranema*. An example is *Chilodonella*, which ingests filamentous algae (Fig. 8-5) as well as bacteria. Others use a different method, in which small organisms such as bacteria are directed towards the mouth by means of currents set up by their cilia, a principle that is also widely employed in the Metazoa.

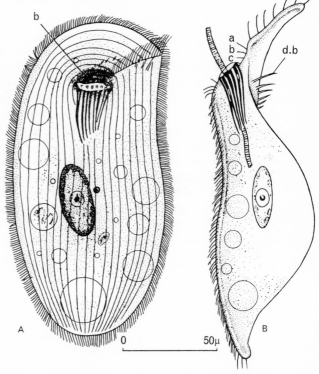

Fig. 8-5. *Chilodonella cucullulus.* × 500. A, from the ventral side; B, from the left, the organism feeding on a filamentous alga. *a, b, c,* pre-oral and circumoral cilia or ciliary lines; *d.b,* dorsal brush. From MacKinnon and Hawes, 1961. *op. cit.*

This latter type of feeding is assisted by trichocysts, which are particularly characteristic of the holotrichous Ciliata, but which are also found in certain dino-flagellates. Trichocysts vary in character, the best known being of the type found in *Paramecium.* Prior to extrusion, they exist in this animal as oval or rod-shaped bodies, lying in the pellicle at right angles to the body surface, and showing no internal structure, even in electron micrographs. When the trichocyst discharges it extrudes from the body surface a long cylindrical shaft which bears a short spine at its tip. In so doing it must undergo some considerable molecular reorganization which is said to be completed in a few thousandths of a second. The effect of this reorganization is detectable under the electron microscope by the appearance of cross-striations and fibrillar patterning in the body of the trichocyst; these extend also into the fully formed shaft. The resting body must presumably contain a fibrous protein which, in certain conditions, can develop a structural pattern; but some trichocysts, such as those of *Prorodon*, one of the gymnostomatous ciliates, are different. They have a curious resemblance to the nematocysts of the coelenterates, and are, for this reason, called cnidotrichocysts. The body consists of a capsule containing a delicate tube, coiled up inside it, that is turned inside out on stimulation. Both the function and the evolutionary origin of trichocysts remain obscure, but it seems likely that they serve to attach the animals to accumulations of bacteria. These structures, like the locomotor mechanisms of Protozoa, illustrate very well the specialized development to which fibrous macromolecules can be subjected.

There is much variation in the details of the ciliary feeding mechanisms of ciliates, but the primitive arrangement is probably to be seen in certain gymnostomes, where rows of body cilia converge upon an apical cytostome. Food particles are driven into the cytostome and then passed on into the endoplasm through the cyto-pharynx, which is an unciliated passage. An elaboration of this arrangement leads to the cytostome being situated at the base of a depression, called the buccal cavity; the somatic cilia extend into this, and may fuse together to form an undulating membrane and smaller membranelles. In *Paramecium* (Fig. 8–6) the buccal cavity lies at the inner end of a vestibulum, but in the Spirotricha, such as *Vorticella*, it is situated at the body surface, where it forms the peristome; in these circumstances its membranellae may play a major part in locomotion as well as in feeding.

Ciliary feeding can readily be observed in *Paramecium*. This animal does not normally ingest any food while it is swimming actively, feeding being restricted to those periods when it is swimming slowly or when it is at rest. At such times the cilia set up currents down the vestibulum and small particles are thus driven towards the buccal cavity. These particles may vary a great deal in character, but they seem to be subjected to some form of selection, for many of them may be passed out again before they enter the buccal cavity. The mechanism of this selection is not understood, but its existence in a protozoan foreshadows the great importance of selective mechanisms in many metazoans that feed in this way upon small particles.

Ciliates have lent themselves well to nutritional studies, and particularly to the development of methods of axenic culture, in which the animals are reared in cultures that are free of all other organisms, including bacteria. In this way the extent of their dependence on preformed organic materials has been determined. Thus we now know the complete requirements of *Tetrahymena pyriformis*, which is a common small

Fig. 8-6. *Paramecium:* the feeding apparatus (diagrammatic). A, ventral view, the animal turned slightly to its right; B, from the right side, with the feeding and rejection paths marked by arrows; C, part of B enlarged, *bc*, buccal cavity; *cy*, cytostome; *fv*, food vacuole; *o*, oral groove; *p, q*, ciliated bands; *r*, rejection path; *v*, vestibulum. (After Mast.) From Mackinnon and Hawes, 1961. *op. cit.*

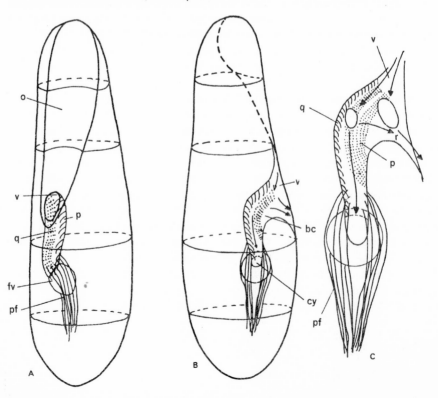

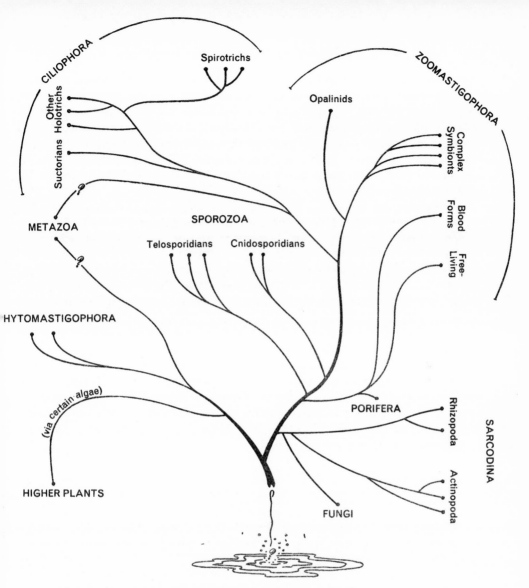

Fig. 8-7. A proposed phylogenetic tree for the phylum Protozoa. Other interpretations are possible. From Corliss, 1959. *Syst. Zool.,* **8,** 169–190.

ciliate of fresh-water and other habitats. This animal requires 10 amino acids, 6 vitamins (including thiamine and riboflavin), and 2 nucleic acid derivatives (guanine and either uracil or cytidine), together with various inorganic ions including magnesium, potassium, iron, copper, and phosphate. Thus far have the Protozoa moved from their autotrophic ancestors; further, indeed, than the higher vertebrates in at least one respect. The rat and pigeon, for example, can synthesize purines and pyrimidines, and can incorporate them into nucleic acids, whereas *Tetrahymena* presumably lacks certain of the enzymes needed to achieve this synthesis. The needs of *Paramecium* have been less completely established, but they are known to include 10 amino acids, and also acetate, phosphate, a sterol, and several vitamins, including thiamine and riboflavin.

Finally, and in complete contrast to the Ciliata, the Class Sporozoa and the

Class Cnidosporidia share in common an osmotrophic nutrition that is an adaptation to their parasitic life, but they show marked differences among themselves in their structure and life cycles. The elongated and flagellated form of the sporozoites of some species suggests a flagellate origin, but other groups develop amoeboid sporozoites during their life history, and may perhaps have had an amoeboid ancestry. The evidence is tenuous, however, and we are hardly justified in doing more than drawing the obvious conclusion that these osmotrophs have had a history that is unknown but almost certainly polyphyletic.

In considering the feeding of Protozoa, as well as their locomotion, we have inevitably referred to the phylogenetic relationships of these organisms. One possible representation of these, which gives general expression to the views stated here, is shown in Fig. 8-7. The basal position of the Mastigophora is not in doubt. The amoeboid Protozoa probably branched off from them at an early stage, while the ciliates evolved later, possibly as a derivative of the complex zoomastigophorans. The relationships of the Sporozoa and Cnidosporidia are, as we have emphasized, uncertain, but it is reasonably likely that these animals represent more than one evolutionary line. The higher plants, the sponges, and the Metazoa are shown as products of three offshoots of the early Mastigophora. That sponges arose independently of true metazoans is generally accepted. Less clear is the path of origin of the metazoans themselves, and the figure expresses this uncertainly. As we shall see later, they may not have a direct relationship with the Mastigophora, but possibly arose by cellularization of a ciliate type of organism. These are matters for interesting and informative speculation (Sec. 18-4), but the evidence is too incomplete to permit a confident resolution of the problem.

8–2 DIGESTION

The form and functioning of digestive systems is largely determined by the properties of their digestive enzymes. For example, enzymes show their optimum activity within sharply defined pH limits, and are highly selective in the type of molecule upon which they act, and in the manner in which they attack it. Thus proteins and polypeptides are digested by proteases that are specific for particular types of molecules, and that break specific bonds in the polypeptide chains. Carbohydrates, too, are attacked by a variety of carbohydrases, adapted for the digestion of particular substrates, although the degree of their specificity is a matter of some dispute. We cannot discuss these biochemical aspects of digestion here, but they are an important factor in determining the range of form and function found in animal digestive systems.

Whatever the mode of food capture, the end result of protozoan phagotrophy is the ingestion of the food material into cavities called food vacuoles; it is within these that digestion takes place. This intracytoplasmic digestion, which must have been the first form of digestion to be practised by animals, has remained widely established in the Metazoa, where it is known as intracellular digestion.

This occurs in a comparatively simple form in *Amoeba*, where the food vacuole initially contains both food and fluid, the latter taken in during ingestion. The entry of this fluid is probably inevitable, and is certainly not surprising, for even when the animal is not feeding it takes up fluid into many small vacuoles, a phenomenon, called pinocytosis, that is also believed to be a widespread activity of the cells of higher organisms (Fig. 2-2, p. 28).

At first the food vacuoles decrease in size, probably as a result of the diffusion of fluid outwards into the cytoplasm, and at this stage an increased acidity is detectable within the vacuole. Superficial comparisons have been drawn between this phase and the gastric phase of digestion in vertebrates, but there is probably no connection between the two. The acidity of the food vacuoles in *Amoeba* is comparatively slight, ranging no further than a pH of about 5.6, and probably results from chemical changes associated with the death of the prey, which ceases its movements during this phase. Later the acidity decreases, the pH increasing to a value of about 7.3; this is probably because of the inflow of fluid from the cytoplasm, a movement that may conceivably be aided by a rise of osmotic pressure in the vacuole. It is during this later, more alkaline, phase that digestion of the prey takes place, for it now be-

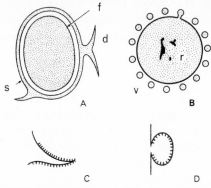

Fig. 8-8. The structural features of food vacuoles. A, a recently formed vacuole in a stage thought to coincide with the secretion of enzymes into the vacuole, and rapid digestion; *f* is the food organism, *d* are tongue-shaped diverticula which may facilitate secretion by increasing the area of the enclosing membrane, *s* is a layer of material which may be either products of digestion or the secreted enzymes. B, an older type of vacuole, probably in the absorptive phase; small vacuoles may be budding off to carry away digested material; *r* represents indigestible fragments. C, tongue-like diverticula of the membrane possibly represent absorption phenomena. D, possibly the budding off of vesicles during absorption. Adapted from Mercer, 1959. *Proc. R. Soc. B,* **150,** 216–237.

comes broken down and diminished in mass. Presumably, then, digestive enzymes are now being secreted into the food vacuoles, and under their influence digestion continues until there remains only a small residue of indigestible material which is discarded from the body. This sequence of events demands a functional organization in the food vacuole which is not fully detectable by light microscopy. The electron microscope, however, reveals features that are strongly suggestive of secretory and absorptive phenomena (Fig. 8–8). The enzymes are initially enclosed in small vacuoles surrounding the food vacuole, and are discharged into the latter by fusion of the small vacuoles with it. These small vacuoles are examples of the organelles called lysosomes, which are believed to be of common occurrence in protozoans and also in metazoan cells. Their enzymes are agents in intracellular digestion in Metazoa (to be referred to later), and also in the phagocytic activity of certain types of blood cell. They also provide for the autolysis of dead cells, a process that facilitates the replacement and repair mechanisms of the body.

Another protozoan in which digestion has been closely observed is *Paramecium*. We have seen how the food of this animal is driven into the buccal cavity. Once it is there the fluid pressure exerted by the ciliary beat forces the food particles towards the distal end, which becomes distended to form a small sac. This sac is then constricted off as a food vacuole, probably in part through the agency of fibres that extend inwards at this point (Fig. 8–6). It is perhaps also a consequence of the action of these fibres that the newly formed vacuole passes quickly backwards towards the hind end of the body. Thereafter it embarks upon a slower movement through the body, probably through the influence of streaming movements in the cytoplasm; eventually it reaches the permanent anus (cytoproct), through which the indigestible residues are discharged.

As in *Amoeba*, there are changes in the pH of the fluid contents of the food vacuoles, but they are here much more marked; an acidity as high as pH 1.4 has been recorded by means of indicator dyes that have been ingested with the food. We cannot be sure whether or not this acidity arises in the same way as has been suggested for that found in the vacuole of *Amoeba*; the possibility that there is a true secretion of acid cannot be excluded, but even so this is not to be compared with the peptic digestive phase of the vertebrate stomach. In *Paramecium*, as in *Amoeba*, the death of the prey takes place during the acid phase, but later the acidity decreases, and digestion takes place at a pH of about 7.8. Further parallels with the digestive mechanism of *Amoeba* are seen in the diminution in size of the food vacuole during the acid phase, and its subsequent enlargement when the acidity decreases; this latter change is presumably associated with the passage into the vacuole of digestive secretion from the surrounding cytoplasm.

Information regarding the nature of the digestive enzymes of the Protozoa can be obtained partly by observing what types of food materials are actually broken down within the food vacuoles, as we have already seen in *Peranema*. It is possible also to identify the enzymes by chemical investigation of extracts prepared from cultures of the animals. By these means it has been shown that the enzyme equipment of these organisms compares well with that present in the digestive systems of Metazoa. This does not mean, however, that all Protozoa can necessarily digest all types of food material.

One element in the adaptive specializations of digestive mechanisms is certainly an emphasis upon the production of those enzymes that are most needed for the characteristic diet of a particular species. How far this principle operates at the protozoan level of evolution is not clear, for our information is still too limited, but it would appear that *Paramecium* can readily digest protein and fat, while only small amounts of ingested starch are broken down. It is said, too, that *Amoeba* is unable to digest starch, but its capacity for digesting protein and fat is well attested, the presence of a protease having been demonstrated by chemical methods. In the Metazoa the digestion of protein occurs in stages, the process being completed by peptidases that act specifically upon the short amino acid chains of dipeptides and tripeptides; this seems to be true also of Protozoa, for a dipeptidase has been demonstrated chemically in *Pelomyxa*. Indeed, the presence of peptidases is clearly indicated by the capacity of ciliates for maintaining growth in media that contain dipeptides and tripeptides; these are presumably broken down by the appropriate enzymes within the body.

As regards the relation between the pH in the food vacuole and the optimum pH of the enzymes, extracts of *Paramecium* show optimum proteolytic activity at pH 5.7 to 5.8. The significance of this result is admittedly limited, for the value may well represent the combined activities of a number of enzymes, including cytoplasmic enzymes that are not necessarily involved in digestion at all. Nevertheless, conditions within the vacuole are evidently quite adequate for the action of digestive enzymes, since the majority of these, as far as we can judge from studies on Metazoa, are likely to have pH optima close to neutrality.

The digestive activity of the Protozoa is confined within a small space, and has no multicellular differentiation to support it; yet it is clearly specialized to an extent that is as adequate for the requirements of these animals as is the alimentary tract of metazoan forms. In this, as in so many other respects, the Protozoa have a complexity of structure and function that is fully comparable with that of the whole body of a metazoan (p. 27).

9
Nutrition of Some Lower Metazoa

9–1 FOOD RESOURCES

The food resources available for exploitation by animals may be broadly classified as liquid, particulate, and massive. Of these three categories, the first might seem especially valuable, for the waters in which so many species live are rich in dissolved nutrients. Inorganic and organic substances are continuously draining into them from the land, and are also in continuous production through the breakdown and decay of plant and animal life. As a result of this, the shallow seas contain dissolved organic matter to a concentration of about 4.5 mg per litre, while the content of fresh-water lakes may be even greater. Aquatic animals would thus be amply provided with nutrients, if only they were able to make direct use of them. This, however, they cannot do to any great extent. At one time it was suggested that they might absorb dissolved nutrients through their gills and other permeable surfaces, but experiments have failed to show that they actually do so in significant amounts. That the seas in particular are highly favourable for animal life is not in doubt; of the 50 or so classes of animals recognized in current taxonomy, 19 are purely marine, and only the Onychophora, myriapods, and Amphibia are wholly absent from the sea. The explanation of this, however, lies in something other than the direct utilization of dissolved nutrients; we shall see later what that explanation is.

Fluid feeding, in fact, is a highly specialized mode of metazoan life. It is seen in the osmotrophy of endoparasites such as cestode worms, which take up material in solution from the intestinal contents of their hosts. There are also many animals that feed by suction (recalling the suctorial ciliates), a habit that is often aided by piercing structures. These are seen in a simple form in the jaws of the gnathobdellid leeches, which draw their food directly from the tissues of their host or prey, a habit that recalls the feeding mechanism of *Peranema*.

The exploitation of liquid food is particularly characteristic of nematodes, arachnids, and certain insects. Many free-living nematodes feed upon decaying products of plant and animal material; they are said to be saprophagous. It is a short step from this to making use of the fluid contents of living organisms, for the transition is facilitated by a characteristic feature of nematode organization, the buccal capsule. This structure, lying immediately behind the mouth, is commonly lined by a sclerotized cuticle, which can be elaborated into varying patterns of teeth and jaws, or may form a protrusible stylet. No less elaborate and variable is the next region of the alimentary tract, the pharynx, which can form an efficient muscular sucking organ. We have already noted that the existence of this may be a direct consequence of the peculiar way in which nematodes exploit hydrostatic principles. But whatever the reason, it is certain that these animals are well equipped for the development of suctorial feeding, either as carnivores or herbivores. This capacity, together with the saprophagous habit that is so widespread among them, has no doubt been an important factor in the evolution of the parasitic habit within the group. It contributes also to their success as members of the soil fauna, in which, numerically speaking, they are second in importance only to the Protozoa. Many of these soil nematodes are saprophagous, and many are predatory, the latter applying their lips to their prey, piercing it with their stylet, and sucking out its fluid content. This is a feeding method well suited to soil dwellers, for it depends upon the animals making use of a resistant substratum while they are thrusting with the stylet.

Fluid feeding among the arthropods depends upon the adaptive versatility of the arthropod limb, which has lent itself to the evolution of complex assemblies of crushing, piercing, and sucking appendages. It is particularly prevalent in the Arachnida, which typically employ a suctorial pharynx to remove the juices from their prey. The anterior appendages cooperate in this by crushing the prey, for instance, as in scorpions and spiders. In ticks the chelicerae form cutting and piercing organs, the fluids being drawn up through a channel formed by these organs and the median hypostome. In spiders a further adaptive device may be brought into use. Some of these animals secrete enzymes into their prey, so that external digestion occurs before the fluid food is taken into the alimentary canal.

Fluid feeding in insects is particularly well developed in the Hemiptera and in certain flies. Some of the latter feed upon decaying organic matter, others upon the nectar and other fluids of plants, while the development of blood-sucking habits has led to dipterans becoming important vectors of disease-producing organisms. In accordance with this diversity of habit, the mouth parts of sucking flies are highly variable in form. Those of Hemiptera are less so, for in this group the members are all adapted for feeding by piercing and sucking. In principle, their maxillae and mandibles are modified to form slender stylets which are protected in a grooved labium. A sucking action draws in the food material, probably aided by capillarity and, in the case of plant feeders, by the pressure of the plant sap. As with flies, this feeding mechanism has led in some instances to the development of close relationships with other organisms. For example, plant-feeding aphids may have to ingest large amounts of fluid in order to obtain the protein that they need; the surplus is extruded as honeydew, which, being rich in carbohydrates, is attractive to ants. This leads in certain species to the establishment of remarkable symbiotic relationships between the two types of insect.

Animals, such as nematodes and hemipterans, that have evolved methods for feeding upon the fluids of plants, have circumvented a major barrier that impedes the exploitation of higher plants by the animal kingdom. This barrier, which is created by the resistant qualities of cellulose and lignin, is one that has not been easily overcome by digestive specialization. We shall refer to this matter later in the context of symbiotic relationships, for it is the use made of micro-organisms by higher animals that has provided another solution to the problem. For many animals, however, the immense food resources represented by the higher plants have remained unavailable as a direct source of nutrition.

These higher plants appeared relatively late in the evolution of life, but prior to their appearance animals must have been exploiting, as they still do today, the vast assemblage of phototrophs that live in the surface layers of the seas and inland waters. Sunlight penetrates water to an average depth of 100 metres, so that within this limit it is possible for phototrophs to carry out photosynthesis and to absorb the dissolved nutrients that they require. Some of these plants are the seaweeds of the seashore and shallow waters, but these are comparatively unimportant. The most important component of this aquatic pasturage, both marine and fresh-water, is composed of micro-organisms that swarm in vast numbers in the upper levels of open waters. It is these that provide the energy-rich compounds upon which the vast aquatic fauna depends for its food supplies; these are provided in the sea to an extent that is fully comparable with the productivity of terrestrial grassland and forest.

That micro-organisms are concerned here, rather than multicellular plants with flotation devices, can be understood in the light of the physical factors that influence life in a fluid medium. There is an advantage in presenting to the medium a surface area that is large in proportion to the body volume, for this facilitates the absorption of nutrients through the body surface. Such a ratio of surface area to volume is found in small organisms, and particularly in unicellular ones; the development of multi-cellular structure would tend to reduce this benefit. There is also another advantage that phototrophs gain from their small size. They must remain in the upper layers of the sea, since it is only there that sunlight is able to penetrate. Consequently they will be aided by any property that retards their rate of sinking through water; small size is exactly such a property, for the relatively large surface area means that frictional resistance between the organism and its surrounding medium counteracts to a considerable extent the effect of gravity.

The phototrophic organisms that compose this floating and drifting pasturage are termed the phytoplankton (*planktos*, wandering). Certain bacteria are included in this assemblage, but first and foremost are the diatoms. These are unicellular algae that are characterized by the possession of a siliceous covering, a feature that in itself has an important limiting effect upon the action of the digestive enzymes of the animals that ingest them. The rest of the phytoplankton are flagellates, and of these the Dinoflagellata are usually the most abundant. In addition there are the cocco-lithophores, which are flagellates with calcareous plates, and there are also enormous numbers of minute flagellates that constitute what is called the nanoplankton (*nanos*, dwarf). It is a remarkable fact, and a striking tribute to the efficiency with which animals have exploited these sources of food, that the existence of this nanoplankton was for a long time unknown, because the organisms were too small to be retained within the usual type of net used for collecting plankton samples. The first demonstration of its presence in the sea came from a study of the filtering activity of the uro-chordates known as Larvacea, which have developed a means of separating these minute organisms out of the surrounding water.

The exploitation of this aquatic pasturage depends largely upon its ingestion by herbivorous animals, which are ingested in their turn by carnivorous forms. Many of these animals are themselves small drifting organisms, living in continuous association with the phytoplankton, and constituting the zooplankton. Others are large, and may feed directly upon the plankton, or they may devour relatively large prey that have themselves fed upon it. In this way are built up the food chains which link organisms of diverse sizes into complex communities. In addition to this ingestion of the plankton, there is also the catabolic activity of heterotrophic microorganisms which bring about the breakdown of organic material without subjecting it to phagotrophy. This results in the production of inorganic nutrients which can then be taken up by the phototrophs in the cycling of nutrients that we discussed earlier. The important part played in this by bacteria has long been recognized, but it is now known that major contributions are also made by diatoms, flagellates, yeasts, and fungi. All of these heterotrophs, then, are added ultimately to the enormous numbers of minute organisms that form such an important part of the food resources available for animals. Those that feed directly upon this microscopic life are said to be microphagous; alternatively, because of the small size of the particles that they ingest, they are said to be particulate feeders. Microphagy is so important in the economy of aquatic life that we must now consider it in some detail.

9–2 MICROPHAGY AND MACROPHAGY

Most generalizations that can be made about animal feeding mechanisms will have their exceptions, but we can begin by recognizing two types of particulate feeding. Both types often depend upon the use of cilia, the animals concerned being then termed ciliary feeders. One of the types, called suspension feeding, makes use of the minute organisms and other particulate material that are suspended in water; this will usually require the filtering of the water and the extraction of the food particles from it, so that organisms feeding in this way are often described as filter feeders. They are highly diversified in form, for the habit is distributed among many groups of the animal kingdom, but they share certain common requirements. Usually filtration demands the setting-up of a current in the surrounding water. This will commonly be created by cilia, with mucus aiding the trapping and sometimes also the filtering, although the crustaceans provide an important exception to this. A great deal of the suspended material may be inedible or positively harmful, so that it is desirable to have some form of rejection mechanism. Further, even if the material is edible, the animal concerned may be limited as regards the size of the particles that it can deal with, so that some sorting mechanism is also desirable, combined, perhaps, with the rejection mechanism. Then, of course, food particles must usually be directed towards a mouth, although there are exceptions even to this apparently self-evident generalization, as, for example, in sponges and pogonophorans. Finally, when the particles have entered the alimentary tract, they must be suitably manipulated to ensure digestion and absorption, and the elimination of waste. Clearly the possibilities here for complexity of adaptation are immense, and under the pressure of natural selection, which tends constantly towards the improvement of the ways in which animals exploit their environment, they have been very fully realized.

Filter feeders include sessile and free-swimming forms, in both of which the capacity for movement, which is so characteristic of animals, is turned to advantage; indeed, the primary reason why movement is so much more typical of animals than of plants is precisely that the former depend upon it so greatly for the securing of their food. The free-swimming filter feeder has the advantage of being able to move directly among its food, but the sessile animal uses cilia or appendages, which are themselves often locomotor structures in their origin. The sessile animal is aided by the existence of natural currents in the water, which help to replenish its food supplies and to remove its waste products. The extent to which these currents are exploited varies, but an extreme example is presented by the hexactinellid sponges, which make use of the steady current of their deep-sea habitat and spread the net-like structure of their bodies across it.

The second type of particulate feeding makes use of the deposits of organic material (detritus) that accumulate on the substratum; this is known as deposit feeding. Animals exploiting this method of feeding usually depend, like suspension feeders, upon ciliary action; indeed, there may not necessarily be a sharp distinction between the two modes of feeding, for one animal may make use of both sources of supply. However, the accumulation of detritus is not confined to the surface of the substratum; material also accumulates within the sand or mud, and so deposit feeding in the sense defined above grades into the swallowing of the substratum itself. This is seen in the lug-worm, *Arenicola*, for example, and in the echiuroids; these animals occupy very much the same ecological niche in the marine environment as do the earthworms on land.

The swallowing of sand, mud, or soil, while relatable to deposit feeding and thus to particulate feeding, may also be regarded as an example of the third method of feeding enumerated earlier: the exploitation of massive food material. Other and very different examples of this are seen in those animals that feed upon encrusting organisms such as algae, Polyzoa, and sponges. Such are the limpets (*Patella*), which use their finely toothed radula to browse upon algae, a method of feeding that is probably primitive in molluscs, and that has had important consequences in the group, as we shall see later. The rasping of the radula results in a stream of fine particles entering the alimentary tract, so that in one sense this, too, is particulate feeding. Here, as so often, is seen the difficulty of framing biological categories in such a way as to avoid any overlap between them. Another example of browsing habits is found in the regular echinoids (sea-urchins), the organ involved in this instance being Aristotle's Lantern. In its fully developed form this comprises five teeth and a number of supporting parts amounting to some 40 pieces altogether. With the teeth growing continuously from sacs, and with complex associated muscles, this organ has a wide range of use; thus echinoids can act as scavengers, feeding on many types of dead animal material, and even upon live animals when these are sufficiently slow-moving to be captured by them.

Feeding upon large masses (often referred to as macrophagy) has the advantage of opening up for a group a wider choice both of food and of habitat, and, on the whole, it favours the attainment of larger size. On the other hand, it commonly involves active predation, or the pursuit of living prey, which demands the development of specialized behaviour patterns and thus makes considerable demands upon muscular and nervous organization. It might be expected, then, that microphagy would be found among the smaller and less highly organized species, and that macrophagy would tend to replace it in the larger and more complex ones. It is certainly true that ciliary feeding occurs today in some decidedly primitive groups (the sponges and pterobranchs, for example), while there is reason to believe that it characterized the earliest echinoderms. Moreover, it occurs also in various other groups of small animals such as the Ectoprocta, the Entoprocta, and the Brachiopoda—groups that are of uncertain relationships, but which are certainly primitive in many features of their organization.

Yet the feeding habits of many phyla show very clearly that events have not always followed such a simple course. For example, in the polychaetes it is the more primitive errant forms that are macrophagous and predatory, while the sedentary species are highly specialized for microphagy. Within the Phylum Mollusca we find ciliary feeding being exploited by the highly specialized lamellibranchs. Here its evolution can be seen as a consequence of the existence of the molluscan gill, or ctenidium, and of the occurrence of rasping feeding in primitive molluscs; both of these factors, as we shall explain later, can be regarded as pre-adaptations favouring the elaboration of filter and suspension feeding. Indeed, the cephalopods are the only molluscs in which predation has become fully developed, and it is significant that these are the members of the phylum that have broken away most completely from the old-established molluscan habits and organization.

The Crustacea form another group in which microphagy is associated with a high level of structural organization. In this instance it is to be attributed to the remarkable versatility of the arthropod limb. It is particularly characteristic of the smaller crustaceans, and it may well have been practised by primitive aquatic arthropods. The larger members of the class, and, in general, the remainder of the living arthropods, are macrophagous, although some, as already mentioned, practise suctorial feeding. These feeding habits are associated in part with the diversification of modes of locomotion, and in part with the assumption of terrestrial life, which, of course, disposes of the possibility of filter feeding.

Finally, the Deuterostomia begin their history, as far as we can judge, with microphagy practised by sessile and tentaculate forms. Within the chordate line the ciliary feeding of the protochordates is succeeded by the macrophagy of vertebrates, a transformation associated with a unique invention called pharyngotremy, which is the development of perforations in the wall of the pharynx.

Already we have encountered an important difficulty in generalizing about feeding or any other aspect of the functional organization of invertebrates. Each major group, endowed with its own characteristic plan of structure, exploits the resources of its environment in its own particular way. The history of one group provides no basis for predicting the history of another. Yet it would be unnecessarily pessimistic to suppose that no general principles can emerge from invertebrate studies. In the present instance we can see that both microphagy and macrophagy are widely distributed in the animal kingdom. This is to be expected, for both are needed in the establishment of organized biotic communities. Moreover, microphagy is not only appropriate for the nutrition of the simpler and smaller animals; it is no less well suited to the specialized organization of more advanced groups. The degree of persistence of microphagy, the extent of its replacement by macrophagy, the secondary development of microphagy in primitively macrophagous groups—all of these are ultimately determined by the possibilities latent in the fundamental plan of organization of any particular phylum. We must therefore consider the more important groups individually if we are to appreciate the success with which animals exploit their food resources. A few examples will serve to show something of the elegance and complexity of the structural and functional adaptations of feeding mechanisms, as well as the principles that have influenced their evolution.

9–3 FILTER FEEDING AND DIGESTION IN SPONGES

Sponges feed by filtering particulate matter from water that enters their body through minute pores. This stream of water is not only nutritive; it also brings a supply of oxygen, and removes the waste products of metabolism, in so far as they do not diffuse direct to the outside. In the calcareous sponges (Class Calcarea) the pores are intracellular canals in specialized cells called porocytes, which are derived from the dermal epithelium. Porocytes may not be present in other sponges, but pores certainly are, and they are always small; consequently they constitute a simple but effective sorting device that permits the passage of only the smallest particles. The course that the water follows may be very complex, but in principle it passes through the pores into the central spongocoel, and leaves this by a large opening, the osculum (Fig. 4–12, p. 69). Each individual initially possesses one such opening. As the body grows, additional oscula may form, and we then regard the sponge as a colony (Sec. 21–2), each osculum representing one individual. The definition is admittedly somewhat arbitrary; individuality is much less well defined in these organisms than it is, for example, in coelenterate colonies.

This weak individualization, like the feeble capacity for movement that we have considered earlier, is indicative of the exceptionally low level of organization at which sponges exist. Another illustration of this is the limited coordination between the constituent cells. The current of water depends upon the completely uncoordinated beating of the flagella of peculiar cells called choanocytes, which form the inner layer of the body. Each of these cells (Fig. 9–4) possesses a single flagellum, surrounded at its base by a protoplasmic collar, and the beat of the flagellum, directed outwards from its base, moves the water. As we shall see later, the choanocytes, together with wandering amoebocytes, abstract the food particles from the water and immediately ingest them, so that no structural specialization for the manipulation of the food is required. What has influenced the body form, however, is the dependence on uncoordinated flagella for the creation of the water flow. Presumably this is a very inefficient way of keeping a mass of water continuously moving in the spongocoel, and this difficulty has undoubtedly conditioned the development of an increasingly complex body form in the sponges.

The essential feature of this complexity is the restriction of the choanocytes to small flagellated chambers (Fig. 9–1), which present a large area of ingestive epithelium. These discharge into a large excurrent chamber through openings called apopyles, the original pores becoming transformed into very small incurrent prosopyles. This is seen at its most efficient in the leuconoid plan of structure (Figs. 9–1 and 9–2), where the water travels to and from the flagellated chambers through a system of narrow canals. These have an effect somewhat like that of the branching vessels of a blood system, for the water, after entering through the prosopyles, moves increasingly slowly as it is passed into canals of diminishing diameter. Eventually it

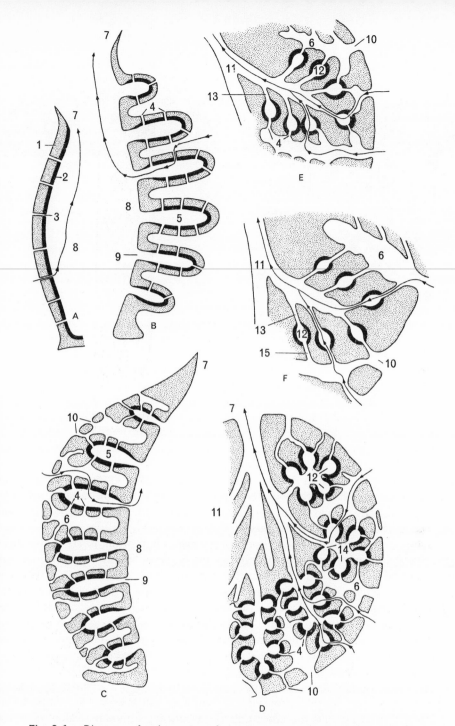

Fig. 9-1. Diagrams of various types of sponge structure. A, asconoid type. B, syconoid type, early stage without cortex. C, final syconoid stage, with cortex. D, leuconoid type with eurypylous chambers. E, leuconoid type with aphodal chambers. F, leuconoid type with diplodal chambers. Choanocyte layer in heavy black, mesenchyme stippled. *1*, mesenchyme; *2*, choanocyte layer; *3*, incurrent pore; *4*, prosopyles; *5*, radial canal; *6*, incurrent canal; *7*, osculum; *8*, spongocoel; *9*, internal ostium; *10*, dermal ostium; *11*, excurrent channel; *12*, flagellated chamber; *13*, aphodus; *14*, apopyle; *15*, prosodus. Adapted from Hyman, 1940. *The Invertebrates: Protozoa through Ctenophora.* McGraw-Hill, New York. Used by permission.

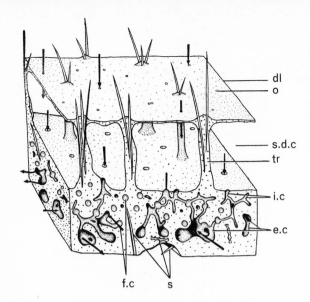

Fig. 9-2. Scheme of the outer layer of the body of *Spongilla*, reconstructed from living and fixed sections. *dl,* pseudo-epithelium; *e.c,* excurrent canal; *f.c,* flagellated chamber; *i.c,* incurrent canal; *o,* ostium; *s,* spicule; *s.d.c,* subdermal cavity; *tr,* trabeculum. Arrows indicate the water flow. From van Weel, 1949. *Physiologia comp. Oecol.,* **1,** 110–126.

dl
o
s.d.c
tr
i.c
e.c
f.c   s

enters the flagellated chambers, and then moves faster as it flows through channels of increasing size. Finally it is expelled from the osculum with considerable force, a result of the diameter of this opening being smaller than that of the channels through which the water has been flowing.

The hydraulics of this feeding mechanism are certainly efficient. The changing rate of water flow at different points of the canal system is itself advantageous, for the choanocytes play an important role in the ingestion of food, and so the water must move past them slowly. On the other hand, the acceleration of the excurrent stream helps to ensure the efficient discharge of the water from the body, with the minimum of contamination of the incurrent stream. This latter condition is an essential element in the successful operation of a ciliary feeding mechanism. It is further ensured in sponges by the form of the body, which often contributes to the efficient separation of the two streams.

Bidder, in his analysis of this aspect of sponge organization, refers to the angle between the intake and outflow currents as the angle of supply. Between the two currents there is established a re-entrant vortex, the diameter of which he calls the diameter of supply. This must be large enough to provide a good chance that surrounding currents or drift will carry away the outgoing water. In non-stalked sponges (Fig. 9–3A) the angle of supply is 90°. The presence of a stalk increases the angle, and thereby reduces the risk of contamination of the intake current. This means that the osculum can be opened out, since the water need not be ejected with as great a force; thus evolves the type of sponge body represented by Neptune's Cup (Fig. 9–3B). If the cup is set on one side, the angle of supply becomes 180°. Oscular velocity is no longer an important consideration, and so the body can open out into a flattened form (Fig. 9–3C); this has the advantage of permitting a maximum flow of water through the body, and hence affords an improved opportunity of securing food.

The achievements of sponges are thus not to be underestimated. They are animals with the minimum of cell differentiation, and with so little coordination that they can almost be regarded as colonies of cells. Nevertheless, by the evolution of their form along lines that can be interpreted in simple hydraulic terms, an effective feeding mechanism is undoubtedly attained. Nor is the elaboration of a complex hydraulic system a necessary condition of this achievement. As we have earlier noted, some of the deep-sea hexactinellid sponges rely upon a body that is shaped as a flat or curved net, with water entering on one side and leaving on the other. In this simplicity of structure they are exploiting, with a minimal expenditure of energy, the steady currents of the abyss. Setting their lattice-like structure across the direction of flow, and filtering particles that are brought to them, they are, in Bidder's words, 'a moment of active metabolism between the unknown future and the exhausted past'.

The low level of coordination in the Porifera is further shown in the digestive processes that follow the filtering of their food material. Our information here is limited by reason of the paucity of species that have been studied, but it would appear that the choanocytes are responsible not only for maintaining the food current, but also for the initial ingestion of the particles. It is known that in the Calcarea, where these cells are particularly large, the food adheres to the outer surfaces of the collars.

Electron microscopy shows these to be composed of microvilli which act as a filter for trapping food particles, which are then passed down the collar surface, presumably by protoplasmic streaming, to be taken up into food vacuoles at its base.

Within these vacuoles a good deal of digestion may take place, very much as in heterotrophic flagellates, but some at least of the material is transferred to wandering amoebocytes in the mesenchyme that separates the flagellated cells from the dermal epithelium. These amoebocytes complete the digestive process, the indigestible residue being

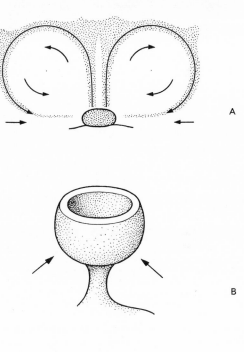

Fig. 9-3. Relationship of the form of sponges to their feeding currents. A, the bath sponge (*Euspongia*), a sessile form in which the angle between the inflow and outflow currents is 90°. B, Neptune's Cup, in which a stalk increases the angle of supply, so that there is less risk of mixing the two currents; the osculum therefore opens out. C, *Phakellia*, in which the body is a flattened fan, with one inflow face and one outflow face. Adapted from Bidder, 1923. *Q. Jl microsc. Sci.*, **67**, 293–323.

Fig. 9-4. Scheme of water flow in the flagellated chamber of *Spongilla*. *p*, prosopyle, lying between choanocytes. From van Weel, 1949. *op. cit.*

p

discarded from them and eventually removed from the sponge body in the outgoing stream of water. These same cells also store reserve material, and thus, in consequence of their movement through the organism, provide the equivalent of a combined storage and transport system. Amoebocytes thus play a central part in the life of these animals; as we shall see, they contribute also in an important way to the reproductive processes.

In the other groups of sponges, the choanocytes (Fig. 9–4) are smaller, and they seem to be concerned more with ingestion than with digestion, for food material is transferred more immediately from them to the wandering cells. This happens, for example, in the fresh-water sponge, *Spongilla*, where the amoebocytes both digest the food and also pass it on to other cells which may complete the breakdown. It is said, however, that they never pass material into the choanocytes, which implies that these cells must have their own self-sufficient digestive mechanism .

Fig. 9-5. *Aurelia:* oblique view of part of the disc from the sub-umbrellar surface, showing some of the currents in two of the four oral arms and in one of the four gastric pouches. The right side shows the path of food (solid arrows) in the lateral tract, and of excretory matter (broken arrows) in the basal groove; the vertical arrows represent the rejection reaction in the lateral tract. The left side illustrates the main paths of the gametes at spawning (path of sperm in male shown by dotted arrows, path of eggs in female shown by dotted and dashed arrows). *a.c,* adradial canal; *b.g,* basal groove tract; *g,* gonad; *gc.g,* gastro-circular groove; *gg.g,* gastro-genital groove; *go.g,* gastro-oral groove; *g.p,* gastric pouch; *i.c,* interradial canal; *l.t,* lateral tract; *o.a,* oral arm; *o.a.t,* oral arm tentacle; *p.c,* pericardial canal. From Southward, 1955. *J. mar. biol. Ass. U.K.,* **34**, 201–216.

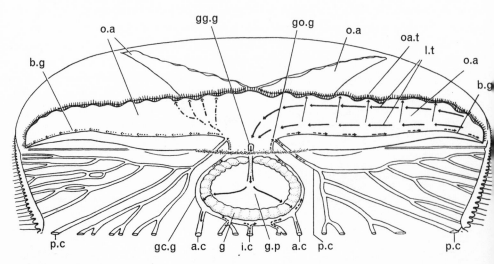

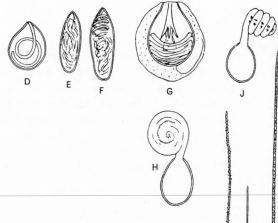

Fig. 9-6. The nematocysts of *Hydra littoralis*, from life. D–G, undischarged: D, desmoneme; E, atrichous hydrorhiza; F, holotrichous isorhiza; G, stenotele inside its cnidoblast. H–M, the same, discharged; H, desmoneme seen from end view showing spiral of thorns; J, desmoneme seen from the side; K, holotrichous isorhiza; L, atrichous isorhiza; M, stenotele. From Hyman, 1940. *op. cit.* Used by permission.

9–4 FEEDING IN COELENTERATES

Coelenterates have a level of cellular differentiation that is notably more advanced than that of sponges, and this is reflected in the greater complexity of their feeding and digestive mechanisms. They are all specialized for a carnivorous diet, and most members of the group are macrophagous, using tentacles to capture prey that is large in relation to the size of their own bodies, and that is selected by a highly discriminatory sensory and motor system. Among the anemones, however, there are microphagous forms that use their tentacles differently. In *Metridium*, for example, the food consists of small particles and minute organisms that are caught by the branched tentacles in a mucous secretion; they are then transferred by ciliary action across the oral disc to the mouth. An example from another group is the scyphozoan jelly-fish *Aurelia*. This collects small organisms in mucus on its outer surfaces, carries them by ciliary action to the inner sides of its oral arms, and then moves them centrally along ciliary tracts (Fig. 9–5).

The remarkable cells called cnidoblasts, which are a diagnostic character of the Coelenterata (or Cnidaria), are important agents in the trapping of food by the tentacles of macrophagous coelenterates. These cells secrete within their cell bodies the structures called nematocysts, which consist of a pear-shaped vesicle with a thread coiled within it. On appropriate stimulation the thread is extruded, to fulfil a function that is determined by its form. The high level of specialization reached in these animals may be judged from the fact that no less than seventeen types of nematocysts have been described, differing in such features as the coiled or straight form of the thread after extrusion, and the presence or absence of swellings and spines upon it. In addition, the Zoantharia have structures called spirocysts, differing from true nematocysts in certain respects, including the structure of the wall, staining properties, and permeability to water.

The range of form of nematocysts is illustrated by the four types found in *Hydra* (Fig. 9–6). One of these is the desmoneme or volvent, which has a coiled thread with minute bristles that winds round any surface projections of the prey. Another type is the stenotele or penetrant; this has a basal enlargement called the butt, on which are situated three rows of spines, the lowest member of each row being much enlarged to form a stylet. This nematocyst is a piercing structure, which is believed to inject poison into the prey. It is a type limited to certain groups of Hydrozoa, and its absence from the Anthozoa may be a feature of some phylogenetic importance. Also present in *Hydra* are holotrichous isorhiza, in which the long slender thread is bristly throughout its length, and atrichous isorhiza, with a smooth thread. Both of these are probably also concerned with the injection of poison.

Considering the exceedingly small size of nematocysts, the capsules of which commonly range in length from only 5 mμ to 50 mμ, these structural specializations are sufficiently remarkable, but they would be of little value in themselves if they were not accompanied by the no less remarkable functional specializations of the cnidoblasts that secrete them. Cnidoblasts, each of which can only discharge one nematocyst, would be largely wasted if their discharge was indiscriminate. It is thus important that their response should be so controlled that it is only evoked in the presence of suitable food material. This control is, in fact, ensured, but it is not exerted by the nervous system, as can readily be demonstrated in larger coelenterates such as the sea-anemone, *Anemonia sulcata*. Electrical stimulation of the tentacles of this animal through the application of micro-electrodes results in the discharge of nematocysts only in the immediate region of stimulation; there is no evidence at all of any conduction to other parts of the body. This is because cnidoblasts are able to respond independently of any other tissue element; they are independent effectors, containing within themselves both the sensory and the motor properties needed to evoke discharge, although the nervous system may sometimes determine the threshold at which they are excited. It is commonly supposed that the projecting cnidocil of the cnidoblasts of *Hydra* is the sensory element, but the presence of this structure is not essential. None is associated with the spirocysts of anemones, nor, probably, are they possessed by all of the true cnidoblasts of these animals.

No less important than the functional independence of the cnidoblast is the nature of the stimulus that triggers its response. Mere physical contact of prey and tentacle would not be sufficiently precise, for such contact stimulus could equally well be given by inanimate objects. A chemical stimulus would be another possibility, but this by itself would again be unsatisfactory, for chemical substances diffusing from the prey might evoke discharge before the tentacles could make the essential contact. To meet this situation the coelenterates have evolved a specialized sensory mechanism requiring mechanical stimulation. The response, however, depends upon the source of the stimulus. If it originates from animal material a discharge of nematocysts is readily evoked, but if the source is inorganic a response will only result from a considerable degree of stimulation. For example, a smooth capillary ball produces no discharge (Fig. 9–7), but some discharge, although still very limited, is seen if the tentacle of an anemone is scratched with a broken capillary rod.

Another requirement is that there must be chemical stimulation by material present in the prey. The effect of this is shown in the copious discharge that takes place when a tentacle is touched by a capillary that has been smeared with molluscan extract. The nature of this stimulating material is not wholly clear, but it appears to

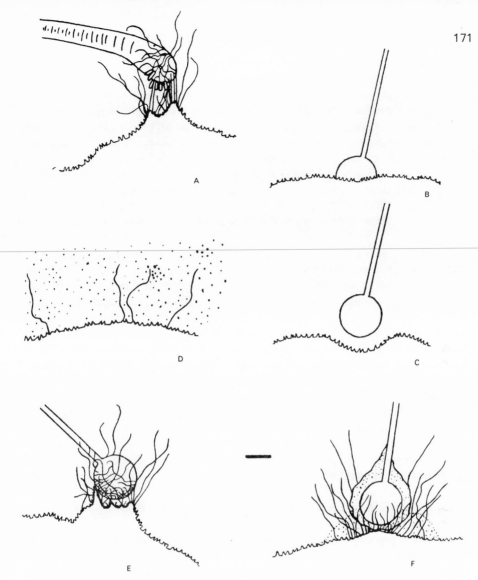

Fig. 9-7. Responses of tentacles of *Anemonia*. Bar = 100μ. A, response of cnidae to touch by human hair; B, C, lack of response to clean glass bead; D, response to immersion in 1% dry weight of human saliva in sea water; E, sensitization of cnidoblasts to glass bead by 5 min immersion in 0.1% dry weight of saliva in sea water; F, response to glass bead smeared with alcoholic extract of *Pecten* mantle. From Pantin, 1942. *J. exp. Biol.,* **19**, 294–310.

be a lipid that is strongly adsorbed on to protein, from which it can be removed by treatment with ethanol or acetone. Its effect is to sensitize the cnidoblasts so that the threshold of their response to mechanical stimulation is markedly lowered. Material with this property seems to be widely distributed in animal products, for a human hair can also evoke discharge of the nematocysts (Fig. 9-7). Human saliva will similarly produce this effect. A tentacle immersed in sea water to which a small amount of saliva has been added will discharge a few nematocysts without any mechanical stimulation at all, and will produce a copious discharge if it is then touched with a capillary ball.

The result of this adaptation is that nematocysts will normally be discharged only in the immediate and close presence of food; diffusion of material from the latter, or direct contact with it, will produce the chemical sensitization, and the mechanical stimulus of contact will complete the process of discharge. The cnidoblast, then, is not merely an independent effector, but an independent effector with a dual sensory mechanism. As Pantin points out, there is no obvious analogy to this situation in any of the tissues of higher Metazoa. It is a good demonstration of the way in which precise adaptation enables animals with an inherently simple organization to secure from their environment the essential requirements for their nutrition.

It is not enough, however, for a macrophagous coelenterate to capture and paralyze its prey with its nematocysts. The food must next be swallowed, and this depends upon a characteristic feeding reaction, in which the mouth enlarges and the coelenteron expands to permit the passage of the food from the tentacles into the cavity where its digestion will be initiated. In this response, as in the capture of the prey, the animal is able to discriminate. It has long been known that *Hydra* will normally swallow only living animal material, although it will ingest other material if this is first moistened with the juice of dead *Daphnia*. It has been suggested that this feeding reaction may be dependent upon the release by living tissues of reduced glutathione. In normal conditions this substance is discharged from the body of the prey when this is pierced by the barbed penetrants, and it is believed that it can evoke the feeding reaction even when it is present at concentrations as low as $10^{-6}M$. Since only living animals seem to contain this compound it follows that the feeding reaction will only be given in their presence. Indeed, so specific is the response that even as closely similar a compound as aspartathione is completely inactive. Thus the cnidoblasts, their nematocysts, and this highly specific chemical sensitivity work together to ensure that the feeding activities of *Hydra* are focused upon material that will be of the maximum benefit to it.

9–5 INTRACELLULAR AND EXTRACELLULAR DIGESTION: COELENTERATES AND PLATYHELMINTHS

The mode of digestion in sponges, in which the food is broken down inside the cell within food vacuoles, is termed intracellular digestion. We must suppose that it has been directly taken over from protozoan ancestors. Indeed, there is at least one striking point of resemblance between the two groups, for the food vacuoles of the amoebocytes are at first acid and later alkaline in reaction, exactly as in the protozoan examples considered earlier.

Obviously, intracellular digestion greatly restricts the size and variety of the food that an animal can utilize. Because of this there has been a widespread tendency for the increase in size of animals to be associated with the establishment of extracellular digestion, in which the digestive processes take place largely within the lumen of an alimentary canal under the action of digestive enzymes that are extruded from the cells of its lining. Such extrusion is already foreshadowed in the Protozoa; the heliozoan *Vampyrella*, for example, is able to extract the cytoplasm of algae by boring through their cell walls with its pseudopodia, apparently by extracellular action.

In the Coelenterata digestion is a combination of the intracellular and extracellular methods. At first sight it may seem that the coexistence of the two is an intermediate stage of evolution, associated with the generally simple organization of those animals. Consideration of other groups, however, shows that the relationship between intracellular and extracellular digestion is by no means always so straightforward as this. If it were, we should expect to see the extracellular method soon replacing the more primitive and restricted intracellular one. This certainly does happen in some groups, but not in all; on the contrary, the intracellular method persists in such highly specialized forms that we must assume that it has been retained because it confers some positive advantage.

The significant fact here is that the presence of well-developed intracellular digestion is commonly associated in higher animals with filter feeding, although this association is not invariable. It is well suited to provide for the digestion of small particles, but only if certain contingent requirements are met. The trapping of food particles during their passage through the alimentary tract demands a relatively large area of ingestive epithelium, which in its turn creates the need for extensive morphological and functional specialization of the alimentary tract. Nor is this all. We shall see examples of collecting mechanisms playing an important part in the sorting of food particles, but often the alimentary tract has also to make a contribution to this. It has further to provide for mixing the food with any extracellular secretion that may be produced by the digestive epithelium, and to delay the passage of the mixture through the alimentary tract. This delay is needed both to allow time for any preliminary extracellular digestion that may be provided for, and also to permit the ingestion of an adequate proportion of the filtered particles.

Extracellular digestion, by bringing a concentration of secretion to bear upon the food, undoubtedly facilitates the breakdown of the latter, but this method of digestion also makes its own demands. It requires a control of pH within the lumen of the alimentary tract, and, in consequence, some degree of regional differentiation. There must also be provision for the movement and mixing of the food and secretion, and for ensuring that the enzymes are economically used by being discharged only when they are actually required. There is, in fact, a balance of advantage and disadvantage to be weighed in comparing one method with the other, and different groups have, so to say, assessed the situation in different ways. A few representative examples may serve to illustrate the range of adaptations that have been adopted, partly in relation to diet, and partly in relation to the evolutionary status of the groups concerned.

Intracellular digestion persists in the Coelenterata, as we might expect from their comparatively lowly position, but extracellular digestion is also well established in them, and it is this that permits them to deal with their relatively large prey. So effective is the extracellular phase in *Hydra* that a *Daphnia* is broken down into small particles within four hours of its ingestion, as a result of the secretion of enzymes into the coelenteron. The secretory cells concerned are clearly recognizable, for their contents are discharged when the prey is swallowed, but the endoderm also includes many absorptive cells which can be distinguished from them, and which are concerned with the intracellular phase. About an hour after ingestion, when the breaking-down of the prey is in full operation, these cells begin to ingest the newly formed food particles into small vacuoles, and it is within these that digestion is completed. Reserve material is stored in the same cells, while indigestible residues also accumulate within them. The disposal of this intracellular waste, an inescapable problem in this mode of digestion, is here dealt with by the fragmentation of the absorptive cells, so that portions containing indigestible residues can be extruded into the coelenteron.

This combination of the intracellular and extracellular methods is found also in the Anthozoa. The structural adaptations are here more complex, for the coelenteron is partially subdivided by the mesenteries, and the secretory and absorptive cells are localized on the mesenteric filaments that constitute the thickened edges of these structures. In macrophagous anthozoans the prey is firmly held by the filaments, which is possible because the latter are armed with many nematocysts. In this way the digestive secretion is directly applied to the food, an arrangement that doubtless increases the efficiency of the action of the enzymes.

It appears, then, that digestion and absorption in coelenterates are no less specialized than the processes involved in the capture and swallowing of the prey, and this is true also of the enzymes themselves. These provide a particularly clear illustration of how an animal's complement of these agents is often adapted to the requirements of its normal food. We have seen that coelenterates are specialized carnivores. In correlation with this they are able to digest protein and fat, but have little, if any, effect upon carbohydrate. It is possible to test this by inserting a piece of sponge into the coelenteron of a sea-anemone and leaving it to absorb some of the digestive secretion. When the sponge is removed, its contents are found to include a protease and a lipase, both with pH optima slightly on the alkaline side of neutrality. Maltase, however, is absent, while the amylase action is very weak; this accounts for these animals being unable to utilize carbohydrate in their food.

The Platyhelminthes provide another example of intracellular digestion playing an important part in a comparatively lowly group of animals, which yet depend on specialized feeding mechanisms. Of particular interest here is the remarkable way in which particulate feeding and intracellular digestion are organized in certain species

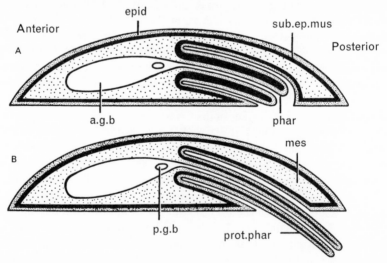

Fig. 9-8. Diagrammatic longitudinal sections of *Polycelis* to show the cylindrical plicate pharynx. A, the normal condition with pharynx retracted; B, pharynx protruded for feeding; *a.g.b*, anterior gut branch; *epid*, epidermis; *m.g.b*, median gut branch; *mes*, mesenchyme; *phar*, pharynx; *p.g.b*, origin of posterior gut branches; *prot.phar*, protruded pharynx; *sub.ep.mus*, sub-epidermal muscles. From Jennings, 1957. *Biol. Bull. mar. biol. Lab., Woods Hole*, **112**, 63–80.

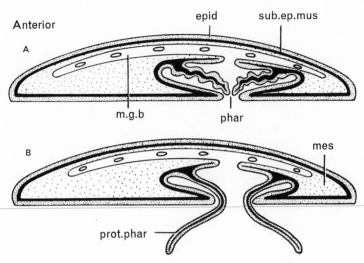

Fig. 9-9.   Diagrammatic longitudinal section of *Leptoplana* to show the ruffled plicate pharynx. A, the normal condition with pharynx retracted. B, the pharynx protruded to envelop food. Abbreviations as in Fig. 9-8. From Jennings, 1957. *op. cit.*

so as to permit the handling of large prey. In the acoelan *Convoluta* the endoderm forms a solid syncytium which is protruded through the ventral mouth. Digestion is necessarily intracellular, and the food is engulfed into food vacuoles much as though the syncytium were a giant pseudopodium.

Digestion is also entirely intracellular in the triclad *Polycelis*, although this animal feeds on bulky prey, which it traps in a mucous secretion. It uses a long protrusible pharynx (Fig. 9-8), which is inserted into the body of the prey so that the whole of its soft contents can be withdrawn. The withdrawal is effected by the passage of waves of muscular contraction over the proboscis; these break up the food into small particles while it is passing to the alimentary canal, and thus prepare it for intracellular digestion. Strictly, the animal is microphagous, judged by the size of the material that it ingests. It is thus practicable for the animal to rely upon this, and yet be able to exploit large prey. In precisely the same way the land planarian *Orthodemus terrestris* is able to feed upon slugs and worms, although its digestion, too, is entirely intracellular.

The diversity shown by closely related forms is apparent when we compare these animals with the polyclad *Cycloporus papillosus*. This is said to feed exclusively upon colonies of *Botryllus* and *Botrylloides* in a very selective manner, sucking the individual zooids into its alimentary tract through its protrusible pharynx. The pharynx of a polyclad (Fig. 9-9) is constructed differently from that of a triclad, however, and it is presumably because of this that the zooids are still undamaged when they arrive within the body. In this instance, and in complete contrast to what we have seen of *Polycelis*, digestion is extracellular; the food is homogenized and broken down within the alimentary tract, with no sign at all of intracellular digestion.

10
Filter Feeding

10–1   FILTER FEEDING IN POLYCHAETES

With the increasing development of cell differentiation and coordination that marks the history of the Metazoa, there arose methods of filter feeding much more elaborate than those of sponges. They are not easy to understand, yet it is worth while trying to do so, for the mechanisms involved are unexcelled for the precision and beauty of their adaptive organization. The principles involved show a considerable degree of uniformity over a wide range of species; this is to be expected, having regard to the uniform character of the food material and to the limited range of structures that animals can deploy in capturing it.

Good examples occur among the polychaetes. Primitively, these worms were probably free-moving and macrophagous, following the mode of life familiar in such animals as *Nereis* and *Nephtys*. These have an eversible pharynx that is used both for burrowing (p. 108) and for feeding. Prey is seized by the hooked jaws that arise from the lining of the pharynx; these are situated at its tip when the pharynx is fully everted. Microphagous feeding is characteristic of the sedentary species, and involves mechanisms so specialized that it is difficult to see immediately any close relationship between the two modes of life. Yet with feeding, as with other functions, we cannot suppose that such specializations arose already fully organized—they must have evolved stage by stage, under the influence of natural selection. Closer analysis often suggests in such instances that the more primitive forms possessed structures suitable for adaptive modification in a particular direction, even though they may have initially served some quite different function. We have earlier referred to this as pre-adaptation; it is a phenomenon that must have been important in facilitating evolutionary change.

Examples of it occur in the errant polychaetes. Like so many creeping and burrowing animals, they produce over their body surface a mucous secretion which protects the surface and forms temporary linings to burrows. Under some circum-

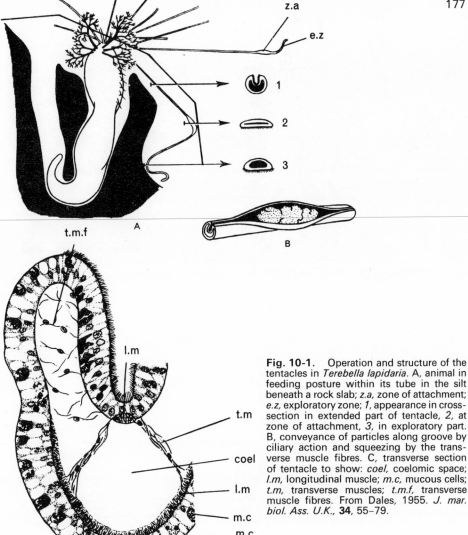

Fig. 10-1. Operation and structure of the tentacles in *Terebella lapidaria*. A, animal in feeding posture within its tube in the silt beneath a rock slab; *z.a,* zone of attachment; *e.z,* exploratory zone; *1,* appearance in cross-section in extended part of tentacle, *2,* at zone of attachment, *3,* in exploratory part. B, conveyance of particles along groove by ciliary action and squeezing by the transverse muscle fibres. C, transverse section of tentacle to show: *coel,* coelomic space; *l.m,* longitudinal muscle; *m.c,* mucous cells; *t.m,* transverse muscles; *t.m.f,* transverse muscle fibres. From Dales, 1955. *J. mar. biol. Ass. U.K.,* **34**, 55–79.

stances *Nereis diversicolor* forms this secretion into a net within its burrow; water can then be pumped through this net, so that it can be used for a simple form of filter feeding. Particles collect in the secretion as though in a bag, and from time to time the material is swallowed. We can visualize that the further elaboration of some such mechanism might have been aided by the presence on the head of tentacles and palps, which are used by errant worms for sensory purposes and to assist in the manipulation of food. These structures have given rise in sedentary worms to complex and beautiful systems of tentacular outgrowths, often called gills, or branchial crowns, because they were at one time regarded as primarily respiratory in function. No doubt they do play a part in respiration, but they also provide mechanisms for the collection and sorting of food particles; they are aided in this by the production of mucus, which is distributed over tracts of ciliated epithelium.

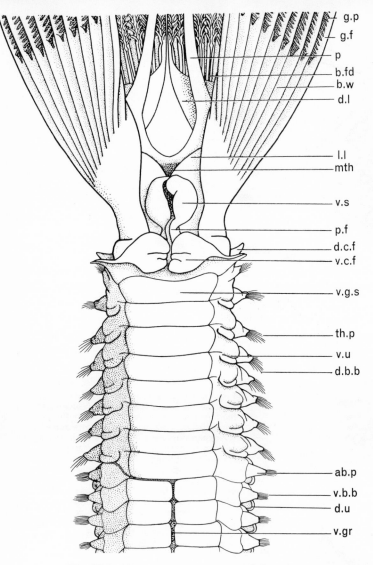

Fig. 10-2. Ventral view of the base of the branchial crown and the first 12 body segments of *Sabella pavonina* to show the external features × 12. *ab.p*, abdominal parapodium; *b.fd*, basal fold; *b.w*, basal web; *d.b.b*, dorsal bristle bundle; *d.c.f*, dorsal collar fold; *d.l*, dorsal lip; *d.u*, dorsal uncini; *g.f*, gill filament; *g.p*, gill pinnule; *l.l*, lateral lip; *mth*, mouth; *p*, palp; *p.f*, parallel folds; *th.p*, thoracic parapodium; *v.b.b*, ventral bristle bundle; *v.c.f*, ventral collar fold; *v.gr*, ventral groove; *v.g.s*, ventral gland shield; *v.s*, ventral sac; *v.u*, ventral uncini. From Nicol, 1930. *Trans. R. Soc. Edinb.*, **56**, 537–598.

With this potentiality as a starting point, ciliary feeding mechanisms could have evolved in the sedentary polychaetes along many independent lines. Terebellid worms (Fig. 10-1), for example, which live in permanent tubes in mud, are deposit feeders; they obtain detritus by extending long ciliated tentacles from their head over the surface of the substratum, the food particles being trapped in mucus and swept along ciliated grooves into the mouth (Fig. 10-1). The tentacles, which are highly mobile, are beautifully adapted for this function. Their shape, as seen in cross-section, varies at different points at any particular moment according to the use to which they are being put. At one point a tentacle will be flattened to form a zone of attachment, distal to which the remainder of the tentacle explores the substratum. Proximally to the attachment point the surface of the tentacle will be folded to form a ciliated groove along which the food is propelled. This propulsion is effected in part by ciliary action, but in part also by muscular contraction.

In complete contrast to this, the lugworm obtains detritus by swallowing the mud in which it is contained. This requires active burrowing, for the detritus beneath the surface is not so quickly replenished as that deposited on the surface; these animals, therefore, although taxonomically sedentary polychaetes, are more active than most worms of this type. They rely upon the sucking action of the anterior end of the alimentary tract to enable them to swallow, and this, coupled with their burrowing activity, accounts for the absence of tentacles.

Sabella, which presents a contrast to both of the above worms, provides an example of the elegance of adaptation that has been achieved in the feeding mechanisms of the polychaetes. It is a comparatively large animal, found in the littoral zone, where it builds tubes that project in large numbers from the surface of the mud. It is a suspension feeder, extracting its food from water currents, which are created by coordinated cilia. These are set upon the branchial crown (Fig. 10-2), which consists of a large number of cephalic tentacles or filaments, differing from those of *Terebella* in being stiff and pinnate, and in being arranged in two groups of about thirty. Each group is united towards its base into a lateral lobe, the two lobes being joined together dorsally but extending back independently on the ventral surface.

The branchial crown forms a wide funnel, with the mouth of the animal lying at the base. The problem, therefore, is to secure the food and to direct it towards that point, and it is for this purpose that the cilia are used. Their operation in feeding depends upon two rows of outgrowths, the pinnules, along each filament. These are

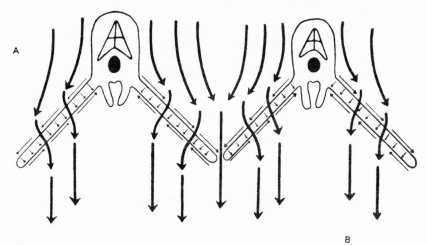

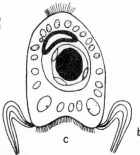

Fig. 10-3. A, diagrammatic section of two gill filaments of *Sabella*, to show the direction of flow of the water entering the branchial funnel, and the direction of beat of the cilia which cause the current. The small arrows indicate the direction of beat of the cilia; the large arrows indicate the direction of flow of the water. B, transverse section through a pinnule to show the ciliation. ×500. *a,* abfrontal cilia; *b,* latero-frontal cilia; *c,* frontal cilia. From Nicol, 1930. *op. cit.*

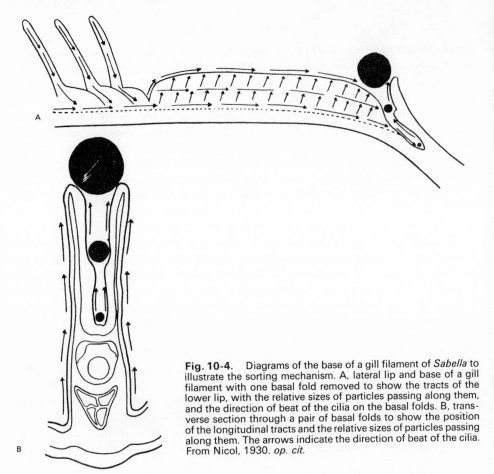

Fig. 10-4. Diagrams of the base of a gill filament of *Sabella* to illustrate the sorting mechanism. A, lateral lip and base of a gill filament with one basal fold removed to show the tracts of the lower lip, with the relative sizes of particles passing along them, and the direction of beat of the cilia on the basal folds. B, transverse section through a pair of basal folds to show the position of the longitudinal tracts and the relative sizes of particles passing along them. The arrows indicate the direction of beat of the cilia. From Nicol, 1930. *op. cit.*

set in such a way (Fig. 10-3) that a pinnule in one row makes an angle of rather more than 90° with the corresponding pinnule in the other row. The pinnules at the distal end of a filament are separated from the ones on the next adjacent filament, but towards the lower part of the branchial funnel they are brought closer together and finally interlock. As a result, they form a filtering system upon which food particles can be trapped.

The outer surfaces of the pinnules (Fig. 10-3) bear cilia, the abfrontal cilia, which beat strongly towards the tip of each pinnule. These cilia draw water into the funnel, the process being completed by latero-frontal cilia, which beat inwards, at right angles to the beat of the abfrontal ones. Food particles enter the funnel with the stream of water, and are thrown, partly by eddies and partly by the beat of the latero-frontal cilia, onto a groove that runs along the inner edge of each pinnule. In this groove are cilia, the frontal cilia, that beat towards the base of the pinnule in the opposite direction to the beat of the abfrontal ones. The frontal cilia thus drive the food particles to the bases of the pinnules. From here they enter a longitudinal groove that runs down the whole length of each filament, and they are driven along this by the cilia that line it.

Towards the base of each filament the two rows of pinnules pass into two continuous folds, the gill folds or basal folds (Fig. 10-4), which are ciliated on both their outer and inner faces. The cilia mostly beat upwards towards the free edge of the folds, but on their inner surfaces the folds bear three ciliary tracts in which the beat is downwards. This downward beat is directed towards the mouth, which is bordered by a dorsal and two lateral lips (Fig. 10-2); these are formed in part from the bases of a pair of long palps, and in part from the bases of the branchial crown. The lips are ciliated, and, in particular, they bear three ciliary tracts that correspond with the three tracts of the gill folds. These various structures constitute part of the sorting mechanism; we have remarked that this is an essential feature of a highly organized ciliary feeding mechanism, ensuring that only suitable particles are directed into the digestive system.

Rejection in *Sabella* depends upon the capacity of the sorting mechanism to differentiate between particles of various sizes. The pinnules play some part in this, because large particles falling from above cannot enter the longitudinal grooves of the filaments since these are protected by the overarching of the expanded bases of the pinnules. Lower down a more subtle differentiation is found, permitting the sorting of large, medium, and small particles (Fig. 10-4). The gill folds are arranged in pairs; the members of each pair enclose a basal groove, but their inner surfaces are so close together that large particles cannot enter between them. Such particles, therefore, do not come under the influence of the ciliary tracts that beat downwards towards the mouth. Instead, they are moved away from the mouth towards the edges of the lips. The smallest particles, however, can pass between the inner surfaces of the gill folds into the basal groove, and they are then carried towards the mouth. The medium-sizes ones follow yet another course, because, although they can enter between the inner surfaces of the gill folds, they are prevented from proceeding as far as the basal groove owing to the existence of a longitudinal ridge. They thus come under the control of a different ciliary tract, which transports them into two expansions of the lateral lips called the ventral sacs (Fig. 10-5). They do not, therefore, enter the mouth, but their selection is none the less important. They are used, after being mixed with mucus, for the building of the mud tube. This is formed through the activity of the collar folds that lie just posterior to the mouth.

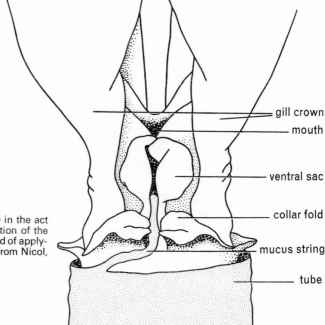

Fig. 10-5. Ventral view of *Sabella* in the act of tube-building, to show the formation of the mucus and sand string and the method of applying it to the edge of the tube. × 12. From Nicol, 1930. *op. cit.*

gill crown

mouth

ventral sac

collar fold

mucus string

tube

The large particles are removed from the animal through the action of rejection currents, the cilia of the lips and palps being important in this. Other débris is removed by the same route, together with the faeces that are passed forwards from the hind end of the animal in a ciliated groove. Not the least striking aspect of the precision of adaptation found in this system is the fact that mucus is extensively used in these rejection movements, where it helps the cilia to pass along the discarded material. Clearly, however, it would not be practicable for mucus to be used in the transport of food, for this depends upon the sorting of individual particles by size. In correlation with this the collection and sorting processes are found to depend largely upon the cilia alone, and upon the currents and vortices that are established by their beat.

There are other polychaetes with feeding mechanisms similar in general principle to that of *Sabella*, but with great variation in detail. One example is *Pomatoceros*, common on rocky shores in its calcareous tubes. The branchial crown, which

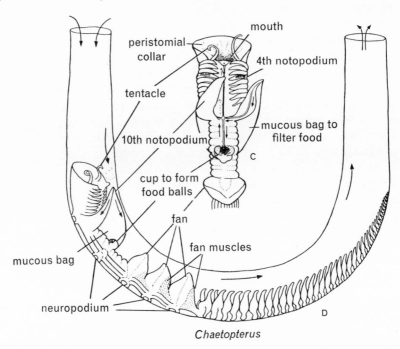

Chaetopterus

Fig. 10-6. *Chaetopterus.* In D, the direction of water is indicated by arrows. From Borradaile et al., 1958. *The Invertebrata* (3rd ed., ed. Kerkut). Cambridge University Press, London.

is very similar to that of *Sabella*, consists of two halves, each of which comprises some 14 to 20 pinnate tentacles borne on an outgrowth of the prostomium. The two halves are joined by the dorsal and ventral lips, between which lies the mouth. The collection and transport of food is similar in principle to that in *Sabella*, but simpler in detail, perhaps because the animal is smaller and possesses a calcareous tube. In particular, there is no specialized sorting mechanism, so that all particles transported by the pinnules are likely to reach the mouth. Some degree of sorting, however, presumably results automatically from the small size of the animal, for this ensures

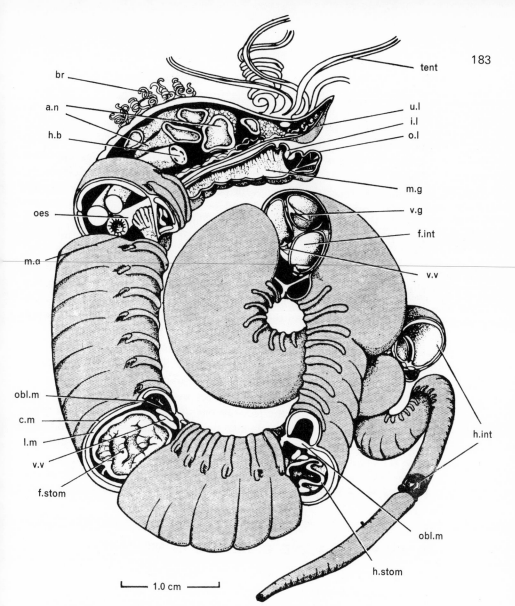

Fig. 10-7. *Amphitrite johnstoni,* illustrating the main regions of the gut in relation to the rest of the body. *a.n,* anterior nephridia; *br,* branchiae; *c.m,* circular muscles; *f.int,* fore-intestine; *f.stom,* fore-stomach; *h.b,* heart body; *h.int,* hind-intestine; *h.stom,* hind-stomach; *i.l,* inner lips; *l.m,* longitudinal muscle; *m.g,* mucous glands; *obl.m,* oblique muscles; *oes,* oesophagus; *o.l,* outer lips; *tent,* tentacles; *u.l,* upper lip; *v.g,* ventral gutter; *v.v,* ventral vessels. From Dales, 1955. *J. mar. biol. Ass. U.K.,* **34,** 55–79.

that only small particles will be transported by the pinnules in the first instance. If, as may sometimes happen, the filaments become clogged with an excess of material, the tip of a filament will bend over and remove the obstruction; further protection is afforded by rejection currents on the palps, lips, and basal folds.

One other example, which shows the variety of these feeding mechanisms even within the limits of one class, is *Chaetopterus,* a highly specialized worm of bizarre form that lives in sand or mud within a U-shaped tube of parchment-like consistency (Fig. 10–6). In this animal there is no branchial crown. Instead, water is drawn through the tube by the beating of three pairs of fans that are presumably derived from the parapodia of related forms. Farther forward another pair of outgrowths forms two wings that are pressed against the wall of the tube. Mucus secreted by these is drawn backwards by cilia in a ventral groove, and is formed into a conical bag, the apex of which lies within a small cup. Food particles are strained out by this mucous bag, the substance of which is continuously secreted by the wings and rolled up into a pellet in the cup. At intervals the secretory process stops and the cilia in the ventral groove move in reverse; as a result the pellet from the cup, with its contained food particles, is transported to the mouth and swallowed.

In the more advanced invertebrates extracellular digestion tends to replace the intracellular method, for reasons that we have earlier indicated, but the mode of feeding may be decisive in determining how far this tendency proceeds. In annelid worms the situation has been comparatively little studied, but there is evidence that the extracellular method predominates. Some phagocytosis may, however, take place, as, for example, in *Arenicola marina*, where digestion is completed in wandering amoebocytes that take up from the alimentary epithelium particles that its cells have ingested. It is surprising that digestion appears to be largely extracellular in terebellids, for their filter-feeding habits would seem to favour the persistence of intracellular digestion. In fact, their gut shows considerable regional specialization for extracellular digestion (Fig. 10–7), being differentiated into an oesophagus, a fore-stomach, a muscular hind-stomach which serves as a mixing region, and an intestine. Enzymes are secreted in the fore-stomach and fore-intestine, absorption taking place in the intestine. Arthropods also, incidentally, rely almost completely upon extracellular digestion, even in microphagous forms; intracellular digestion is restricted to the final stages in the digestion of proteins, more especially in arachnids. This contrasts strikingly with the situation that we shall find in lamellibranchs, where microphagy is associated with the retention of a highly specialized form of intracellular digestion.

10–2   FILTER FEEDING AND DIGESTION IN MOLLUSCS

No animals provide better illustrations of filter feeding than do the lamellibranch molluscs, for all the members of this class, with the exception of the secondarily modified septibranchs, obtain their food in this way. As with the polychaetes, we can see that a substantial element of pre-adaptation has been involved, although the course of events has been quite different in the two groups. To judge from the type of feeding found in the chitons and in the most primitive living gastropods, the earliest molluscs must have been microphagous, using a rasping radula to break up encrusting algae, and then transferring particles of these organisms, together with deposits of detritus, into the mouth. We shall see later that the molluscan alimentary tract is highly specialized to deal with the intake of particulate material. What the lamellibranchs have done is to exploit certain potentialities inherent in this molluscan plan of organization. Making use of the protective value of the shell, and of the muscular power of the foot, they have become typically semi-sessile animals, inhabitants of sandy or muddy substrata. Here, with an alimentary system already adapted for microphagy, they have utilized the food resources of their habitat to the full by modifying the ciliated molluscan gills; these are now organized so as to enable them

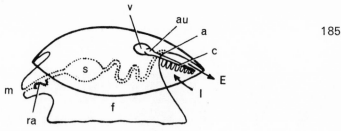

A

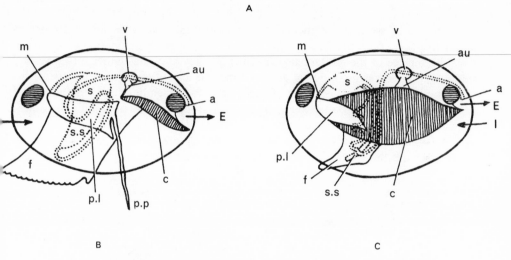

B   C

Fig. 10-8. Diagrams illustrating stages in the evolution of the Lamellibranchia, showing significant changes in the orientation of the body, form of the shell, foot, ctenidia, and heart, alimentary canal (stippled), and labial palps. A, structure of hypothetical primitive Mollusca (modified after Pelseneer); B, protobranch stage; C, final condition in typical Eulamellibranch without siphons. *a*, anus; *au*, auricle; *c*, ctenidium; *f*, foot; *m*, mouth; *p.l*, palp lamellae; *p.p*, palp proboscides; *ra*, radula; *s*, stomach; *s.s*, style sac region; *v*, ventricle. From Yonge, 1939. *Phil. Trans. R. Soc. B*, **230**, 79–147.

to filter suspended and deposited material from a current of water that was doubtless initially developed for its respiratory value (Sec. 11-4).

The current, which enters in lamellibranchs through an inhalent siphon and leaves through an exhalent one, is maintained by the action of the cilia on the ctenidia. In this group these are greatly elongated (Fig. 10-8). Each ctenidium consists of a long axis which bears two demibranchs, each of these being composed of a parallel row of filaments. In the primitive protobranchs the filaments are unfolded, but in filibranchs and eulamellibranchs they are folded so as to form ascending and descending limbs (Fig. 10-9). In the filibranchs (e.g. *Mytilus*) adjacent filaments are joined by ciliary junctions; in the eulamellibranchs (e.g. *Anodonta*) they are joined to each other by vacular interfilamental junctions (Fig. 10-10). Each demibranch thus forms a folded lamella, and the ascending and descending plates of this are joined to each other by interlamellar junctions.

In lamellibranchs, as in polychaetes, we find use made of cilia that are arranged in frontal and lateral series, but their action is complex, and shows much variation in detail from species to species. The lateral cilia (Fig. 10-10) draw water into the mantle

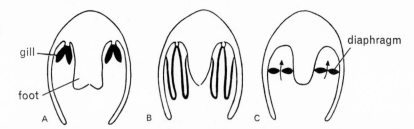

Fig. 10-9. Vertical sections of Lamellibranchiata to show different stages in the development of the ctenidia A, protobranch; B, filibranch and eulamellibranch; C, septibranch. The arrows in C show the direction of water flow through the 'diaphragm' when the latter moves downwards. From Borradaile et al., 1958. *op. cit.*

chamber, and from there into the interlamellar and suprabranchial cavities. As the water passes between the filaments, the latero-frontal cilia catch the food particles and throw them onto the frontal cilia, which then sweep them, entangled in mucus, over the surface of the gill lamellae. From here they may pass either into a ventral marginal groove, or into a dorsal groove along the axis of the gill, at the base of the demibranchs. Along one or other of these grooves, depending upon the particular species concerned, the food material is carried to the two pairs of labial palps; these are triangular structures, one pair lying on either side of the mouth.

It would take too long to describe the possible courses of these particles in detail, so complex are the specialized ciliary mechanisms involved, but as far as sorting is

Fig. 10-10. The ctenidia of the Lamellibranchiata. The arrows indicate the direction of the food current and the path of the food particles it contains. *Mytilus* = Filibranch; *Anodonta* = Eulamellibranch. From Borradaile et al., 1958. *op. cit.*

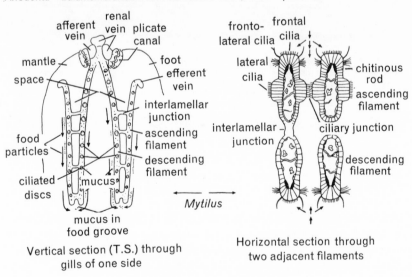

Vertical section (T.S.) through gills of one side

Horizontal section through two adjacent filaments

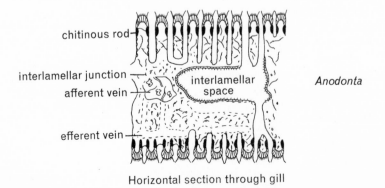

Horizontal section through gill

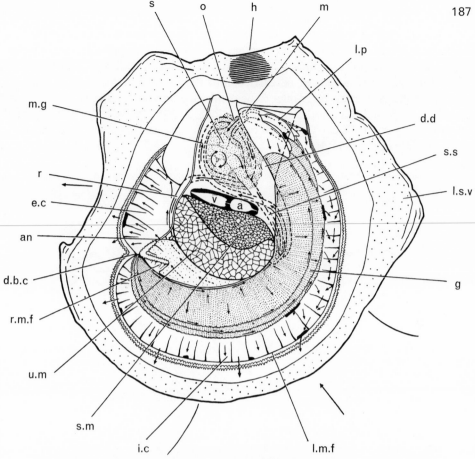

Fig. 10-11. *Ostrea edulis*, right shell valve and mantle removed. *a*, auricle; *an*, anus; *d.b.c*, division between inhalent and exhalent chambers; *d.d*, digestive diverticula; *e.c*, exhalent chamber; *g*, gills; *h*, hinge; *i.c*, inhalent chamber; *l.m.f*, left mantle fold; *l.p*, labial palps; *l.s.v*, left shell valve; *m*, mouth. *m.g*, mid-gut; *o*, oesophagus; *r*, rectum; *r.m.f*, right mantle fold; *s*, stomach; *s.m*, adductor muscle, portion with striated fibres; *s.s*, style sac; *u.m*, adductor muscle, portion with smooth fibres; *v*, ventricle. Large arrows external to shell indicate direction of ingoing and outgoing currents. Broken arrows denote currents on under surfaces. From Yonge, 1926. *J. mar. biol. Ass. U.K.*, **14**, 295–386.

concerned this occurs partly on the gills and partly on the palps. It is common to find a differentiation of ciliary tracts on the gills. Some tracts are provided with fine cilia, and are adapted for conveying the fine particles required for food; other tracts have coarse cilia and deal with the rejection of larger particles. Coupled with this simple differentiation, however, are complex and highly diversified patterns of ciliation, associated in their turn with variations in the form of the gills.

For example, the gill lamellae are sometimes folded (plicate), as they are in *Pecten* and *Ostrea*, with the ciliary beat on the crests of the folds differing from that in the grooves. The smaller particles required for food are carried chiefly upwards by fine cilia to the dorsal grooves, while coarse particles, such as sand grains, are carried downwards. The latter tend to drop off from the gill edge (Fig. 10-11), or are shaken off by muscular movements of the demibranchs.

In other forms the ventro-marginal grooves may contribute to the sorting in a way reminiscent of that which we have seen in *Sabella*. For example, they may be divided into a deep channel lined by fine cilia and a superficial one lined by coarse cilia. Fine particles may then be carried into the bottom of the groove, whereas closure of this may cause large ones to be conducted only to its edge, so that they are eventually rejected. As another possibility, long cilia on the edges of the marginal groove may permit the entry of small particles, but prevent the entry of larger ones; this principle operates in *Mya*.

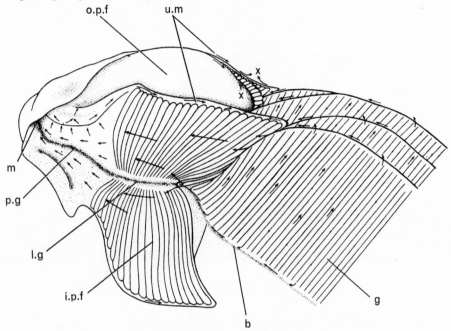

Fig. 10-12. Junction of palps and gills of *Ostrea*, right palps opened out so as to expose inner, ridged surfaces. × 8. *b*, base of demibranch; *g*, gill; *i.p.f*, inner palp face; *l.g*, lateral oral groove; *m*, mouth; *o.p.f*, outer palp face; *p.g*, proximal oral groove; *u.m*, upper margin of palps; *x*, point where material is rejected from palps. From Yonge, 1926. *op. cit.*

The labial palps (Fig. 10–12) are ciliated structures; their sorting function depends particularly on the structure of their internal faces, which are crossed by a series of diagonal folds. These folds overlap each other in the direction of the mouth, all but the uppermost part of one fold being covered by the next adjacent one. The sorting mechanism is here said to depend solely on the weight and not on the size of the particles. Of the particles that are carried over the top of the surface, the heavier ones settle down into the grooves between the slope of one fold and the crest of the next; in this position they come under the influence of a powerful ciliary current that sweeps them to the upper margin of the palp. Lighter ones avoid this current because they do not sink in the same way; as a result, they are swept from one slope to the next and pass towards the mouth. A similar sorting takes place among particles that pass down between the folds, heavier ones being carried by another current towards the upper margin and lighter ones towards the mouth. Thus these structures have their cilia arranged so as to produce a diversity of ingeniously integrated currents.

We shall follow later the fate of those particles that finally enter the mouth and pass into the alimentary canal. The rejected particles pass onto the ciliated epithelia of the mantle or visceral mass, where the strong ciliary currents produced by these epithelia give rise to vortices. These entangle the particles in mucus to form masses that eventually accumulate below the internal opening of the inhalent siphon. Periodically the animal closes its exhalent siphon and, by a sudden movement of contraction, forces the rejected material (pseudofaeces) out of the inhalent siphon in a current of water.

We have suggested that the rasping method of feeding of primitive molluscs was a pre-adaptation to the evolution of the specialized filter feeding of lamellibranchs. This rasping method is essentially a form of microphagy. Thus the requirements for the handling of small particles must have influenced the organization of the alimentary canal of molluscs from the beginning of their history, and must further have facilitated the establishment of the feeding methods of lamellibranchs. Moreover, the ingestion of small particles probably determined the retention of the intracellular method of digestion, which is so widespread in molluscs. Indeed, the group as a whole provides a good illustration of the supplanting of the intracellular method by the more advanced extracellular one, and the retention of the former in microphagous forms.

Particularly characteristic of the molluscan alimentary tract is the stomach, an organ that demonstrates very strikingly the problems of combining microphagy with intracellular digestion. We have earlier mentioned that intracellular digestion requires a large area of phagocytic epithelium. To take full advantage of this, the food must be delayed in its passage through the alimentary tract and distributed over the epithelium. The satisfying of these two requirements has determined the evolution of the molluscan stomach. In the lamellibranchs there projects into the lumen of this organ a long and flexible rod, composed of layers of mucoprotein. This structure, the crystalline style, is secreted by a style sac (Fig. 10–13); this is an extension of the stomach that may open widely into that organ, or be more or less completely cut off from it. Cilia in the style sac cause the style to rotate, and at the same time drive it forwards into the stomach. Here its free end is worn away by friction against the gastric shield (Fig. 10–14), which is a thickening of the cuticular lining of the stomach wall. The wearing away is aided by the alkaline stomach contents, which cause the style substance to dissolve. This substance contains a digestive amylase adsorbed to its mucoprotein base, while in some species a cellulase is probably also present. Thus the dissolution of the style results in these enzymes being added to the contents of the gastric lumen.

The effect of all this is that the food-bearing strands of mucus that enter the stomach are caught up and wound into a spiral mass by the rotation of the style, and are simultaneously mixed with its digestive secretion, so that the extracellular digestion of carbohydrate is initiated. But more than this is involved, for particles of food and mucus are continually being broken off from the main mass, partly because of its rotation, and partly because the pH of the stomach contents (about 5 to 6) lowers the viscosity of the mucus. These detached particles are now subjected to sorting by the stomach wall (Fig. 10–14), much of which is lined with ciliated ridges and grooves that have an action similar in principle to that of the labial palps. The larger and heavier particles enter the deeper grooves, and come under the influence

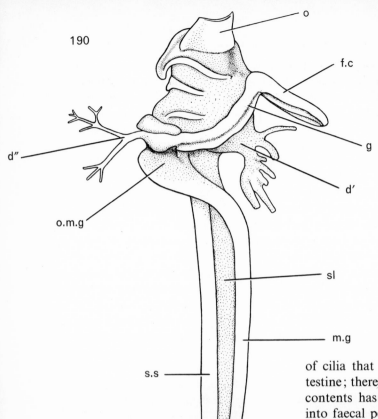

Fig. 10-13. Gelatin cast of stomach of *Ostrea* with style sac and first part of mid-gut and portion of oesophagus, from ventral aspect. ×4. *d'*, larger, left duct of digestive diverticula; *d"*, smaller, right duct of same; *f.c*, food-sorting caecum; *g*, ventral groove; *m.g*, mid-gut; *o*, oesophagus; *o.m.g*, opening of mid-gut; *s.s*, style sac; *sl*, slit connecting mid-gut and style sac. From Yonge, 1926. *op. cit.*

of cilia that transport them into the intestine; there the more alkaline pH of the contents has the effect of forming them into faecal pellets that are eventually extruded through the anus. Finer particles, however, take a different route, and one which promotes their further digestion; they are borne over the cilia on the ridges of the stomach wall towards the openings of the digestive diverticula (or glands), which constitute another characteristic feature of the molluscan alimentary tract.

There are two of these diverticula, each consisting of a highly branched system of blind tubules opening into the stomach by a ciliated duct. The epithelium of the tubules is also ciliated, and in lamellibranchs is usually composed of a single type of highly vacuolated cell. This cell is phagocytic, capable of ingesting fine particles into food vacuoles, and it is within these vacuoles that the digestive process is completed. In fact, digestion is very largely intracellular in the lamellibranchs, except in so far as the secretion of the style sac initiates the digestion of carbohydrates. We see here very clearly how the retention of the intracellular method demands a sorting mechanism of the type provided by the stomach. Only fine particles can be taken up into the phagocytic epithelial cells, and the entry of large ones into the digestive diverticula would clog their delicate ducts. A supplementary means of ingestion is, however, available; larger particles, including whole diatoms or blood corpuscles that have been artificially fed to the animals, can be ingested by wandering amoebocytes in the stomach, a procedure that recalls the part played by the amoebocytes of sponges.

We have already seen in our discussion of coelenterates that intracellular digestion results in the phagocytic cells becoming loaded with waste material. This is very evident in the digestive diverticula. It leads to the epithelial cells undergoing fragmentation; spherical masses with vacuoles, ingested material, and waste are thus given off from the epithelium, and are conveyed out of the diverticula into the stomach and thence into the intestine. Such masses must contain enzymes that have been secreted by the phagocytic cells, and this probably accounts for the fact that weak enzyme activity can be detected in the stomach even though it does not itself possess a digestive epithelium. Whether such residual enzymes are of any importance in normal digestion may be doubted. On the other hand, it is quite conceivable that their discharge from phagocytic epithelia, an inevitable consequence of the course of intracellular digestion, might have been a factor promoting the evolution of the extracellular method.

The lamellibranchs have specialized to the full in the exploitation of the food sources provided by suspended organic matter and detritus, and their feeding and digestive mechanisms are, with one exception, very uniform. The exception is provided by the septibranchs, a group of carnivorous lamellibranchs that draw in dead or dying animals by means of contractions of a muscular septum that replaces the gills as the organ of feeding. In correlation with this, the crystalline style is reduced in size.

The gastropods, by contrast, are altogether more varied in their feeding habits. In consequence, there is a corresponding diversity in the structure of their alimentary canal, with a marked tendency for intracellular digestion to be replaced by the extracellular method. Some gastropods are herbivores, and of these there are genera in which the organization of the digestive system shows a general resemblance to that of the lamellibranchs. *Crepidula*, for example, is a ciliary feeder, with amylase as its only extracellular digestive enzyme, and with digestive diverticula that are solely absorptive in function and that contribute no external digestive secretion. What is particularly interesting, however, is that this animal, like lamellibranchs, possesses a crystalline style, a structure that is also found in a number of the other herbivorous gastropods, especially in the Taenioglossa but also in the Rhipidoglossa and the thecosomatous pteropods.

The distribution of the style in gastropods raises some interesting considerations, for it is not present in all of the herbivorous forms. Those that do possess it are microphagous herbivores, and this is significant, for it is possible to see two factors that would promote the establishment of a style in such forms. Only some of them are ciliary feeders; indeed, the majority depend upon their radula for the securing of their food, but this method of feeding, like ciliary feeding, results in a continuous

Fig. 10-14. Diagram of the anatomy of the stomach of *Glycymeris*. *c,* caecum; *f,* fold; *g.i,* intestinal groove; *g.s,* gastric shield; *g2,* groove; *i,* intestine; *l.c,* left wall of caecum; *l.d,* opening of duct from left lobe of digestive gland; *o,* oesophagus; *r.c,* right wall of caecum; *r.d,* opening of duct from right lobe of digestive gland; *s.a.c,* sorting area of caecum; *s.a.p,* posterior sorting area of stomach; *s.s,* style sac; *t1, t2,* typhlosoles. From Graham, 1949. *Trans. R. Soc. Edinb.,* **61**, 737–761.

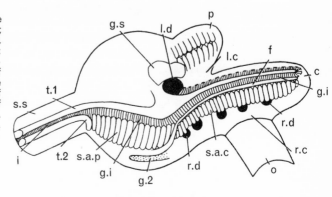

stream of small particles passing into the alimentary canal. It is in precisely such conditions that the crystalline style confers an advantage; not only does it wind the food into a spiral mass and mix it with the amylase, but it also provides a means for the continuous release of small quantities of that enzyme.

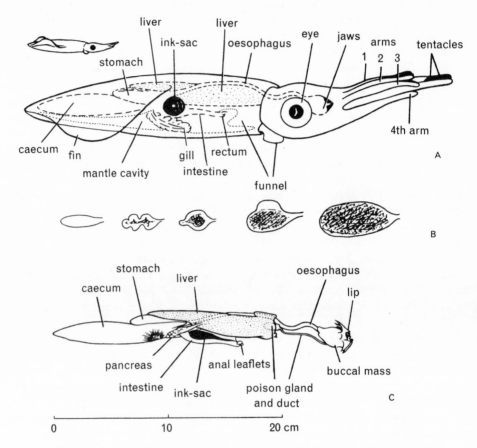

Fig. 10-15. A, young living *Loligo vulgaris* as seen swimming in tank. Optical section of mantle-cavity in dotted outline. Pancreas and details of gills not visible in life. Oesophagus, stomach, and caecum only visible when containing food. B, stomach empty, half-full and actively churning, and fully distended. C, digestive system from animal's right side. A, B, and C to same scale. From Bidder, 1950. *Q. Jl microsc. Sci.,* **91**, 1–43.

A further factor is the absence of an extracellular protease. If this were present it would, of course, digest the style. No doubt this is one reason why this structure is lacking in carnivorous forms, for many of these, including carnivorous proso-branchs such as *Murex*, have both an amylase and a protease present in their digestive secretions. Another relevant consideration is that gastropods possess oesophageal glands, which provide an alternative source of extracellular enzymes. Carnivorous species commonly obtain their food at irregular intervals, so that glands like these, which may well be under nervous or hormonal control, probably meet their needs better than would the continuous release of enzymes from a style. It has been sug-gested that the two modes of secretion, by a crystalline style and by oesophageal glands, are mutually inconsistent; their distribution in prosobranch gastropods certainly goes some way to confirm this, for in that group they do not coexist in the same species, but seem rather to be developed as alternative mechanisms.

We have mentioned that the style is not universally present in herbivorous gastropods. *Patella*, *Haliotis*, *Aplysia*, and *Helix* are among those forms that lack it, but there seems to be no single reason for this. A tendency for the replacement of intracellular digestion by extracellular is doubtless one factor that determines it. This situation exists in *Helix*. In this herbivore no solid particles at all enter the cells of the alimentary tract, although the digestion of protein is probably completed within them after they have absorbed soluble peptides. *Patella*, on the other hand, has its digestive system organized at a more primitive level, in that most of its digestion is intracellular, with amylase as the only extracellular enzyme. This is not produced, however, through the mediation of a crystalline style, but is secreted from the oesophageal glands, known in these animals as sugar glands. It has been suggested that in this instance the lack of the style is conditioned by the mode of life of this herbivore in the intertidal zone. Its feeding is restricted to those periods when the tide is in and it can move without danger of desiccation; it could well be, therefore, that a style mechanism would be ill adapted for sporadic feeding of this sort, much as it is in carnivores.

The molluscs generally display a remarkable diversity and elaboration of digestive specialization. Among them the cephalopods, as might be predicted of such a highly organized group of predators, have an exclusively extracellular digestive mechanism. This (Fig. 10-15) bears some superficial likeness to the alimentary system of vertebrates, for the first stage of digestion occurs in a so-called 'stomach', and the second stage in the 'caecum', while the digestive gland has become subdivided into two regions known as the 'liver' and the 'pancreas'. The terms, however, are misleading. The pH of the stomach contents is 6.2, with no indication of an acid peptic phase such as is found in most vertebrates, while the 'liver', at least in *Octopus*, is a typically molluscan organ, carrying out the three functions of secretion, absorption, and excretion.

An interesting adaptive feature is said to be involved in the functioning of the 'liver' in *Octopus*, in that each cell performs each of these three functions in a cycle. The organ cannot, therefore, release enzymes into the 'stomach' while absorption is in progress. The squid, *Loligo*, however, differs in that its 'liver' is not concerned with absorption, so that this organ can secrete enzymes without interruption. This difference may be correlated with the bottom-dwelling habit of *Octopus* and the active swimming and predation of the squid. Digestion in a sedentary *Octopus* can, perhaps, be successfully completed over a considerable period of time, whereas in *Loligo* the ceaseless activity demands a more rapid handling of the food .

10-3   FILTER FEEDING AND DIGESTION IN DEUTEROSTOMIA

Consideration of annelids and molluscs has already shown us how systems of microphagy, not fundamentally dissimilar in their ciliary mechanics, may yet differ widely in the circumstances that condition their origin and in their subsequent evolutionary history. In annelids they arise as a later development in a group that seems initially to have been more predatory in its habits. In molluscs they appear as a logical development from an initially microphagous habit, although one that was of a peculiar character and that was not based upon ciliary mechanisms. One other major group that merits attention from this point of view is the Echinodermata, not so much because of the history of ciliary feeding within the group itself, but because of its bearing upon wider evolutionary issues.

The origin of this group is unknown, but the earliest fossil members exist in Palaeozoic deposits as sessile forms that possess in their body wall an armour of calcareous plates. Subsequently the sessile life has been abandoned for independent movement, such as we find today in the sea-urchins, starfish, brittlestars, and sea-cucumbers. Many of these are predatory and macrophagous, although some, such as the heart-urchins and certain holothurians, ingest mud and sand, while the use of cilia and mucus is not unknown. These free-living echinoderms constitute the Subphylum Eleutherozoa, while the sessile forms are placed in the Subphylum Pelmatozoa, a group of animals that is now wholly extinct apart from the Class Crinoidea. Crinoids are found today as forms that are attached to the substratum for at least part of their life (although not necessarily for the whole of it) by a stalk, and they are all ciliary feeders. The central disc of their body bears five pairs of arms, each arm possessing a double series of pinnules. Along the pinnules and arms there extend ciliated grooves that run to the mouth. These grooves bear ciliated podia or tube-feet, organs that in the Eleutherozoa are used for locomotion. In crinoids they set up a current from which food particles are collected, to be driven towards the mouth along the grooves. As the outline of similar grooves exists in the early fossils, this was probably the primitive method of feeding in echinoderms; indeed, it is a type of feeding mechanism that is very characteristic of sessile forms.

Change of habits evidently determined the reduction of ciliary feeding in the other surviving lines of the phylum, but it persisted in several groups that are closely related to them. We have already commented on the association of the Echinodermata with the vertebrates, and their relations with the assemblage termed the Deuterostomia. One justification for grouping several phyla in this association is that the history of their feeding mechanisms, despite their diversity of specialization, can be interpreted within a logical and consistent framework. The ciliated tentacles that we believe to have been primitive in the echinoderms are represented today in the Pogonophora, which capture food by means of these structures. These animals are remarkable in having secondarily lost their alimentary canal; digestion is believed to be external, in a cavity which is enclosed by the tentacles, and into which enzymes are secreted.

Within the Phylum Hemichordata the use of ciliated tentacles as a feeding mechanism persists in the pterobranchs *Cephalodiscus* and *Rhabdopleura*. In *Cephalodiscus* (Fig. 10–16) it is associated with the pharyngotremy mentioned earlier, for this animal draws into its mouth a stream of water which leaves by a pair of gill slits in the wall of the pharynx. Judging the value of this device is difficult, because pterobranchs have almost certainly become secondarily simplified in correlation with a reduction in size. Perforation of the pharynx may facilitate the expulsion of the excess water that is driven in by the ciliary feeding mechanism, but possibly it was initially developed as a respiratory adaptation. This is suggested by the pharyngotremy found in the remaining group of hemichordates, the Enteropneusta, where the pharynx is perforated by a series of gill pores that seem to be primarily respiratory in function.

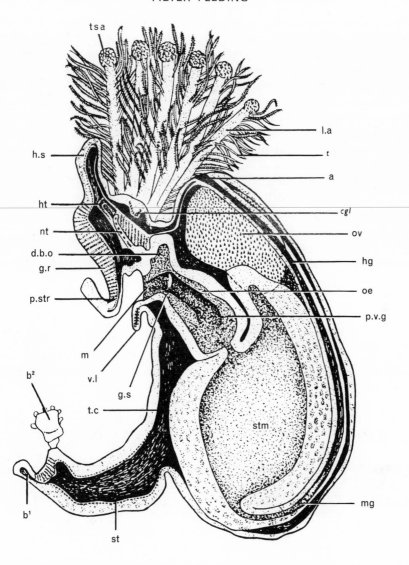

Fig. 10-16. Anatomy of *Cephalodiscus*, seen in median L.S. *a*, anus; *b¹*, *b²*, buds; *c.gl*, cerebral ganglion; *d.b.o*, dorsal median blind projection of oesophagus; *g.r*, glandular region; *g.s*, gill slit; *hg*, hind-gut; *h.s*, head shield; *ht*, heart; *l.a*, lophophore arm; *m*, mouth; *mg*, mid-gut; *nt*, notochord; *oe*, oesophagus; *ov*, ovary; *p.str*, pigment streak; *p.v.g*, posterior vacuolized groove; *st*, stolon; *stm*, stomach; *t*, tentacle; *t.c*, trunk coelom; *tsa*, terminal swelling of arm; *v.l*, ventral lip. From Schepotieff, 1907. *Zool. Jb. Abt. Anat.*, **24**, 553–608.

Enteropneusts, which are mostly burrowing forms, feed on detritus and sand, engulfing vast quantities of the substratum and discarding it at the surface of their burrows as sand castings. They probably evolved from pterobranch-like ancestors, and their feeding mechanism shows some trace of this history. The ciliated proboscis can trap food particles in mucus and pass them towards the mouth—a process clearly reminiscent of the food-trapping action of ciliated tentacles.

The relationship of the Phylum Chordata to these several groups is demonstrated by two chordate subphyla, the Urochordata (Fig. 10-17) and the Cephalochordata. In these two groups, collectively termed the Protochordata, pharyngotremy has become the basis of a new type of ciliary feeding mechanism; the pharynx is used both for feeding and for respiration, and there is no longer any sign of ciliated tentacles. Despite the novelty of this device, however, the ciliary mechanics of the pharynx prove similar in principle to those of the branchial crown of the polychaetes and of the gills of lamellibranchs, for the feeding of amphioxus and the ascidians depends upon groups of cilia beating at right angles to each other.

Lateral cilia on the delicate fenestration of the pharynx draw water through the pharyngeal wall into an atrial cavity that has been secondarily developed as protection for this vulnerable structure. The filtering of this water depends upon the presence in the floor of the pharynx of a longitudinal groove, the endostyle. A secretion

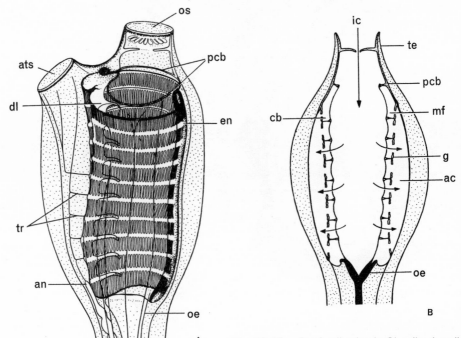

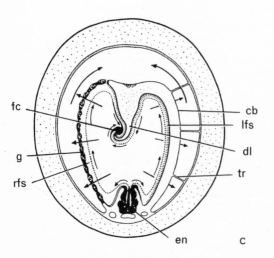

Fig. 10-17. Food collection in *Clavelina lepadiformis*. A, lateral view of anterior region of body. B, diagrammatic frontal section. C, diagrammatic transverse section through the pharynx, passing on the left through a row of stigmata, and on the right through a ciliated bar. *ac*, atrial cavity; *an*, anus; *ats*, exhalant siphon; *cb*, ciliated bar; *dl*, dorsal languet; *en*, endostyle; *fc*, food cord; *g*, gill; *ic*, inhalant current; *lfs*, left mucous filtering sheet; *mf*, funnel of mucus; *oe*, oesophagus; *os*, inhalant siphon; *pcb*, peripharyngeal ciliated bands; *rfs*, right mucous filtering sheet; *te*, tentacle; *tr*, supporting trabecula. In *B*, the arrows indicate the direction of the water currents. In *C* the small arrows indicate the direction of movement of the filtering sheets, and the large arrows the direction of the water currents. Adapted from E. and B. Werner, 1954. *Helgoländer wiss. Meeresunters.*, **5**, 57–92.

produced by this organ is moved up the pharyngeal wall by frontal cilia, which are the functional equivalent of the frontal cilia of worms and molluscs; thus the food particles are caught up in a moving filter formed by this secretion. The material is moved up to the mid-dorsal line, and from there is passed backwards as a food cord which is digested in a manner to be briefly considered below. This feeding mechanism is well suited for sessile and bottom-dwelling animals, but inevitably it is much modified in the pelagic urochordates, such as the salps and doliolids. In the latter, for example, the flow of water is maintained by pulsations of the body wall, and the food is trapped by strands of mucus in the lumen of the pharynx.

The endostyle is very characteristic of the protochordates, but a curious parallel to it is found in the gastropod *Crepidula*. This animal, which uses its gills for ciliary feeding, has developed an organ that seems to fulfil a function very similar to that of the endostyle, and which, in consequence, has been given the same name although it is, of course, an entirely independent development. This organ of *Crepidula* is a ciliated and mucus-secreting groove, from which a secretion is swept onto the food-collecting surface of the gills, where it contributes to the trapping of the food particles. Naturally, this imitation of an endostyle has been evolved quite independently of the endostyle of the protochordates. Indeed, this is where its interest lies, for it reveals how similar requirements may condition the evolution of similar organs in wholly diverse groups. Like the patterns of ciliation that we have been considering, it is an example of how the common factors that underlie the diverse organization of animal groups may, from time to time, find expression in the building of closely similar types of adaptation.

The ciliary and pharyngeal feeding mechanisms of the early Deuterostomia certainly had potentialities of exceptional importance, for they contributed powerfully to the evolution of vertebrates. We cannot follow this aspect in any detail here. It must be sufficient to say that the substitution of muscular for ciliary action led on to the type of microphagous feeding that we see today in the ammocoete larva of the lamprey. Probably it proved a more efficient method of securing food, and permitted increased size and activity. The crucial stage, however, was the development of macrophagous feeding. This process was absolutely dependent upon the initial establishment of pharyngotremy, for it was made possible by the development of jaws out of parts of the supporting skeleton of the perforated pharynx.

The digestive processes of the Deuterostomia are less well known than could be wished. They have been most closely studied in amphioxus, which provides another example of the retention of intracellular digestion in association with ciliary filter feeding, showing also some remarkable parallelisms with the digestive processes of lamellibranchs and of certain other invertebrate filter feeders. The food cord formed in the pharynx is passed back by ciliary action into the mid-gut, at the hind end of which its passage is arrested in a specialized region called the ilio-colon ring (Fig. 10-18). Here cilia set it into rotation around its longitudinal axis. This rotation ensures the necessary delay in the backward movement of the food cord; at the same time it mixes the cord with digestive enzymes that are passed into the ilio-colon ring, again by ciliary action, from the mid-gut caecum where they are secreted. The rotation also breaks up the mass of food and secretion into fragments; the smallest of these are swept forwards by ciliary currents into the caecum, while the larger ones drop back into the mid-gut and are returned to the rotating mass. Within the caecum the small particles come to rest on the epithelial surface and are ingested by the cells, so that while the initial stages of digestion are extracellular, the process is finally intracellular.

The rotatory action of the ilio-colon ring presents a remarkable analogy with the style mechanism of molluscs. The style probably originated in a mechanism similar to that seen today in the Protobranchiata, where a mixture of secretion and food particles is rotated by the action of a specialized zone of cilia developed at the junction of stomach and intestine. In lamellibranchs this device has evolved into the firm rotating style already considered, but this has not happened in the protochordates. The two groups show, however, the independent evolution of a fundamentally similar device for delaying the passage of the food, for mixing it with secretion, and

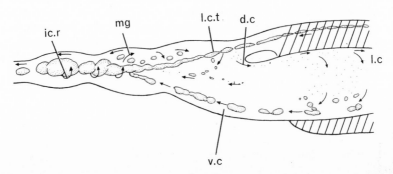

Fig. 10-18. Diagram to show the currents and movements of material in the alimentary tract of amphioxus. *d.c*, dorsal current carrying small particles into the caecum; *ic.r*, ilio-colon ring, containing a rotating mass of food and secretion; *l.c*, small particles deposited and ingested on the lateral wall of the caecum; *l.c.t*, lateral ciliated tract; *mg*, mid-gut, in which material is thrown forwards; *v.c*, ventral current carrying secretion from the caecum into the mid-gut. From Barrington, 1965. *The Biology of Hemichordata and Protochordata.* Oliver and Boyd, Edinburgh.

for distributing it to the ingestive regions of the alimentary epithelium. The digestive gland of lamellibranchs also resembles in principle the mid-gut caecum of amphioxus. Both provide for an increase in surface area for secretory and ingestive activity, and in both groups the distribution of food particles is so controlled that only the finer particles enter these blind alimentary diverticula. The two groups thus illustrate yet again how similar needs, acting within the inevitable limits of animal organization, must evoke similar, yet independent, solutions to functional problems. Nor do the lamellibranchs and cephalochordates supply the only example of this. A rotation of material in the alimentary canal, essentially similar in principle to that described above, occurs also in the Ectoprocta, the Entoprocta, the Brachiopoda, and the Phoronida.

10–4 FILTER FEEDING IN CRUSTACEA

Although cilia lend themselves particularly well to the organization of filter-feeding mechanisms, they are not the only means available for this, as is shown in the microphagy practised by Crustacea. This group, sharing with other arthropods a general lack of cilia (p. 40), has exploited instead the potentialities of the arthropod limb. The mechanisms involved are quite different from those that we have so far considered, and they are the more interesting because of this. They show how similar ends may sometimes be attained by quite different means, determined by differences in the fundamental plan of structure of the groups concerned.

We have already seen something of the ways in which the crustacean limb has become diversified in relation to habitat and to method of locomotion. It has also been profoundly influenced by its involvement in crustacean feeding mechanisms. We can only speculate as to the starting point for its diversification, but among living forms the Branchiopoda seem to shed the most light on this problem. Branchiopods have a variable number of segments and an elongated tubular heart with segmental ostia, and they often use their antennae for swimming. The first two of these features are certainly primitive, and the last one may well be so also, for the Devonian *Lepidocaris* probably used its antennae in the same way. Indeed, it may be that initially the antennae were the chief locomotor organs, with the abdominal appendages serving primarily for respiration, and that these were later drawn into use for swimming and feeding, as they are in branchiopods today. At first they would doubtless have been simpler in form than the limbs of present-day species; we have seen that they might have been of a simple foliaceous type, already with filtering gnathobases, such as were possessed by *Lepidocaris*. Metachronal rhythm would have prevented the limbs interfering with each other, and their orderly beat would have provided for an economical expenditure of energy, in that locomotor movements could have contributed also to the requirements of filter feeding, and would have aided respiratory ventilation.

In this way the early crustaceans could have begun to exploit the rich food resources of open waters. To say this, however, is not to imply that such was necessarily the primitive mode of life of the group. Filter feeding has certainly evolved along many independent lines in the course of crustacean history (in malacostracans, for example, quite independently of branchiopods), while many crustaceans have also exploited the nutritive resources of the substratum. We shall see that the phylogenetic interrelationships of these diverse methods of feeding (bottom-dwelling and pelagic, raptatory and suspension feeding) are complex, and that the course of history has not always followed the same pattern in the various lines. One conclusion, however, is self-evident: the ability of crustaceans to achieve in their feeding mechanisms the perfection of mechanical adaptation that we shall now be examining must have been a major factor in establishing the success of the group as aquatic animals.

As a first example of these filter-feeding mechanisms we may consider the anostracan Branchiopoda. These animals swim by means of the metachronal beat of thoracic appendages which are of the foliaceous type that we have called phyllopodia (Fig. 10-19). The inner edge of each of these bears a series of endites, the most basal of which is much larger than the others and is possibly formed by the fusion of two. These endites in their turn bear a fringe of large setae, which, together with the endites themselves, are directed somewhat backwards. The outer edge of the limb bears several lobes; the most distal of these, which is also provided with setae, is the exopodite, while the more basal ones are the epipodite and the proepipodites.

The beating of these limbs produces currents in the surrounding water, and it is these that are used in feeding. Thus the animal economically employs the limbs simultaneously for feeding as well as for locomotion, while their delicate structure

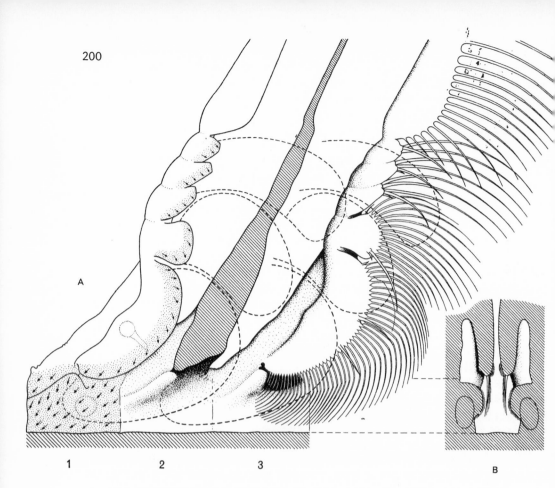

Fig. 10-19. A, median view of three consecutive trunk limbs of the branchiopod *Branchinella australiensis*. Only the median parts of the limbs are shown. *Limb 1:* The setae are omitted. The setules on the edges of the endites and on the wall of the food grooves are indicated by stippling, their direction being shown by arrows. *Limb 2:* The endites have been cut away to show the shape of the inter-limb space behind and its exit channel. *Limb 3:* The endites complete with setae are figured. The extent of the setae on limbs 1 and 2 is indicated by dotted lines. B, posterior view of lower edge of basal endites of a pair of trunk limbs of *Branchinecta gaini*, showing the exit grooves opening into the food groove between the filter setae and the main axis of the limb. From Cannon, 1933. *Phil. Trans. R. Soc. B*, **222**, 267–352.

enables them also to serve for respiratory exchange. An important factor in the feeding mechanism is the existence between any two limbs of one side of the inter-limb space (Fig. 10-20), which is delimited on the outside by the exites of the more anterior of the two limbs, and on the inside by its endites. Normally the animal swims upon its back, so that the inter-limb space will be closed above by its large distal endite (or endopodite), and below by the ventral body wall. All the inter-limb spaces communicate with the continuous mid-ventral space that extends between the two rows of limbs.

The metachronal rhythm of locomotion is so organized that the phase of each limb is slightly in advance of the one immediately in front of it. At the end of the backstroke the limbs are inclined back at such an angle that their inter-limb spaces are reduced to their minimum volume; as they move forwards in succession (Fig. 10-21, limbs 6-10) their inter-limb spaces are correspondingly enlarged. This

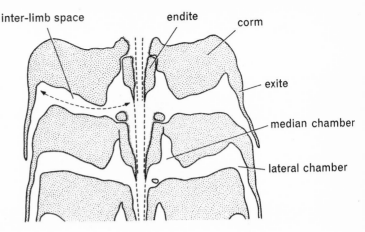

Fig. 10-20. Frontal section through three consecutive pairs of trunk limbs of *Branchinecta gaini* to show the shape of the inter-limb spaces and the valvular arrangements of the exite series. Adapted from Cannon, 1933, *op. cit.*

inter-limb space

endite

corm

exite

median chamber

lateral chamber

enlargement creates a suction which results in the endopodites and exites of one limb pressing backwards on the limb behind it, and so closing off the upper and side entrances to the inter-limb space. The suction draws water into the enlarged inter-limb space from the mid-ventral space between the pairs of limbs. Because of the closing action of the endopodites and exites, however, this water can only enter the inter-limb space by passing through the fringe of setae along the edges of the endites. When the limbs beat backwards (Fig. 10-21, limbs 1–5) the situation is different. It is in the backward phase that the animal is driven forwards. During this phase the limbs are comparatively rigid, and they become separated from each other during their extension; this opens up the inter-limb spaces and allows water to pass out backwards from them. It is, in fact, this stream of water that causes swimming.

Thus the swimming movements of the limbs result in water passing from the mid-ventral space between the limbs into the inter-limb spaces. To replace it more water must enter the mid-ventral space from the water surrounding the animal, and it is this inflow that brings the supply of food material. As the water passes into the inter-limb space, this material is trapped on the setae of the endites, which thus act as the filtering elements of the mechanism.

Another important factor in this complex process is the presence of very fine setules (Fig. 10–19) that form a feltwork on the median faces of the endites close to the main filtering setae. As the limbs move forwards, and each one presses against the

Fig. 10-21. Outline sketch of left half of an Anostracan (based on *Branchinella australiensis*) to show swimming and feeding currents. The arrows below the trunk limbs indicate their relative movements; limb 5 is completing its backward stroke, while limb 6 is beginning to move forward. All setae have been omitted. Adapted from Cannon, 1933. *op. cit.*

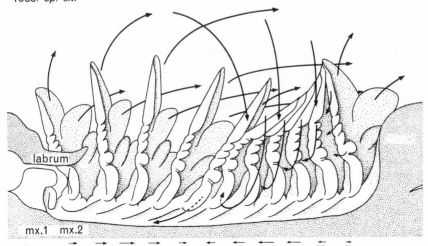

labrum

mx.1   mx.2

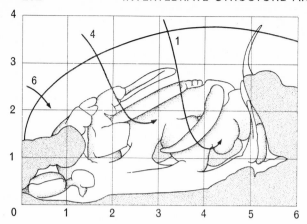

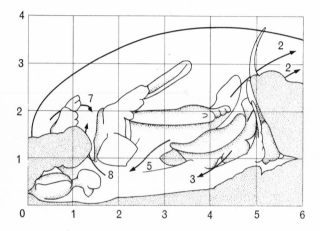

Fig. 10-22. Outline sketches of left half of *Daphnia magna*, to show movements of limbs and feeding currents. *Above*, the third and fourth trunk limbs are approximately at the end of their forestroke and *below*, at the end of their backstroke. A coordinate frame has been traced over the figures so that the movements of the limbs can be seen. Adapted from Cannon, 1933. *op. cit.*

one behind it in the way already explained, the setules of any one limb will project between the setae of the limb in front of it; as a result, they comb off the accumulated food material, which is then drawn by the water currents into a food groove. This groove is a channel that runs forwards along the mid-ventral line of the body wall, immediately between the bases of the limbs. In ciliary feeders the passage of food material along a corresponding path would be effected by cilia. Here it is probably brought about by anteriorly directed spurts of water which leave the inter-limb spaces during certain phases of the limb movements. In this way the food reaches the labrum, where it becomes entangled in a mucous secretion discharged from labral glands. This secretion facilitates its passage into the mouth, into which it is pushed by the maxillules, a pair of small appendages bearing long setae.

All branchiopods, and many filter-feeding Malacostraca, exploit essentially the same mechanical principle in their feeding mechanisms: the formation of a suction chamber by the expansion and contraction of inter-limb spaces, and the drawing in of water through filtering setae. The principle has been deployed, however, with much diversification of detail. To take another example, the mechanism found in *Daphnia* (Fig. 10–22) shows the effect of a reduction in the number of limbs, and of some degree of division of labour among them, while the development of the bivalved carapace means that this can act as the outer wall of the water chamber. The limbs of *Daphnia* also differ from those of *Chirocephalus* in the reduction of the distal parts and in the development of a prominent gnathobase from an enlarged basal endite.

In all there are five pairs of trunk limbs in *Daphnia* (Fig. 10-23), and of these it is the third and fourth pairs that act as a filtering mechanism similar in principle to that of the Anostraca. This they are able to do because of the presence of a fringe of setae, representing their gnathobases. The fifth limb lacks these setae, and plays no direct part in filtering, but it contributes by its movements to the maintenance of the feeding currents; its outer part hinges forwards and backwards on its inner part, so that it closes the inter-limb space at one stage and opens it at another. The first limb probably aids the forward passage of food along the ventral food groove by increasing the suction in this region, while its setae, together with those of the second

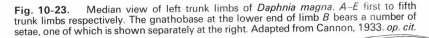

limb, probably prevent over-large particles from entering the groove. The gnathobase of the second limb possesses a fringe of setae, one of which is particularly elongated; these seem to play some part in assisting the removal of food particles from the filtering setae of the more posterior limbs, and in influencing their movement towards the mouth. There is some disagreement regarding the exact operation of the anterior limbs, but their action results eventually in the food being entangled with a labral secretion as in anostracans; the material is then passed into the mouth by the action of the maxillules and mandibles.

Fig. 10-23. Median view of left trunk limbs of *Daphnia magna*. *A–E* first to fifth trunk limbs respectively. The gnathobase at the lower end of limb *B* bears a number of setae, one of which is shown separately at the right. Adapted from Cannon, 1933. *op. cit.*

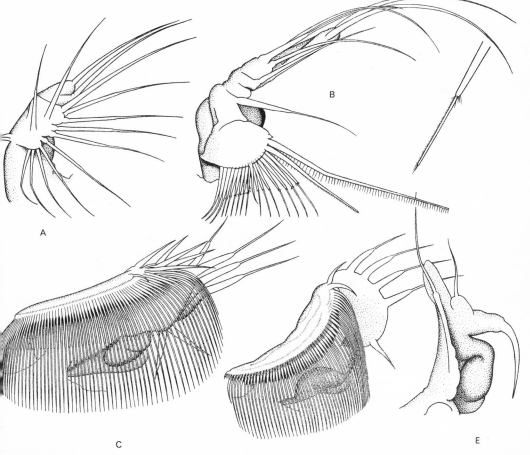

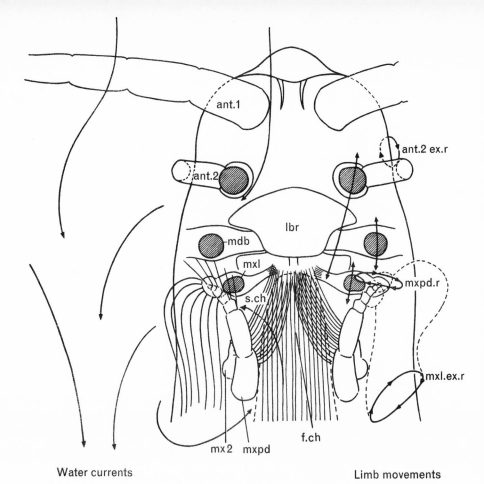

Water currents   Limb movements

Fig. 10-24. Diagram of anterior region of *Calanus finmarchicus*. The endopodite of the antenna, the mandibular palps, and the distal parts of the maxillules have been removed. The position of the swimming trunk limbs is indicated by the shaded area inside the dotted line. On the *right* side of the figure the limb movements are indicated, on the *left* the water currents. *ant.1*, antennule; *ant.2*, antenna; *ant.2 ex.r*, rotation path of tip of exopod of antenna; *f.ch*, filter chamber; *lbr*, labrum; *mdb*, mandible; *mxl*, maxillule; *mxl.ex.r*, rotation path of tips of setae of maxillulary exite; *mx.2*, maxilla; *mxpd*, maxilliped; *mxpd.r*, rotation path of tip of maxilliped; *s.ch*, suction chamber. From Marshall and Orr, 1955. *The Biology of a Marine Copepod.* Oliver and Boyd, Edinburgh.

Filter feeding of a different type, associated with a considerable degree of divergent specialization among the limbs, is seen in copepods such as *Diaptomus* and *Calanus* (Fig. 10-24), in which the feeding current is created by a swimming vortex. Fryer has suggested that this may be an example of the secondary development of filter feeding in a group that was primitively raptatory. The first thoracic segment is here fused with the head (p. 127), and bears a pair of maxillipeds, while the remaining five free thoracic segments each bear a pair of swimming limbs. These latter are not primarily involved in the feeding mechanism, which is the concern of the maxillipeds and of the head appendages: the maxillae, maxillules, mandibles, antennae, and antennules. The antennae, mandibular palps, and maxillules are kept in rapid vibration, which, because of the long setae that they carry, sets up a large vortex in the water on each side of the thorax (Fig. 10-25). Internally to these main vortices are smaller ones, partially established by the maxillules and maxillipeds.

The filter chamber of *Calanus* is bounded dorsally by the body wall, ventrally by the tips of the more anterior swimming limbs, medially and anteriorly by the maxillary setae and the labrum, and laterally by the maxillulary setae. Water is first drawn into this chamber by the suction created by the outward swing of the setae of the maxillipeds, and is then drawn out of it, through the maxillary setae, by the forward beat of the maxillules. The effect of this is that food is collected on the fringe of the maxillary setae, which thus act as the filter; the maxillae form a stationary filter, which does not show the rhythmical movement that is displayed by the other limbs. Finally, the food is removed from the maxillary setae and passed towards the mouth by setae on the maxillular endites and on the maxillipeds.

Maxillary filtering plates are also used in the Malacostraca, as, for example, in *Hemimysis*; in this animal they act both as a suction pump and as a filter, drawing a food-bearing stream forwards from a ventral food groove by their vibration. The food stream in this animal is produced by the swimming movements of the thoracic exopodites, much as in anostracans, but there is an important difference in their mode of action, for the limbs of Malacostraca bend forwards, whereas those of the Branchiopoda bend backwards. This suggests that the method of producing the food stream in the two groups evolved independently, for any stage intermediate between them would inevitably have been hydraulically inefficient.

Many other complications are revealed when we attempt to trace out the evolutionary pattern underlying these various systems. For example, *Nebalia bipes*, a malacostracan of the group Leptostraca, is a mud-living form that is common under stones in the littoral zone. It favours areas that are rich in organic débris, and feeds on particles that are filtered from a food stream produced by the oscillatory movements of the foliaceous trunk limbs. This stream, however, differs from that described in our other examples in that it enters the food-collecting zone anteriorly and leaves at the posterior end of the carapace. Moreover, the filter is here formed by the setae on the endopodites of the limbs.

One explanation of the origin of this unusual mechanism is that the Leptostraca may be derived from primitive mysid-like forms that took to a burrowing life, as a result of which they abandoned their swimming movements and, in consequence,

Fig. 10-25.. Diagram of ventral view of *Calanus finmarchicus* slowly swimming, to show water currents. From Marshall and Orr, 1955. *op. cit.*

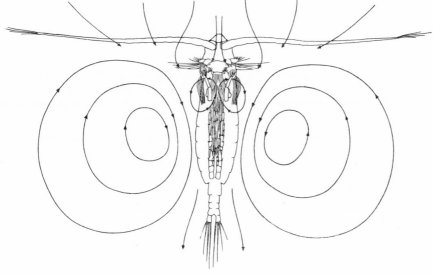

their primitive filter-feeding mechanism. The use of oar-like movements of the antennules to pull the animal through the mud might then have tended to suck particles into the anterior opening of the carapace. An increasingly folicaeous development of the trunk limbs might have encouraged this backward current, and have led eventually to the evolution of a new type of filtering mechanism. Mechanical principles similar to those employed in more primitive forms would in this way have found a new structural expression.

The complexity of the evolutionary interrelationships of crustacean feeding mechanisms and modes of life will be sufficiently evident, even from this brief survey. To some extent they are an expression of the parallelism and convergence found in so many aspects of arthropod organization. Thus, the caridoid facies of the Malacostraca, although probably developed in bottom-dwelling forms (p. 131), has nevertheless lent itself to the exploitation of pelagic life, and filter feeding has evolved as a natural accompaniment. Despite this, however, the higher Malacostraca have come to rely on crawling or burrowing in the littoral zone and on the sea bottom. Increasing emphasis upon macrophagy is natural in these conditions, and is aided by the versatility of the crustacean limb, and notably by the development of chelae on the walking limbs. This in turn favours continuing increase in size, and so we arrive at the large and varied raptatorial decapod fauna of today.

11
Respiration

11–1 SOME PHYSICAL FACTORS

The processes involved in securing and utlizing oxygen are grouped under the general category of respiration, but this term comprises two distinct aspects of those processes. Firstly, there is the exchange of oxygen and carbon dioxide between the organism and the external environment: this is external respiration. Secondly, there is the complex of reactions that takes place within the cells, and that results in the release of energy by the oxidation of the energy-rich molecules derived from the food: this is internal respiration. Linking these two are the transport mechanisms that convey the oxygen and carbon dioxide between the external respiratory surfaces and the metabolizing tissues.

We are here concerned with external respiration and transport. The organization of these is influenced by certain physical considerations that have been clearly stated by Krogh, whose analysis we may conveniently follow. The availability of oxygen for living organisms depends upon its concentration in the surrounding medium, and in this respect conditions are more favourable in air than in water. Air consists of 20.95 % oxygen and 0.03 % carbon dioxide, the remainder being composed of inert gases, mainly nitrogen (78 %) and argon (0.94 %). In respiratory uptake, however, the pressure rather than the volume of these gases is important; consequently it is more meaningful to express their concentrations in terms of pressure. Thus at sea level, at a normal barometric pressure of 760 mm of mercury, the oxygen pressure will be of the order of 20.95/100 × 760 mm, i.e. 155 mm, whereas at 16,000 ft it will have fallen to 88 mm, and life will be correspondingly more difficult to maintain.

The situation in water is very different from this. The component gases of the air are soluble, but only to a limited extent, and less so in salt solutions than in pure water. Solubility is expressed as the absorption coefficient. This, in Krogh's definition, is the quantity of gas, measured dry at 0°C and at atmospheric pressure, which can be taken up by one volume of water from an atmosphere of that gas at normal pressure (760 mm); it can conveniently be expressed as a percentage of the water volume. Absorption coefficients vary with temperature. At 15°C, to give one example, the values for oxygen, nitrogen, and carbon dioxide in pure water are respectively 3.5%, 1.7%, and 100%. Normally, of course, organisms are concerned with the mixed gases of the atmosphere, each of which is independently absorbed according to its partial pressure. Thus 100 volumes of water at sea level and at 15°C will take up $155/760 \times 3.5 = 0.72$ vol of oxygen, and $605/760 \times 1.7 = 1.35$ vol of nitrogen. It follows from all of these considerations that oxygen is very much less available in water than in air, and that it is less available in sea water than in fresh water (Table 11-1).

Other factors, however, are relevant in judging the availability of oxygen for the organisms living in any particular habitat. In the sea, despite the relatively low solubility of the gas, there is certainly enough in most regions to meet the requirements of animal life—not only at the surface, where it is taken up directly from the atmosphere, but in the deep waters of the abyssal zone, where it is continuously replenished by the massive currents of the oceans. The same is true for fresh water, provided that

Table 11–1   Volume of oxygen (ml/l) in fresh and salt water saturated with atmospheric air at the stated temperature. (From Krogh, A., 1941. *The Comparative Physiology of Respiratory Mechanisms.* Pennsylvania University Press.)

Temp. °C	fresh water	10% Cl	20% Cl
0	10.29	9.13	7.97
10	8.02	7.19	6.35
15	7.22	6.50	5.79
20	6.57	5.95	5.31
30	5.57	5.01	4.46

there is ample circulation of the water. Where circulation is reduced, as in swamps and ponds, or in lakes at a level below the summer thermocline (where contact with the surface is lost), there may be oxygen deprivation, particularly where abundant organic material is undergoing bacterial decay. Conversely, the occurence of much photosynthesis may raise the oxygen content of water above what could be secured by diffusion from the atmosphere; the water is then said to be supersaturated.

The rate of uptake of oxygen by an organism is limited by the gradient of concentration between the organism and the layer of the medium that immediately surrounds it. Regardless of whether an animal is living in water or in the air, this layer will be aqueous, for even in terrestrial forms the respiratory surfaces are kept moist by a thin film of fluid; it is this that maintains their permeability. Efficient respiratory exchange depends also upon the continuous replacement of the oxygen that is taken up from the medium, a replacement which is effected partly by diffusion of oxygen through the medium, and partly by movement of the medium itself. This movement may be partially provided for by convection currents, but the more important factor will usually be ventilation, which comprises the movements set up in the medium by the organism itself. It is essential for air-breathing animals to keep their respiratory surfaces moist, and to prevent an undue loss of water through them. Provided that these conditions are satisfied, the balance of respiratory advantage lies with them rather than with those animals that take their oxygen from water. One reason for this is that oxygen diffuses much more readily in air than in water. This has been expressed by Krogh in terms of diffusion constants, which are based upon the difference in partial pressure of the gas per unit length of the phase through which it is diffusing. The diffusion constants for oxygen at 20°C are 11.0 in air and only 0.000034 in water. A further advantage for air-breathing animals is the lower density of air as compared with water; the specific gravity of air at 20°C, when it is dry and at atmospheric pressure, is 0.0012. This means that convection currents are more readily established in air than in water, and also that ventilation movements in the former demand a smaller output of energy.

We shall see many ways in which the form and organization of the animal body have been influenced by the factors outlined above. In addition, they have been influenced by the problem of ensuring the transport of oxygen from the surrounding medium into the area of metabolic activity within the body. Small size brings the advantage of a high ratio of surface area to volume. Because of this the smallest animals need rely on no more than passive diffusion of the oxygen into and around their body. This is most obvious in Protozoa, but it holds also in sponges and coelenterates, where thin layers of epithelium are directly bathed by the external medium.

There are sharp limits, however, to the value of unaided diffusion. These can be appreciated from the calculation that the difference in oxygen tension between the surface and the centre of an organism, if constant metabolic rate is to be maintained, will be proportional to the square of the radius of the organism. Krogh has drawn from this the conclusion that organisms relying solely upon diffusion can only maintain a high rate of metabolism if they are of 1 mm diameter or less. Larger animals that continue to rely upon diffusion alone must necessarily, therefore, have a low metabolic rate. It is true that animals have some room for manoeuvre in this regard, for their relations with the environment can be improved by appropriate modifications of their shape. The point here is the well-known one, fundamental to the design both of the whole body of an animal and of its constituent parts, that a sphere provides the smallest possible ratio of surface area to volume. Departures from a strictly spherical shape will, therefore, benefit the organism by increasing this ratio and so facilitating respiratory exchange by diffusion. This factor must have influenced the evolution of the shape of platyhelminths and nemertines, for their flattened form both increases the ratio and reduces the distances over which diffusion has to take place.

Two other developments have been important in attaining large size. Both are related to the need for providing internally some system of convection to replace diffusion, and to provide an equivalent to the external convection secured by the ventilation movements. The first has been the establishment of a circulatory system providing for the movement of a fluid transport medium through the body. To some extent the movement of tissue fluids resulting from locomotion and feeding goes a little way to meet this need; but the crucial advance in this connection was the evolution of a blood system, which provides for a continuous and comparatively rapid circulation of fluid to all parts of the body.

We have already seen, however, that a saline medium, which is what the body fluids necessarily are, can only absorb comparatively small amounts of oxygen in simple solution. Consequently many animals have a circulatory system which is fortified for respiratory functioning by the presence in it of oxygen carriers, or respiratory pigments. These have properties of remarkable adaptive advantage, being able to take up oxygen where it is abundant, to release it where it is scarce, and to transport it in concentrations greater than could be secured by its simple solution. By developing these substances many animals have obtained an invaluable basis for metabolic efficiency. Curiously enough, however, one of the major groups, the insects, together with certain other members of the Phylum Arthropoda, have not adopted this device. Instead, they have secured a high level of metabolic efficiency through the aid of physical diffusion, sometimes, although not always, supplemented by ventilation movements. For this they have paid the price of small size.

11–2 RESPIRATORY PIGMENTS

We can only account for the distribution of oxygen carriers in the animal kingdom if we assume that these compounds have been independently evolved in many different lines, for more than one type of compound has been employed, and the distribution of these follows no simple phylogenetic plan. The most widespread of these substances is the group of compounds called haemoglobins; these have certainly evolved quite independently in unrelated groups, doubtless as a consequence of the capacity of living organisms for synthesizing the compounds known as porphyrins. These are synthesized in natural conditions from glycine and other simple substances, but they may be regarded theoretically as derivatives of a parent compound called porphin (Fig. 11-1). This substance, known only from laboratory synthesis, consists of four pyrrole rings linked by four methane bridges into a cyclic system which is evidently of great stability, for porphyrins of biological origin occur in mineral deposits such as coal and oil. They are widely distributed in living organisms, in bacteria and plants as well as in animals. In fact, the capacity for synthesizing them is universal in aerobic organisms, with the exception of certain bacteria, and they are probably another example of a molecular pattern that appeared very early in the history of evolution.

A particularly important property of porphyrins is their ability to associate with metals to form coordinated compounds known as metallo-porphyrins. These compounds serve as the prosthetic groups of proteins that have a wide range of catalytic functions in the cell. Thus iron porphyrins are the prosthetic groups of the peroxidases that are found largely in plant tissues, and also of the catalases of bacteria and animal tissues, while chlorophyll is a magnesium–porphyrin complex. Furthermore, the cytochromes, which we have seen to be essential components of intracellular oxidation mechanisms, are composed of proteins having iron porphyrins as their prosthetic groups. Probably the capacity for synthesizing this type of molecule led to the evolution of adaptively valuable compounds, with the consequent development of certain oxygen carriers.

One of the porphyrins that can be derived from porphin is protoporphyrin. The addition to this of one ferrous iron atom produces ferrous protoporphyrin (haem, Fig. 11-1), in which the iron atom is joined by four of its coordination bonds to the four nitrogen atoms of the protoporphyrin. One of the remaining six coordination bonds can then be joined to a molecule of a protein called globin. The result is the formation of the compounds known as haemoglobins, which are the best known of all

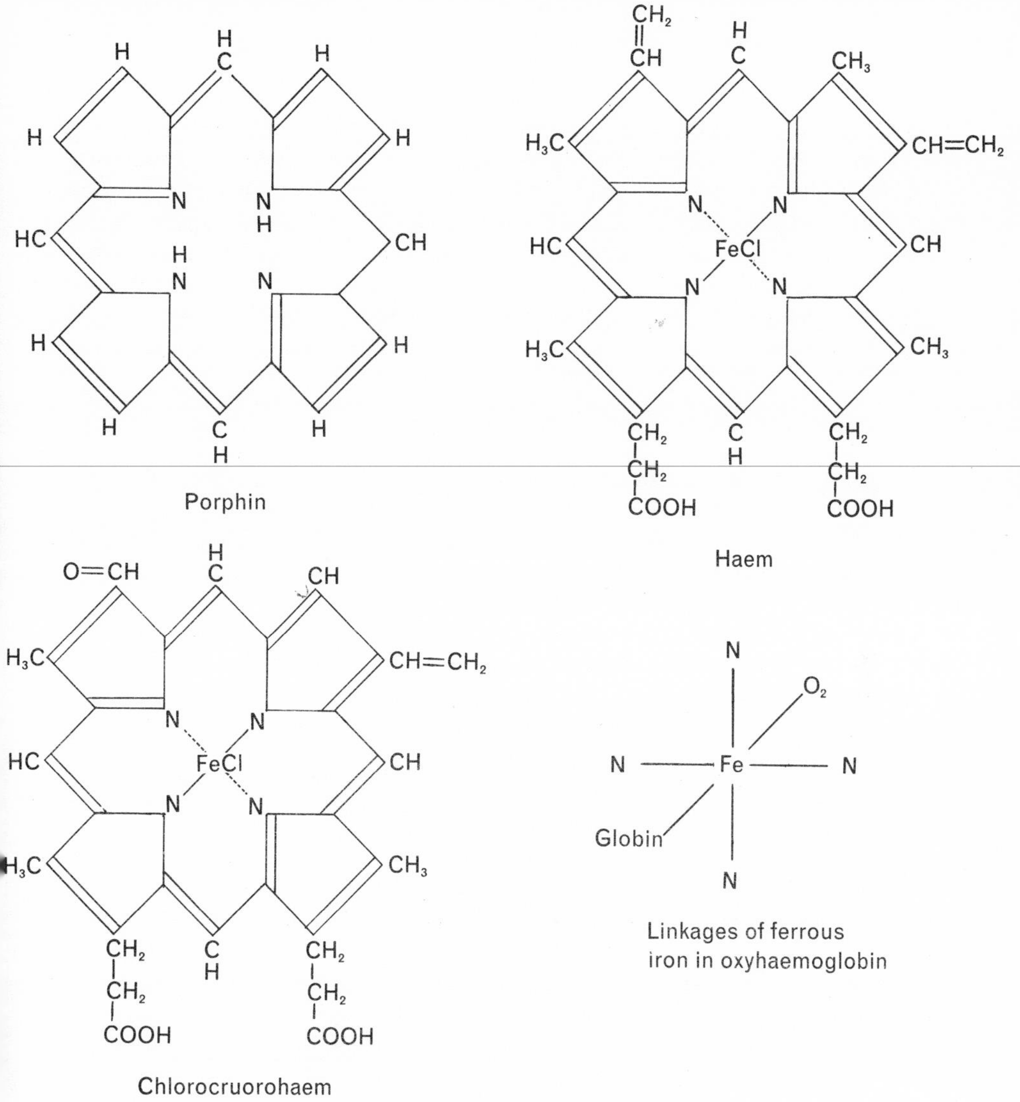

Porphin

Haem

Chlorocruorohaem

Linkages of ferrous
iron in oxyhaemoglobin

Fig. 11-1.   Haem and related compounds.

of the oxygen carriers. The haemoglobin molecule can carry an oxygen molecule attached to the remaining coordination bond, with the iron remaining in the ferrous state (Fig. 11–1); this is of peculiar value in oxygen transport. The oxygen is readily taken up at the respiratory surface, and is equally readily given up within the tissues at regions of low oxygen concentration; this latter process, called dissociation, involves the replacement of a molecule of oxygen by a molecule of water. The two forms of the compound, oxygenated and deoxygenated, are known respectively as oxyhaemoglobin and deoxyhaemoglobin. They must be distinguished from the oxidized form, methaemoglobin; in this the iron is in the ferric form, and the sixth bond carries a hydroxyl group, with the result that the molecule is no longer available as an oxygen carrier.

Haemoglobins occur in all vertebrate animals, with some very rare exceptions (the leptocephalus larva of the eel is one), so that they can be regarded as a biochemical characteristic of the group. In invertebrates the situation is quite otherwise. It has been known since the early investigations of Ray Lankester in the nineteenth century that haemoglobin is widely distributed in these animals, but its appearance is curiously sporadic, and of no obvious phylogenetic significance. As suggested above, this is most readily explained as a consequence of the widespread capacity for synthesizing protoporphyrin. Conceivably haemoglobin could have arisen because of changes in the cytochromes resulting from mutation. Cytochromes, however, depend for their functioning upon oxidation, with an associated change in the valence state of the iron from the ferrous to the ferric form. Thus, as Munro Fox and Vevers remark, it is probably easier to imagine haemoglobins arising from the chance association of protoporphyrin with various globins.

Among the invertebrates haemoglobin is particularly characteristic of the Annelida and the entomostracan Crustacea, where it is typically dissolved in the blood fluid, although it may also be present in the tissues. It occurs only rarely in other arthropods, the blood of the midge larva, *Chironomus*, providing one example. In molluscs its occurrence is sporadic; when present it is usually in the tissues, but it is dissolved in the blood of one pulmonate, *Planorbis*, and it occurs in blood corpuscles in a few lamellibranchs. *Phoronis* provides an example of its occurrence in the blood corpuscles of an interesting and isolated animal; it has been identified also in organisms as diverse as *Paramecium* and yeast. Finally, the production of haemoglobin, so characteristic of animals, is not beyond the capacity of the higher plants, for it has been identified in the root nodules of the Leguminosae. There it results from the interaction between the plant itself and its symbiotic micro-organism. *Rhizobium*; neither of these can produce it unaided.

Oxyhaemoglobin and deoxyhaemoglobin are respectively red and purple in colour, and are characterized by well-defined absorption bands in the visible spectrum. Oxyhaemoglobin has alpha and beta bands in the yellow and green regions (the alpha nearer the red end) and a larger gamma band in the violet region. Deoxyhaemoglobin has the gamma band, although at a slightly different position, together with only one other band, lying in the green region. The positions of these bands vary in haemoglobins from different sources, which means, of course, that there must be many different haemoglobins. Indeed, spectroscopic characteristics are not the only differences between them. They are distinguishable also by physical properties, such as their isoelectric points and their amino acid composition, and these are reflected in differences in the kinetics and equilibria of their interactions with oxygen. These characteristics arise solely from differences in the globin portion of their molecules, the haem portion being always identical. This can be demonstrated by taking advantage of the capacity of pyridine for displacing the globin and combining with the haem to form a pyridine–haem complex. The spectroscopic properties of this complex are always precisely the same, irrespective of the properties of the haemoglobin from which it is derived.

In general, the invertebrate haemoglobins differ from the vertebrate ones in having less histidine and lysine, and more arginine and cystine, but they also differ among themselves. Their molecular weights, for example, range from 17,000 to several million. This variability, which may even be found between two species of the same genus, illustrates the variability that is often shown by complex protein molecules, and it has doubtless provided the basis for the adaptive evolution of haemoglobins that are particularly suited for use in different types of environment. There are, however, other differences to be found in respiratory pigments, showing that substances that are similar in principle in their oxygen-transporting properties may yet be very different in their molecular structure.

One example of these is chlorocruorin, a type of green respiratory pigment found only in four families of the Polychaeta: the Ampharetidae, Chlorhaemidae, Sabellidae, and Serpulidae. It is closely related chemically to haemoglobin (Fig. 11-1); the protein is different, as is to be expected, but the iron porphyrin of its prosthetic group differs only in having one of the two vinyl groups ($-CH=CH_2$) substituted by a formyl (aldehyde, $-CHO$) group. Its molecular weight, however, is extremely high, amounting to about 3 million, and it contains some 190 iron atoms in its complex molecule. Chlorocruorin is described as dichroic, for it has two colours which are dependent on its concentration. green in dilute solutions and red in concentrated ones. Worms with this pigment are not necessarily green, however, for the colour may be masked by other pigments, as it is, for example, in the tentacles of serpulids. More confusing is the fact that closely related species may differ in the presence or absence of the pigment, as in the genus *Spirorbis*. One species, *S. borealis*, possesses chlorocruorin; another, *S. corrugatus*, has haemoglobin; a third, *S. militaris*, has no respiratory pigment at all.

The close similarity of chlorocruorin to haemoglobin makes it likely enough that chlorocruorin could evolve from haemoglobin by genetic mutation, and that it might well have arisen independently in different species. Thus the presence of this pigment is not necessarily evidence of the close phylogenetic relationship of the groups concerned. The need for caution in making such interpretations is shown by the presence of chlorocruorohaem, which is the prosthetic group of chloro-cruorin, in two starfish, *Luidia* and *Astropecten*; these animals have not, however, developed the respiratory pigment itself.

The devious pathways of biochemical evolution are further illustrated by the haemerythrins. These are reddish-violet iron-containing respiratory pigments that are known only in the sipunculids (including *Sipunculus* and *Phascolosoma*), the polychaete *Magelona*, the priapulids *Halicryptus* and *Priapulus*, and the brachiopod *Lingula*. Haemerythrin is thus a rare pigment, and, apart from the fact that it has been identified in all sipunculids examined, its distribution is sporadic and without any phylogenetic significance. The sipunculids are possibly related to annelids, but the priapulids are non-coelomate forms, while the brachiopods are perhaps related through the structure of their lophophore to *Phoronis* and the Ectoprocta. There are other curious facts about this pigment. For one thing, it is always present in cells, which are usually in the coelomic fluid; in *Magelona*, however, they are true blood corpuscles, this animal being the only polychaete to carry a respiratory pigment in this particular way. Then again, haemerythrin, despite its oxygen-carrying capacity and its red colour, is not closely related to haemoglobin. Its spectrum shows no strong absorption bands, and in molecular structure it is a protein, with iron in its molecule, but with no associated porphyrin. Thus in haemoglobin and haemerythrin we find a similar result achieved by different chemical means.

There is also another and more important type of respiratory pigment that also lacks the haem group. This pigment is haemocyanin, a protein that differs from all of the preceding in having copper instead of iron as the metal that enters into dissociable combination with oxygen. It thus shows some relationship to the copper-containing phenol oxidases, a relationship analogous to that of the haemoglobins to the iron-containing oxidases and peroxidases. The oxygen combines with two atoms of copper in haemocyanin, as compared with the one iron atom of the haemoglobin, and in so doing produces a blue compound, a deoxygenated form of the pigment being colourless. The molecular weights are considerable—units with two copper atoms range from 50,000 to 74,000, and are associated into complex molecules with molecular weights as high as 6,650,000 in *Helix pomatia*. Not surprisingly there is variation here, as with the haemoglobins, in the properties of the pigment.

Haemocyanin, like chlorocruorin, occurs only in solution, in this instance in the haemolymph of certain arthropods and molluscs, where its distribution shows a certain phylogenetic pattern. It is the only respiratory pigment of malacostracan Crustacea, occurring in the decapods and the stomatopods. It is found in no other crustaceans, nor does it occur at all in insects, but it appears in some chelicerates: *Limulus*, *Euscorpius*, and spiders. As regards molluscs, it is found in chitons, in cephalopods, and in many gastropods, including particularly the prosobranchs and the pulmonates, but it has not been identified in the lamellibranchs. Molluscan haemocyanins have molecular weights of several million, while those of crustaceans are of the order of several hundred thousand; the difference doubtless reflects the independent origin of these substances in the two groups.

The wide distribution of respiratory pigments, and their occurrence in such different groups, is sufficient indication that respiratory advantages must, in general, accrue from their possession. Yet it needs to be emphasized that, as in the case of *Spirorbis*, one species may exist without any of these pigments, while related species possess them. Indeed, it is not always easy to decide just what their function is in certain species. As we have already suggested, the molecules of these pigments seem well suited for undergoing adaptive modification. Yet we must judge their function not only from the properties of the particular pigment, but also with an understanding of the conditions of life of the species concerned.

In general, respiratory pigments function either as oxygen carriers, or as oxygen stores, providing reserves to be used at times of shortage. The former function may reasonably be attributed to those pigments that are present within the blood stream, but where they are present in other tissues (as, for example, in the muscles of *Arenicola*) they are more probably serving for oxygen storage. However, storage is not sharply separable from transport, for the tissue pigments, by combining with the oxygen arriving in the blood stream, must accelerate the passage of oxygen into the tissues. This is likely to be particularly important in organs that carry out rhythmical bursts of activity; it is significant, therefore, that there is evidence of haemoglobin being particularly abundant in the muscles of gizzards and radulae. It is often supposed that storage is also the main function of the respiratory pigments of the body cavities, such as the coelomic haemoglobins of some annelids and the coelomic haemerythrins of sipunculids. This may be so, but we have noted that the use of such fluids in hydrostatic skeletons results in a good deal of movement in them, and certainly brings them into close functional relationship with contractile tissues; some transport function cannot, therefore, be excluded in such instances.

One factor of particular relevance to the mode of functioning of these pigments is their oxygen affinity, which is indicated by the partial pressure of oxygen at which they are half-saturated with oxygen. If the value (referred to as the p_{50}) is high, the pigment has a low affinity, for it will give up its oxygen while this is still relatively plentiful in the surrounding medium. If the p_{50} is low, the pigment has a high affinity, for it will only yield up its oxygen when the partial pressure of oxygen in the surrounding medium has become very low. A low affinity has been thought to indicate a transport function, and a high affinity a storage function, but this may not always be so. The problem may be illustrated by reference to *Arenicola*.

The oxygen affinity of the haemoglobin of this animal is relatively high; it is completely saturated at an oxygen concentration equivalent to 5 mm to 10 mm of mercury, and has a p_{50} of about 1.8 mm. The presence of haemoglobin in the blood increases the oxygen capacity of the fluid by about 10 times, yet this capacity is low in relation to the known metabolic rate of the animal. Even if the pigment were functioning solely as a store, the oxygen would only be sufficient for about 21 minutes of activity. Admittedly even as small a store as this could be of value in the intervals between the rhythmic irrigation movements which, as we shall see later, the worms carry out in their burrows, and which provide a regular replenishment of oxygen supply. However, it is probable that the pigment does, in fact, provide a mechanism for transporting oxygen. The water in the sand around the burrow at low tide will contain an oxygen concentration equivalent to about 6.7 mm of mercury. This is sufficient to saturate the haemoglobin, so that there seems no reason why this should not transport oxygen to the tissues and release it to the haemoglobin of the muscle. We shall see that the respiration of *Arenicola* is further aided by the animal's ability to draw oxygen into its burrow when the tide is out; presumably, therefore, it is not dependent for long periods upon stored oxygen.

Nephtys hombergi, in contrast to *Arenicola*, has a haemoglobin with a low oxygen affinity; its p_{50} is 6 mm of mercury. This animal, an active burrower (Sec. 6–3), is believed to use its haemoglobin for oxygen transport when the tide is in, and it may well be that its tissues, like those of the higher vertebrates, can only continue to function if a certain critical oxygen tension is maintained in the blood. Where so many invertebrates differ from mammals is in their ability to maintain metabolism at very low internal oxygen tensions. This is probably the situation in *Arenicola*, and it is probably true also of *Tubifex* and earthworms, which can continue their metabolism even when their haemoglobin is completely immobilized by the presence of carbon monoxide.

11–3 GILLS AND LOPHOPHORES

The thin flat body of platyhelminths facilitates respiratory exchange, and also ensures that metabolites can readily be transmitted throughout the body by diffusion; in correlation with this there is no blood system in these animals. A simple type of circulatory system is, however, present in nemertines, and is probably associated with the elongation of the body. In its simplest and presumably primitive form, as seen in *Cephalothrix*, it consists of no more than a pair of longitudinal vessels, united in front and behind; in other genera this plan is further elaborated by the development of transverse vessels and a mid-dorsal one. The larger vessels are contractile, with circular muscle fibres in their walls, and there is a true circulation of the blood.

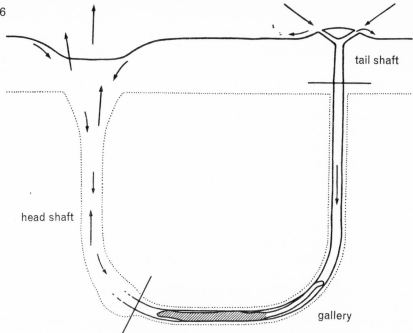

Fig. 11-2. Generalized diagram of a lugworm burrow, with the worm lying quietly in the gallery. The cross lines are drawn at the boundaries between head shaft, gallery, and tail shaft. The dotted line is the boundary between yellow and black sand. The long, thin arrows show the movement of water, and the short, thick ones that of sand. From Wells, 1950. *Symp. Soc. exp. Biol.,* **4**, 127–142.

This movement can be seen in smaller animals, the flow being forwards in the dorsal vessel, as it commonly is in invertebrates.

The blood of nemertines is usually colourless, with cells suspended in it, but sometimes these cells contain pigment, and in a few instances this has been shown by spectroscopic examination to be haemoglobin. Presumably, then, the vascular system of nemertines may sometimes be of significance for respiration. But the vessels lie below much or all of the well-developed muscle layers of the body wall; here they are so far from the body surface that they must often be unable to play much part in respiratory exchanges with the external medium. Probably the system is chiefly important as a transporter of metabolites; we would expect, however, that once established a circulatory system would become associated, sooner or later, with the uptake and movement of oxygen and carbon dioxide; in fact, we find a system functioning in this way in the Phylum Annelida.

In many annelids, particularly in oligochaetes and leeches, respiratory exchanges take place through the body surface. In earthworms the epidermis is sufficiently thin for diffusion to take place through it, and the vessels run at its base; in leeches, with a more specialized body wall, capillaries penetrate among the epidermal cells. Even within this simple type of arrangement there is room for adaptation to specialized habitats, as may be seen in *Tubifex*. This oligochaete is well adapted for withstanding oxygen shortage. It is, in fact, the first species to become re-established in rivers below points where animal life has been destroyed by the discharge of effluents, and for this reason it is a useful biological indicator of high pollution. It lives head downwards in burrows in the mud, and obtains its oxygen by uptake through the posterior body wall. Ventilation is effected by a rhythmic waving of its tail at a frequency that increases as the amount of available oxygen declines. The arrangement of the posterior segmental vessels is influenced by this; they are long and convoluted, and are closely applied to the body wall, so that they are well suited for the uptake of oxygen. A similar arrangement at the anterior end, however, would result in the loss of oxygen to the deoxygenated mud, and it is presumably in adaptation to this difficulty that the more anterior segmental vessels are shorter, and are not so closely applied to the body surface.

The respiratory exchange of errant polychaetes is aided by the parapodia; these are hollow and mobile extensions of the body surface, and are also well vascularized. True gills or branchiae are also common in polychaetes. An outgrowth of the parapodium of *Nephtys* is probably respiratory in function (Fig. 6–6), but gills are more particularly characteristic of sedentary worms such as *Amphitrite* (Fig. 10–7), where the parapodia are of a different form. In *Arenicola* we find gills are developed as branched and highly vascularized outgrowths on a number of the trunk segments, and the adaptations of this animal for life within a burrow (Fig. 11–2) include a mechanism for ensuring efficient ventilation. This is carried out by outbursts of irrigation movements, which recur with great regularity at intervals of about 40 minutes. The movements are initiated by a tailward locomotion of the animal, which takes it towards the posterior end of the burrow. This is followed by the chief phase of irrigation, which consists of anteriorly directed peristaltic waves of the body surface, combined with some headward creeping. During this phase water is drawn forwards and over the gills. Finally, there is a brief phase of tailward irrigation.

One means for bringing about such irrigation movements would, in theory, be for them to arise as reflex responses to shortage of oxygen, but this is not the means adopted in *Arenicola*. Instead, they are the product of an innate spontaneous rhythm with a period of about 40 minutes; this rhythm is uninfluenced by oxygen shortage, and is probably evoked by a pacemaker situated in the central nervous system. Similar outbursts of activity occur if the worm is pinned out in a dish of well-aerated sea water (Fig. 11–3); they are even shown by strips of its body wall, always provided that these include a piece of the ventral nerve cord. Innate rhythms of this type are

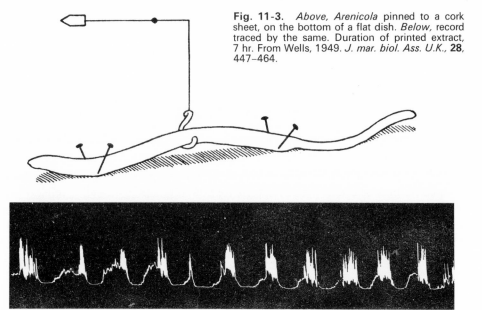

Fig. 11-3. *Above, Arenicola* pinned to a cork sheet, on the bottom of a flat dish. *Below,* record traced by the same. Duration of printed extract, 7 hr. From Wells, 1949. *J. mar. biol. Ass. U.K.,* **28**, 447–464.

sometimes referred to as 'animal clocks'. They are of great importance in animal behaviour patterns, and the irrigation movements are not the only example of them in *Arenicola*. There is also a periodicity of feeding movements, smaller in amplitude and with a period of about 7 minutes; it probably arises from a pacemaker located in a nerve plexus on the oesophagus (Sec. 16–3).

The potentialities of this mode of behaviour, and its suitability for life in a burrow, are illustrated by the fact that the irrigation movements can be used when the tide is in and the burrow filled with water, as well as when the tide is out and the burrow deprived of fresh supplies of water. In the latter circumstance the same rhythmicity results in the worm extending its tail to the surface of such water as may be present over the sand. The forward-directed irrigation movements then draw air bubbles over the dorsal body surface to the gills. Wells has shown that this behaviour allows a worm to spend as much as 120 hours in an artificial burrow in the laboratory, with the same 15 ml of water, and still be in good condition at the end of that period. It may be expected from our discussion of blood pigments that the haemoglobin of *Arenicola*, which is present in its muscle as well as in its blood stream, will further increase the efficiency of its respiration.

Many sedentary polychaetes have a crown of tentacles at the anterior end. These, as we have seen, can serve as filter-feeding mechanisms. Before this function was understood the tentacles were generally termed gills, or branchial crowns, and the term is not necessarily inappropriate, for respiratory exchange may be one of their functions. It is possible that here, as with the gills of molluscs, respiration was actually the primary function of these tentacular crowns, and that their incorporation into the feeding mechanism was a later step. The polychaetes, however, provide no special evidence regarding this.

The development of branchial crowns at the oral end of the body is by no means restricted to polychaetes. A similar principle is seen in a number of the smaller invertebrata phyla, including the Phoronida, the Ectoprocta (Fig. 5–3), the Brachiopoda, and the Entoprocta (Fig. 5–2). Of these, the first three share common features of organization in that the ring of tentacles surrounds the mouth but not the anus, and the tentacles are hollow and contain an extension of the coelom. To this specific type of branchial crown the term lophophore has been applied. Because the three groups concerned have this feature in common they may be closely related. The Entoprocta, which have no close relationship with the Ectoprocta, are of a more archaic organization, and lack a coelom. In them the tentacles enclose the anus as well as the mouth, and they are not retractile. Nevertheless, the term lophophore is sometimes applied to their tentacular crown also, and, indeed, to all such rings of tentacles, irrespective of their morphological organization, and including those of the polychaetes.

In all of the groups mentioned above the tentacles serve as ciliary feeding organs; they can reasonably be assumed also to assist in respiration, by providing a large surface area for gaseous exchange. In the Phoronida and the Brachiopoda there is the additional advantage of a blood system. In the former this includes a ring vessel running in the coelom at the base of the lophophore, and giving off a single vessel into each tentacle. The circulation of blood passes up and down the tentacular vessels, and must considerably increase the efficiency of the respiratory exchange, particularly since haemoglobin is present.

11–4   GILLS AND LUNGS IN MOLLUSCS

The examples so far considered suggest the possibility of a close relationship between respiration and ciliary feeding. There are good grounds for this supposition. Respiratory surfaces must be kept clean, and a flow of water maintained over them, if they are to function efficiently. Wherever these needs arise in animals, and whether or not the function of the surfaces concerned is respiratory, they are often met by the secretion of mucus, and by the development of cilia to maintain movement over the surface. (The arthropods, of course, are an obvious exception to this.) Clearly this is precisely the situation that also best lends itself to the collection and transport of food particles, but unfortunately we often lack the evidence to determine whether or not events have followed this course. In the molluscs, however, we have a group of animals in which the close interlocking of respiratory and nutritional requirements is particularly well shown, and in which there is evidence that enables us to trace something of the history of the organs concerned.

As already noted, we can regard the body of a mollusc as composed of two components: a ventral portion (the head and foot), in which the activity is predominantly muscular, and a dorsal portion (the visceral hump), in which ciliary action and mucus secretion predominate (Fig. 11–4). The surface of the visceral hump extends into an overhanging fold, the mantle, which secretes the shell, and which encloses between itself and the visceral hump a space called the mantle cavity. This cavity is the centre of external respiration, for protected within it are the gills or ctenidia. It has been generally assumed that, in the primitive state, there were two of these, but some doubt now attaches to this since the discovery of *Neopilina*, with its five pairs of ctenidia (Fig. 11–5): However, even if the earliest molluscs did have serially repeated ctenidia (and we cannot be sure that this was so), these organs must have been reduced to a single pair at a very early stage of molluscan history. Their condition at that stage was the basis for the later history of the respiratory organs in the group, and we can develop our analysis from that point.

The structure of the early molluscan ctenidium can be deduced from its condition in primitive living forms, such as the zeugobranchiate prosobranchs. Yonge has defined it as consisting of a longitudinal axis from which triangular filaments were given off alternately on its two sides (cf. Fig. 11–4). Essentially it was a hollow outgrowth of the body, supplied with branchial muscles, nerves, and blood vessels; the blood travelled up and down the axis in a dorsal (afferent) and ventral (efferent) vessel, and flowed from one to the other of these through the filaments. If we assume that only two ctenidia were present, oxygenated blood would have flowed from them into a single pair of auricles, and so into the ventricle for general distribution (Fig. 11–5).

The functional relationships of this system, so simple in principle, are subtly adapted in present-day molluscs to ensure the maximum efficiency of respiratory exchange. The protection of the filaments within the mantle cavity makes ventilation the more essential, and this is secured by lateral cilia on the face of each filament. These cilia, which draw the respiratory stream of water into the mantle cavity, lie near the efferent limb of the circulation. Here they create a current of water that is directed upwards and inwards, in the opposite direction to the flow of the blood. This arrangement therefore involves counterflow; its effect is to increase the efficiency of gaseous exchange between the blood and the water. The gill filaments must be

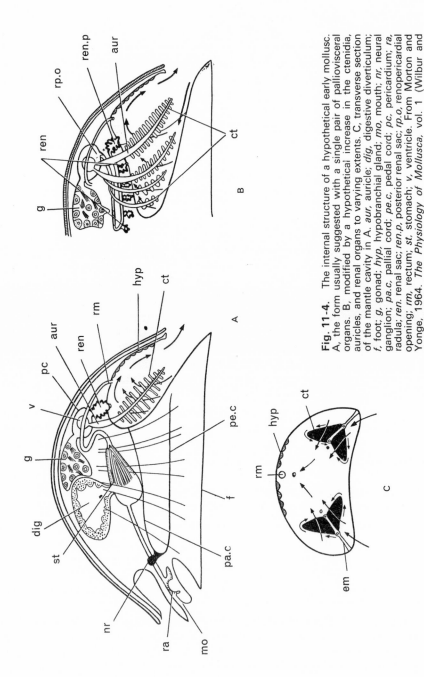

Fig. 11-4. The internal structure of a hypothetical early mollusc. A, the form usually suggested with a single pair of pallovisceral organs. B, modified by a hypothetical increase in the ctenidia, auricles, and renal organs to varying extents. C, transverse section of the mantle cavity in A. *aur*, auricle; *dig*, digestive diverticulum; *f*, foot; *g*, gonad; *hyp*, hypobranchial gland; *mo*, mouth; *nr*, neural ganglion; *pa.c*, pallial cord; *pe.c*, pedal cord; *pc*, pericardium; *ra*, radula; *ren*, renal sac; *ren.p*, posterior renal sac; *rp.o*, renopericardial opening; *rm*, rectum; *st*, stomach; *v*, ventricle. From Morton and Yonge, 1964. *The Physiology of Mollusca*, vol. 1 (Wilbur and Yonge, eds.). Academic Press, New York.

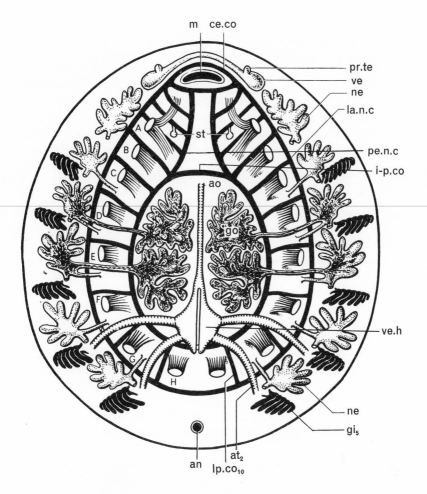

Fig. 11-5. Diagram of the relations between the 'segmented' organ systems in *Neopilina*. The gill nerves, the gill vessels, and many smaller muscles are also repeated, but are not included in the drawing. *A–H*, foot retractor muscles; *an*, anus; *ao*, aorta; *at$_2$*, 2nd atrium of heart; *ce.co*, cerebral commissure; *gi$_5$*, 5th gill; *i-p.co*, inter-pedal commissure; *la.n.c*, lateral nerve cord; *lp.co$_{10}$*, 10th latero-pedal connective; *m*, mcuth; *ne*, excretory organs; *pe.n.c*, pedal nerve cord; *pr.te*, preoral tentacle; *st*, statocyst; *ve*, velum; *ve.h*, ventricle of heart. From Lemche and Wingstrand, 1959. *Galathea Rep.*, vol. 3, 9–71. Danish Science Press, Copenhagen.

supported against the flow of water, and chitinous supporting rods provide for this. Further, the surface of the filaments needs to be kept clear of foreign material which will tend to settle on them from the water, and in adaptation to this requirement there are frontal and abfrontal cilia situated on the afferent and efferent edges of the filaments (cf. Fig. 10-10). These sweep material towards the central axis, where it is removed by a ciliary current along the afferent surface.

As Yonge points out, these arrangements will not in themselves ensure the protection of the ctenidia from sediment, particularly as these organs increase in size, for the ciliary currents may prove too weak to remove heavy deposits of material. It is probably because of this that two other paired structures, the osphradia and the hypobranchial glands, are present in the primitive mantle cavity; these structures, with the ctenidia, form a functionally associated system which can be called the pallial complex. The osphradia, which are universally present in the mantle cavities of aquatic gastropods, irrespective of their habitat or the nature of their food, are receptors, consisting of raised areas of epithelia that are rich in mucus, and in ciliated and sensory cells. They test the quality of the incoming water, perhaps by chemical sensitivity, for they are extremely large in carnivores such as *Buccinum*. Perhaps they also estimate through mechanoreception the amount of sediment entering the mantle cavity. The hypobranchial glands (Fig. 11-4), present in gastropods and in some lamellibranchs, are folds of mucus-secreting epithelium lying on the roof of the mantle cavity. They vary in size and complexity, apparently in relation to the amount of sediment that is likely to enter the mantle cavity in the particular habitat favoured by the species; their function seems to be to aid the removal of the sediment by consolidating it into larger masses. Their absence from cephalopods is thought to be correlated with the exceptionally powerful currents in those animals, which remove the need for such consolidation.

Not surprisingly, the highly organized respiratory systems of the pallial cavity reflect a great deal of adaptive evolution in relation to changes in the habits and organization of the members of this highly diversified phylum. This is already apparent in the primitive chitons. In these animals the number of gills is secondarily increased in correlation with the forward extension of the mantle cavity, and the osphradia lie posteriorly, where the outgoing current of water leaves. Within the gastropods the respiratory process has been profoundly affected by two characteristic features of the group. The first of these is the asymmetrical coiling of the visceral mass, which is an adaptation to secure a more compact arrangement of the internal organs. The second is torsion, a process that takes place early in development (Sec. 19-2), quite independently of coiling, which brings the mantle cavity of the veliger larva from its primitively posterior position round to the anterior end (Fig. 11-6).

The significance of torsion for the respiratory process is that the visceral and pallial organs are rotated through 180°, so that, as Morton points out, the mantle

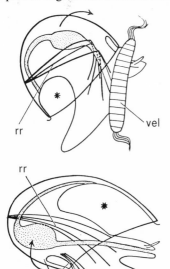

Fig. 11-6. The process of torsion in a prosobranch veliger larva, showing the position of the asymmetrically developed shell muscle. Asterisk indicates position of the mantle cavity. *rl*, left retractor muscles; *rr*, right retractor muscles; *vel*, velum. From Morton and Yonge, 1964. *op. cit.*

cavity is now in more sensitive touch with its surroundings. Additional advantages are that the forward movement of the animal will now reinforce the incurrent stream instead of opposing it, while the gills receive water direct from in front of the animal, and the osphradium is in the anterior position that is suitable for a major receptor organ. On the other hand, a serious problem now arises in disposing of the excurrent water stream with its contained faeces. It would be unsatisfactory for these to be discharged anteriorly into the path of the animal, and so we find various arrangements of openings in the shell (the row of openings in *Haliotis* is an example of this) to direct this stream away from the incurrent one.

Other solutions to the problem are influenced by the fact that asymmetrical coiling produces on one side of the mantle cavity a compression that favours reduction of the corresponding part of the pallial complex. Thus we find that one of the ctenidia and its associated auricle may be lost, while as a further stage of reduction the original two rows of gill filaments of the ctenidium are reduced to one. The ctenidia may even be completely lost, respiration taking place through the body wall or with the aid of accessory respiratory organs. This condition is found in nudibranchs, and also characterizes the Pulmonata. In the latter, as their name indicates, the mantle cavity functions as a lung, its epithelium forming the respiratory surface. The cavity usually retains its anterior position, but it has only a single external opening, the pneumostome, which can be opened and closed. Because of this change of function, the hypobranchial gland is lost, as would be expected from what we have said above regarding its supposed role in the removal of small particles, while the osphradium is usually outside the mantle cavity. The respiratory surface is now the lining of that cavity, and, as in other types of lung, its area is greatly increased by ridges that are richly supplied with blood vessels. These ridges are said to increase the respiratory surface of air-breathing snails by as much as 2 or 3 times.

We are accustomed to regard lungs as being organs that require ventilation if they are to function satisfactorily, and this is obviously true of vertebrates. Probably because of this, it has been thought that the pulmonate lung also requires ventilation, but Krogh makes it clear that this is not necessarily so. He points out that in slugs (*Arion*) of about 10 g weight, with a pneumostome of 4 mm to 6 mm diameter, and with a respiratory surface of 6 cm^2 to 7 cm^2, a pressure difference of only 2 mm will ensure diffusion of atmospheric oxygen to the wall of the mantle cavity; even larger animals could therefore be satisfactorily supplied in this way. This conclusion applies, of course, to animals with a relatively low metabolic rate; ventilation of the lungs certainly becomes necessary with increasing oxygen consumption, and with increase in size of the body.

It would be an equally false analogy with the vertebrates to suppose that the pulmonate lung was purely a terrestrial respiratory organ, or that it was confined in aquatic animals to aerial respiration. We shall deal elsewhere with some of the factors that operate as animals of different phyla move to and fro between water and air in the course of their evolutionary history. It will be sufficient here to note some examples of the varied respiratory potentialities of the pulmonate lung. The siphonariid limpets are marine pulmonates that are completely aquatic in habit; the mantle cavity is filled with water, and has developed secondary pallial gills, formed by folding of the wall of the cavity. Many other examples, showing different degrees of adaptation to aquatic or amphibious habits, are provided by the fresh-water pulmonates. Thus *Lymnaea truncatula* has its lung filled with air; this animal, living an essentially aerial life in marshy habitats, plays a role of no small economic importance in providing an intermediate host for the sheep liver fluke, *Fasciola hepatica*. At the other extreme is *L. abyssicola*, which lives in deep water without coming to the surface, while *L. stagnalis* is intermediate in habit, living in water, but returning to the surface to refill its lung with air. Oxygen lack will be a major factor in stimulating this return, but another factor in fresh-water pulmonates is the use of the lung as a hydrostatic organ. If the cavity is artificially filled with oxygen, the animal will return to the surface before it has exhausted the supply, being driven to do so by the reduction in the volume of the gas enclosed in the lung.

Planorbis corneus resembles *Lymnaea stagnalis* in this respect, but is able to handle the, situation with greater efficiency because it possesses dissolved haemo-globin in its blood. This is a good example of the pigment acting as an oxygen storage device, and of the ecological advantage that results from this. The oxygen content of the lung of *Planorbis* necessarily diminishes if the animal is kept under water, but it does not fall to 4% until after at least 150 minutes, and the metabolism of the animal is meanwhile well maintained. In the same circumstances, but lacking haemo-globin, *L. stagnalis* shows a fall in the oxygen content of its lung to 6% in 1 hour, while its metabolism becomes much reduced. It is to be expected that oxygen lack will be a major factor in stimulating the return of these animals to the surface of the water, but another factor is the hydrostatic property of the lung. If the cavity of a fresh-water pulmonate is artificially filled with oxygen instead of air, the animal will return to the surface before it has exhausted the supply; it is driven by the reduction in the volume of the gas enclosed in the lung.

The most complex of all molluscan ctenidia are those found in the Lamelli-branchia, where they are involved in the elaborately specialized ciliary feeding mechanisms of this group. In our earlier discussion we saw that the respiratory functioning of the ctenidium demands the presence on it of mucus glands and ciliated tracts that serve to keep its delicate surface clean from detritus, so that molluscs may be said to have been pre-adapted for ciliary feeding. We have observed that certain gastropods have taken advantage of this to become ciliary feeders, but it is clearly the lamellibranchs that have most fully exploited the situation.

Yonge has outlined a course of events that could have led to the elaboration of the gills of the most advanced lamellibranchs. The first step, according to his analysis, was the overgrowth of the body by the mantle lobes, for this led to the anterior and ventral extension of the mantle cavity, and to the forward movement of the ctenidia. This movement brought them into functional association with the mouth, through the intermediation of the labial palps. Initially, while the ctenidia were primarily respiratory, they were horizontally disposed, but later the filaments bent downwards to form a V-shaped pattern. The outer filaments became fused with the mantle, and the inner ones to their partners on the other ctenidium or to the visceral mass; thus the mantle cavity became subdivided into inhalent and exhalent chambers. The filaments then became elaborated into an increasingly complex sieve by the develop-ment of interlamellar junctions, and of ciliary and tissue junctions (Sec. 10–10).

The increasing ciliation which would have accompanied these structural ad-vances probably increased the intake of sediment with the respiratory stream, and the development of latero-frontal cilia would serve to counteract this by preventing the passage of particles between the filaments. In correlation with this the abfrontal cilia, still present in *Nucula*, would have been lost. It is obvious that all of these advances, serving primarily to improve respiratory exchange by increasing the flow of water and by elaborating the surface of the gills, would also have improved the collection of suspended food material. Indeed, the two functions were presumably elaborated side by side in this group, together also with the specialization of the sorting and transport mechanisms. At quite the opposite extreme is the situation in the anomalous and highly specialized Septibranchia, where a muscular pumping organ is formed by a septum, which is perforated by ciliated pores, and which probably evolved from the fusion of modified ctenidia.

The active life of the Cephalopoda presents a remarkable contrast with that of the sedentary forms that we have just considered. In this class the ctenidia are contained within a mantle cavity that has become elongated in a dorso-ventral direction, and that is usually itself involved in the respiratory movements. A primitive form of the respiratory mechanism is found in the Tetrabranchia, represented by *Nautilus*. The presence in this genus of two pairs of ctenidia, instead of the single pair that is so generally characteristic of molluscs, has been regarded as a secondary specialization. The existence of five pairs in *Neopilina*, however, creates a possibility that the number of ctenidia in *Nautilus* may itself be a more primitive character than had previously been suspected.

In respiration the important functional characteristic of cephalopods is the production of the respiratory current by muscular action. *Nautilus* creates this ventilation by pulsations of the funnel, which is formed, as we have seen, from two halves of the foot that are not yet fused at this primitive stage of evolution. In the Coleoidea fusion is complete, and the current correspondingly more vigorous; it is now brought about by contractions of the mantle wall as well as of the muscles of the foot and head, this being made possible by the reduction of the shell and its overgrowth by the body. Cilia are thus no longer a necessary part of the respiratory mechanism, and they are absent from the gill surface, which is greatly increased in area by primary and secondary folding of the filaments.

The cephalopods are beautifully designed for rapid locomotion. The power for this is dependent upon the expulsion of a jet of water from the funnel, and is thus directly and economically linked with the respiratory mechanism. As with all such active animals, there is a demand for the most efficient possible oxygen supply; the elaborate folding of the gill surface is one contribution to this, while the presence of a respiratory pigment is another. Significantly, of all the animals that possess haemocyanin, cephalopods have the blood with the highest oxygen-carrying capacity. Yet this is not as great as the capacity of the blood in many animals with haemoglobin. Representative values for the latter are 21 volumes of oxygen per 100 volumes of blood in man, 5.5% to 7.8% for the dogfish *Mustelus*, and 8.4% to 9.7% for *Arenicola*. Corresponding values for the haemocyanin-containing blood of molluscs are 3.1% to 4.5% for *Octopus vulgaris*, 3.8% to 4.5% for *Loligo pealei*, and 1.15% to 2.2% for *Helix pomatia*. The blood of cephalopods is saturated only at high pressures, so that the animals are very sensitive to oxygen lack; under favourable conditions, however, they can achieve a very high level of activity.

The efficiency of their respiratory mechanism is further increased by a capillary circulation in the gills, contrasting markedly with the haemocoelic type of system found in other molluscan groups. Associated with this are branchial hearts at the bases of the gills. Thus the whole system is organized for maximum efficiency of respiration within the limits of the molluscan plan of structure. The complex of respiratory, locomotor, and circulatory mechanisms in cephalopods provides an instructive example of the way in which the parts of highly specialized animals can become closely integrated, so that each contributes to the successful functioning of the others.

11–5 GILLS AND TRACHEAE IN ARTHROPODS

The organization of the respiratory mechanisms of the Arthropoda reflects the evolutionary history of the group, which, as we have already shown, began in the sea and continued later in fresh water and on the land. The most primitive method of respiratory exchange is found in the smaller aquatic crustaceans, such as early larvae, adult copepods, and most ostracods and cirripedes. These animals, like many worms, respire through their general body surface. It is reasonable to assume that the thin-walled and foliaceous appendages of the branchiopods, like the parapodia of polychaetes, facilitate gaseous exchange, and that they have, therefore, a respiratory function additional to their use in feeding. The maintenance of the filter-feeding current would, of course, serve also for ventilation. In fact, it may well be that in these animals, as in the lamellibranchs, the feeding mechanism was a specialization of a more primitive respiratory one, but we cannot be sure of this.

The larger crustaceans develop specialized outgrowths that are regarded as gills, although there is often a lack of physiological evidence for their respiratory function. Structures of this type are particularly well developed in the Malacostraca, where they take the form of foliaceous outgrowths of the coxae of the thoracic limbs. These outgrowths, which are termed podobranchs, may be supplemented, particularly in the decapods, by similar outgrowths arising from the arthrodial membrane at the base of the limb (arthrobranchs), or from the body wall (pleurobranchs). In their simplest form such gills may be no more than hollow, flattened outgrowths, but they become much more complex, with a central axis and various types of lateral branch. They are well vascularized, with an afferent and efferent circulation, but they do not develop either capillaries or branchial hearts such as are found in the cephalopods. Ventilation is maintained by the rhythmic beating of one or more appendages; primitively a number of these are concerned, as in *Anaspides*, but in the decapods this function is restricted to the scaphognathite of the second maxilla.

Another example of the use of limbs in respiration is probably to be seen in the Trilobita (Fig. 11–7), although here we are restricted to inferences drawn from their fossil remains. We have seen that these animals show a uniformity of structure in their biramous limbs, apart from the differentiation of the antennules. Of the two rami, the inner one supposedly functioned as a walking leg, since it bore a terminal claw. The outer ramus, with its fringe of broad filaments, presumably had some respiratory function.

A third example of the respiratory use of the limb occurs in *Limulus* (Fig. 7–12). Five pairs of swimming paddles exist on the opisthosoma of this animal, each of these limbs consisting of a slender internal ramus and a broad external one. The latter bears a peculiar type of gill formed of as many as 200 delicate branchial leaves, for which reason it is called a gill book. Ventilation of the gill book is readily provided by the locomotor actions of the limbs. For much of its time the animal is shovelling its way through sand and mud, and the moulding of the ventral surface of the body into a trough probably provides some protection for the delicate gill books. The overhanging genital operculum, regarded as the fused limbs of the first opisthosomatic segment, provides a further safeguard.

We have seen that few crustaceans have achieved any success in the invasion of land (Sec. 7–3). Some malacostracans, however, have surmounted the difficulties, examples being found among the anomuran decapods, and also among the true

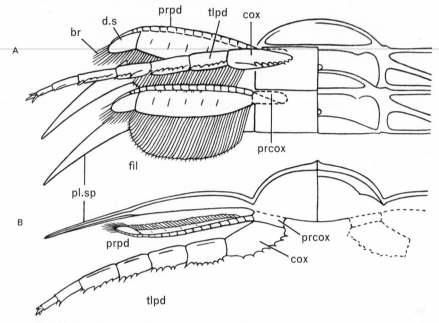

Fig. 11-7.   Reconstructions of the appendages of the trilobite *Olenoides* (*Neolenus*) *serratus* Rominger, 100 mm, Middle Cambrian. After Størmer. *br*, bristle; *cox*, coxa; *d.s*, distal segment of pre-epipodite; *fil*, filaments; *pl.sp*, pleural spine; *prcox*, precoxa; *prpd*, pre-epipodite; *tlpd*, telopodite. From Tiegs and Manton, 1958. *op. cit.* Used by courtesy of the Cambridge Philosophical Society.

crabs. Here the solution of the respiratory problem has been the development of vascularized folds of the wall of the branchial chamber; a development that is not greatly different in principle from the possession of pleurobranchs. These adaptations may be called lungs, and the same term is applicable to the air-filled sacs that are formed in certain terrestrial isopods (*Oniscidae*) by the hollowing-out of the exopodites of the pleopods. An interesting variant of this is found in other terrestrial isopods, the Porcellionidae and Armadillidiidae, in which the appendages contain branched tubules (pseudotracheae, p. 265), opening to the outside by a narrow aperture. This is a simple illustration of the possibility of distributing gases through tissues by tubular ingrowths of the body surface. The principle has been widely exploited in the arthropods, where it has presumably been encouraged by the development of the hard cuticle; it provides one of the clearest indications of the widespread convergent evolution that has marked the history of the group.

It is convincingly demonstrated, for example, in the Chelicerata. We have already found that the recognition of *Limulus* as being related to arachnids leads inescapably to the conclusion that this class must have developed its terrestrial adaptations independently of other arthropods. The line of evolution seems likely to have passed through the scorpions, which are known from the Upper Silurian. These animals bear some resemblance to the eurypterids, an extinct group of aquatic forms that were more generalized in structure than is the highly specialized *Limulus*. Unfortunately the respiratory organs of the eurypterids are not satisfactorily known, but we may assume that they were of the same type as the gill books of *Limulus*, and that the aerial respiratory organs of scorpions were evolved from them. These are invaginated organs that are called lung books, because they consist of closely apposed leaflets, which are set, like the pages of a book, within a pit that opens to the outside through a narrow aperture. No special provision is made for ventilation, so that gaseous exchange must depend upon diffusion.

It is known that *Limulus* can survive for several days out of water; it has been suggested, therefore, that primitive chelicerates had a similar capacity, and that lung books evolved as a consequence of this. It may be, for example, that the limbs were closely applied to the ventral body surface, that the gill books became enclosed by fusion of the limbs with the body wall, and that the gill lamellae in their turn fused with the wall of the chamber. Four pairs of lung books exist in scorpions, which have remained conservative in their respiratory equipment, but other arachnids are more specialized. Thus some spiders have two pairs of lung books, some have only one pair, and in one family there are none at all. This reduction is doubtless correlated with the tendency for lung books to be replaced in these animals by tracheae, which resemble in principle those of insects and other groups to be mentioned below, but which have clearly been developed quite independently. In the spiders they may perhaps have evolved as diverticula of the missing lung books. Tracheae are also found in other

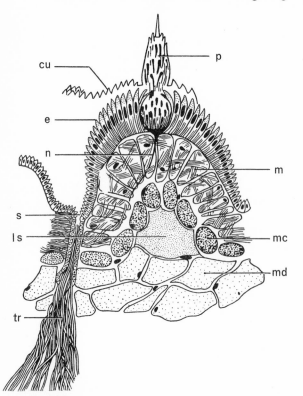

Fig. 11-8. T.S. *Peripatus trinitatis. cu,* cuticle, detached; *e,* epidermis; *ls,* blood lacuna; *m,* subepithelial muscles; *mc,* circular muscles; *md,* diagonal muscles; *n,* nerve of sensory papilla; *p,* sensory papilla; *s,* stigma; *tr,* bundle of tracheae. From Grassé, 1949. *Traité de Zoologie,* vol. 6. Masson, Paris.

arachnids: the Solifugae, the Phalangidae, and some of the Acarina. In these groups there is no evidence for a primitive lung-book phase, and it is at least possible that they may have developed tracheal respiration independently of the spiders.

We have already seen evidence that *Peripatus*, the myriapods, and the insects may constitute a natural group of terrestrial arthropods, the product of an invasion of the land that was achieved quite independently of the arachnid line. All of these forms have developed tracheal respiration, but their tracheae are not uniform in structure, and we cannot assume that they necessarily had a common evolutionary origin. They could, in theory, be independent expressions of a common genetic potentiality in these several groups. We have no means of judging this, and the dangers of speculation are shown by the fact that the tracheae of the Solifugae show detailed resemblances to those of insects, despite their undoubted independent origin. In *Peripatus* (Fig. 11–8) the tracheae are delicate tubules, passing inwards to the organs, and arising in tufts from pits of the body surface. Each pit opens by a spiracle, the spiracles being scattered irregularly instead of showing the segmental arrangement seen in insects. A fact of great physiological and ecological importance for the Onychophora is that they are unable to close the spiracles. Because of this they cannot resist desiccation, a feature that is correlated with their occupation of sheltered and damp habitats. In the myriapods the tracheae are more complex in structure, and are commonly supported, as they are in insects, by a spiral thickening. In centipedes they usually branch and anastomose; in millipedes they may branch but anastomoses do not develop.

The operation of tracheae has been most closely studied in insects. In this group they achieve an efficiency in operation that makes a major contribution to the diversity of specialization and high level of activity that these animals attain. Tracheae have, however, one major disadvantage, since transport of gases by diffusion is suited only to small organisms. Thus they are one of the features of insect organization (the exoskeleton is another) that severely limit the size of these animals; a limitation for which the rest of the animal kingdom should be thankful.

Tracheae are ectodermal structures, formed by invagination, or ingrowth, from the surface. As a result they are lined with cuticle, called the intima, which is thickened to form delicate ridges arranged either as a continuous spiral or as separate rings. These thickenings, the taenidia, serve to maintain an open lumen throughout the tracheal system, and thereby ensure the passage of gases. Communication with the outside is by means of openings called spiracles, referred to above; they may be regarded as the sites of the original invagination. Typically these are found in the thorax and abdomen (Fig. 11–9), situated on the pleura, but there is much variation in detail, and distinctions can be made in the insects between holopneustic, hemipneustic, and apneustic systems. The first of these, with eight pairs of spiracles on the abdomen and two on the thorax, is the most primitive, and is particularly characteristic of adult stages. Hemipneustic systems, in which one or more of the pairs of spiracles are closed, are particularly characteristic of those larvae in which respiratory exchange has become localized at one end of the body; this is usually an adaptation to life in a fluid or semi-fluid medium. In apneustic systems all of the spiracles are closed, so that respiratory exchange must now occur either through the body surface, or through outgrowths of it that are called gills. This mode of functioning is particularly characteristic of endoparasites and of fully aquatic insects.

The essential feature of the fully developed tracheal system of insects is that it transports oxygen to the tissues by tracheal tubes that branch to supply all parts of the body, and form extremely fine terminations called tracheoles. These terminations possess thin walls that are permeable to water, and that are provided, like the tracheae, with taenidia so delicate that they can only be seen by electron microscopy. Because of the minute size of the tracheoles they enter into so close a relationship with the tissues that they surround the cells and end blindly within them. Moreover, the degree of their development and branching can be adaptively adjusted to meet fluctuations in the oxygen demands of particular tissues.

It is difficult sometimes to make a clear-cut distinction between pulmonary and

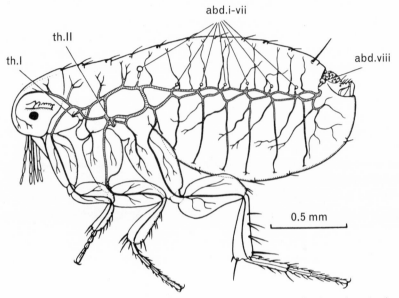

Fig. 11-9. Tracheal system of *Xenopsylla cheopsis*. *th.I*, *th.II*, thoracic spiracles; *abd. i–viii*, abdominal spiracles. From Wigglesworth, 1947. *The Principles of Insect Physiology* (3rd ed.). Methuen, London.

tracheal respiration. As Krogh points out, the tracheae of spiders may function essentially as lungs, for they do not convey oxygen to the tissues, but merely aerate the blood in the adjacent ventral sinus. Even in insects there is a blood stream which must necessarily play some part in gas transport; the tracheoles may sometimes be found suspended in the blood, and presumably provide a source of oxygen that it can then transport. Moreover, tracheae are sometimes expanded to form thin-walled air sacs. These may sometimes serve as hydrostatic organs, but they are probably of particular importance in increasing the capacity of the respiratory system as a whole, so that the respiratory movements result in the exchange of a correspondingly greater volume of air. There is an analogy here with the function of the air sacs of birds, and a further analogy is implied in a suggestion that the air sacs of insects may aid flight by reducing specific gravity. A similar function has been suggested in birds, for in these animals the air sacs penetrate extensively into the bony skeleton.

As with other types of respiratory system, the mode of functioning of tracheae is closely governed by the physical properties of air and water. We have seen that air is a more favourable medium for respiratory exchanges than is water, and that this is particularly apparent in connection with the diffusion of oxygen, which is very much more rapid in air than in water. Krogh's calculations showed that in a large *Cossus* larva, 60 mm long and weighing 3.4 g, the tracheae had an average length of 6 mm, with a cross-sectional area of 6.7 mm². In these circumstances diffusion is ample for supplying the necessary oxygen; it requires a pressure difference of only 11 mm, so that the animal need not expend any energy at all upon ventilation movements. The same is probably true of very many tracheate arthropods, including the Onychophora, the arachnids, the myriapods, and a large number of the smaller insects, together with larvae and pupae.

Two factors that modify this situation are size and activity. Many insects are smaller than the larva mentioned, and are in an even more favourable position, but conditions deteriorate with increased size, as Krogh showed. If, for example, the linear dimensions increase by a factor of 10, giving tracheae 6 cm long and 6.7 cm² in cross section, the rate of diffusion could be increased by a factor of 10, but the animal would be 1,000 times heavier, and its metabolism at least 100 times greater. Diffusion would now be totally inadequate for meeting its needs, and this is why tracheal respiration limits the size of arthropods. Conditions are at their most difficult in insects. The expenditure of energy during flight is formidably high, and transport of oxygen by diffusion is thought to become inadequate when the body weight reaches 0.1 g. Respiratory movements are now needed to ensure an adequate supply of oxygen, and so these are seen in bees, for example, which weigh 100 mg. A particular difficulty arises in species in which the legs are unduly long relative to the size of the body; reliance upon diffusion over such distances may result in the oxygen concentration in the tracheae of these limbs falling to very low levels. It is doubtless in adaptation to this that harvestmen (*Opiliones*), with exceptionally long legs, have spiracles on their tibiae.

With tracheae, as with lungs, there is bound to be some loss of water vapour through the respiratory membranes; this constitutes a serious drawback in the tracheal system, particularly as terrestrial animals must achieve maximum economy in the use of water. Since the general body surface is impermeable, the spiracles become the main site of water loss. Primitively this loss was doubtless accepted, as it still is today in *Peripatus*.

The extraordinarily successful exploitation of aerial life by insects has depended upon overcoming this particular limitation by developing devices for closing the spiracles and thereby controlling diffusion through them (Fig. 11–10). The spiracles thus become complex organs, varying greatly in the details of their organization, but commonly provided with muscles, with which cuticular elements may be associated. These form closing mechanisms by which the opening can be completely occluded. Further, the tracheae arise from a vestibule that is provided with filtering hairs; these serve to reduce any diffusion of water vapour through the spiracle, in addition to preventing foreign particles from entering the system.

For successful operation, these closing mechanisms must be regulated to meet the respiratory needs at any particular moment. Here again there is much variation. In air-breathing vertebrates use is made of the carbon dioxide concentration in regulating the rate of pulmonary ventilation. The respiratory centre in the medulla of the brain is stimulated by the small increases in the carbon dioxide tension in the arterial blood that result from increased metabolism—an example of the use of a by-product of metabolism as a chemical signal. A similar principle seems to be used by at least some insects. The cockroach, for example, opens its spiracles with increasing activity; this is thought to be a result of increased production of carbon dioxide, for experiments have shown that the spiracles are provided with receptors that are specifically sensitive to this gas.

In the locust (Fig. 11-11) the respiratory movements are under the control of a ventilation centre in the metathoracic ganglion. This is regulated by impulses transmitted from carbon dioxide receptors situated in the nerve ganglia themselves. The centre can also be controlled by external stimuli acting through the cephalic ganglion; for example, respiration may be momentarily interrupted if the insect is handled.

In the flea *Xenopsylla cheopsis*, on the other hand, no specific carbon dioxide receptors are present, and in this animal the opening of the spiracles is apparently due to increased acidity of the tissues. Spiracular closing mechanisms sensitive to carbon dioxide are found also in the scorpion *Buthus* and the tick *Ornithodorus*; an example of physiological convergence in insects and arachnids. We may recall in this connection that the effect of carbon dioxide on mammalian respiration was once thought to result from the increased acidity caused by its presence, rather than from the direct action of this metabolite on the respiratory centre. The situation in insects shows that this mechanism is a feasible one, and it may also play a part in mammals, although in this group direct action is probably also important.

One further remarkable specialization in tracheal systems remains to be described. This is a mechanism, discovered by Wigglesworth, that makes it possible for the insect to increase the availability of oxygen for the tissues, and thereby supplement the effect of the closing mechanisms in reducing gaseous diffusion. We

Fig. 11-10. Closing mechanisms of the spiracles of *Xenopsylla*. A, abd. viii in surface view; B, abd. vi in transverse section; C, abd. vi as seen in living insect, open; D, the same, closed. E, th. II in horizontal section; F, th. II as seen in living insect, open; G, the same, closed. *m*, muscle; *n*, nerve; *r*, chitinous rod; *tr*, trachea. From Wigglesworth, 1935. *Proc. R. Soc. B*, **118**, 397–419.

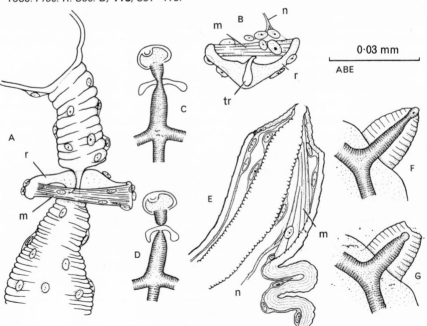

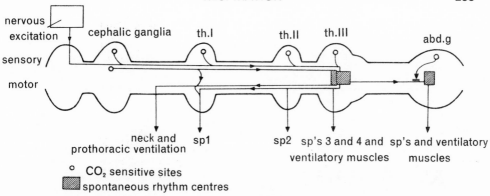

Fig. 11-11. A summary of the control of ventilation in the locust. Sensory fibres coupled to carbon dioxide receptors in each ganglion run in the nerve cord to the metathoracic ventilation centre; other fibres run from the head to the metathoracic ganglion and then to the neck and prothoracic ventilation muscles. From Miller, 1960. *J. exp. Biol.,* **37,** 224–236.

have seen that the tracheae end in tracheoles that surround and penetrate the cells. These tracheoles are necessarily permeable to water, for without such permeability the oxygen could not diffuse through their walls. As a result, water passes into them from the tissues. The amount that does so is determined by the relationship between the osmotic pressure of the tissue fluids and the force of capillarity within the tracheole tubules. When the tissues are respiring with an inadequate oxygen supply, as happens at times of great activity, metabolites accumulate in the tissue fluids and raise their osmotic pressure. This results in water being withdrawn from the tracheoles into the tissue fluids, the space left in the tracheoles being filled by air moving along them. Since oxygen diffuses much more rapidly through air than through water, the effect of this will be to improve the supply of oxygen to the cells. This result, as Krogh remarks, is analogous to the opening-up of the capillaries in the active muscles of the vertebrate body.

It remains to add that the possession of such a highly specialized respiratory system has not prevented insects from returning to an aquatic life, any more than the possession of lungs has prevented mammals from doing the same. Various devices are adopted for this purpose. The animal may return to the surface to breathe through its spiracles, and it may supplement this by carrying down under the water a store of air on its body surface. It will be recalled that pulmonate molluscs use their lung in a similar way. Air may also be obtained from aquatic plants. Many aquatic insects, however, have become fully aquatic by developing tracheal gills, which make it possible to obtain oxygen by diffusion from the surrounding water. The essential feature of these is the presence of many fine tracheae immediately below the cuticle, ventilation being sometimes provided by the movements of the animal, and sometimes by movements of the gills themselves. Krogh pointed out in this connection a curious analogy between the respiratory system of the nymph of the dragonfly *Aeschna* and that of the cephalopods. The former has tracheal gills that lie in the rectum, and that are ventilated by muscular movements that also provide for the locomotion of the animal. In principle, this is the same combination of respiratory movement and locomotion that has been developed with such success in the operation of the cephalopod pedal siphon.

12
Excretion

12–1 EXCRETORY ORGANS

While knowledge of animal organization has been advancing, there have inevitably been occasions when structures were described and named before their function was understood, and before their relationships with superficially similar structures could be determined. It is for this reason that so much confusion has in the past surrounded the study of the so-called excretory organs of animals. We say 'so-called', because the very term excretion is used in more than one sense. Strictly speaking, it refers to the removal of the waste products of metabolism, which comprise the carbon dioxide and water that are released by the oxidation of energy-rich compounds, and the nitrogenous waste that results from the metabolism of proteins and nucleic acids. But the removal of carbon dioxide is part of the respiratory process, and because of this, and because there is more than one route for the passage of water, excretion has commonly been thought of as the removal of nitrogenous waste. We shall use the term in that sense here, but with the immediate proviso that the process is closely bound up with the regulation of the flux of water and certain electrolytes between the organism and its external environment. We have, in fact, to find sites of operation of functions that were not appreciated when invertebrate organs were first described and named. This is true also of many other aspects of animal organization, but it is particularly important in studies of excretory function not to be misled by traditional nomenclature.

We owe to Goodrich the foundations of our modern understanding of the history of excretory systems. It was he who first clearly formulated, in 1895, the fundamental principle that the animal body may be connected with the external environment by two distinct sets of tubular structures, the nephridia and the coelomoducts (Fig. 12-1). He defined a nephridium as an organ that is developed centripetally, and quite independently of the coelom, being probably derived from the ectoderm. Its lumen is formed by the hollowing-out of the nephridial cells, and is consequently intracellular. Primitively this lumen is closed internally, but frequently it secondarily

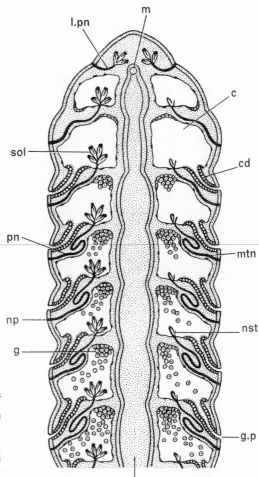

Fig. 12-1. Diagram of primitive annelid in longitudinal section, showing relations of coelomoducts and nephridia to segmental coelomic cavities. Protonephridia, *pn*, on left; metanephridia, *mtn*, on right. *c*, coelom; *cd*, coelomoduct; *g*, gonad; *g.p*, genital pore; *int*, intestine; *l.pn*, larval protonephridium; *m*, ventral mouth; *np*, nephridiopore; *nst*, nephridiostome; *sol*, solenocyte. Adapted from Goodrich, 1945. *Q. Jl microsc. Sci.*, **86**, 113–392.

acquires an opening into the coelom, this opening being the nephridial funnel or nephrostome. In complete contrast to a nephridium, a coelomoduct is developed centrifugally as a mesoblastic structure, formed as an outgrowth of the gonad or of the wall of the coelomic cavity. Its lumen, which is an extension of that cavity in coelomate animals, is not intracellular, but is bounded by a layer of epithelial cells; it opens into the coelom by a ciliated funnel, the coelomostome.

The distinction between a nephridium and a coelomoduct is not purely developmental and morphological, but involves also functional criteria. Both types of organ are present in the lower coelomate invertebrates, and in these the primary function of the coelomoducts is to convey to the outside the germ cells that develop in the coelomic epithelium. In the acoelomate platyhelminths and nemertines these ducts are represented by the gonoducts, which, on the gonocoel theory of the origin of the coelom, would therefore be the direct forerunners of coelomoducts. The nephridia, on the other hand, seem primitively to have had no connection with reproduction, although such a connection may be secondarily established in a relatively small number of species. The primitive function of these organs is usually said to be excretory; this is correct if we use the term in a broad sense to include regulatory functions, but it is by no means clear that the removal of nitrogenous waste is an important aspect of their function.

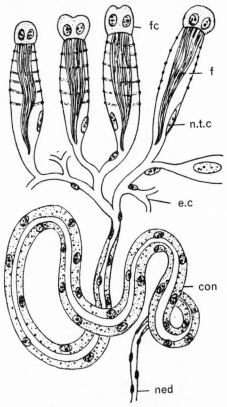

Fig. 12-2. *Geonemertes agricola.* Diagram of single protonephridium (from Coe, 1930). *con,* convoluted canal; *e.c,* end canal; *f,* flame of cilia; *fc,* binucleate flame-cell; *ned,* efferent duct; *n.t.c,* nucleus of terminal chamber. From Goodrich, 1945. *op cit.*

These are matters that will become clearer as we pursue our analysis. For the moment it is important to appreciate that nephridia are essentially characteristic of the earlier stages of invertebrate evolution, and, to some extent, of the larvae of higher forms, although their presence in amphioxus reminds us that they have also persisted side by side with considerable advances in other aspects of organization. What created confusion for those who first described and named these organs is that in the course of evolution the coelomoducts have extended their field of activity to take over functions originally carried out by the nephridia, so that the distinction between the two sets of organs is obscured. The distinction remains, however, of fundamental importance. Possibly the disappearance of nephridia is associated with the increasing metabolic complexity of the more advanced animals. Increasing exploitation of a wider range of habitats and modes of life has demanded an increasing specialization and diversification of function from the excretory and regulatory systems, and it may well be that coelomoducts have proved better able to provide for this than have nephridia. Indeed, we shall see that in the arthropods even the coelomoducts proved insufficient for these needs, and that in this group there evolved another type of excretory organ that belongs to neither of these two primary categories.

The nephridium occurs in two main forms, the protonephridium and the metanephridium. The first of these, which is certainly the more primitive of the two, is characterized by the canals ending blindly in cells of a peculiar type, variable in form, but usually either flame cells or solenocytes. Flame cells have cell bodies with branching processes and with central cavities, continuous with the cavities of the tubules, and containing a bunch of cilia, the flame. Solenocytes may be regarded as derived from this type of cell, the cell lumen having been prolonged into a delicate tube (which gives the name to the cell, from the Greek *solen*, a channel), and the flame having been reduced to a single flagellum.

Protonephridia are found in the Platyhelminthes, which may be thought of as having a pair of these structures, their canals being much branched and bearing flame cells at the ends of the branches. These cells, therefore, are scattered throughout the parenchyma. Similar protonephridia are found in the nemertines, sometimes as a single pair situated far forwards. Sometimes they may be extended into longitudinal collecting canals, into which open many smaller efferent canals that lead from the scattered flame cells. Such is the arrangement in the terrestrial form *Geonemertes* (Fig. 12-2), where the system consists in effect of many hundreds of separate protonephridia, each discharging through its own efferent canal. From such an arrangement the nephridial system of annelids might have been derived. Here each typical segment primitively possesses a pair of the organs, opening independently of each other at segmental nephridiopores. The nephridia themselves are intersegmental in position, their inner end penetrating the anterior septum of the segment in which the main body of the organ lies.

The nephridia of the annelids show many variations upon this simple ground plan, and for this reason it is particularly important to understand the history of the nephridial system of these animals. The particular complication in the polychaetes is that their nephridia frequently bear ciliated funnels; they are then termed metanephridia. It was at one time supposed, because of the presence of the funnels, that organs of this type were homologous with coelomoducts, especially since they sometimes serve for the passage of germ cells. The situation was finally clarified by Goodrich, who clearly established the homology of these nephridia with those of platyhelminths, and at the same time showed that nature had set a trap for investigators by developing more than one variant of these organs.

The trochophore larva of certain polychaetes (e.g. *Nereis*, *Pomatoceros*, Fig. 19-2) possesses a pair of simple and typical protonephridia, the so-called head kidneys. These structures, each with a flame cell bearing a single flagellum, disappear later, and the nephridia of the adult worms are metanephridia, with open ciliated funnels. This history is in itself good evidence for the serial homology of protonephridia and metanephridia, but Goodrich was able to clinch this part of the argument by his discovery that certain adult polychaetes (e.g. *Nephtys*, *Phyllodoce*) possessed only protonephridia, which in these instances have solenocytes. Coelomoducts are also typically present in polychaetes, not necessarily in every segment, but at least in those in which germ cells develop. They give rise, however, to two modifications. One of these is found in the nereid worms, where the coelomoducts are reduced to inconspicuous areas of ciliated epithelium, discovered by Goodrich and named by him the dorsal ciliated organ. These are possibly phagocytic, but they have certainly lost their primitive function of conveying the germ cells, which in these worms escape by rupture of the body wall.

The other modification is more widespread. It is remarkable that only one family of the polychaetes, the Capitellidae, preserves the primitive arrangement of coelomoducts and nephridia (in this instance metanephridia). In the other families the two structures become associated to form a compound organ called a nephromixium, in which the nephridial tube bears a ciliated mesodermal funnel. The nephridial component of this may be a protonephridium, as, for example, in the Phyllodocidae; here

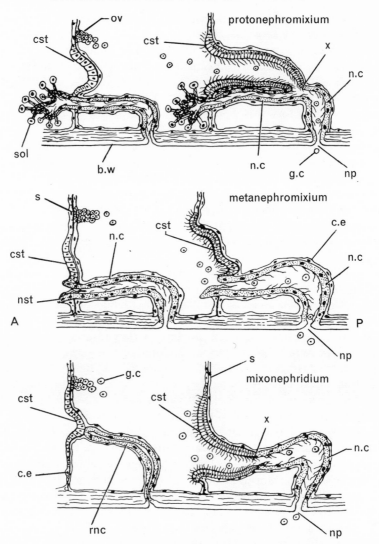

Fig. 12-3. Diagrams showing structure and formation of nephromixia by combination of coelomoduct with nephridium. A, anterior, young stage before combination. P, posterior, combination completed. *b.w*, body wall; *c.e*, coelomic epithelium; *cst*, coelomostome; *g.c*, germ cell; *n.c*, nephridial canal; *np*, nephridiopore; *nst*, nephridiostome; *ov*, ovary; *rnc*, rudiment of nephridium; *s*, intersegmental septum; *sol*, solenocyte; *x*, point where coelomoduct opens into nephridial canal. From Goodrich, 1945. *op. cit.*

the developing coelomoduct has been observed to grow backwards alongside the protonephridial canal, an open communication between the two arising at sexual maturity. The organ thus formed is a protonephromixium (Fig. 12–3). Alternatively, and more commonly, the nephridial component of the nephromixium is a metanephridium, the resulting compound organ being called either a metanephromixium or a mixonephridium, according to the way in which the junction is formed (Fig. 12–3). An example of the latter is seen in *Arenicola*, where there are usually six pairs of these organs, present in segments 5 to 10. These organs, conspicuous with their rich vascularization, frilled funnel lip, and attached gonad, serve both for the passage of germ cells and, presumably, for the regulatory functions that we shall be considering later. Probably the elaborate structure of the funnel aids in the selection of ripe ova and in their removal from the coelom.

Such, in outline, is the disposition of coelomoducts and nephridia in the polychaetes, although it is accompanied by much variation in detail from family to family. Elsewhere in the annelids the situation is much simpler. In the oligochaetes the nephridia are all of the metanephridial type, familiar in the nephridium of the earthworm. The evolutionary relationship between the complex funnel of this type of organ and the flame cell and simpler funnel of many polychaetes can readily be appreciated in such a form as *Enchytraeus*, where the nephridiostome is small and possesses a flame of cilia recalling the arrangement of the endings of protonephridial tubes. Coelomoducts are also present, but the tendency for the restriction of these to the genital segments, seen in polychaetes, is here carried further, one duct now being associated with each gonad. The arrangement in the Hirudinea, closely related to the oligochaetes, is very similar, despite the more complicated form of the metanephridia.

Other groups of animals also possess nephridia. In the Archiannelida, an artificial assemblage of worms of rather doubtful affinity, but presumably related to annelidan ancestors, we find either protonephridia or metanephridia, and probably also nephromixia. The Polyzoa Entoprocta, the Rotifera, the Gastrotricha, and the Kinorhyncha have a pair of protonephridia, with gonoducts representing coelomoducts. Protonephridia have also been found in the Priapulida and in the Acanthocephala. In the latter the nephridial and genital ducts join to form a median urogenital canal, giving rise, therefore, to a peculiar type of nephromixium. The actinotrocha larva of *Phoronis* has a pair of protonephridia, but the corresponding organs of the adult have wide ciliated funnels, and are probably nephromixia, since they carry the genital products to the outside. The Sipunculida, the Echiuroidea, and the Myzostomaria are other groups in which the so-called nephridia are probably nephromixia, although this is not certain; nephromixia are probably also present in the Brachiopoda.

The generalization with which we started, then, is of wide applicability, and among the lower invertebrates there are only a few groups that cannot be readily fitted into it. The Chaetognatha and the Polyzoa Ectoprocta have no nephridia at all, but coelomoducts are represented by ciliated ducts leading to the outside. Another exceptional group is the Nematoda. These highly specialized animals have no coelom, but the gonoducts may be held to represent the coelomoducts of other groups, as they do in the platyhelminths. The excretory system of nematodes is supposed to be represented by a pair of longitudinal canals lying in the lateral thickenings of the body wall. These show no resemblance at all to nephridia; they have no internal opening, nor do they possess cilia, which are not present at all in this group. Moreover, the whole system is believed to be formed by the enlargement and excavation of two cells (cf. p. 76).

Another important group in which there is no sign of nephridia, either in the larval or adult stages, is the Echinodermata, and this applies also to the Hemichordata and the Urochordata, which, as we see in other contexts, are probably related to the echinoderms. Whether this means that these groups have lost these organs during their evolution is very difficult to say, but it is certainly of significance that protone-

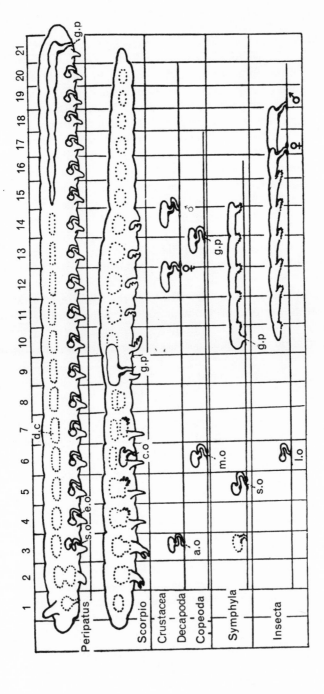

Fig. 12-4. Diagram showing excretory and genital coelomoducts in various Arthropoda. *Peripatus* and *Scorpio* drawn complete, with embryonic coelomesoblastic somites and their dorsal portions shown in dotted line. Crustacea, Symphyla, and Insecta simplified; transient vestigial coelomoducts shown in dotted line. Opening of antennary organ, *a.o;* of coxal organ, *c.o;* of excretory organ, *e.o;* of lingual gland, *l.o;* of maxillary organ, *m.o;* of salivary organ, *s.o.* Dorsal coelom, *d.c;* genital pore, *g.p* (both sexes indicated in Decapoda and Insecta). From Goodrich, 1945. *op. cit.*

phridia, with typical solenocytes, are present in amphioxus, lying in the coelom above the gill bars. What we have said elsewhere regarding the remarkable possibilities of convergence (in arthropod evolution, for example) must make us cautious in regarding the protonephridia of the invertebrates as having necessarily been inherited from a remote common ancestral group; but it would certainly be surprising if these organs had appeared in amphioxus without being represented at all in the protochordate and echinoderm line. This, then, seems to be an instance in which nephridia may have been lost without trace.

The history and relationships of the excretory systems of arthropods are no less complex than other aspects of the organization of this group. The characteristic excretory organ of many of these animals is a tubular mesodermal structure, which, before the distinction between nephridium and coelomoduct had been clearly formulated, was often referred to as a 'nephridium'. It follows from our earlier definition, however, that this was a misnomer, and that the organ must, in fact, be a coelomoduct.

The primitive arrangement is well seen in *Peripatus* (Fig. 12-4), which possesses a pair of these structures, called coxal glands, in almost every one of its segments. Their development is particularly illuminating. Hollow coelomic follicles, or somites, appear in each segment, and, in the trunk region, become divided into a dorsal and a ventro-lateral portion (Fig. 12-5). The latter grows into the appendages, but its cavity persists to form the end sac of the coxal gland; this becomes connected with the outside by a mesodermal duct which grows from it towards the ectoderm. Thus arises a structure which we may regard as the prototype of the coxal glands of other arthropodan groups. The end sac opens by a ciliated canal, which we can regard as the coelomostome, into a coiled excretory canal; the terminal portion of this is enlarged

Fig. 12-5. Scheme illustrating the development of the coelom in *Peripatus*. A, each coelomic sac divides into dorsal (*d*), lateral (*l*), and ventral (*v*) cavities, the dorsal enclosing the germ cells. *ov*, ventral organ. B, the dorsal cavity forms the gonad cavity, the lateral one the lateral body cavity by disintegration of its walls, and the ventral one the sac of the excretory organ with its canal, *cn. ie*, epidermal invagination; *n*, ventral nerve cord. C, section at the level of the gonads. The body cavity is traversed by cords of mesenchyme. *co*, heart; *sp*, pericardial septum. D, section at level of genital opening. *cn*, excretory canal forming oviduct. From Grassé, 1949. *Traité de Zoologie*, vol. 6. Masson, Paris.

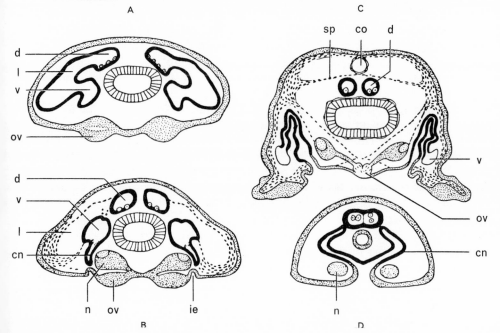

to form a vesicle or bladder. There is no sign at all of nephridia in *Peripatus*. The derivation of the coxal glands from coelomoducts is perfectly clear, and is emphasized by the mode of formation of the gonads and their ducts. The dorsal portions of the coelom become reduced anteriorly, but posteriorly they fuse on either side to form the paired gonads, which open to the outside at the last segment. At this point the coelom has not divided into dorsal and ventral portions, so that each of the gonads becomes continuous with a duct that meets its partner at a median ventral pore. As a result, no coxal glands are formed in this particular segment.

Coxal glands of similar structure are also found in the Arachnida and the Crustacea, but are greatly reduced in number (Fig. 12–4). In the Crustacea they are found only in the third and sixth segments, where they open respectively at the base of the second antenna (antennal gland) and second maxilla (maxillary or shell gland). In the Branchiopoda, Ostracoda, Copepoda, Branchiura, Cirripedia, and lower Malacostraca, the antennary gland is present in the larva and the maxillary gland in the adult. In the Amphipoda, Euphausiacea, and Decapoda the antennary gland persists into the adult, while the maxillary gland either disappears or fails to develop; but in the Mysidacea, generally conceded to be primitive animals, both of the glands may be functional in the adult. Given this facility of the coxal glands for disappearing, the restricted glands of modern crustaceans can readily enough be derived from a hypothetical continuous series such as that of *Peripatus*. Support for this interpretation is found in various crustacean species where groups of cells at the bases of other appendages can take up injected foreign material, such as indigo-carmine. In doing this they resemble cells of the glands themselves, and they are probably to be regarded as vestiges of former coxal glands. The openings of the genital ducts, which vary in position from the eleventh to the nineteenth segment, would have formed part of the same series of structures. As in *Peripatus*, there is no certainty that nephridia were ever present in crustaceans. There is, however, some evidence that the terminal portion of the duct of the gland forms from ectoderm; this has led to the suggestion that it may be the vestige of a nephridial canal.

Most arachnids possess a pair of coxal glands opening on the sixth segment, at the base of the fifth pair of appendages (third pair of walking legs). Doubtless there were originally more of these, for in *Limulus* the gland also receives contributions from the three next anterior segments, while during the development of the scorpion vestiges of glands are detectable in the fourth, fifth, and seventh segments; they appear as diverticula of the coelomic cavities, and can reasonably be regarded as traces of coelomoducts. Outgrowths of the coelomic cavities in segment 9 form the mesodermal parts of the gonoducts.

In those arthropods that have become fully adapted to terrestrial life there is an important development in the organization of the excretory system: the appearance of Malpighian tubes. These are outgrowths of the alimentary canal, and are thus an entirely new introduction, owing nothing either to nephridia or to coelomoducts. We shall see that their appearance is correlated with the novel physiological situation presented by life on dry land. They are, therefore, new adaptive devices, and it is understandable, although none the less remarkable, that they have arisen by convergence along more than one evolutionary line. They are found in Myriapoda, Insecta, and Arachnida, and we are bound to conclude, in view of what has been said earlier regarding the history of these groups, that the Malpighian tubes of arachnids must have been evolved independently of those of the other two groups. This interpretation is strengthened by their development in arachnids from the end of the embryonic mid-gut, whereas in the other groups they are ectodermal structures, arising from the proctodaeum. The difference is a small one, but of the sort that we expect to find when comparing convergent features of organization.

We have suggested earlier the possibility that the myriapods and Insecta evolved from a remote common ancestor. Perhaps, therefore, the Malpighian tubes of these two groups had a common ancestry, but we cannot assume that this must have been so. If convergence in this respect has occurred in the arachnids, it may well have occurred in other lines also. As we have earlier emphasized, not the least interesting feature of arthropod relationships is that however we interpret them we are bound to postulate some degree of convergence in their evolutionary history. It is hardly necessary to add that no trace of nephridia remains in any of these groups. As for coelomoducts, these persist as the genital ducts, of course, and it is possible that the 'head' or 'salivary' glands of certain myriapods may represent the coxal glands.

There remain the molluscs, a group that preserves a good deal of uniformity in the excretory system, despite the variety of form shown by other organs such as the ctenidium and the foot. As with the crustaceans, nephridia are absent from the adults; in this instance, however, we have some evidence that they have been second-arily lost, for protonephridia have been identified in the larvae of certain Pulmonata (e.g. *Ancylus*, *Planorbis*, *Lymnaea*, *Arion*, *Helix*) and Lamellibranchia (e.g. *Dreissensia*).

The coelomoducts of the adult (Fig. 12-6) consist typically of a pair of tubular structures, leading from the coelomic cavity to the outside, and primitively consti-tuting the genital ducts. It has been generally assumed that the molluscs originally possessed a pair of coelomic cavities, which met dorsally to enclose the heart, and the walls of which proliferated the germ cells, but we have seen that it is not easy to decide how these cavities might have arisen in the first place. We can only suppose that some simple arrangement of paired cavities gave rise by further differentiation to an anterior region, the gonad; a central region, the pericardial coelom; and a posterior region, the gonoduct. The last of these also came to take over excretory function, presumably in correlation with the disappearance of the nephridia. Thereafter there was a progressive tendency for the renal and genital ducts to separate, just as happened also in the vertebrates; presumably there is much functional advantage in this separation. The coelomic cavities, whatever their precise origin, are clearly tripartite structures as we see them today. There is no reason, however, to suppose that this subdivision represents any form of metameric segmentation, for these cavities arise by the hollowing-out of a pair of coelomoblast masses. In so far as segmentation is to be found at all in the coelom of molluscs, it is present in the six pairs of excretory organs of *Neopilina* (Fig. 11-5), but it is by no means certain that this repetition is truly metameric.

In the Aplacophora the arrangement of the coelomic cavities still corresponds closely to the primitive plan, but in other molluscs modifications have been developed along several evolutionary lines (Fig. 12-6). One result of these is the appearance of some degree of asymmetry; another is the separation of genital and excretory regions. This separation is achieved in the Polyplacophora by a splitting of the coelomoduct in the region of the coelomostome, while the gonadial cavities become closed off from

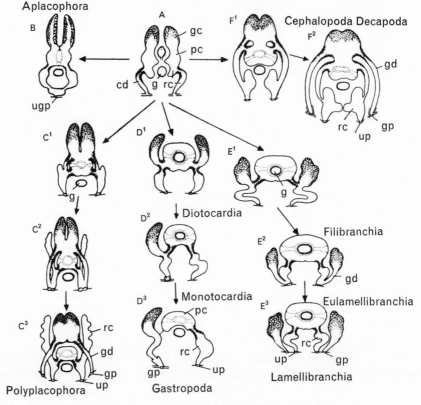

Fig. 12-6. Diagram showing specialization and subdivision of coelom and coelomo-ducts in Mollusca. A, primitive plan. B, Aplacophora. *cd*, coelomoduct; *g*, gut; *gc*, gonadial coelom; *gd*, genital duct; *gp*, genital pore; *h*, heart; *pc*, pericardial chamber; *rc*, renal organ; *ugp*, urinogenital pore; *up*, excretory pore. Along line C coelomoduct becomes split from coelomostome outwards and genital coelom closed off. Along line D (Gastropoda represented as untwisted) both heart and pericardial chamber may surround gut, and left genital chamber comes to open into renal organ and left coelomostome may be closed, left coelomoduct remaining as genital duct. Along line E gonadial chamber comes to open into coelomoduct which may become split into separate excretory and genital ducts. In line F coelomoduct also becomes split into two, and generally they are asymmetrically developed. From Goodrich, 1945. *op. cit.*

the pericardial coelom. The excretory coeloms remain connected with the latter at the coelomostomes, but are increased in relative size by forward prolongation and by the development of branched outgrowths.

In the gastropods a marked asymmetry develops in the coelomic complex. The right gonad disappears, and in the Mesogastropoda the surviving left gonad opens into a coelomoduct that has lost both its renal function and its connection with the pericardial coelom. The excretory organ is now present on the right side only, and is commonly large and thick-walled. The position of the external renal opening varies in relation to the other factors influencing the organization of the pallial complex. In the prosobranchs, for example, the opening is in the posterior part of the mantle cavity, while in the pulmonates the duct extends alongside the rectum, so that it opens outside the respiratory mantle cavity.

The lamellibranchs lack the complications of asymmetry that are such a feature of gastropod organization, but in them, too, the genital and renal ducts become separated. In the more primitive protobranchs the gonads discharge their products into the renal organs just beyond the renopericardial funnel; in the filibranchs the connection is much nearer the posterior end of the kidney, while in the eulamellibranchs the two organs have developed separate openings. During the course of this transformation there is also a modification in the renal organs themselves. Initially, in the protobranchs, the whole of the coelomoduct is excretory, but later it becomes bent into a U shape; the lower limb is now glandular, while the upper, and more distal, limb forms a bladder. Finally, the separation of the genital and excretory components of the coelomic complex has been achieved also in the cephalopods, where the genital duct comes to run separately from the renopericardial canal and kidney. Some degree of asymmetry may be present in this group, as, for example, in *Sepia*, where a renal papilla is present on each side, but a genital papilla on the left side only.

12–2 EXCRETION OF NITROGEN

Amino acids, absorbed from the alimentary tract or arising from the metabolism of proteins, are subjected to two main types of metabolic process. One of these, known as transamination, is a reversible process in which amino nitrogen is transferred from one compound to another:

$$\underset{|}{\overset{R}{}}\qquad \underset{|}{\overset{R'}{}}\qquad \underset{|}{\overset{R}{}}\qquad \underset{|}{\overset{R'}{}}$$
$$NH_2CHCOOH + O=CCOOH \rightleftharpoons O=CCOOH + NH_2CHCOOH$$

This reaction, which is probably operative throughout living tissues, both plant and animal, involves an interaction between the amino acid and α-ketoglutaric acid, and is catalyzed by specific enzymes.

The second main type of process is known as oxidative deamination, and results in the breakdown of the amino acid to a keto acid and free ammonia:

$$\underset{|}{\overset{R}{}}\qquad\qquad\qquad \underset{|}{\overset{R}{}}$$
$$NH_2CHCOOH + \tfrac{1}{2}O_2 \rightleftharpoons O=CCOOH + NH_3$$

This, too, is a reversible reaction, catalyzed by specific enzymes, and is known to occur in plants and micro-organisms as well as in animals. Both processes, therefore, are presumably part of the fundamental biochemical equipment of living tissues.

Animal tissues can assimilate some of the ammonia produced by deamination, but usually their catabolic activity produces far more than can be dealt with in this way, and it is here that the problem of nitrogenous excretion arises. There seems no reason to doubt that ammonia is the major waste product of protein metabolism in all animals, but it need not leave the body in that form. To determine whether or not it does so, it is necessary, ideally, to identify the organs responsible specifically for the removal of nitrogenous waste, and to establish the chemical nature of their product. There are obvious difficulties in the way of doing so, however; not the least is that the animals concerned are often small. Fortunately, much valuable information can be gained with aquatic animals by analyzing the medium in which they are living, and determining the nature of the nitrogenous products that accumulate in it.

No group limits its nitrogen excretion to one product, but it is well established that aquatic invertebrates commonly excrete much of their nitrogen in the form of ammonia. This constitutes 52.7% of the total nitrogen excreted by actinians, other representative figures being 80% (*Aphrodite*), 60% (*Astacus*), 67% (*Sepia*), and 39.3% (*Asterias*); a relatively low value in echinoderms is associated with the excretion of large amounts of amino acids. All such animals, in which ammonia is the predominant form of nitrogenous waste, are termed ammonotelic. Ammonia is a substance that diffuses readily through body surfaces into surrounding water, so that its removal is unlikely to demand the development of specialized excretory organs. This is confirmed by data obtained from crustaceans, which show that ammonia may be plentiful in the blood but very scarce in the excretory fluid. In *Maia squinado*, for example, the ammonia content of the blood may be as high as 2.4 mg/100 ml, but the amount of nitrogen lost in the urine accounts for less than 10% of the total nitrogen excreted by the animal. The explanation seems to be that ammonia is lost largely through the permeable body surfaces, and particularly through the gills. In consequence of this, a considerable amount of ammonia can still be lost even after the excretory pores have been blocked. Evidently, then, some function other than nitrogenous excretion is needed to account for the specialized excretory organs that we have described, but before seeking for this it will be well to examine why certain animals have departed from this primitive pattern of ammonia excretion.

Compounds other than ammonia may be excreted by ammonotelic animals, including urea, uric acid, guanine, and amino nitrogen, but all of these substances are secondary in importance to ammonia. Even *Asterias* excretes only 23.8% amino nitrogen, while for *Astacus* the figure is 10.1%. There are, however, other invertebrates in which uric acid is the predominant nitrogenous waste product; in *Rhodnius*, for example, as much as 92% is excreted in this form. These forms, which are termed uricotelic, comprise most of the insects and many gastropods. The two groups have thus developed, quite independently of each other, a specialized form of nitrogen excretion, and one that they share with birds and many reptiles.

The principles underlying the establishment of uricotely were first formulated by J. Needham, who approached the problem from the standpoint of vertebrate embryology; they were then extended to adult invertebrates by Delaunay. The argument is that ammonia is highly toxic, and must therefore be excreted rapidly from the body. This, as we have already seen, presents no difficulty to aquatic animals with permeable surfaces. Terrestrial animals, however, are no longer surrounded by water, and must reduce their loss of this essential substance to a minimum, perhaps by the development of an impermeable body surface, as commonly occurs in arthropods. This means that nitrogenous excretion can no longer take place through the surface; instead, it is now dependent on the specialized functioning of excretory organs, which thus take on an importance in excretion that they have not achieved in ammonotelic forms. Nevertheless, the urine that they produce cannot be used for the removal of nitrogen in the form of ammonia, for this would require the loss of an extravagant quantity of water if the concentration of the ammonia were to be kept below the level of toxicity.

To deal with this difficulty animals make use of two main devices. One of these is to combine the ammonia with carbon dioxide to form urea, which is much less toxic than ammonia, and can therefore be excreted (ureotely) in more concentrated solution with a consequent reduction in the loss of water. This device is used in mammals (and is employed for a different reason in elasmobranch fish), but it has found no significant application in invertebrates. Indeed, it has the disadvantage of still demanding a considerable output of water. The second device is the excretion of nitrogen predominantly as uric acid (uricotely). This is of particular advantage to terrestrial animals. Uric acid is relatively insoluble, so that it can be precipitated from solution and removed in a solid or semifluid form, and this is undoubtedly one reason why the use of uric acid as the chief nitrogenous waste product is particularly characteristic of birds and terrestrial reptiles.

For the same reason a dry urate excretion is found in the Onychophora, myriapods, insects, and certain gastropods. In myriapods and insects it is correlated with the development of Malpighian tubes as excretory organs. The Onychophora lack these, but are able to excrete their uric acid from the intestinal epithelium into the intestinal lumen. It is removed from here within a peritrophic membrane, which is expelled at intervals of about 24 hours. Despite the development of this adaptation, the Onychophora still possess coelomic excretory organs, which retain their primitively segmental arrangement. Water containing ammonia is expelled from them, but only at infrequent intervals. It would seem that these organs must be regarded as a vestige of the aquatic ancestry of the group, with their activity now reduced to a minimum so as to avoid unnecessary waste of water.

Another reason for the establishment of uricotely is that uricotelic animals usually develop from cleidoic eggs, which are eggs that are protected against water loss by being surrounded by a relatively impermeable membrane. Uricotely permits the retention of nitrogenous waste within this membrane in the form of uric acid. Thus, to take one example, the uric acid content of the egg of *Lymnaea* increases from 0.5 mg/100 ml at cleavage to 4.5 mg/100 ml at hatching. *Peripatopsis*, the onychophoran in which nitrogenous excretion has been most closely studied, is viviparous, but here, too, the embryo accumulates uric acid, ridding itself of this after birth. This provides an instructive contrast with mammals, for the mammalian foetus relies upon its mother to remove its nitrogenous waste through her blood stream. It is because of this that it can afford, unlike the chick embryo, to excrete its nitrogen as urea; a circumstance that may well have influenced the establishment of ureotely in mammalians.

Uricotely has manifestly been evolved independently in several quite unrelated evolutionary lines, and may well have evolved independently within individual groups. This has certainly happened in the gastropods, which have developed uricotely in correlation with terrestrial life regardless of their phylogenetic relationships. Crystals of uric acid accumulate in the secretory cells of the kidney of these animals, to be discharged from the body at intervals. As a result, large amounts of uric acid may collect within the excretory organ, as much as 100 mg per gramme dry weight of kidney in the terrestrial *Pomatias* (*Cyclostoma*), for example. In contrast, the excretory organs of marine operculates may contain as little as 2 mg to 4 mg per gramme.

The adaptive significance of uricotely is well shown by comparisons of closely related forms living in different habitats. Thus the four species of *Littorina*, adapted for life in different regions of the littoral zone, show a gradation in their uric acid content, ranging from 1.5 mg per gramme dry weight of kidney in *L. littorea* to 25 mg per gramme in *L. neritoides*, which lives an almost completely terrestrial life in the splash zone. Similarly, there is a reduction in uricotely in those forms that have returned to an aquatic life. The fully terrestrial *Helix pomatia* may contain 700 mg of uric acid per gramme dry weight of kidney; by contrast, *Planorbis corneus* and *Lymnaea peregra* may contain respectively 41 mg and 1.5 mg. *Hydrobia jenkinsi* is instructive in this connection, for it is a fresh-water gastropod with very little uric acid. The explanation of this is that it has entered rivers from brackish water, and only quite recently; *Lymnaea*, on the other hand, is believed to have invaded fresh water from the land, and thus to have retained in its excretory mechanism some part of the terrestrial adaptation of its ancestors.

Part of the nitrogenous waste of animals comes from the metabolism of the pyrimidines and purines of the nucleic acids. The pyrimidines yield ammonia. The purines may be excreted direct, as adenine or guanine, or they may undergo degradation along the sequence

purine → xanthine → uric acid → allantoin → allantoic acid → urea → ammonia

The sequence may be interrupted at any stage, the excretory product often being correlated with the general nature of the excretory adaptation. Ammonotelic forms may excrete purines as ammonia, for example, whereas in terrestrial insects they may be removed as uric acid or allantoin. Evidently there is a close link between the degradation of proteins and purines, and this is of considerable evolutionary interest. It will be appreciated that the pathways of purine and nucleic acid metabolism are common to all animals. The existence within these pathways of uric acid thus suggests that the evolution of uricotely as an adaptation for terrestrial life may have been based upon the modification of already existing enzyme systems. Similar considerations apply to ureotely, for urea is formed from arginine through the mediation of arginase. Animals in general can synthesize arginine, while arginase is widely distributed in microorganisms, plants, and animals. Here again a specialized mode of excretion might have evolved by the modification of existing metabolic pathways. To this extent aquatic animals may have possessed in their mode of nitrogen metabolism some measure of biochemical pre-adaptation to terrestrial life. We shall find that their mechanisms of ionic regulation also provided them, in marine conditions, with some pre-adaptation towards the exploitation of fresh-water habitats.

But this argument cannot be pressed without reservations. Considering the high degree of elaboration of the crustacean excretory organs (see also p. 262), it is very remarkable that the terrestrial members, as well as the aquatic ones, have remained ammonotelic. The only fully terrestrial ones are the Oniscoidea, isopods which live on land and also reproduce there. Small amounts of uric acid have been identified in them, but their nitrogen is excreted predominantly as ammonia; this accounts for as much as 70% to 80% of the non-protein nitrogen excreted by *Ligia oceanica*, and 50% to 60% of that excreted by the woodlouse, *Porcellio scaber*. It may be significant, however, that these terrestrial forms excrete much less nitrogen per unit weight than do their aquatic relatives. It has been suggested for this reason that their chief adaptation to terrestrial life has been the reduction rather than the modification of their nitrogen metabolism. We have discussed elsewhere the paucity of terrestrial forms among crustaceans. Whatever explanation may be suggested, it is apparent in the present context that not all groups have exploited paths of biochemical evolution that, on theoretical grounds, would seem to have been available to them. Another illustration of unpredictability is seen in the Arachnida. Spiders conserve water by excreting nitrogen predominantly as guanine, which appears as crystals in the Malpighian tubes.

While, therefore, ammonia, urea, and uric acid are the main types of nitrogenous waste material discharged from the animal body, it would probably be rash to assume that there are no other excretory products to be identified, even though they may be present in only very small quantities. Chromatography makes possible the separation of substances that would never be detectable by classical methods of analysis, and it is sobering to learn that this technique has disclosed the presence of no less than 45 components in the urine of the octopus. It is not surprising, therefore, that published data of the composition of the nitrogenous waste of animals customarily leave a substantial proportion as unidentifiable non-protein nitrogen. The physiological importance, if any, of these unknowns has not yet been determined; as Ramsay remarks, the imagination recoils from contemplating the magnitude of the effort required to attack the problem. In the meantime, however, our knowledge of nitrogen excretion is sufficient to show that this process, particularly in aquatic invertebrates, is not enough in itself to account for the complexity of the various types of excretory organ. It is this that brings us to consider the problems of osmotic and ionic regulation.

13

Osmotic and Ionic Regulation

13–1　IONIC REGULATION IN MARINE ANIMALS

Studies of the osmotic pressure of body fluids are favoured by the comparative ease with which the osmotic pressure of a small volume of fluid can be determined by measuring the depression of its freezing point (expressed as Δ) below that of water. Data obtained for the body fluids of a wide range of organisms show that the great majority of marine invertebrates have an internal osmotic pressure that agrees very closely with that of the sea water in which they live. This is one reason why we believe that life originated in the sea, or at least became associated with it at an early stage, for it suggests that protoplasm may at one time have been adjusted to carrying on its metabolic activities while being directly bathed by sea water.

Osmotic relationships, however, are not the only ones that have to be considered in this context; the ionic composition of the body fluid is no less important. Information regarding this aspect has been slower to accumulate, but much accurate information has now been secured as a result of the development of flame photometry and other techniques adapted for the chemical analysis of the small quantities of fluid available. Earlier work had shown that there was a general resemblance between the ionic composition of the sea and of the body fluids of animals, a resemblance indicative, like the osmotic data, of a close relationship between all living organisms and the marine environment. At one time, indeed, it was suggested that the body fluids were essentially sea water. It is now well recognized, however, that marine invertebrates, despite being usually iso-osmotic with the sea, maintain an ionic composition of their body fluids markedly different from that of normal sea water. This is even true of the coelenterates, for fluid from the mesogloea of *Aurelia* has significantly more potassium and less sulphate than the surrounding sea water. Other groups of the less highly organized invertebrates show a similar state of affairs; echinoderms have high potassium values, as also do polychaetes, while the latter may show a reduced sulphate content, like *Aurelia*.

250

When these differences were first demonstrated it was argued that the body fluids of present-day animals might reflect the chemical composition of the sea as it was during earlier periods of evolution. This view, however, is not supported by geological evidence, which suggests rather that there has been very little change in composition, and certainly not enough to account for the observed differences. Consequently the ionic peculiarities of body fluids are now regarded as being of adaptive significance, and there is good reason for believing that they were established at a very early stage of evolution. Nevertheless, there is sufficient general resemblance between the ionic composition of the sea and of body fluids to justify a belief that the composition of the latter was established in a marine environment.

That these differences are the result of active regulation on the part of the animals can be demonstrated by comparing the composition of freshly drawn plasma or coelomic fluid with that of a similar sample that has been dialyzed against sea water, and which is thus in passive equilibrium with the latter. The composition of this dialyzed sample will differ from that of the sea, because body fluids contain large quantities of protein, the indiffusibility of which gives rise to Donnan effects, and calcium ions may form insoluble complexes with them. But its composition differs from that of the freshly drawn fluid—a difference that must result from the active regulation that goes on in the living body (Table 13-1). This phenomenon is

Table 13–1   Ionic regulation in some marine invertebrates

	Na	K	Ca	Mg	Cl	SO$_4$
COELENTERATA						
Aurelia aurita	99	106	96	97	104	47
ECHINODERMATA						
Marthasterias glacialis	100	111	101	98	101	100
TUNICATA						
Salpa maxima	100	113	96	95	102	65
ANNELIDA						
Arenicola marina	100	104	100	100	100	92
SIPUNCULOIDEA						
Phascolosoma vulgare	104	110	104	69	99	91
ARTHROPODA						
Maia squinado	100	125	122	81	102	66
Dromia vulgaris	97	120	84	99	103	53
*Carcinus maenas**	110	118	108	34	104	61
Pachygrapsus marmoratus†	94	95	92	24	87	46
Nephrops norvegicus	113	77	124	17	99	69
MOLLUSCA						
Pecten maximus	100	130	103	97	100	97
Neptunea antiqua	101	114	102	101	101	98
Sepia officinails	93	205	91	98	105	22

The header spans: Concentrations in plasma or coelomic fluid as percentage of concentration in body fluid dialyzed against sea water

*Webb (1940).   †This grapsoid crab is the only animal in the table which is hypo-osmotic (ionic concentration 86% that of sea water).   From Robertson, 1957. In *Recent Advances in Animal Physiology* (B. T. Scheer *et al.*, eds.) University of Oregon Publications, Eugene, Oregon.

known as ionic regulation, which we may define, following Robertson, as the maintenance in a body fluid of concentrations of ions differing from those that would result from a passive equilibrium with the external medium.

Ionic regulation of the body fluids, while always apparent, is comparatively limited in the lower invertebrates, but in the most highly organized ones, such as the decapods and the cephalopods, it may extend to every ion. On the whole, calcium and potassium tend to be more concentrated in the extracellular body fluids than in the external medium, while magnesium and sulphate are less concentrated; an increase in chloride compensates for the reduction in sulphate. We must conclude, therefore, that the tissues of marine invertebrates require a medium of specialized ionic composition. Since this situation is detectable in coelenterates, it was probably established at an early stage of evolution.

From the point of view of cell function the composition of the body fluids is merely a means to an end, for the cells have to maintain their own specialized ionic composition. Thus the excitability of nervous and muscular tissues depends upon the maintenance of a high internal concentration of potassium, some 20 to 50 times that of the ambient fluid. Sodium and chloride, by contrast, are relatively dilute, their concentrations outside the cells being, respectively, 3 to 15 and 5 to 50 times that within. This distribution of ions, which is responsible for the potential drop across the cell membrane known as the resting potential, appears to depend upon the resting membrane being moderately permeable to potassium and chloride, and relatively impermeable to sodium. Such sodium as does pass in is pumped out by an active metabolic process, essentially secretory in nature, and called the sodium pump. When these cells are excited by the application of a stimulus, there is a change in the permeability relationships, which leads to sodium entering the cell and potassium passing out; the immediate result is the establishment of a reversed potential called the action potential, the resting condition being rapidly restored again during a recovery period. This principle of operation is certainly very widespread in animals, and may even be universal. It seems possible, therefore, that ionic regulation may have been established very early in evolution as a mechanism for securing the essential requirements of irritability and response.

We are chiefly concerned here with the part played by excretory organs in the ionic regulation of the body fluids. For many invertebrates there is unfortunately no direct evidence regarding the way in which the composition of the body fluids is regulated, but something is known of the mechanism in higher arthropods and molluscs, where the excretory organs are large enough for experimentation, and for analysis of their contents. It is known that there is a continuous outflow of water through the excretory organs of marine members of the groups. This is readily demonstrable by closing the excretory apertures, for this leads to an increase in body weight as a consequence of the accumulation of fluid. But these organs are not merely passive ducts. If the composition of the fluid passing through them is compared with that of the blood plasma it is found that there are important differences. As Table 13-2 shows, sulphate is passed out in excess of its concentration in the blood; sodium, potassium, and calcium, however, are clearly being conserved, for their concentrations in the excretory fluid are less than their concentrations in the blood.

By thus controlling the removal of ions from the body the excretory organs contribute to the regulation of the composition of the body fluids, but in doing so they inevitably bring about a loss of both water and salts, and this loss has to be made good. Because of this there is a continuous entry of water into the body, probably to some extent through the gut epithelium, but mainly through the permeable external surfaces of the body, particularly those of the respiratory organs. How this inflow of water is contrived in animals that are iso-osmotic with the sea is by no means clear, but in any case it is only part of the problem, for ions must also be taken up. Some of these will be entering against the concentration gradient, for, as we have seen, certain ions are maintained internally at a concentration higher than that in which they are found in the sea. Their passage into the body must therefore be a metabolically active process (active uptake). This is evidently an essential part of ionic regulation, and it must therefore have been established early as a fundamental property of living organisms.

These facts have important evolutionary implications. It is generally accepted that marine animals have repeatedly given rise, along many evolutionary lines, to forms that have been able to colonize successfully both brackish and fresh-water habitats, and that have also been able to pass onto dry land These habitats are exacting ones, more 'difficult' (p. 3) than the sea. The fresh-water fauna is notably less extensive in variety than is the marine fauna; more than one reason can be given for this (Sec. 20–3), but one limiting factor is the continued dependence of protoplasm on osmotic and ionic conditions comparable with those of the sea. Fresh-water forms are faced with the difficulties of maintaining life in a dilute medium, with the associated low availability of essential ions. Yet certain groups and species have been able to deal with this, in part by adaptive modification of the structure and mode of functioning of their excretory organs, although reduced permeability and improved active uptake are also important factors. Undoubtedly the foundations of their success were laid in their marine ancestors, which, like the marine forms of today,

Table 13–2   Antennal gland secretion and renal sac fluid compared with blood plasma

	Concentrations as percentages of plasma values (on water-content basis)					
	Na	K	Ca	Mg	Cl	SO$_4$
CRUSTACEA						
(Antennal gland secretion)						
Maia squinado	100	98	99	109	101	214
Cancer pagurus	97	81	90	125	96	134
*Carcinus maenas**	95	78	94	390	98	224
Palinurus vulgaris	98	65	86	137	101	98
Homarus vulgaris	99	91	64	180	101	159
Nephrops norvegicus	98	83	81	130	101	106
Palaemon serratus†	82	86	95	670	106	380
CEPHALOPODA						
(Renal sac fluid)						
Eledone cirrosa	102	90	87	89	97	136
Sepia officinalis	79	50	70	68	100	215

*Webb (1940).   †Parry (1954), on ml basis. *Palaemon* shows hypo-osmotic regulation, but 'urine' is iso-osmotic with blood.   Remainder of analyses from Robertson (1939, 1949, 1953). From Robertson, 1957, *op. cit.*

were presumably exerting, through their excretory organs or other tissues, an active control of ionic fluxes. Marine invertebrates are thus to some extent pre-adapted for extending their habitat. Because of this, animals have been able to contrive more than one type of solution to these osmotic and ionic problems; not all of these solutions, however, have been equally successful, nor, it would seem, have they been easy to achieve.

13–2 PROTOZOA AND FRESH-WATER LIFE

The passage to fresh water has proved to be well within the capacity of protozoans, a fact so familiar that it is easily taken too much for granted. In view of what has been said above regarding the dependence of protoplasm on conditions comparable with those of a marine environment, we might expect the internal osmotic pressure of these fresh-water forms to be substantially above that of the external medium. Measurements of their volume changes in solutions of different molarity have given direct evidence that this is so.

For example, if *Amoeba proteus* is placed in various lactose solutions it is found that the weakest concentration in which a decrease in its volume can be detected is 0.005 M, which suggests that this is about the value of its internal osmotic pressure. Hence there must be an osmotic flow of water into its body, and presumably into other fresh-water protozoans. Even if the frequent presence of a cuticle reduces the

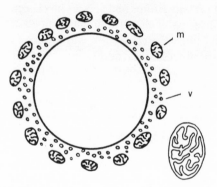

Fig. 13-1. The contractile vacuole and associated structures. The vacuole is enclosed in a membrane having a triplet structure similar to that of the external membrane and is surrounded by mitochondria (*m*). Between the layer of mitochondria and the membrane are found vast numbers of small vacuoles (*v*), which presumably burst into the main vacuole. The small vacuoles appear to form spontaneously in the space between the mitochondria and the vacuolar membrane. The smaller figure shows the arrangement of the internal membranes of a mitochondrion. From Mercer, 1959. *Proc. R. Soc. B, 150*, 216–237.

permeability of their surface, and we cannot be sure that it does, the animals must still maintain nutritive, respiratory, and excretory relationships with the external medium. We may expect them to accumulate water as a result of their own metabolism, of uptake in food vacuoles, and of their surface permeability. Of these three factors the last must present a particularly acute problem to animals which, because of their minute size, have an enormous ratio of surface area to volume. As for ionic regulation, we know virtually nothing of this in Protozoa, but we have earlier seen that protozoans possess contractile mechanisms that may well be similar in principle to those of the Metazoa. If this is indeed so, we may expect these mechanisms to depend upon the regulation at least of the movements of potassium and sodium ions, although at present this is no more than supposition.

It is evident, even from these limited considerations, that fresh-water Protozoa must certainly be able to control the water content of their bodies, and it has long been suspected that this is one of the functions, and possibly the primary one, of the

contractile vacuole. This structure, which accumulates fluid and periodically discharges it, is a well-known feature of most fresh-water protozoans. It has often been
said that it is restricted to these, but this is not so, for it occurs in many marine
flagellates and ciliates, although it is usually absent from parasitic forms. It is found
also in the motile stages of some fresh-water algae, and in some of the cells of fresh-
water sponges.

The functional importance of this organelle is indicated by its high level of
organization. In *Amoeba* (Fig. 13-1) it has a simple spherical form, with a bounding
membrane that is about 0.5 μ thick. The presence of many mitochondria around it
indicates that it is involved in a high level of metabolic activity. During its period of enlargement (diastole) it is carried forwards in the plasmasol; small vacuoles have been
observed to contribute to it at the beginning of this phase. Eventually it becomes
enclosed in the plasmagel, and may then be left in a posterior position, but discharge
(systole) will soon take place through a temporary pore in the surface, and a new
vacuole then starts to grow in the same region. In protozoans with a more defined
body form the contractile vacuole has a fixed position and structure, and its condition
in *Amoeba* is doubtless a secondary simplification. In *Euglena*, for example, it lies
close against the so-called 'reservoir', which is, in fact, no more than part of the
pharynx; here a group of small vacuoles contributes to form the main one, a procedure not fundamentally different from that in *Amoeba*. In the ciliates, in conformity
with their generally advanced organization, the contractile vacuoles (commonly
more than one) are more complex. Fibres may be associated with them, and they
are fed by a complex and fixed system of secondary channels, which extend considerable distances through the body as minute vacuoles (Figs. 13-2, 13-3).

The underlying mechanism of these contractile systems is little understood.
Kitching, to whom much of our knowledge is due, has pointed out that the fluid
cannot enter by filtration, as it is often believed to do in the excretory organs of
metazoans, because the contractile vacuole is only connected to the outside medium
at systole. For this reason, the internal hydrostatic pressure could not be relieved by
filtration of fluid into the vacuole, since the total volume within the limiting cell
membrane would not be reduced. He therefore favours the view that during diastole
there must be active secretion of water through the vacuolar wall. As regards systole,
he is inclined to ascribe this to contractile properties in the wall. Its thickness suggests
that a layer of structural protein might well be present in it, and it has been observed
that it is weakly birefringent during diastole but that this property disappears at
systole. This behaviour could be interpreted in terms of the folding or displacement
of protein molecules such as has been postulated as a basis for amoeboid movement.

It was natural for early observers of contractile vacuoles to compare them with
the kidneys and analogous organs of higher forms, and to regard them as being
organelles of nitrogenous excretion, but this interpretion no longer seems plausible,
at least as an explanation of the primary function of the vacuoles. There is direct
evidence that protozoans excrete their nitrogen as ammonia, and perhaps to some
extent as urea, and it seems likely that these substances could be readily lost through
the body surface. The favoured view is that contractile vacuoles are primarily osmoregulatory. This does not destroy, of course, the validity of comparisons drawn
between them and excretory organs, for the latter, too, are by no means restricted in
function to nitrogenous excretion, even in the most advanced animals. Moreover, we

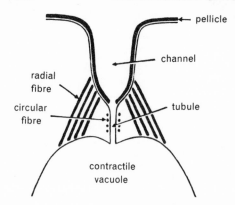

Fig. 13-2. Diagram showing the complex structure of the duct of the contractile vacuole in the suctorian *Tokophrya*. The existence of the circular fibres is highly probable but not yet definitely established. After Rudzinska, from Grimstone, 1961. *Biol. Rev.,* **36**, 97–150.

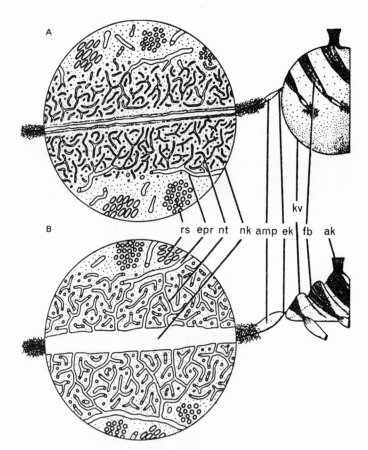

Fig. 13-3. Schematic drawings of the contractile vacuole apparatus in *Paramecium* showing main vacuole to right and one radial canal, with enlarged circular inset, to left. Upper drawing (A) shows radial canal in systole, main vacuole in diastole; lower drawing (B) shows radial canal in diastole, main vacuole in systole. *ak*, discharge canal; *amp*, ampulla of radial canal; *ek*, injector canal; *epr*, endoplasmic reticulum, showing continuity of this system with *nt*, 'nephridial' tubules forming a sponge around *nk*, 'nephridial canal'; *fb*, bundles of fibrils in vacuole wall; *kv*, main contractile vacuole; *rs*, clusters of membranous tubules. From Schneider, 1960, and from Pitelka, 1963. *Electron Microscope Studies of Protozoa*. Pergamon Press, Oxford.

have seen that the first appearance of excretory organs may well have been conditioned primarily by the need for regulating the flux of water and ions.

Belief in the osmoregulatory function of contractile vacuoles has rested partly upon the fact that these organelles are particularly characteristic of fresh-water forms; the conclusion may thus seem somewhat weakened by their presence in many marine ones. The weakness is not, however, serious, for the presence of protonephridia in so many of the lower marine invertebrates sufficiently shows that the need for such regulatory organs (see below) is felt in the sea as well as in fresh water, and we have seen good reasons why this should be so.

In any case, there is experimental evidence to support the osmoregulatory interpretation. For example, the rate of output of the vacuoles can often be decreased by increasing the osmotic pressure of the medium, and increased by decreasing it. The output from marine peritrichous ciliates increases as much as 70 to 80 times when these animals are immersed in 10% sea water. Moreover, new contractile vacuoles appear in marine, and also in parasitic, forms if these are subjected to osmotic pressures lower than those to which they are adjusted. Then again, the addition of cyanide to the external medium suppresses the activity of the vacuoles, presumably because of its inhibitory action on respiration; this results in an increase in the volume of the body. There are good grounds, then, for concluding that one of the many functional resemblances of Protozoa to Metazoa is the use of devices for solving the osmotic problems encountered when animal life, adjusted to maintaining itself in a marine environment, began to exploit fresh water.

We have mentioned above that contractile vacuoles occur also in fresh-water sponges. Their presence in these animals was first reported over 100 years ago, but it is only quite recently that it has been confirmed by Jepps, who has found them in the amoebocytes and choanocytes of finely teased fragments of the fresh-water sponges *Ephydatia* and *Spongilla*. Two or three of them exist near the base of the collar of the choanocytes, where they are said to be particularly large in 'that revealing moment just before death'. Significantly, in view of what we have said of their importance in fresh-water Protozoa, they have not been positively identified in any marine sponge. We can only surmise that these vacuoles are fulfilling, in the sponge body, functions similar to those that we have attributed to them in Protozoa. Their presence is a striking indication of the particularly close association that is held to exist between the two groups. They have not been reported in any other metazoan; not even in the coelenterates, where, in the absence of any differentiated excretory or osmoregulatory organs, we might have expected to find them.

This lack is perhaps associated with the almost exclusively marine distribution of coelenterates. Penetration into fresh water has been achieved by only a very few species; some medusae are included among these, but the best-known examples are *Hydra* and its relatives. *Hydra* is a good example of the way in which familiarity can blind us to the unexpected, for, with no obvious sign of surface protection or of specialized osmoregulatory structures, it is yet well able to maintain hypertonicity in its fresh-water habitat. The ectoderm and endoderm cells, which are highly permeable to water, probably maintain an internal osmotic pressure equivalent to about 0.04 M to 0.05 M sucrose, for they begin to shrink in concentrations of 0.04 M. Moreover, studies with radioisotopes have shown that sodium, potassium, and bromine are concentrated in *Pelmatohydra oligactis* at levels above those of the external medium, so that these animals, like *Aurelia* in the sea, are evidently able to carry out ionic regulation. Unfortunately, the mechanisms by which they achieve these results remain unknown; presumably they depend upon properties of the epithelia that form the internal and external surfaces of the diploblastic body.

13–3 METAZOA AND FRESH-WATER LIFE

The problems involved in the responses of marine invertebrates to changes in salinity are of great interest because of their bearing on the colonization of fresh water. As we have seen, these animals are highly permeable, and live in dynamic equilibrium with sea water as far as their water and ion relationships are concerned. Usually, and particularly when they live below the tide marks, they do not encounter changes of salinity in the external medium, and they are not adapted to deal with them. In consequence, when they are confronted with such changes under experimental conditions, the osmotic pressure of their body fluids varies with that of the water in which they are placed, and is virtually iso-osmotic with it; they are said to be poikilosmotic, or to be osmo-conformers. An example is *Hyas araneus* (Fig. 13–4).

When osmo-conformers are placed in dilute sea water, water enters the body as a result of osmotic uptake, while salts are lost along the gradient of concentration through the excretory organs and through the permeable body surface. Soft-bodied forms therefore swell in dilute sea water, and shrink in concentrated sea water. Often, however, they show some capacity for regulating their volume. This necessarily involves some adjustment of the salt content of the body, since they continue to remain iso-osmotic with the external medium. For example, if *Aplysia* is placed in 75% sea water, it at first gains weight for several hours as a result of the osmotic uptake of water. It then enters on a recovery phase of active regulation, during which it loses weight, as a result of loss of water, and at the same time makes a corresponding reduction in its total salt content. If, during this recovery phase, it is transferred back to normal sea water, it continues to lose weight; this is because it now suffers an osmotic loss of water, consequent upon its loss of salts during the recovery phase.

The cells of these animals will be affected in the same way, for a reduction in the salinity of the blood will cause swelling of the cells and tissues, as well as disturbance of their ionic balance. The extent to which poikilosmotic forms can survive changes in the salinity of the external medium therefore depends upon the extent to which their tissues can continue to function at different salinities. Those that can withstand only a very narrow range of salinity are termed stenohaline; those with a wide range of tolerance are termed euryhaline. The range is sometimes surprisingly wide. The osmotic pressure of the blood of *Mytilus edulis*, for example, closely follows that of the surrounding water, whether it is living in the North Sea, at a salinity of 30‰, or in the Baltic, at 15‰. It can even survive in dilutions of 4‰ to 6‰, which must clearly involve considerable adaptation on the part of its tissues. Other examples of this are seen in *Aurelia aurita*, which tolerates a salinity of 6‰ in the Baltic, *Membranipora pilosa*, which tolerates 4‰, and *Mya arenaria*, which tolerates 5‰.

This type of response probably leads to considerable stress, which must reduce the metabolic efficiency of the organisms. It is known, for example, that at a salinity of 15‰ the oxygen consumption of *Mytilus* is lower than in normal sea water, and there is also a reduction in its ciliary activity and rate of heart beat. One would not expect, therefore, that tolerance of very low salinities could provide a basis for the exploitation of fresh-water habitats, yet the swan-mussel, *Anodonta cygnea*, succeeds in defying this expectation. It survives in fresh water because its tissues are adapted to a blood plasma with a freezing point depression Δ of only −0.08°C. This indicates an extraordinarily low value for the osmotic pressure of an internal medium, and it must surely make the animal's body fluid one of the most dilute among living organisms.

Contrary to the more usual situation in fresh-water invertebrates, *Anodonta* is highly permeable to water. Considerable quantities of fluid are passed out through its pericardial coelom and kidneys, the amount in intact animals being of the order of

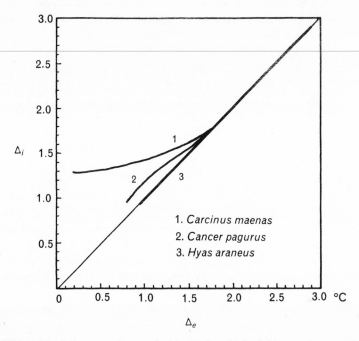

Fig. 13-4. Blood concentrations as freezing points (Δ_i) of three marine crustaceans as a function of the external medium (Δ_e): *1, Carcinus maenas* (Δ_e 2·88–0·19°C); *2, Cancer pagurus* (Δ_e 2·41–0·82°C); *3, Hyas araneus* (Δ_e 1·80–0·96°C). From Robertson, 1960. In *The Physiology of Crustacea*, vol. 1 (T. H. Waterman, ed.), 317–339. Academic Press, New York.

1.9 ml per hour for a 100 g animal at 15°C. The fluid within the pericardial cavity is relatively free of protein and is isotonic with the blood. Probably it is formed by ultrafiltration from the blood through the wall of the pericardial coelom, for the hydrostatic pressure of the blood is high enough to provide for this. From here the fluid passes into the kidneys, which are active in ionic uptake, for they discharge a hypotonic urine.

It may at first seem surprising that *Anodonta* is not able to make use of this active uptake in its kidney to maintain a much higher internal osmotic pressure, comparable, for example, with that achieved by fresh-water fish. Potts has suggested that part, at least, of the explanation of this is found in an analysis of the kinetics of the situation. A factor of great importance is the surface permeability. We have seen that this is high, and it is necessarily so in *Anodonta* because of its ciliary feeding habit and the large surface area of its ctenidia (p. 185). This must result in a prohibitively heavy influx of water. It has been calculated that if *Anodonta* had to exist in fresh water with an internal osmotic pressure equal to that of sea water it would have to carry on osmotic work demanding an energy consumption of 62 cal per hour per 100 g body weight in order to maintain its salt content. A low internal osmotic pressure reduces the amount of metabolic work required, and the exceptionally low value in *Anodonta* probably reduces it by a factor of several thousand. In one sense, then, this solution of the osmotic problem of fresh-water life is an efficient one. Yet, as we have suggested earlier, so dilute an internal medium must be far from ideal for the functioning of highly specialized cells, and this may well account for the lamellibranchs remaining predominantly marine animals.

Anodonta does, however, maintain an internal osmotic pressure higher than that of fresh water. It thus has some capacity for osmoregulation, which we may define, following Robertson, as the regulation of the total particle concentration of body fluids at levels different from those of the external medium. Other osmoregulators are able to regulate to a higher level of internal osmotic pressure, and it is these that provide a more promising basis for the exploitation of fresh-water habitats. *Nereis diversicolor*, for example, is a euryhaline form that may be found in natural conditions at a salinity of 4 ‰. Here it can regulate so that it is hyperosmotic to the external medium, although its internal osmotic pressure is lower than that of normal sea water. In this it differs from *Perinereis cultrifera*, which swells in salinities as high as 20 ‰, and from *Arenicola*, which also swells at reduced salinities and cannot survive at salinities lower than 12 ‰. Both of these species are osmo-conformers. The success of *Nereis diversicolor* as an osmoregulator depends partly on its reduced permeability to ions and water when it is in dilute sea water, and partly on its capacity for active uptake of chloride. It has been thought, too, that its nephridia may produce a urine that is hypo-osmotic to its blood, as happens in earthworms (p. 264), but this does not seem to be an essential requirement.

Osmoregulation in dilute sea water is better understood in certain decapod crustaceans. We have seen that *Hyas* is poikilosmotic; so also are many other crabs and lobsters that normally live in full-strength sea water. Some decapods, however, have penetrated into brackish water, an example being the common shore crab, *Carcinus*, which ranges from below low tide level to estuarine water of less than half the concentration of sea water. At high salinities *Carcinus* is iso-osmotic with the medium, but at lower ones it can maintain, by active uptake (mainly through its gills), a hyperosmotic state (Fig. 13-4). This enables the animal to survive the fluctations of salinity to which it is exposed in its littoral and estuarine habitats; yet the osmoregulation is only partial, and the cells are subjected to considerable changes in the osmotic pressure of the fluids that surround them.

A limiting factor in the maintenance of the ion and water balance of *Carcinus* is that its antennal glands, unlike the kidneys of *Anodonta*, can do no better than produce a urine that is iso-osmotic with the blood. In other words, when the surrounding medium is dilute, and ions are consequently scarce, the kidneys do nothing at all to help to conserve these ions by active uptake. They are simply maintaining ionic regulation, as they do in osmo-conforming crustaceans in normal sea water. In brackish water, therefore, *Carcinus* loses ions in its urine as well as by diffusion outwards through the surface of the body. This loss must be overcome by active uptake through the surface, and this requires the expenditure of energy. There is, however, one adaptation that reduces the demand for this: the permeability of the body surface is reduced, so that it is less than in osmo-conforming marine species. We have already referred to the value of reduced permeability, which is an adaptation common in brackish-water forms as well as in fresh-water ones. The degree of its development is related to the nature of the habitat, the fresh-water species showing the greatest reduction of permeability. Its effect is to reduce both the osmotic inflow of water and the outward diffusion of ions, so that the amount of work needed to maintain the osmotic gradient between body fluids and the external medium is correspondingly diminished.

Even with the advantage gained by reduced permeability, however, the type of adaptation seen in *Carcinus* would be a metabolically extravagant way of exploiting fresh-water habitats. The limits to its possibilities are probably reached by the grapsoid crab *Eriocheir sinensis*, which has penetrated into fresh water and which succeeds in maintaining there a relatively high internal osmotic pressure ($\Delta = -1.18°C$). It does so, however, by no more than the mechanism that we have just described, succeeding in this because of its rapid active uptake of ions. The gills are probably the seat of this uptake, for they can absorb sodium chloride from concentrations of no more than 1/40 that of the blood. This animal, therefore, must work very hard to maintain its fresh-water life, and is compelled to do so because, like *Carcinus*, it receives no help at all from its antennal glands; these continue to exercise their old function of producing a urine isotonic with the blood.

Eriocheir has to migrate to the sea to breed, although young animals can penetrate hundreds of miles up river, and its osmoregulatory capacity is adapted to facilitate this change of medium. Not only can it remain hyperosmotic in fresh water; it can also remain hypo-osmotic in concentrated saline, differing in this respect from *Carcinus*. The regulatory capacity of the latter is confined to maintaining hypertonicity in dilute sea water. Like *Eriocheir*, however, it depends upon a high salinity for breeding, its larvae being unable to develop in salinities of less than 28‰.

The fresh-water crayfish, *Astacus*, shows a more effective mode of adaptation than those that we have so far considered. So well is it adapted to fresh water that it can breed as well as live in it; moreover, although it can adapt under experimental conditions to sea water, it does not survive in this medium for more than a few days. Its internal osmotic pressure ($\Delta = -0.6°$ to $-0.8°C$) is lower than that of *Eriocheir*, and there are other fresh-water crustaceans, such as *Gammarus pulex*, that maintain even lower ones. This lowering represents an important saving of energy, for, by reducing the gradient between the internal fluids and the external medium, it reduces the loss of ions by diffusion. By reducing also the osmotic uptake of water, it decreases the volume of the urine, and hence the loss of ions through the excretory organs.

The internal osmotic pressure of *Astacus* is notably higher than that of *Anodonta*, and this will enhance the metabolic efficiency of the tissues. This advantage is made possible by the low surface permeability of the crayfish, but this is not the animal's only resource. Like *Anodonta*, and unlike *Eriocheir* and *Carcinus*, *Astacus* also has the capacity for producing from its excretory organs a urine that is hypotonic to the blood; ions can therefore be conserved while the surplus water is removed. This capacity, which is found also in the fresh-water *Gammarus pulex* and the brackish-water species *G. duebeni* and *G. zaddachi*, constitutes an important contribution of the coxal glands to the exploitation of fresh and brackish water, and is reflected in the structure of these organs.

The significant element in this structure is the presence in *Astacus* of a long secretory tubule following the labyrinth (Figs. 13-5 and 13-6). This tubule, which is absent from the excretory organs of the marine *Homarus*, is known to be the region in which the urine is diluted. The study of samples of urine removed from the excretory organ of the crayfish shows that the fluid in the end sac is iso-osmotic with the blood, and that it becomes less concentrated during its passage through the tubule. The situation in *Astacus* is closely analogous to the mode of life of teleost fish in fresh water, for they, too, absorb ions through their gills and excrete a hypotonic urine. By analogy with the vertebrate kidney tubule, filtration in the excretory organ of *Astacus* might be expected to occur in the end sac, and re-absorption of ions in the tubule, but we have no right to assume that natural selection will have produced identical results in crustaceans and vertebrates. The situation in the crayfish could be achieved, or at least aided, by the secretion of water in the tubule as well as by the re-absorption of salts, and the precise course of events is still not clear.

Gammarus shows a modification of the antennal gland similar to that seen in *Astacus*, and to a degree that is well correlated with the habitats of the several species mentioned. The marine *G. locusta* has a short excretory tubule, the fresh-water

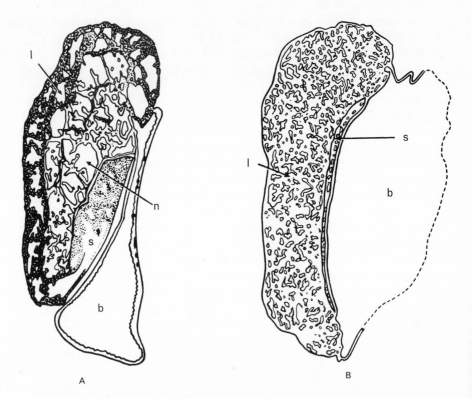

Fig. 13-5. Transverse sections of the antennal glands of *Astacus astacus* (A) and *Homarus gammarus* (B). *s*, end-sac; *l*, excretory tubule or labyrinth; *n*, additional tubule; *b*, bladder. From Parry, 1960. In *The Physiology of Crustacea*, vol. 1 (T. H. Waterman, ed.), 341–366.

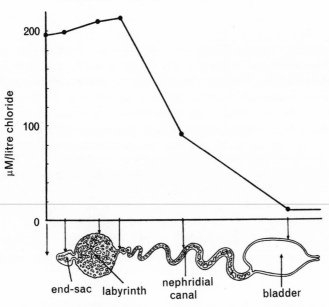

Fig. 13-6. Diagram of the antennal gland of *Astacus astacus* (after Marchal) with a graph of Peters' data of the chloride content of the excretory fluid. From Parry, 1960. *op. cit.*

G. pulex a long one, and the brackish-water *G. duebeni* one of intermediate length. In correlation with these differences the two latter species can both produce a hypotonic urine. *G. duebeni* is notable for the speed with which it can vary the concentration of its urine in response to changes in the salinity of the external medium; this capacity is probably to be correlated with its frequent occurrence in salt marshes, which are particularly liable to sudden fluctuations in salinity.

From all of this we can conclude that the coxal glands of crustaceans are heavily involved in osmotic and ionic control, and that they have played a significant part in the adaptation of the group to fresh-water life. These glands are far more important in this respect than in nitrogenous excretion, and they are clearly very much more than excretory organs, in the limited classical sense of that term.

13–4 FROM WATER TO DRY LAND

The water relationships of terrestrial animals, and the mode of functioning of their excretory organs, depend very much upon the route by which they entered onto dry land, and their degree of specialization to that habitat. Earthworms can be regarded as having evolved from fresh-water animals, their nearest relations being the fresh-water oligochaetes. Their adaptation to terrestrial life remains imperfect, for they commonly require moist soil for their surroundings, and can readily survive immersion in fresh water. Their body surface is highly permeable, as it must be for them to be able to respire through it; thus transference from damp soil to fresh water results in an uptake of fluid sufficient to produce an increase in weight of some 15% in 5 hours. This is a passive entry, the water following the osmotic gradient between the external medium and the inside of the body.

In view of the necessity for terrestrial animals to guard against water loss, it is remarkable to find that earthworms have metanephridia that are specialized for the removal of it. The osmotic pressure of the coelomic fluid is equivalent to $\Delta = -0.31°C$, while the blood is slightly less concentrated ($\Delta = -0.29°C$). The fluid from the metanephridia, however, is markedly hypotonic ($\Delta = -0.06°C$), which shows that these organs, like other excretory organs, can exert some regulatory function. The production of this dilute urine is a measure of the essentially fresh-water character of this group of animals (their excretion of ammonia is in conformity with it), but it may very well be of value on land when the soil is very wet. Some earthworms, however, have become adapted for life in drier soils by the development of complex nephridial systems which discharge in part into the intestine (entero-nephridia) instead of directly to the outside. An example is the Indian earthworm, *Pheretima posthuma*. In this species, as in *Lumbricus terrestris*, the nephridial fluid becomes less concentrated during its passage through the organ.

There is also evidence that protonephridia have some regulatory function, at least as far as water relationships are concerned. In trematodes, for example, the protonephridia bear contractile vesicles, which can accumulate fluid and discharge it periodically, while in the cercaria larvae the rate of discharge decreases with increase in the osmotic pressure of the external medium. We have already mentioned that the protonephridial system is particularly well developed in the terrestrial nemertine, *Geonemertes*. It is certainly more extensive than in the marine nemertines from which this animal has presumably been derived, and this suggests that, like the meta-nephridia of earthworms, it may be producing a copious flow of water. Pantin has shown that the protonephridia of *Geonemertes* certainly do excrete fluid, and that the activity of the flame cells is related to the water contents of the animal; partial drying results in a cessation of their activity. Undoubtedly this animal may lose water at a great rate, not only by evaporation from its body surfaces, but also in laying eggs, and in secretion of the mucus which it uses in locomotion. It reduces the loss by living in sheltered and damp situations (under logs and stones, for example), and it buries itself when it begins to become dry. As in the earthworm, then, the functioning of the excretory system of *Geonemertes*, and its capacity for removing water, has to be evaluated in the light of the types of habitat into which the normal reactions of the animal will take it. Pantin points out that its preference for damp logs may result in it being sometimes surrounded by pure dew or rain water. It will then be in danger of excessive hydration rather than of desiccation, and in this circumstance the action of the protonephridia will be highly advantageous.

Another instructive illustration of the problems of terrestrial life is provided by the Oniscoidea. We have earlier referred to these isopods as being one of the few groups of crustaceans to have made any progress towards terrestrial life. The dorso-ventral flattening of their bodies, and the possession of a ventral brood pouch, might be said to constitute a measure of pre-adaptation for terrestrial life. Yet these isopods have developed little in the way of specific adaptations for such a life, and they remain dependent to varying degrees upon a damp environment. They have not waterproofed their exoskeleton, and they continue, like their marine ancestors, to rely upon their pleopods for respiration. The modifications of their pleopods are, however, modest terrestrial adaptations; it is known that those isopods possessing pseudotracheae (Fig. 13-7) can respire better in dry air than can those without them.

To judge from the habits of their immediate relatives, these isopods must have evolved from marine ancestors, their path of entry onto land being through the littoral zone. This is suggested by *Ligia oceanica*, a familiar isopod of the splash zone, which has not quite emancipated itself from the sea shore, and which has unmodified pleopods. What little is known about the water relationships of isopods indicates that these animals have remained as much marine forms as the earthworms have remained as fresh-water ones. The osmotic pressure of their blood is high, as would be expected if they are of marine origin, but they seem to have little power of regulating it. They appear to survive by being able to tolerate the internal osmotic fluctuations that result from their surface permeability. Thus *Ligia* can tolerate fluctuations in the composition of its blood ranging from $\Delta = -1.44°C$ to $\Delta = -3.48°C$. All of these isopods are further aided by behavioural responses which are evoked by loss of water. *Oniscus*, *Porcellio*, and *Armadillidium* drink water (as also, incidentally, does *Birgus latro*), while *Ligia* takes up water by the anus.

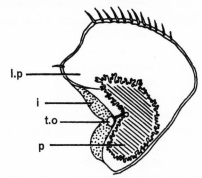

Fig. 13-7.   Exopodite of the first pleopod of *Porcellio scaber*, to show the extent of the pseudotracheae. *i*, interior border of the pleopod; *l.p*, lamina of the pleopod; *p*, pseudotracheal area; *t.o*, tracheal opening shown by presence of air bubble. After Verhoeff, from Edney, 1960. In *The Physiology of Crustacea*, vol. 1 (T. H. Waterman, ed.), 367–393.

Edney has pointed out that a possible explanation of the limited extent of the terrestrial adaptations of isopods may be found in the problems presented by passage through the littoral zone, as compared with passage through the water of estuaries and swamps. In the latter, and particularly in swamps, aerial respiration can become established while the animals concerned are still protected by an aquatic habitat from the large temperature fluctuations that are encountered on dry land. This was, in fact, the background of the evolutionary origin of terrestrial vertebrates. In the littoral zone, however, aerial respiration has to be established at the same time as temperature fluctuations are being encountered; and in these conditions the retention of a permeable body surface could be highly advantageous. The reason for this is that transpiration through the surface is an important means of lowering the body temperature during periods of potential heat stress, for, just as in the temperature regulation of birds and mammals, it removes the latent heat of vaporization of the water. This use of a permeable skin is a capacity that the Amphibia possess today, and it is perhaps a fair judgment of terrestrial crustaceans to say that they have so far not managed to proceed beyond that amphibian stage of adaptation to dry land.

We have, however, seen in various contexts that arthropod structure has great potentialities for adaptation to terrestrial life. These potentialities are most fully realized in insects, the achievements of which present the most striking contrast possible with the meagre ones of crustaceans. As with vertebrates, their primary adaptation is the waterproofing of the surface, here by the laying-down of the wax layer near the surface of the cuticle; a device that is not, of course, restricted to insects, but that is found also in other terrestrial arthropods, including mites, ticks, and probably spiders. Because of this, insects are outstanding in their ability to survive in really dry conditions; they are further aided by their invaginated respiratory surface, and their spiracular closing mechanisms. Associated with these features is the development of the Malpighian tubes, which replace the coxal glands as excretory organs. Our discussion of arthropod phylogeny has already shown that this adaptation must have evolved at least twice: in the Arachnida on the one hand, and in the myriapod–insect assemblage on the other.

Even within the insects Malpighian tubes vary in detail, but in principle they have walls composed of a single-layered epithelium, and they are bathed in the blood of the haemocoel. Water passes into the lumen of the tube, together with nitrogenous waste and dissolved salts, but how these substances enter is not entirely clear. There is some evidence for the occurrence of filtration in the end sac of the coxal glands, although even in that instance the evidence is not conclusive. In insects the position is a different one, for the blood pressure is very low, and the Malpighian tubes are surrounded on all sides by the blood, so that it is difficult to see that external pressure could have any other effect than to cause the collapse of the tubes. It seems likely, then, that the initial entry of the fluid and of its solutes must involve active secretion. In any case this certainly takes place in the reverse direction, either in the lower parts of the tubes, or in the rectum, for the material finally voided by the animal is a concentrate in which urates have been precipitated. This, as we have suggested earlier, can be regarded as a contribution of the excretory system to the conservation of water.

The mode of functioning of Malpighian tubes may well vary in detail as much as does their structure, but the observations of Wigglesworth have provided valuable information regarding their operation in *Rhodnius prolixus*. Here the upper (distal) two thirds of the tubule has a granular epithelium, and fluid is present in the lumen; the lower (proximal) one third has a relatively non-granular epithelium, but its lumen is filled with crystals of urates. When the animal feeds it ingests a large volume of blood. Within 3 to 4 hours the water contained in this has been absorbed and excreted through the Malpighian tubes, the result being that the proximal parts of the tubes are flushed free of their urates. After this phase is over, crystals appear again in the proximal parts of the tubes; they are derived, it is believed, from sodium or potassium urate that is secreted with the water into the distal end of the tube. The contents increase in acidity as they pass down, presumably because water and bases are re-absorbed into the blood from the proximal region, so that they become available for combination with more nitrogenous waste.

A fully terrestrial animal does not have to deal with osmotic problems in the way that aquatic and semi-terrestrial ones do, but ionic regulation remains important. Little is known of this aspect of insect excretion, although there is some evidence that sodium and potassium can be regulated, as one would expect. On the other hand, many insects have returned to water for part or the whole of their life cycle, and their problems now become the same as those that we have already discussed for primitively aquatic forms. One might expect that they would rely upon their impermeable surface for reducing salt loss and water gain, and this seems to be so in the larva of the alder fly, *Sialis*; the plasma chloride of this animal ranges from 0.15% to 0.34%

sodium chloride, and no less than 6 weeks starvation in distilled or tap water is needed to reduce this value to 0.06%. Re-absorption in the Malpighian tubes doubtless contributes to this retention, for the urine contains little sodium or potassium, and is devoid of chloride. The success of these protective mechanisms may be judged from the fact that the animal has no capacity for active uptake of ions, and presumably obtains all that it requires from its food.

It has been mentioned earlier that aquatic insects may develop structures that have been called tracheal gills. These are present in the *Sialis* larva, and in this animal they seem to be truly respiratory. In some other aquatic forms, however, their appearance is deceptive, and their name unjustified. Examples are the larvae of *Chironomus*, *Culex*, and *Aedes*, which have outgrowths that are now called anal papillae. These structures were formerly called gills, but it is now known that they are organs through which water can enter or leave the body, according to the osmotic pressure of the medium; they are also capable of active uptake of ions. Among the evidence for this may be mentioned that larvae of *Aedes aegypti* shrink in hypertonic media, but do not do so if their hind end is tied off, while larvae of *Chironomus* and *Culex* can take up chloride from very dilute solutions, but are unable to do this if the anal papillae are destroyed or ligated. Moreover, it can be demonstrated, in both experimental and natural conditions, that there is a good correlation between the state of development of the anal papillae and the salinity of the medium in which the larvae live. In general, the papillae are large in fresh-water forms and reduced, or even absent, in those living in saline waters. Anal papillae, then, like the other regulatory organs that we have discussed, illustrate the danger of naming organs, and of inferring their function and mode of operation, without adequate experimental evidence.

14

Sources of Information

14–1 CODED SIGNALS

It is self-evident that the maintenance of animal life demands continuous adjustment of the organism to changing conditions in its environment. Some of these changes will have no significant effect upon an animal's life—to these it may be insensitive. Others may influence its capacity to survive or to reproduce, or at least to carry out with efficiency its normal range of activities—to these it must be adapted, which means that it must be able to respond to them in such a way as to promote its survival. An animal must therefore possess sensitive structures, called receptors, which can be excited by an appropriate range of signals or stimuli from the environment. They provide it with the information which enables it to formulate its adaptive responses.

This pattern of stimulus and response must have existed from the very beginning of life, which could not have survived without it. It probably depended in the first instance upon the disturbance by the environment of some fundamental property of protoplasmic organization. This property is perhaps to be found in the structure of the living membrane that forms the surface of the cell. The significance of the membrane in this connection is well seen in two types of cell that are intimately concerned in animal behaviour: the nerve cell (neurone) and the muscle cell. We have seen that their composition differs from that of the surrounding medium in having a higher concentration of potassium and lower concentration of sodium. In association with this the membrane carries an electric charge; it is said, therefore, to be polarized, the charge being termed the resting potential. An active control of potassium concentration is a widespread feature of living systems (p. 252), and it is likely, as we have already suggested, that polarization of the surface membrane is a common, and perhaps universal, property of living matter. This suggests that from an early stage of evolution the primary effect of environmental disturbance was to create localized states of instability in surface membranes, involving changes in their ionic permeability. This would have resulted in a flow of ions which could bring about some measure of depolarization.

Such membrane disturbances can certainly be conducted over cell surfaces, but the effect diminishes with distance from the point of initial disturbance, and the conduction is said to be decremental. It provides a rudimentary mode of conveying information, but clearly it can only be of significance over very short distances. Theoretically it could provide for transmission through the body of a protozoan, particularly one like *Amoeba* in which there are no visibly differentiated organelles that might serve for conduction. Unfortunately, the small size of these animals makes it difficult to secure data sufficiently precise to confirm this, although there certainly are differences of potential across their surface membranes.

In the giant amoeba *Pelomyxa carolinensis* the potential difference at the surface is about 80 mV to 100 mV, with the positive charge external; this is associated with an internal potassium concentration greater than the external, and if the external concentration is increased the potential difference is correspondingly lowered. It is impossible to judge for certain whether or not such changes in surface charges are involved in the responses of Protozoa, although there is no evidence against this. Increased excitation of *Opalina* changes the direction and wave pattern of the ciliary beat, and theoretically we could account for this by supposing that there are corresponding changes in the polarization of the body surface.

On the other hand, it has been suggested that kinetodesmata and other intracytoplasmic fibrils may play a part in conduction and coordination in certain Protozoa. If this is so, it is difficult to see how the conducting mechanism could be similar to polarization changes at the cell surface. This could mean that the fibrils of protozoans are the result of the independent evolution of conducting mechanisms different from those of metazoans, but we know too little of the function of these fibril systems to judge whether this is a real possibility.

There is equal uncertainty regarding the condition in sponges. Mechanical stimulation of these animals produces contraction of the body, so that some form of signal can evidently be transmitted from one cell to another. The contractions remain localized, however, so that all that sponges seem to have achieved is some decremental spread of response over short distances. In this respect, as in others, they are essentially assemblages of cells with little coordination between them. Something much more is needed to provide for the long distance signalling that is essential for the organized responses of the highly differentiated bodies of metazoans, and it is this that is the special province of the nervous system. It is believed that this system is absent from sponges, but it is well established in the Coelenterata, and is a familiar and characteristic feature of all metazoan animals.

The nervous system is the result of the exploitation of an important invention, the specialized cell called the neurone. The significance of this cell lies in its ability to translate excitation into coded signals termed nerve impulses, which it can distribute (or propagate) over long distances without decrement. Neurones are highly diversified in form, but we may follow Bodian in recognizing that the common principle of their organization is the possession of three components: a cell body, a dendritic zone, and an axon (Fig. 14–1).

Like other types of cell, the neurone must carry out trophic or vegetative functions. These are mainly located in the cell body, which is responsible for the maintenance of the dendritic field and axon, and for the production of certain secretions, called the neurohumours and the neurohormones. The dendritic zone is the receptor

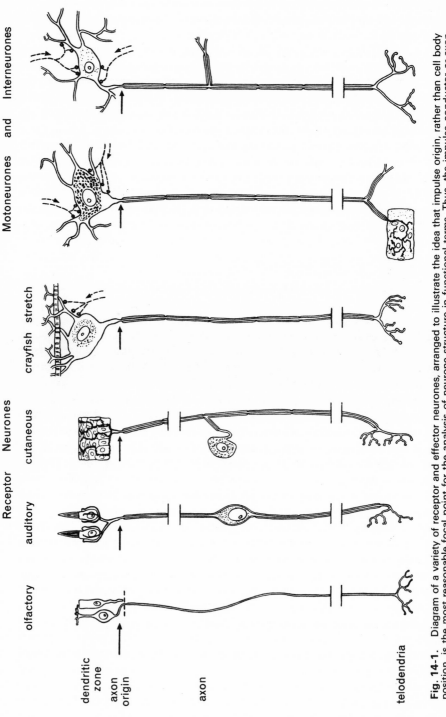

Fig. 14-1. Diagram of a variety of receptor and effector neurones, arranged to illustrate the idea that impulse origin, rather than cell body position, is the most reasonable focal point for the analysis of neurone structure in functional terms. Thus, the impulse conductor or axon may arise from any response generator structure, whether transducing receptor terminals or synapse-bearing surfaces (dendrites, cell body surface, or axon hillock). Except for the stretch receptor neurone of the crayfish, the neurones shown are those of vertebrates. From Bodian, 1962. *Science, N.Y.,* **137,** 323–326. Copyright 1962 by the American Association for the Advancement of Science.

region of the cell. It may be specialized as a receptor structure, sensitive to environmental stimuli; or it may be part of a motor neurone or internuncial neurone, in which cases it will receive the endings of the axons of other neurones, and be excited by their activity. It will then often consist of a series of branched processes called dendrites.

The axon, or nerve fibre, is a specialized outgrowth which conducts nerve impulses away from the cell body. It branches at its distal end to form the axon telodendria, a region that differs from the rest of the axon, and resembles the dendritic zone in that it is not concerned with the propagation of the nerve impulse itself. Instead, it is typically specialized so that when a nerve impulse reaches it, it transmits a chemical signal across a barrier called the synapse; these signals bring about the excitation of the dendritic zone of other neurones, or they may excite the effector structures (usually muscle or gland cells) that are the agents of response. A further possibility is that the axon ending may be associated with blood vessels to form neurohaemal organs, specialized for the release of neurohormones into the circulation (Sec. 17–2).

14–2 PROPERTIES OF RECEPTORS

We may begin our analysis of the nervous system by considering some aspects of the organization and mode of functioning of receptors. These structures are differentiated in all multicellular animals above the level of the sponges. Their characteristic properties are well seen in the stretch receptors of the lobster and crayfish (Fig. 14–2), as studied by Eyzaguirre and Kuffler. In this instance the receptor is the dendritic zone of a neurone that sends dendrites into a strand of muscle (Fig. 14–3) and that gives off an axon that runs into the central nervous system. The dendrites are excited when the muscle is stretched or contracted, and it is supposed that the excitation normally begins in the peripheral ends of the dendrites. These, it is thought, are specifically sensitive to stretch, which causes their surfaces to become depolarized. By inserting micro-electrodes into the interior of these neurones (Fig. 14–4) we can take direct readings of the initial (resting) potential, and of the changes that result from excitation of the cell.

In this way we find that the dendrites become depolarized when they are excited by the stretching of the muscle (Fig. 14–5), and that the change in potential is a graded one, varying according to the intensity of the stimulus. The potential resulting from excitation is called the generator potential, for it spreads to the cell body and there causes a corresponding fall in resting potential. Normally this resting potential has a value of 70 mV to 80 mV. If it is reduced by a certain critical amount, between 8 mV to 12 mV, a localized depolarization is evoked at a point that is probably near to the junction of the axon with the cell body. This depolarization is not a graded one; it is an all-or-nothing response evoked by a critical fall in the resting potential of the cell body. Moreover, it evokes a similar response in its immediate neighbourhood, so that a wave of depolarization is propagated without decrement along the whole length of the axon. This propagated disturbance is the nerve impulse. The potential associated with it, called the action potential, is the electrical expression of its passage.

Continued stimulation of a receptor cell will produce continued excitation (within the limits mentioned below), but any one response is followed by a brief period of absolute refractoriness during which no response can be shown. Continuous

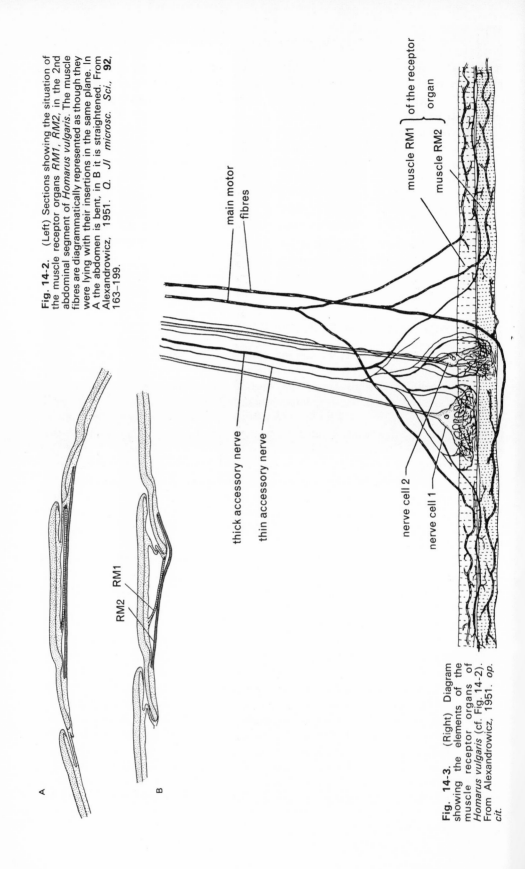

Fig. 14-2. (Left) Sections showing the situation of the muscle receptor organs *RM1*, *RM2*, in the 2nd abdominal segment of *Homarus vulgaris*. The muscle fibres are diagrammatically represented as though they were lying with their insertions in the same plane. In A the abdomen is bent, in B it is straightened. From Alexandrowicz, 1951. *Q. Jl microsc. Sci.*, **92**, 163–199.

Fig. 14-3. (Right) Diagram showing the elements of the muscle receptor organs of *Homarus vulgaris* (cf. Fig. 14-2). From Alexandrowicz, 1951. *op. cit.*

main motor fibres

thick accessory nerve

thin accessory nerve

nerve cell 2

nerve cell 1

muscle RM1 ⎫
muscle RM2 ⎬ of the receptor organ

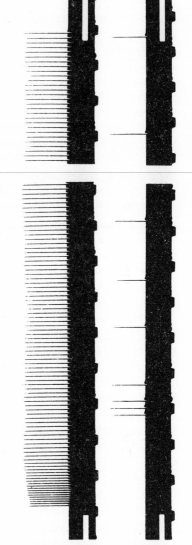

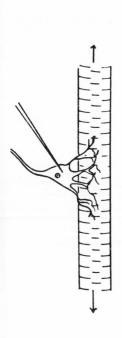

Fig. 14-4. (Above) Diagram showing a nerve cell making contact with a receptor muscle strand, seen through the dissecting microscope, with a capillary electrode in position. From Eyzaguirre and Kuffler, 1955. *J. gen. Physiol.,* **39,** 87–119. Reprinted by permission of the Rockefeller University Press.

Fig. 14-5. (Right) Membrane potential changes during stretch in the absence of sensory discharges. Intracellular record from the cell body of a slowly adapting cell in the third abdominal segment of the crayfish. Stretch and relaxation marked by arrows. From Eyzaguirre and Kuffler, 1955. *op. cit.* Reprinted by permission of the Rockefeller University Press.

Fig. 14-6. (Right) Oscillograms of action potentials of a single optic nerve fibre of *Limulus* in response to prolonged illumination of the eye. For the top record, the intensity of stimulating light was 10,000 times that used for the bottom record. Eye partially light-adapted. Signal of exposure to light blackens out the white line above time marks. Each record interrupted for approximately 7 sec. Time marked in 1/5 sec. From Hartline et al., 1952. *Cold Spring Harb. Symp. quant. Biol.,* **17,** 125–141.

stimulation therefore produces a series of discrete responses; continuous illumination of the eye of *Limulus* (Fig. 14-6), for example, results in the passage of a train of responses, each involving a characteristic sequence of ionic fluxes and changes in polarization in the nerve fibres concerned. These changes can be electrically recorded as spikes which are our visible evidence of the transmission of information along the axon. The rate of discharge of these impulses varies with the level of the graded generator potential, and hence with the intensity of the stimulus, the rate increasing with increased intensity. Commonly, however, the continued application of a stimulus to a receptor eventually stops the discharge of impulses. The receptor is no longer being excited, and has adapted to the stimulus. The discharge of impulses from some of the stretch receptors of the lobster can persist for several hours if the stimulus is maintained; these are slow-adapting receptors. Others are fast-adapting, for in them the discharge ceases in less than a minute.

This course of events is, we believe, generally applicable to the action of receptors which we think of as initiating a train of nerve impulses by establishing a local depolarization at the proximal end of the nerve fibre. This fibre may be a product of the receptor cell concerned, as in the example of the crustacean stretch receptors. Such a cell is known as a primary sense cell, and, in the form of single cells, it may well represent a primitive form of receptor equipment. In other instances the nerve fibre may belong to another nerve cell, which is then said to innervate the receptor cell, the latter being termed a secondary sense cell.

The sequence of events is a complex one, and it presents a number of problems of interpretation that have only recently begun to yield to experimental analysis. The primary function of the receptor element is to capture from the stimulus some energy which causes the organism to respond to the stimulus. The amount of energy involved may sometimes be infinitesimally small, as when a male moth detects the scent of a female at a great distance. Even in man, where the sense of smell is relatively feeble, the evil smelling substance, skatol, can be smelt when its concentration is so low that there may be little more than one molecule of it for each olfactory cell of the nasal epithelium. We must suppose, then, that the receptor includes some amplifying device, although we can only speculate as to what this may be.

By some means or other the energy initially provided by the stimulus is transformed into a series of electrical events in the axon—the train of action potentials that constitute the nerve impulses. This transformation is called transduction. One result is that a continuous stimulus is coded into a series of discrete nerve impulses. It is in this coded form, therefore, that information obtained from the environment is transmitted through the nervous system. The code is a very simple one, the only variable in it being the frequency of the nerve impulses, which increases with increase in strength of the stimulus. Yet, for all its simplicity, it is adequate to provide the organism with a very wide range of information. This is because each type of receptor, sensitive—as we shall see—to one particular type of stimulus, transmits impulses along a particular set of nerve fibres to its own particular region of the central nervous system. The information can thus be interpreted and acted upon according to the source from which it has been received. It is important that this should be so. An animal needs a great variety of information if it is to have an adequate basis for adaptive response.

14–3 MECHANORECEPTION

The maintenance of a rich input of information demands a high level of specialization among receptors, for it is generally supposed that each type of receptor element is organized so that it responds to one particular mode of stimulation. A useful way of considering this aspect is to relate the receptors to the physical character of the stimuli to which they are sensitive. On this basis we can classify invertebrate receptors into mechanoreceptors, responding to mechanical deformation; chemoreceptors, responding to changes in the chemical composition of the environment; and electromagnetic receptors, responding to quanta of light and radiant heat over a spectrum that varies in different species, but that extends from the infrared to the ultraviolet. In considering these three types, we shall refer to a few of the more closely studied examples. It is probable that the principles involved in their operation will be shown by future work to be of wide general applicability.

The primary source of mechanoreception was presumably the sensitivity of cell surfaces to contact with stationary or moving objects. Changes in membrane potentials and ionic composition may have ensued, and any of these that evoked responses leading the organism to move away from harmful material would from the beginning have been of adaptive value. It is likely that free nerve endings in the body surface often serve for mechanoreception in Metazoa, but more complex structures have also been evolved, particularly in the arthropods. In these animals, as in the vertebrates, information regarding the position of the joints of the skeleton and the tension of the muscles is essential for the rapid and effective execution of responses. One example from the crustaceans is the muscle stretch receptor that we have already considered; it may be compared with the muscle proprioceptor of vertebrates. Another is the statocyst, particularly striking in showing that the arthropods and the vertebrates have independently evolved two very similar types of receptor, sensitive both to gravity and to acceleration. No less striking is the resemblance in these respects between vertebrates and *Octopus*.

The statocyst (Fig. 14–7) occurs among the Crustacea in the Malacostraca, more particularly in the Mysidacea and the Decapoda, situated either at the anterior or posterior ends of the body. Morphologically it is an invagination of the body surface which forms a sac filled with fluid. The wall of the organ bears sensory setae which may be of two types, as they are, for example, in crabs. One of these types is the statolith hair, stimulated by movements of particles called statoliths, which consist either of a secretion of the animal itself, or of sand grains cemented by a secretory product. The statoliths, together with the sensory hairs and fluid, are shed at the moult. In classical experiments Kreidl demonstrated that if iron filings are sub-

Fig. 14-7. Inside of isolated ventrocaudal corner of left statocyst of *Carcinus maenas*, seen from dorsofrontal aspect. The hair fields surrounded by interrupted lines are clearly transparent in contrast to rest of statocyst wall. *t.h,* caudal end of thread hair row; *s.h,* statolith (hook) hairs touching statoliths with their tips; *f.h,* free hook hairs with tips directed laterally. From Cohen and Dijkgraaf, 1961. *The Physiology of Crustacea*, vol. 2 (T. H. Waterman, ed.), 65–108. Academic Press, New York.

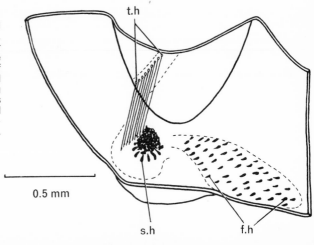

t.h

0.5 mm

s.h   f.h

stituted for the statolith grains—as they can be, for example, in *Palaemon*—the position of the animal can be controlled by a magnet. This component of the statocyst therefore functions as a position receptor, the orientation of the body being maintained in response to excitation of the statolith hairs produced by gravitational force acting on the statoliths. The mode of action is remarkably similar in principle to that of the maculae acusticae of the membranous labyrinth of vertebrates. Just as in the latter animals, angular displacement of crustaceans brings about compensatory reflexes which affect the limbs and eye stalks. Moreover, the position receptors of both groups resemble each other in that, irrespective of stimulation they spontaneously generate a continuous discharge of nerve impulses. The receptors can therefore respond to a change of stimulus in either of two directions, corresponding to an increase or decrease in rate of discharge, while in both groups spontaneous discharge also contributes to the maintenance of muscular tone.

No less remarkable is the parallelism between the functioning of the second type of sensory setae found in the more specialized statocysts. These hairs, called the thread hairs, have no contact with the statoliths, but instead are stimulated by movements of the fluid within the statocyst, being highly sensitive to changes in angular rotation about any of the three main axes of the body. Stimulation is followed by compensatory reflex movements of the eye stalks (Fig. 14–8), which turn contrary to the direction of rotation when the rate of rotation is increasing, and resume a normal position when the speed becomes constant. The results are similar to those evoked by changes in angular rotation in vertebrates, with the difference that in crustaceans there is no structural elaboration comparable with the semicircular canals. In both groups this particular reflex movement of the eyes contributes to maintaining a uniform field of vision during acceleration.

Considering the degree of convergence between crustaceans and vertebrates in this form of mechanoreception, it is surprising that position receptors of this type are almost wholly absent from insects. The Diptera are an exception, for they possess halteres which evoke reflex reactions to rotational movement during flight. Cohen and Dijkgraaf suggest that this difference may be related to differences between the state of equilibrium of crustaceans and vertebrates on the one hand, and insects on the other. The equilibrium of the two former groups is unstable. Insects differ from them in having a lower centre of gravity, and a greater surface area relative to their weight, factors that make them mechanically more stable, even when flying.

Nevertheless, other forms of mechanoreceptors are well developed in insects, as they must be in active animals with an articulated skeleton. Connective tissue is conspicuous in this connection, and neurones have become associated with it to form organs that are specialized for signalling the stresses that result from movements of

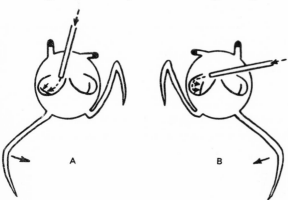

Fig. 14-8. Compensatory eyestalk and limb reflexes evoked in *Astacus astacus* by bending statocyst hairs in opposite directions with a fine water jet (statoliths removed). A, bending the hairs laterally. B, bending the hairs medially. From Cohen and Dijkgraaf, 1961. *op. cit.*

A   B

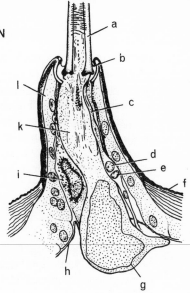

Fig. 14-9. Section through base of tactile bristle in larva of *Vanessa urticae* (after Hsü). *a*, base of hair; *b*, articular membrane; *c*, scolopoid body; *d*, sense cell; *e*, neurilemma cell; *f*, cuticle; *g*, trichogen cell; *h*, basement membrane; *i*, tormogen cell; *k*, vacuoles in trichogen cell; *l*, epidermis. From Wigglesworth, 1947. *The Principles of Insect Physiology* (3rd ed.). Methuen, London.

the body wall. In the simple form found in *Periplaneta* these receptors each consist of a multipolar neurone embedded in a strand of connective tissue. In grasshoppers and locusts the neurone has become encapsulated by connective tissue, and the whole is attached to a muscle. In Lepidoptera there is still further specialization: the muscle fibre that bears the receptor complex has become separated from the remainder of the muscle, has developed a separate motor innervation, and contains two giant nuclei. At this stage it has something in common with the vertebrate muscle spindle; its functions are similar in principle to those of the spindle, and also to those of the crustacean stretch receptor, but the latter differs structurally in being a compound organ with as many as four neurones on one muscle fibre. We see in these examples how similar needs condition the evolution of similar receptor mechanisms, with sufficient differences in detail to indicate the independence of their origins.

Mechanoreceptors are also associated with the exoskeleton of insects, occurring as hair sensilla and campaniform sensilla. The former (Fig. 14–9) are often arranged as the sensory cells of hair plates which are stimulated by the movements of the intersegmental folds of the cuticle. They serve, therefore, to signal the position of the parts of the body, without being dependent, like the muscle receptor organs, upon the development of muscular tension. The campaniform sensilla are essentially domes of cuticle, their associated receptor cells being stimulated by the strains produced by the bending of the skeleton. These sensilla are often found on the legs, in positions suggesting that they signal the forces acting on the skeleton of the stationary animal.

Finally, insects possess chordotonal sensilla, lying on elastic strands extending between two regions of the body wall. These receptors, too, can signal changes in tension, but they also give rise to highly evolved auditory organs. In this form they are stimulated by vibrations of a membranous tympanum that overlies them, and which presents an obvious analogy with the ear drum of higher vertebrates. They are highly sensitive, sometimes to frequencies that are far above the limit of perception of the human ear. Audioreception, indeed, is an important factor in the life of insects, not only because of their terrestrial life, but because the exoskeleton lends itself to the production of sounds, as is well seen in the bowing of the tegmina of male grasshoppers by their hind legs. Experimental study has clearly demonstrated that insects can recognize the sounds characteristic of their own species. Moreover, the grasshopper *Chorthippus* produces a number of distinctive sounds which are associated with equally distinctive situations that, from a human standpoint, would have emotional overtones. Faber has been able to distinguish, among no less than twelve such sounds, the song of the male in the absence of the female, the serenading of the female by the male (ending, if uninterrupted, in a shout of triumph), the duet of rival males, and the song of the copulating male.

Just as insects lack the statocysts of crustaceans, so the latter seem to lack hearing organs. It is true that crustaceans are sensitive to vibration, but this, as Cohen and Dijkgraaf point out, is not the same as possessing specialized sound receptors which are stimulated by pressure waves of characteristic velocity. Hearing, defined in this formal way, has not yet been clearly demonstrated in any crustacean. Perhaps the predominantly aquatic habit of the group is a contributory factor, but it cannot be the whole explanation, for teleost fish often have an acute sense of hearing, aided in many of them by the development of Weber's ossicles. We can only remind ourselves that groups and species have receptors that are adapted to respond to particular ranges of sense modalities, and that it is upon these that their behaviour depends. The consequence for us is that the world is full of noises and other sources of information that are quite unavailable to human receptor systems, unless, of course, we choose to supplement them with electronic equipment.

14–4   CHEMORECEPTION

The limitation of our own receptors is evident in chemoreception. It is difficult for us to appreciate the significance of this sense modality in animal life, for in man it is greatly reduced in importance. In many other species the situation is wholly different, for they possess an acute sensitivity to extraordinarily small chemical changes in the environment. Later we shall consider how products of metabolism, for example, provide a basis for animal communication and responses. We have, in fact, already noted this in the feeding processes of coelenterates. It is not clear which of the receptor cells of these particular animals are specifically concerned with chemoreception, but some information is available for certain other groups.

In turbellarians chemoreceptive cells occur in the cephalic pits or grooves. Ablation experiments demonstrate that these receptors are responsible for increasing the movement of the animals in the presence of food and for guiding them towards it. This is essentially a 'seeking' reaction; other chemoreceptors on the head operate when the animal is sufficiently close to the food, and initiate feeding. The chemoreceptors of flatworms are primary sense cells, elongated and slender, with stiff cilia-like processes projecting from their distal ends. Similar cells in the surface epithelia of annelids may be chemosensitive, but this assumption is based only upon observations of the intact animal, and experimental evidence at the cellular level is commonly lacking. It is known, however, that the whole surface of earthworms is sensitive to saline solutions, whereas sensitivity to sugar solutions is restricted to the prostomial region. This indicates that chemoreceptors must be widely distributed over the body, and that they are differentiated into more than one type.

Much more precise information is available for certain arthropods, for in these animals the association of receptor cells with differentiated outgrowths of the cuticle greatly facilitates their study by electronic techniques. In certain flies the legs and labellum bear chemoreceptors that are excited by contact with chemical substances, and that initiate such feeding responses as the protrusion of the proboscis. As with so many arthropod receptors, these structures are innervated setae. In the blowfly, *Phormia*, to take one example that has been extensively studied, the chemoreceptors of the labellum are setae, each with a sac of cells suspended beneath it. Within the sac are the trichogen and tormogen cells that are concerned respectively with the secretion of the seta and with the formation of the socket. Associated with these are chemoreceptive neurones, which may be as many as five in number. Of these, several have distal processes that extend up to the tip of the seta. This is the permeable region of the seta, and it is at this point that the processes can be chemically stimulated. One process, however, ends at the base of the seta. This is believed to be a mechano-receptor, for the seta remains sensitive to touch after its tip has been removed, but will no longer respond to chemical stimulation.

These and other observations on sensitivity depend upon applying fluid-filled micro-pipettes to the setae and using them as recording electrodes. They can be inserted either in the side walls of the setae or in their tips, the advantage of the latter position being that the fluid in the micro-pipette can then serve as a source of chemical stimulation. By inserting one electrode into a seta and another into the head of the animal we can record action potentials from a single seta. As with the stretch receptor considered earlier, the stimulus is coded into nerve impulses, the frequency of which varies with the strength of the stimulus. The responses of the individual receptor cells can be distinguished by analyzing the action potentials.

These studies have shown that the chemoreceptors are sensitive to at least eighteen sugars, and that stimulation of a single hair will elicit the characteristic feeding response of proboscis protrusion. The sensitivity is extraordinarily high, so much so that the complete behavioral response can be produced by stimulating a single hair with sucrose in a concentration of only 0.00001 M. A variety of other substances, including salts, acids, and alcohols, will also stimulate the hair, but with them the response is rejection, shown by a withdrawal of the proboscis, if this is already extended.

Are these two contrasted responses, feeding and rejection, mediated by the same receptor cell, or are these cells differentiated in their sensitivity? An answer to this is suggested by the electrical responses resulting from the two forms of stimulation. The rejection response is accompanied by a discharge of large spikes from the sensilla fibres, whereas the feeding response is accompanied by a discharge of small ones. This suggests that the two responses arise from two different cells, one sugar-sensitive, the other a non-sugar receptor. But this is not all. Rejection proves to be not a single modality of response, but one that can be evoked in two different ways. One of these involves stimulation of the rejection receptor, which is believed to be specific-ally sensitive to monovalent salts. The other depends on inhibition of the acceptance receptor by substances that do not stimulate the rejection receptor. Furthermore, there is evidence of the existence of a specific water-sensitive receptor, distinct from the carbohydrate receptor, while female flies, at certain stages of their reproductive cycle, seem able to distinguish between protein and carbohydrate acceptance.

The mechanism of this differential sensitivity is by no means understood. It appears to depend in part upon the structural configuration of the molecules concerned, but there is evidence also that different molecules may act at different sites on the receptor cells. Many suggestions have been made as to how the action is exerted. Presumably it must involve some disturbance of the surface membrane; this, according to the general concept outlined earlier, would result in ionic movements that could establish a generator potential. Davies has argued that the disturbance may result from the odorant molecules becoming temporarily incorporated into the membrane, the specificity of the association being determined by the characteristic shapes of the molecules.

Other factors influencing the feeding responses of *Phormia* are the general state of excitation of the nervous system, and the adaptation of the receptors. Thus a tactile stimulus, the bending of a seta, will not normally evoke extension of the proboscis, but it will do so if the fly has been without water and food for a day, when the animal is apparently hypersensitive. After further tactile stimulation the response disappears; the seta has thus adapted to this particular stimulus, but neighbouring setae will be found to be unaffected. Similarly, any one seta can be successively adapted to water and to increasing strengths of sucrose solution. Finally, the extension of the proboscis is only the initiation of the feeding process. Once it has occurred, stimulation of chemoreceptors on the labellae is necessary to bring about sucking, and, indeed, to regulate the extension, while further stimulation of papillae between the labellae is needed if the feeding process is to be continued.

Thus, starting with a sensory seta, which itself contains several functionally distinct receptor elements, our analysis leads us to see even a simple behaviour pattern as dependent upon coded signals from a large number of diverse receptors. Under normal conditions, of course, many sensory setae will be involved in the feeding response of *Phormia*, and many receptors additional to the chemical ones. This is a measure of the complexity of organization needed in the nervous system, which is responsible for the handling of these signals. We shall later consider some of the steps by which this has been achieved.

14–5   PHOTORECEPTION

One of the unresolved problems of receptor systems is the means by which they initially capture energy from the environment. We know enough about photoreceptors, however, to realize that here the initial stimulus must be the absorption of quanta of light by photosensitive pigments, and that the resultant chemical change in these pigments is in some way the source of the generator potential. It is also known that in the vertebrate eye there are four such pigments. All of these are carotenoid derivatives, consisting of a substance called retinene (vitamin A aldehyde) combined with a specific type of protein called an opsin. One or other of two main types of opsin may be joined with one or other of two types of retinene, retinene$_1$ being derived from vitamin A$_1$, and retinene$_2$ from vitamin A$_2$. Thus are formed rhodoposin, iodopsin, porphyropsin, and cyanopsin.

It is a striking demonstration of the unity underlying organic diversity that carotenoids are widely, and perhaps universally, used in photoreceptor systems, not only in animals, but also in the systems that are concerned with the phototropisms of moulds and higher plants. Moreover, pigments similar to those of vertebrates, although not containing either vitamin A_2 or retinene$_2$, have been demonstrated in the complex eyes of both arthropods and cephalopods. It is not clear whether these similarities of biochemical organization have been independently evolved, or whether they are derivatives of a fundamental pattern achieved very early in the history of life. Such, however, is the importance of sensitivity to radiant energy that the latter alternative would seem the more probable.

An explanation of the wide use of carotenoids in visual receptor systems has been put forward by Wald. He ascribes it to the peculiar capacity of these compounds for geometrical isomerization. Other types of natural pigments lack this capacity, for their atoms are held firmly in position in ring structures. Carotenoids, however, possess straight-chain conjugated systems, the stereochemical configurations of which can be readily modified. What is particularly remarkable is that the pigments involved in photoreception seem always to have a certain configuration known as 11-*cis*-, meaning that there is a *cis*-configuration at the eleventh carbon atom. Isomerization involves the transformation of this into the more stable all-*trans*-configuration, and it is this change that occurs when a quantum of light (a photon) is absorbed. The selection of this particular configuration is a consequence of its possessing a unique degree of photosensitivity; in other words, it can be isomerized by light with the maximum efficiency of energy transfer.

The most primitive manifestation of photosensitivity is the so-called dermal light sense, a diffuse sensitivity that does not depend upon any obviously recognizable receptor system. Indeed, since the nature of the receptor structures is unknown, it is not even certain that they are dermal, so that the designation of this phenomenon may be something of a misnomer. The property is widely spread through all the major phyla, more particularly in aquatic forms, and often co-exists with morphologically differentiated eyes. It is apparent in *Amoeba*, which changes its direction and speed of movement in response to stimulation by light. It is seen, too, in the isolated mesenteries of anemones, which contract in response to local illumination. They continue to do so even after the nervous system has been immobilized by anaesthesia, so that local reflexes cannot be involved. This suggests that certain coelenterate cells may be able to act in response to illumination as independent effectors, preserving a type of response similar to that of *Amoeba*.

In more complex animals the dermal light sense may play an important part in orientation, either through general or local reactions. Thus local illumination of the body of *Ciona* brings about a bending of the animal, produced by local contraction of the musculature, whereas general illumination causes closure of the siphons. We might suppose this latter effect to be caused by stimulation of the pigment spots that are conspicuous around the rims of the siphons, yet this is not so. They can be removed without affecting this reaction, so that the name of eye spots, frequently applied to them, is misconceived. Other examples of such reactions are to be seen in *Holothuria*, which retracts its tentacles when these are locally illuminated, but reacts to general illumination by moving and turning. They also occur in tubicolous polychaetes, where the orientation of the tubes may be influenced by illumination. With regard to the evolution of photosensitivity it is significant that the maximum sensitivity of the dermal light sense lies at wavelengths between 470 mμ and 580 mμ. This agrees with the known properties of photosensitive pigments, and certainly suggests that the dermal light sense, and primitive photosensitivity in general, depend upon the presence of small amounts of pigments similar to those of differentiated receptor systems. This could well have been the starting point of the evolution of such systems.

Two main types of highly differentiated photoreceptor system have appeared in the invertebrates: the compound eyes of arthropods and the camera-type eyes of cephalopods. Enough is known of the mode of functioning of these, and of their probable past history, to show that they represent the evolution, along two very different lines, of organs that have some striking points of similarity with the vertebrate eye, not only in their pigments but also in certain details of their structural organization. Indeed, this is an aspect of animal organization to which we have more than once referred—a convergence resulting from the widespread distribution of a common biochemical ground plan. In this instance the common feature is, of course, the nature of the photosensitive pigments.

Simple types of eyes are seen in the free-living Platyhelminthes and in the Annelida, where they are often composed of sensory cells associated with screening pigment cells. In their simplest form they may be no more than pigment spots, forming part of the general epithelium, but more usually they sink inwards to form cups. In the Turbellaria the pigment cells are often arranged to form the wall of an open bowl, the bipolar receptor cells projecting into this through its aperture. In such an eye there can be no possibility of forming an image, for there is no refractive structure. These organs are doubtless restricted to the differentiation of light and darkness, and in this way they make it possible for the animal to orientate itself with respect both to the intensity and to the source of the illumination. The distal ends of the receptor cells are differentiated to form a rod border, in which longitudinal striations can be seen with the light microscope. The function of this border is unknown, but it may have something in common with the rod-like differentiations that are seen in the receptor cells of more complex eyes, and that are known, as we shall see below, to be an essential element of these photoreceptors.

Cup-like arrangements of pigment cells are common in the eyes of polychaetes,

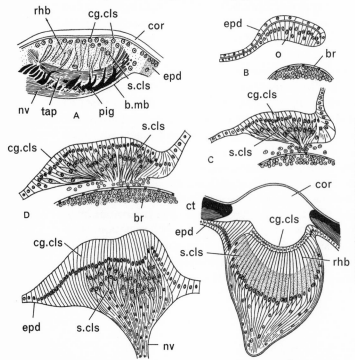

Fig. 14-10. Examples of the structure and development of dorsal ocelli of insects. A, dorsal ocellus of *Machilis*. B–F, stages in the development of a dorsal ocellus of male of *Formica pratensis*, and mature median ocellus of same. *b.mb,* basement membrane; *br,* brain; *cg.cls.* corneagenous cells; *cor,* cornea; *ct,* cuticula; *epd,* epidermis; *nv,* nerve; *o,* ocellar rudiment in epidermis; *pig,* pigment; *rhb,* rhabdome; *s.cls,* sense cells; *tap,* tapetum. Adapted from Snodgrass, 1935. *Principles of Insect Morphology.* McGraw-Hill, New York. Used by permission.

Fig. 14-11. Schematic drawing, representing a section of lateral eye of *Limulus*, in a plane perpendicular to surface of cornea, as seen in fresh preparations. Transparent cornea at top, showing crystalline cones of the ommatidia; the heavily melanin-pigmented conical bodies of these form a layer on the inner surface of the cornea. On the left, a group of ommatidia is represented, with indications of bundles of nerve fibres traversing the plexus behind the ommatidia, collecting in larger bundles that become the optic nerve still farther back. One of these ommatidia has been represented as if the section had passed through it, revealing the sensory component, also as if sectioned. On the right an ommatidium with its nerve fibre bundle is represented as it appears after having been isolated by dissection and suspended, in air, on electrodes (moist cotton wicks, from chlorided silver tubes filled with sea water) represented by the solid black triangles. From Hartline et al., 1952. *op. cit.*

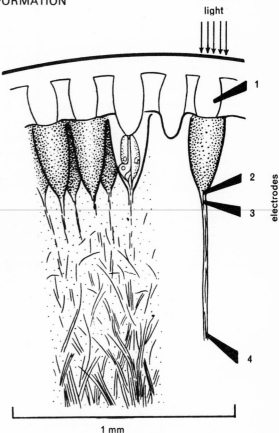

but a higher level of differentiation is reached in this group. Not only do the receptor cells themselves have a rod-like tip, but the epithelium of the cup may produce secretions that fuse to form one or more lenses. Moreover, groups of sensory cells may be closely collected together to form ommatidia, recalling the unit structures of the compound eye of arthropods. Indeed, in sabellids (*Branchiomma*, for example) the ommatidia themselves may be grouped together to form a rudimentary type of compound eye. No doubt a similar tendency played an important part in the ancestors of arthropods, contributing to the establishment of their characteristic compound eyes. Convergence was probably involved in the process of arthropodization, so much so that it is necessary to envisage the possibility of an independent evolution of compound eyes in more than one line. The situation in annelids goes some way to make the possibility of the independent evolution of compound eyes acceptable, although it does not reveal the actual ancestry of these organs.

Evidently the optic cup is the foundation upon which the varied types of arthropod eye have been formed. It is seen in the Onychophora, in which the eyes are a pair of closed vesicles into which a lens is secreted. It is seen also in the median eye of the nauplius larva, and in the dorsal ocelli of insects (Fig. 14–10). From a purely morphological point of view it is not difficult to visualize the evolution of such structures into the vertically elongated groups of cells that make up the ommatidia of the compound eye. This type of eye is seen at its simplest in the lateral eye of *Limulus*, which has

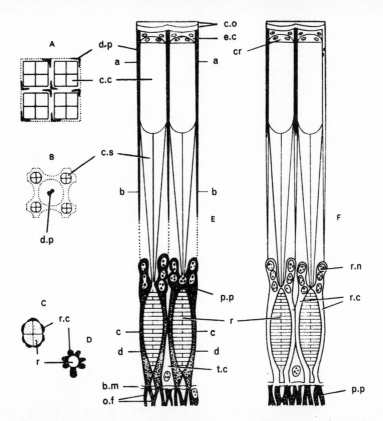

Fig. 14-12. Structure of the ommatidia of *Astacus astacus* (redrawn from Bernhards). A, B, C, D, tangential cross sections of four (A, B) ommatidia or one (C, D) ommatidium at the levels indicated in E by *aa*, *bb*, *cc*, and *dd*, respectively. E, radial (axial) section of two ommatidia showing the pigment in the light-adapted condition providing maximum shielding of each single unit. F, similar view in the dark-adapted condition with a condition of minimum light shielding by pigment. The facet diameter of such an eye is about 60µ. *b.m*, basilar membrane; *c.c*, crystalline cone; *c.o*, cornea (lens); *c.s*, stalk of crystalline cone; *cr*, crystalline cone cells; *d.p*, distal pigment; *e.c*, corneagenous cells; *o.f*, optic nerve fibres of retinal cells; *p.p*, proximal pigment; *r*, rhabdome; *r.c*, retinular cells; *r.n*, retinular cell nucleus; *t.c*, tapetal cell. From Waterman, 1961. *The Physiology of Crustacea*, vol. 2 (T. H. Waterman, ed.), 1–64.

provided material for experimental analysis of much elegance. It consists of about 1,000 ommatidia, each of which is formed of twelve retinula cells, together with an eccentrically placed nerve cell (Fig. 14–11). The retinula cells are arranged like the segments of an orange, packed radially around the dendrite of the nerve cell. Within the ommatidia is a photosensitive pigment based upon vitamin A_1 and retinene$_1$; these, as we have seen, occur in the vertebrate eye, but the analogy with the latter is even closer than this.

Electron microscopy reveals that the rods and cones of the vertebrate retinula cells contain membranes arranged as closely packed discs. It is supposed that the visual pigments are arranged on or in these membranes, and that isomerization causes permeability changes, resulting in ionic movements and changes in membrane potential. Within the retinula cells of *Limulus* there are arrays of parallel tubules that suggest an obvious analogy with the ultrastructure of the vertebrate rods and cones. The similarity of the pigments makes it highly probable that the mechanisms of energy capture and transduction are fundamentally the same in the two groups. It is thus all the more significant that by using microelectrodes we can recognize generator

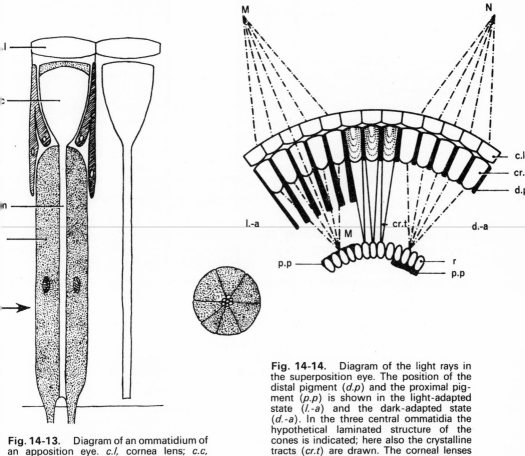

Fig. 14-13. Diagram of an ommatidium of an apposition eye. *c.l,* cornea lens; *c.c,* crystalline cone; *s.c,* sense cells. In the cross-section the individual rhabdomeres can be recognized in the rhabdome (*r.m*). From Kuiper, 1961. *Symp. Soc. exp. Biol.,* **16**, 58–71.

Fig. 14-14. Diagram of the light rays in the superposition eye. The position of the distal pigment (*d.p*) and the proximal pigment (*p.p*) is shown in the light-adapted state (*l.-a*) and the dark-adapted state (*d.-a*). In the three central ommatidia the hypothetical laminated structure of the cones is indicated; here also the crystalline tracts (*cr.t*) are drawn. The corneal lenses (*c.l*) are usually not drawn in such diagrams though they often have a greater refractive power than the cones. *m* and *n* are two light sources and *r* is the retinula. From Kuiper, 1961. *op. cit.*

potentials in the ommatidium of *Limulus,* and show that the eccentric nerve cell (the corresponding elements are, of course, arranged quite differently in the vertebrate retina) gives rise to the nerve impulses already mentioned.

Compound eyes of a more advanced type are found in crustaceans and insects; while varying greatly in detail, they are essentially of the plan in Fig. 14–12. Two refractive bodies are present; the lens, which is a biconvex thickening of the general cuticle, and the crystalline cone, secreted by a group of vitrellar cells. Below these is a group of seven to eight receptor (retinula) cells, each of which forms a fibrillar rhabdomere along its length, the several rhabdomeres fusing to form the rhabdome. The visual pigment is probably located within the rhabdome, which may therefore be compared with the rods and cones of the vertebrate retina. Photostimulation is presumably initiated within the rhabdome, its result being the propagation of nerve impulses into the optic nerve along the nerve fibres that arise from the base of each retinula cell.

We can distinguish two main morphological types of compound eye, the apposition eye and the superposition eye (Figs. 14–13, 14–14). In both types the ommatidium is structurally a separate and self-contained unit, separated from its neighbours by groups of distal and proximal pigment and reflecting cells. Where the types differ is in the degree of functional independence of the ommatidia, a factor that has an important influence on the mode of functioning of the eye.

The apposition type is particularly characteristic of terrestrial, littoral, and diurnal species, including the Hymenoptera and Diptera amongst the insects. Its receptor cells are greatly elongated, extending distally as far as the crystalline cone. According to the classical mosaic theory of vision, each ommatidium receives light from the very small area that corresponds to its geometrical projection. This means that the image formed by the eye as a whole must be a mosaic of areas corresponding in number to the ommatidia. In the superposition eye—found, for example, in lobsters, crabs, and nocturnal insects—the retinal cells are widely separated from the crystalline cone, and it is supposed that each receptor cell is stimulated by light that has entered through a number of ommatidial lenses. This type of eye is suited for vision in dim light, which might not be an adequate stimulus if each receptor cell received only the rays that had entered through its own ommatidium. The resulting overlapping of images, however, will yield poor resolution, whereas much better resolution is to be expected from the isolated images formed by the apposition eye.

This interpretation would indicate that the pigment cells cooperate in visual function by modifying the degree of isolation of the ommatidia. Their behaviour varies greatly from species to species, but in general they seem to be of greater importance in the superposition eye. Here, in conditions of strong illumination, the pigment moves within the cells to screen the retinal cells, so that they can only be stimulated by light entering along the ommatidial axis. In this condition the eye is said to be light-adapted (Fig. 14-12). In dim light the pigment moves to expose the retinal cells, which can now be reached by light from a wider source, a condition in which the eye is said to be dark-adapted (Fig. 14-12).

Evidently, many arthropods are unable to secure precise discrimination of form in their visual field. Often they will only distinguish degrees of shade and illumination, but even so the compound structure of the eye probably aids detection of movement, because of the continuously changing pattern of ommatidial illumination. These matters are still very imperfectly understood, but new experimental approaches are leading to re-assessments of old problems. For example, it has been widely supposed that the apposition eye favours the discrimination of form through acuity of resolution. Recent electronic studies, however, have shown that the field of vision of a single ommatidium is much larger than was formerly believed. Thus a single ommatidium of the eye of *Locusta* receives light over an angle of 20°, which means that a single point source must stimulate many ommatidia. Yet this same eye can detect movement, and discriminate pattern, when the angle subtended by the movement or source is only of the order of 0.3°. The sensitivity of the compound eye in this instance is certainly much higher than might have been predicted—perhaps, according to a suggestion of Burtt and Catton, because additional images are formed deeper in the eye by groups of ommatidia. It is at least quite clear from behaviour studies, to which we shall be referring later, that some insects are well able to discriminate form and, by virtue of this capacity, to learn the landmarks in their neighbourhood.

It is equally clear that certain insects can discriminate colour, so that this capacity, too, must be latent in the structure of the compound eye. It has been supposed that the basis of colour vision in vertebrates is the presence of three pigments, differing from each other in their spectral sensitivity, and there are now some reasons for believing that a similar explanation may apply to the compound eye. This is a field of investigation only recently opened up with the aid of electronic techniques. Already, however, it has been possible to explore the responses of single retinal cells in the compound eyes of the blowfly, *Calliphora erythrocephala*, and to show that the degree of depolarization depends upon the wavelength of the light, as well as upon its intensity. This has led to the recognition of three types of receptor cell in this eye. All three show a peak response at a wavelength of about 350 mμ, in the ultraviolet range, but they differ from each other in respect of a second peak. In one of the types, the most abundant one, this peak lies at about 490 mμ (green-type receptor), while in the other two it lies respectively at below 470 mμ (blue-type receptor) and at above 520 mμ (yellow-green type). Obviously the differences between these several pigments are very small, and so the central nervous system must be highly specialized to differentiate between the varying patterns of excitation that are transmitted to it from the eyes. In this there is nothing either surprising or improbable. On the contrary, as Burkhardt points out in his discussion of these results, it is much easier to imagine the evolution of colour vision by the accumulation of small changes in pigment properties rather than by the sudden emergence of entirely new types of photosensitive substance.

We have suggested that the history of the arthropod eye is to be traced through the increasing elaboration of the simple vesicular eyes found in lower invertebrates; this also seems to be the case in the molluscan eye. In the more primitive forms, as, for example, in *Patella*, the eyes are no more than open invaginations of the epidermis, lined with pigment and receptor cells, but with no lens. In more advanced forms the opening of the vesicle is narrowed and closed, the vesicle then containing either a fluid secretion or a lens. Such organs are presumably used for orientation, since they can have no capacity for form discrimination. More specialized arrangements are seen in the more active molluscs, such as *Pecten*, where the pallial tentacles bear highly differentiated eyes, each with a lens and an inverted retina. Even here, however, these organs can do no more than detect movements and shadows, capacities that are none the less of first importance in animals that are capable of such rapid swimming responses.

As might be expected, it is in the cephalopods, with their generally high level of activity and response, that the molluscan eye reaches its peak of differentiation. Superficially, the eye of dibranchiates such as *Octopus* greatly resembles that of vertebrates, and presents in this respect a classical example of convergence (Fig. 14–15). Yet its mode of development is different, while in some ways its retinal organization is more akin to that of the compound eye of arthropods. In *Nautilus* the eye is still simple, being a cup-shaped invagination with a small opening to the outside, and lacking any lens. The dibranchiate eye still develops in this way, so that it is formed in its entirety direct from the epidermis; the vertebrate eye, by contrast, develops centrifugally as an outgrowth of the central nervous system. These differences in mode of development account for the cephalopod retina being the direct type, with the sensory ends of the receptor cells directed towards the source of light, whereas the retina of vertebrates is inverted, with the sensory ends turned away from the source of light. The eventual resemblances between the eyes, however, are all the

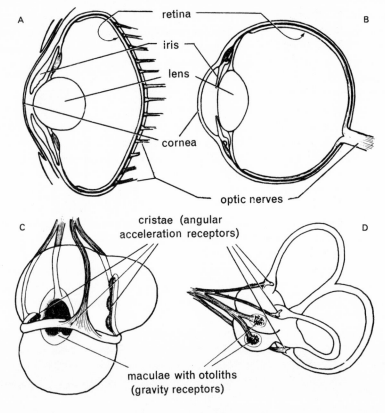

Fig. 14-15. Parallel development of sensory receptors in man and the octopus. A and B are longitudinal vertical sections through the eyes of an octopus and of a man respectively. C and D show the statocysts of *Octopus* and the labyrinth of the inner ear of man. (C is adapted from Young, 1960, *Proc. R. Soc. B,* **152**.) From Wells, 1961. *Advmt Sci., Lond.,* **17**, 461–471.

more remarkable. In the cephalopod the invagination closes over, the lining forming the retina while a lens develops at the point of fusion. Later an iris is formed, so that a pupillary opening is delimited, and the whole becomes covered by a transparent cornea associated with eyelids. Focusing is effected through the ciliary muscle which contributes to the suspension of the lens, relaxation of the muscle leaving the lens in position for distant viewing.

The optic potentialities of this eye, by analogy with the vertebrate eye, would seem to be excellent, yet it is limited in its capacities by the organization of the retinal elements. These are arranged (Fig. 14–16) in groups that recall to some extent the ommatidia of the arthropod eye. The retinula cells, which are pigmented, are arranged in groups surrounding a rhabdome, which is composed of four rhabdomeres. Like the rods and cones of vertebrates, and the rhabdomes of arthropods, these rhabdomeres have a complex fine structure, each consisting of piles of tubules. The important feature of these piles, and one that probably has a fundamental effect upon the mode of behaviour of these animals, is that the piles are so arranged that two of them lie in the horizontal plane and two in the vertical plane. Each pair (vertical or horizontal, as the case may be) is related to a distinct nerve fibre.

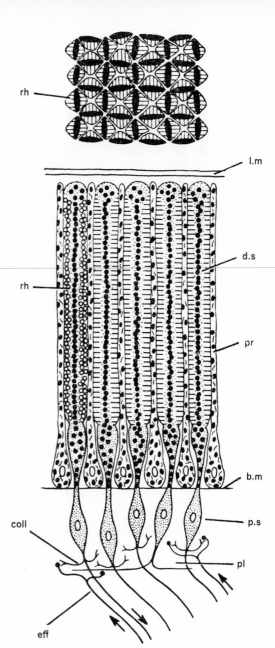

Fig. 14-16. Diagram of probable arrangement of the elements of the retina of *Octopus.* *Above,* as seen in tangential section; *below,* in radial section. *b.m,* basal membrane; *coll,* collateral of retinal fibre; *eff,* efferent axon to the retina; *d.s,* distal segment of retinal cell; *l.m,* limiting membrane; *p.s,* proximal segment of retinal cell; *pl,* plexus beneath retina; *pr,* process of supporting cell (probably thinner); *rh,* rhabdomes. The second retinal cell from the right has been wrongly shown; it should carry a fibre to the optic nerve. From Young, 1961. *Biol. Rev.,* **36**, 32–96. Used by courtesy of the Cambridge Philosophical Society.

Behaviour studies of the octopus show that this animal has marked powers of form discrimination, but that these depend largely upon the estimation and comparison of horizontal and vertical extents. Thus it can readily discriminate between horizontal and vertical rectangles but cannot discriminate between oblique ones. It has been suggested that this limitation is a consequence of the horizontal and vertical orientation within its receptor elements, an orientation that is also detectable in the dendritic fields of the optic lobes into which the impulses from the eyes are discharged. The importance of this orientation is further suggested by the octopus maintaining a constant orientation of its eyes, irrespective of the position in which the body may be held (Fig. 14–17). This orientation depends upon information received from the

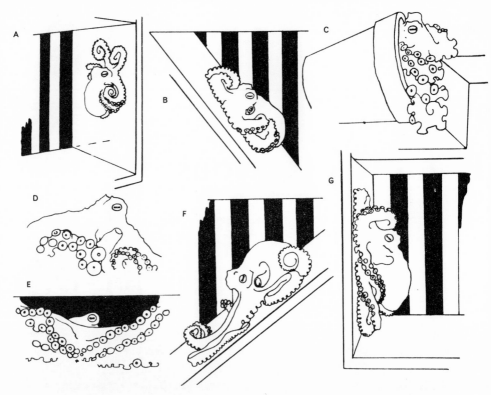

Fig. 14-17. Orientation of the eyes before and after bilateral statocyst removal. In unoperated animals the slit-like pupil normally remains horizontal or very nearly so (A–E), whatever the position of the octopus. After removal of both statocysts this ceases to be true, and the orientation of the retina, as indicated by the position of the pupil, thereafter depends upon the position in which the animal is sitting (F–G). Pictures traced from projections of Kodachrome transparencies: C, D, and E are of comparatively large (500 g) octopuses, the rest of small (15–25 g) animals in an aquarium set up in front of a vertically striped background; in B and F the aquarium, with the animals sitting on the bottom, has been tipped through 45°. From Wells, 1960. *J. exp. Biol.*, **37**, 489–499.

statocysts. If these organs are removed the orientation of the eyes is disturbed; for example, they may be held at an angle of 90° from their normal position, and in these circumstances the animal may interpret vertical rectangles as horizontal ones, and vice versa. Clearly the apparent convergence of the cephalopod and the vertebrate eye is superficial and deceptive, and is applicable only to the more general features of the structure of these organs. Closer analysis shows that the mode of functioning of the dibranchiate eye, and its relationships with the statocyst, attain a very high level of specialization in details that have no parallel in the vertebrates.

15
Primitive Nervous Systems

15–1 COMPONENTS OF BEHAVIOUR

We have so far viewed animal behaviour in the simplest possible terms of a pattern of stimulus and response, dependent upon the transmission of coded information from receptors to effectors. In exceptional cases a receptor cell may also be responsible for the final reaction to the stimulus. Such a cell (the cnidoblast of coelenterates is an example) is called an independent effector. Much more often, however, the excitation is propagated from receptor to effector through pathways formed by chains of two or more neurones. Commonly this includes passage through a central nervous system, which interconnects different pathways, but this is not an essential feature of neural organization; there are primitive types of nervous system without a differentiated central nervous system.

Where a central nervous system does exist the neural pathways constitute the familiar reflex arcs of classical physiology. The fundamental features of these are afferent limbs, conveying impulses centrally, efferent limbs conveying impulses peripherally to the effectors, and a central nervous system providing central connections. These pathways may be laid down during development, in which case they are genetically determined just as are other structural features. They are thus independent of the experience of the individual, and they form the neural basis of inborn reflex actions. These are characterized in general by the simplicity of their neural pathways, by the association of a sharply defined stimulus with a correspondingly restricted response, and by the termination of the response when the stimulus ceases to act. Such simple and inborn reflex responses are by no means restricted to animals with a central nervous system, as we shall particularly see in coelenterates. Hence we usually extend the concept of reflex response beyond its classical limits to include the behaviour of animals with primitive and non-centralized nervous systems.

Reflex responses, as defined above, appear as unitary components of behaviour. The observed behaviour of animals, however, is commonly of much greater com-

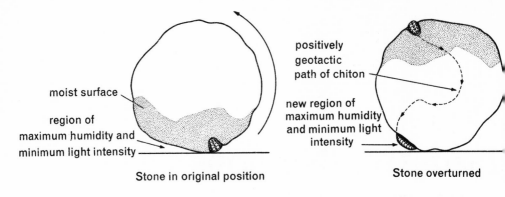

Fig. 15-1. Movements of a chiton when the stone bearing it is overturned. Adapted from Evans, 1951. *J. Anim. Ecol.,* **20**, 1–10.

plexity. When inborn it is expressed as instinctive behaviour, which typically consists of reflex actions that are unified or integrated into patterns of activity involving the whole organism. In contrast to reflex responses, instinctive behaviour is usually excited by a complex pattern of stimulation, termed a releaser. Moreover, it is associated with an internal drive which is manifested in seeking, or appetitive, behaviour, in which the animal actively explores the potentialities of its environment instead of passively waiting, as it were, to be stimulated. Although the effect of drive is often clearly evident, the concept is somewhat abstract, and its physiological basis is not well understood. Perhaps it results from characteristic patterns of activity in the nervous system, and more particularly in the central nervous system.

How adaptive behaviour can be effectively organized out of a relatively small equipment of reflex responses is illustrated in the behaviour of the polyplacophoran mollusc, *Lepidochiton cinereus,* as analyzed by Evans. His analysis starts with the observation, readily made in the intertidal zone, that when the tide is out the animal

Fig. 15-2. Movements of two chitons placed in the illuminated halves of Petri dishes. Adapted from Evans, 1951. *op. cit.*

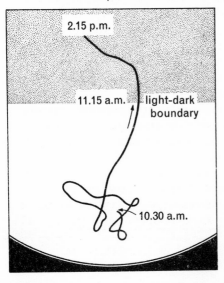

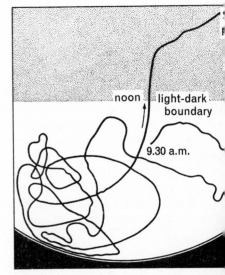

A

B

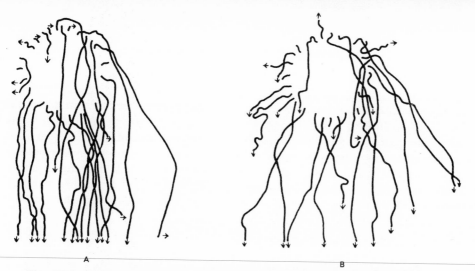

Fig. 15-3. Paths of chitons on vertical plates out of water; A, on glass, B, on roughened Perspex. Arrows show orientation of the head after 2½ hr. From Evans, 1951. *op. cit.*

is usually on the under-surfaces of stones. If one of these stones is turned upside down in bright sunlight, the animals creep over its surface until they are again on the surface that is now lowermost (Fig. 15-1). Clearly this is adaptive behaviour, protecting the animals from the adverse effects of exposure. Evans has shown that it depends upon responses to three factors in the environment: light, gravity, and humidity.

When exposed to bright light the animals move at random, the rate of movement being to some extent dependent upon the intensity of illumination. They do not orientate their movements by the direction of illumination, at least under experimental conditions, although possibly they can do this if they are exposed to strong sunlight. Nevertheless, despite their lack of orientation, they collect in the shadowed area of a Petri dish, simply because they arrive there by chance, and then, having done so, slow down and stop (Fig. 15-2). A locomotory reaction of this type, in which the stimulus brings about a variation in linear velocity, is called an orthokinesis (*orthos*, straight); *Lepidochiton* shows a negative orthokinesis, a response which is one factor determining its position below stones.

Another factor is humidity, together with the degree of immersion. Chitons will not move across a dry surface. But on a moist surface they are active, much more so than when completely submerged in water. Consequently they are stimulated to move when they become exposed as the tide falls, so that they are likely to find protection before the substratum dries. In this they are aided by their response to gravity, which varies according to whether they are exposed or immersed. If they are placed on a glass plate below the surface of the water they move in all directions, showing no response to gravity. When, however, the plate is removed from the water they move downwards (Fig. 15-3), a response to gravity that, in the intertidal zone, will lead them to the underside of stones when the tide falls. A response like this, in which movement is orientated with reference to the source of the stimulus, is termed a taxis; *Lepidochiton* is negatively geotactic.

Effective though the adaptive behaviour of *Lepidochiton* clearly is, it is based upon a few comparatively simple reflex responses. Perhaps it would not usually be described as instinctive behaviour, for this term might be thought more appropriate to the much more elaborate behaviour patterns in, for example, the lives of social insects. This, however, is a field of analysis in which we cannot draw rigid boundaries. Behaviour that is apparently complex may yet depend upon very simple neural mechanisms, as, for example, when the feeding response of *Phormia* is evoked by the stimulation of a single receptor. To some extent, then, we can look in animal behaviour patterns for a continuous spectrum of organization, ranging from simple reflex responses to the grouping of these into highly elaborate behaviour patterns. Underlying all of this is the phenomenon so very characteristic of living organisms, and so very difficult to analyze: the fact that they behave as wholes rather than as the sum of their constituent parts. Their behaviour shows integration, which we have already mentioned as a process unifying the actions of an organism into patterns that involve the whole individual. We can formally define this as a phenomenon in which the generation of a single nerve impulse by a receptor may evoke in the effector system a response greater or less than could be produced by the arrival of one impulse. We shall see that integration is provided for in even the simplest of nervous systems. But one of the advantages gained by the increasing elaboration of neural organization is undoubtedly improvement in integration, with all the possibilities of behavioural elaboration that flow from this.

There is also another aspect of behaviour to be considered. Survival in a constantly fluctuating environment would be difficult, if not impossible, if it depended solely upon rigidly determined patterns of activity, established during individual development under the influence of genetic control. Some degree of flexibility of response is also necessary, and this is provided to varying extents and in diverse ways. It depends in part upon the interconnection of nervous pathways, which permits efferent pathways to be linked with a wide range of incoming information. To this are added the physiological properties of nerve cells, and particularly of the synapses which make the connections between them. Normally a nerve cell will receive a train of impulses, the arrival of which may exert an additive effect called summation. This may be temporal summation, when many impulses arrive at the same synapse, or spatial summation, when they arrive at different synapses on the same cell. The effect of summation may be excitatory—the cell may respond more readily to a number of impulses than to a few, a phenomenon called facilitation. Conversely, the cell may become less responsive, so that the summation in this instance may result in inhibition, or a failure to respond. Commonly inhibition occurs in the central nervous system, but this is not always so; peripheral inhibition is a characteristic feature of crustacean neural organization. In either case both inhibition and facilitation provide a means by which the pattern of activity of the nervous system, and hence of effector response, can be very delicately adjusted to changing patterns of stimulation.

Other factors also promote flexibility of neural action. Responses depend very much on the internal state of the animal; thus the reactions of a hungry animal will differ from those of a well-fed one. We have seen an example of this in *Phormia*. Another example is the sheep tick, which is found at the tips of blades of grass when hungry, but which moves downwards when it has had a meal. Reactions will also vary with age and state of development; in particular, the state of sexual maturity will be of paramount importance. Here, as in other conditions, the secretion of the chemical regulators known as hormones is often important in influencing the excitability of the nervous system.

Lastly, and most significant of all, behaviour can be modified in the light of the previous experience of the animal. This is the phenomenon called learning, which we may define, following Thorpe, as that process which manifests itself by adaptive changes in individual behaviour as a result of experience. Learning takes many forms, which are inevitably influenced by the structure and complexity of the nervous system in which it is being manifested. Probably its simplest form is habituation, or the cessation of response to a repeated stimulus when the stimulus is without significance in the mode of life of the animal concerned. The capacity for habituation is clearly a fundamental need of animals. Without it there must be a waste of energy which could be more usefully employed to promote survival. Not surprisingly, therefore, it is widespread in the animal kingdom; it is seen in Protozoa (p. 296), and it may very well be a universal property of excitable living material.

Another type of learning is called associative learning. One example of this is known in classical physiology as the development of a conditioned reflex. This is observed when two different stimuli are applied simultaneously and repeatedly to the animal. In these circumstances the reflex response that is normally given to one of the stimuli (this stimulus is called the reinforcement) becomes transferred to the other stimulus. This can now evoke a reflex response that is not an inborn one, and the animal is said to be conditioned to this second stimulus, or to have developed a conditioned reflex.

Another form of associative learning is that known as trial-and-error learning. In this the animal develops an association between a stimulus and some element of its appetitive behaviour, the stimulus in this instance being received in advance of the reinforcement. Such behaviour is seen when an animal, moving away from some unsuitable environment, learns to turn in a particular direction at a particular point as a result of receiving a stimulus on each occasion that it reaches that point. An earthworm, for example, moving from the light into the dark, may be trained to turn into the right-hand limb of a T-shaped tube because it receives an electric shock whenever it turns into the left-hand limb. This type of learning is associated with a reward; the earthworm, in the experiment just mentioned, is allowed to arrive in the dark on each occasion that it turns in the 'right' direction; the dark is its 'preferred' environment, and provides the reward.

A reward is not, however, an essential feature of learning. Students of behaviour recognize also what is called latent learning, in which associations are formed without any obvious immediate reward. We shall see illustrations of this in the lives of social insects; worker bees, for example, learn landmarks in the neighbourhood of the hive preparatory to undertaking long foraging flights. Finally, there is insight learning. We can recognize this in ourselves, but find it difficult to define what it involves in terms of neural structure and functioning. We can only remark that it appears to be expressed as the sudden solution of a problem, perhaps through the sudden reorganization of the past experience of the animal. It is the foundation of scientific method, for it is out of this capacity that hypotheses are born.

Enough has now been said to show that there is much variation in the behaviour patterns shown by animals, and in the flexibility manifested in their responses. To a large extent these variations reflect differences in the level of organization of the nervous system. We shall now examine these differences to see something of how the requirements of adaptive behaviour are met in the main groups of invertebrates.

In doing this, we should remember that in the evolution of the nervous system, as of other systems, there has been an exploitation of fundamental properties of living material that do not depend upon the existence of a differentiated nervous system. The behaviour of *Paramecium* is not completely predictable. According to Jennings, it is variable in a way that shows at times the slight beginnings of the modification of behaviour through previous experience. In *Stentor* there are even signs of habituation. Jennings found that after it has responded a few times to some very weak stimulus it begins to react differently; the change is not due to fatigue, but seems rather to have some regulatory character. When a current of water from a capillary tube is directed against its disc the animal at first contracts. But soon it expands again, and next time it does not react to the current, but continues its normal activities unmoved.

Attempts to demonstrate associative learning in protozoans have been less successful, but they have certainly served to illustrate problems of experimental design and interpretation. In one example a single paramecium was placed in a drop of culture medium which was arranged so that one half of the drop was at 15°C and the other half at 42°; the cooler half was darkened, while the warmer half was illuminated. In these circumstances the animal remained predominantly in the cooler half, giving the characteristic avoiding reaction at the boundary. After 90 minutes both halves were brought to 15°. For a time the paramecium still gave the avoiding reaction and so remained in the darker half, but the reaction slowly weakened until after about 15 minutes the animal was swimming freely throughout both the dark and illuminated zones. This behaviour was at first attributed to the temporary establishment of a conditioned response to illumination, the stimulus of high temperature having acted as the reinforcement.

Later, however, a simple control experiment carried out by another investigator showed that this was a misinterpretation. In this new experiment the illuminated half of the drop was heated before the animal was placed in it, and then after 90 minutes the temperature was equalized to 15°. The animal was now introduced for the first time. It immediately gave an avoiding reaction at the boundary, although it had had no experience of encountering a temperature barrier there, nor did one now exist. The explanation proved to be that heating of the water modifies its chemical composition by driving off dissolved gases, resulting in a difference in chemical composition between the two halves. The animal in the first experiment was responding to this chemical difference after the temperature had been equalized, while the disappearance of the response after 15 minutes was a consequence of the drop acquiring uniformity of composition through diffusion. There had, in short, been no conditioning at all.

Not the least interesting aspect of this episode is that Jennings had long before shown that *Paramecium* was sensitive to just such changes in chemical composition of the medium. As Jensen points out, there are two modes of approach to behaviour studies. An investigator may study one topic (such as responses to light or to temperature) throughout a range of species, or he may elect to study the whole range of reactions throughout one species alone. Both modes of approach are required, and they really need to be coordinated. In the present instance much confusion would have been avoided from the beginning if the results obtained by Jennings from his comprehensive studies of *Paramecium* had been applied to the interpretation of an experimental situation that was not as simple as it seemed.

15–2 COELENTERATES AND THE NERVE NET

A very primitive nervous system exists in three groups of invertebrates: the Coelenterata, the Hemichordata, and the Echinodermata. In each of these groups a dominating feature of neural organization is the arrangement of nerve cells in a continuous layer to form an irregular nerve net or plexus. Neural pathways become differentiated within this net, to a varying degree in the three groups. This we may regard as foreshadowing the association of fibres into the macroscopically visible tracts that constitute the nerves of more advanced nervous systems. As this association develops, the primitive nerve net diminishes in importance, although it may still have some significance.

From previous discussion we know that the responses of the coelenterates show a high level of adaptive efficiency. How the requirements of this adaptive behaviour are met within the structural limitations of what appears to be a very simple plan of neural organization is of particular interest. Our knowledge of the structure of the coelenterate nerve net derives from the nineteenth-century studies of Schäfer and of O. and R. Hertwig. Within the ectoderm and endoderm of coelenterates there exists a plexus of nerve cells that are usually bipolar or tripolar, although occasional multipolar ones may be present. These cells lie immediately above the muscle fibres, and apparently never within the mesoglea.

This localization was clearly emphasized in the descriptions given by the early authors, although, as Pantin has shown, a debasement of text figures has led to the belief that the nerve net extends into the mesogloea. This error has been encouraged by later accounts based upon the use of silver impregnation. The results of this technique are difficult to interpret, for it also impregnates connective tissue fibres; it is then possible to confuse them with nerve fibres. It is important, therefore, that descriptions of the distribution of these fibres should be checked against observations made with other techniques as well. For this purpose *intra vitam* staining with methylene blue is particularly valuable, although the action of this dye is erratic, and not all species respond well to it. The studies of Pantin and his colleagues, however, have shown very clearly how this procedure not only confirms the main conclusions of the earlier workers, but also reveals more of the structural basis of behaviour.

To illustrate this, consider the responses of anemones to mechanical or electrical stimulation of the column. Stimulation of the column of *Calliactis* evokes various symmetrical responses which can be related to the several components of the muscular system (p. 63), the contractions of which can be recorded separately (Fig. 15–4). A weak stimulation may result in a local contraction of the circular musculature, leading to the initiation of a peristaltic wave, or the animal may shorten. During this shortening the disc may remain expanded, the parietal muscles being the only effectors involved. A stronger stimulation will also cause withdrawal of the disc through contraction of the mesenteries, while a very strong mechanical stimulation will evoke an immediate protective contraction of the marginal sphincter. These varied responses occur irrespective of where the stimulus is applied, which shows that there is a diffuse conduction of excitation in all directions through the net. The form of the responses varies, however, with the strength of the stimulus: as the strength increases so also does the distance over which its effect spreads.

At one time it seemed that these properties were irreconcilable with the fundamental principle that nerve impulses are propagated without decrement of excitation.

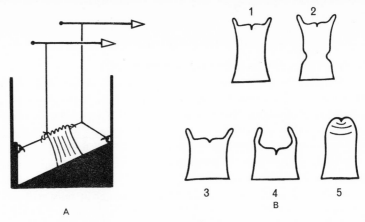

A

Fig. 15-4. A, method of recording sphincter and mesenteric movements in the anemone *Calliactis parasitica*. B, diagrammatic representation of symmetrical responses of the animal. From Pantin, 1935. *J. exp. Biol.,* **12**, 139–155.

Pantin's analysis of the situation was the first to show clearly that the diffuse and apparently decremental conduction was simply a result of the morphological organization of the nerve net, and that its physiological properties were not fundamentally different from those of typical nerve cells. The explanation depends firstly upon the fact that the net is composed of separate cells that are not fused together, but that connect with each other at synapses. This was, indeed, the view of the early workers, and later studies have confirmed it, although it should be added that it does not follow that all nerve nets are constructed in this way. It is believed, for example, that the atrial (visceral) nerve net of amphioxus is a continuous structure, without synaptic barriers. In coelenterates, however, the nerve impulses are propagated through a series of cells, and not simply along a continuous and uninterrupted path; this, in conjunction with the properties of the synapses, accounts for the observed peculiarities of response.

In the oral disc, to take one example, a single electrical stimulus will produce either no response at all, or at best only a slight one. If the stimulus is repeated, muscular contraction begins, and then, as the frequency of stimulus is increased, so the size of the response increases and also the distance over which it is propagated. Now if this were a result of decremental conduction of nerve impulses we might expect a single wave of muscular contraction that would diminish in extent as it passed farther away from the point of stimulation. What we actually find, however, is something quite different. At first the only muscles to respond are those close to the point of stimulation; those farther away do not do so until a number of stimuli have been given, after which these muscles, too, are drawn into the response. The

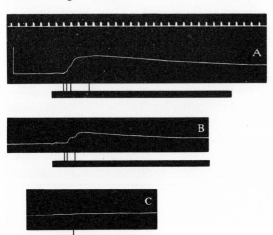

Fig. 15-5. Graded responses of the sphincter of *Calliactis parasitica* to mechanical stimulation of pedal edge. Black band shows duration of mechanical stimulus. Vertical lines show arrival of impulses at sphincter. First line corresponds to arrival of second impulse; first impulse causes no response. Note occurrence of adaptation. From Pantin, 1935. *J. exp. Biol.,* **12**, 119–138.

explanation is that the responses of the anemone are normally evoked not by a single stimulus but by a series of stimuli, arising, perhaps, through the touching of a number of mechanoreceptors. The early nerve impulses travel only short distances, being arrested at the synaptic barriers, but they leave the system in a state of excitation. This excitatory state aids the passage of subsequent impulses, provided that they follow immediately; thus the impulses resulting from prolonged stimulation can travel progressively farther. This is the phenomenon earlier referred to as facilitation; in the form described here it is called interneural facilitation.

Another illustration (Fig. 15-5) is the effect of stimulating the pedal edge of *Calliactis* by dropping a weight upon it. This mechanical stimulus is followed by a discharge of impulses leading to contractions of the sphincter muscle. Fig. 15-5 shows that the time between the impulses increases, even though the mechanical stimulus is maintained. This is the phenomenon of sensory adaptation; the receptors adapt to the stimulus as it continues to act upon them, and may eventually cease to respond altogether. Facilitation is demonstrated in the way that the contraction increases when the impulses follow close together (Fig. 15-5A, B); as they become less frequent the response diminishes, because facilitation falls off.

A further factor that influences the responses of *Calliactis* is the specialization of its muscles; this accounts for the varied character of the responses mentioned earlier. Each muscle gives a facilitated response at a characteristic frequency range of stimulation, this range being related to the natural speed of contraction of each muscle. For example, contractions of the circular muscle of the column are called forth by an extraordinarily low frequency of stimulation, ranging from 1 every 10 seconds to 1 every 6 seconds; this muscle takes many minutes to reach its maximum contraction. When the frequency of stimulation is 1 every 3 seconds (Fig. 15-6) there is a very slow contraction of the parietal muscles. At 1 every 2 seconds the longitudinal mesenteric muscles contract in advance of the parietals. At 1 every 1.1 seconds there is a response from the sphincter, longitudinal mesenteric, and parietal muscles. At 1 every 0.6 seconds the sphincter response predominates, and there is no response from the parietals. Thus, although the nerve net of the column provides, from the morphological point of view, a simple unit of diffuse conduction, interneural facilitation and specialization in the effector system allow varied and graded responses.

Fig. 15-6. Successive facilitation of parietal (*P*), longitudinal mesenteric (*L*), and sphincter muscles (*S*) in *Calliactis parasitica* with increasing frequency of stimulation. Time in half-minutes. From Pantin, 1935. *J. exp. Biol.*, **12**, 139–155.

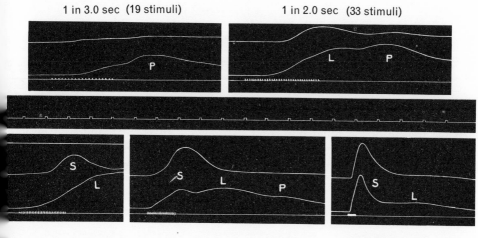

1 in 3.0 sec (19 stimuli)   1 in 2.0 sec (33 stimuli)

in 1.45 sec (29 stimuli)   1 in 1.10 sec (24 stimuli)   1 in 0.60 sec (13 stimuli)

Even this by no means exhausts all the specialization involved in the action of the primitive nerve net. Examination of the rates at which nerve impulses are propagated through the net shows that there are certain tracts, called through-conduction tracts, in which propagation is very rapid. These tracts are especially pronounced in the mesenteries, where they can conduct vertically at a rate of 120 cm per second, as compared with the much lower rates in the column. These vertical mesenteric pathways connect with a ring of rapid conduction near the sphincter, the system as a whole providing for the rapid protective contraction referred to earlier. The existence of these through-conduction tracts was inferred initially from physiological studies; it has since been confirmed by direct observation of the structure of the nerve net. For example, the retractor muscle of the mesenteries mediates the retraction reflex, and it is precisely on this face of the mesenteries that there is a well-developed plexus composed mainly of large bipolar cells. On the opposite (exocoelic) face of each mesentery is a sheet of radial muscle. This is a weak muscle, functionally distinct from the retractors, and its nerve cells are correspondingly fewer and smaller. Probably they are quite separate from the other plexus, which clearly provides the through-conduction pathways that are indicated by the physiological evidence.

We have now seen enough of the actinian nervous system to understand something of the principles upon which it is built, and to judge of its fitness to serve the needs of these animals. *Calliactis* lives on stones on the sea bottom, but is often found also in a mutualistic relationship (p. 475) on shells of *Buccinum* that are inhabited by hermit crabs, and its nervous system is particularly well adapted to this mode of life. Following Pantin's analysis, we can regard the column as a machine for bearing the disc, which is itself concerned with feeding. As the anemone is carried around by the crab the column must necessarily be subjected to a great deal of mechanical shock, but it is to the animal's advantage if much of this is ignored, for it involves no danger, and response to it would interfere with feeding. On the other hand, there will sometimes be more severe disturbance, to which the anemone must give some protective reaction. Facilitated responses, leading under severe stimulation to contraction of the sphincter and retractor muscles, are ideally fitted for these requirements. It is equally advantageous for the feeding reactions of the disc to be separated from the protective reactions of the column. Moreover, we have seen earlier that the feeding of anemones involves asymmetrical behaviour of the tentacles and mouth. Local stimulation of a tentacle causes it to bend over towards the centre of the disc, while prolonged stimulation brings into action the mouth and the other tentacles. This sequence, in itself highly adaptive, is an expression of interneural facilitation. The emphasis in the disc upon this, rather than upon through-conduction pathways, allows the individual responses of the tentacles and the efficient manipulation of the food.

When we have said all this, however, we must avoid being over-optimistic regarding the present state of our understanding of coelenterate organization. D. M. Ross has described the way in which *Calliactis* becomes attached to shells (Fig. 15-7). The process involves first the attachment of the tentacles and oral disc to the shell, then the freeing of the pedal disc from its previous attachment, followed by its adhesion to the shell, and finally the release of the oral attachment and the establishment of normal posture. The sequence of movements shows a remarkable degree of

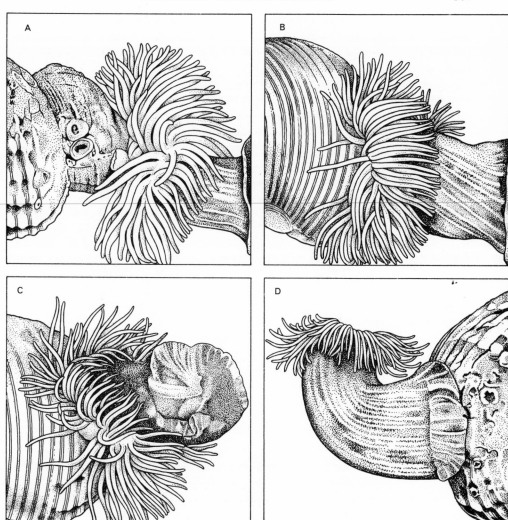

Fig. 15-7. Stages drawn from a series of photographs showing the attachment and settling of *Calliactis parasitica* on a shell occupied by *Pagurus bernhàrdus*. A, establishment of contact between anemone attached to wall of tank and shell (small area of pedal disc not securely attached). B, tentacles establishing firm attachment to shell; column of anemone twisting; pedal disc loosening its hold on glass. C, oral disc expanded to provide large area adhering to shell; pedal disc freely suspended; column bending to bring pedal disc into position for attachment to shell. D, most of pedal disc now attached, assisted by a constriction of the column immediately above it; oral disc detached and column beginning to straighten out. Approximate times involved from A: B, 5 min; C, 9 min; D, 22 min. After photographs by Ross, 1960. *Proc. zool. Soc. Lond.,* **134**, 43–57.

coordination, during which the animal receives a flow of information about the chemical and physical properties of the shell. It will not, for example, attach to shells that have been boiled in alkali. This information is translated into a series of responses, some of them asymmetrical, which are adapted to the achievement of a precisely defined goal. We may claim to know something of the component parts of these responses, but we can hardly pretend to understand how these are unified, or, as we say, integrated (p. 294), into the behaviour of the whole animal. Here, as so often, we are describing aspects both of the life and of the organization of an invertebrate, while still remaining a very long way indeed from understanding what the animal is really doing.

The division of the actinian nervous system into partially distinct functional components shows the possibility of elaboration that is latent in the superficially simple plan of the nerve net, but the elaboration does not stop at this point. Further possibilities are illustrated by the situation in more active coelenterates, of which the ephyra larva of *Aurelia* will serve as an example. The locomotor movements of this larva consist of rhythmic and symmetrical contractions that can be called the

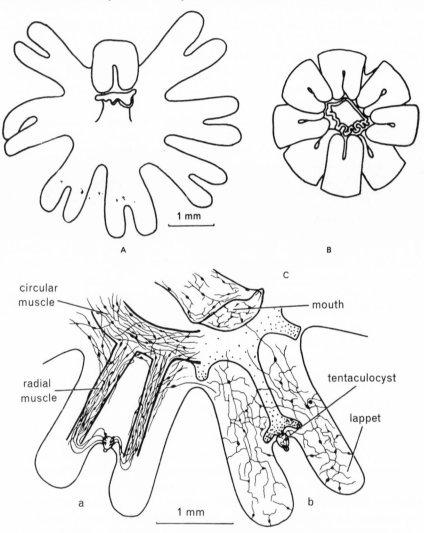

Fig. 15-8. A, the coordination of the mouth and one arm in the feeding response of the ephyra larva of *Aurelia*. B, the long-lasting contraction of all the arms in the spasm. C, two arms of the bell of the ephyra larva, showing *a*, the muscle-strips and the giant fibre system, and *b*, the cells of the diffuse net and the underlying gastric cavity. From Horridge, 1956. *Q. Jl microsc. Sci.*, **97**, 59–74.

swimming beat. These are sharply differentiated from the specialized feeding re-actions (Fig. 15–8). When the larva comes into contact with food material, such as a small copepod, an arm bends over to the mouth, which itself moves to meet it. Each arm can act independently in this respect, so that several arms can each catch copepods in rapid succession. On the other hand, a strong stimulus may cause a sustained contraction called the spasm, in which all of the arms fold tightly over the oral surface.

The functional dichotomy of locomotion and feeding is reflected in the nervous system. This includes two distinct nerve nets, one of which is thought to be associated with the swimming beat and the other with the feeding reactions. Indeed, it would be difficult to account for the behaviour of the ephyra larva in terms of only one nerve net, for the feeding response can occur in the absence of any swimming beat, while regular locomotor contractions can occur without any trace of the maintained contraction of an arm. What is needed is a further development of functional isolation within the nerve net, which we have seen to be partially attained as between the disc and the column of the anemone; the differentiation of two nets provides for exactly this (Fig. 15–8).

One of these nerve nets is a synaptic system consisting of large bipolar cells, $6\,\mu$ to $10\,\mu$ long, with fibres that are usually less than $1\,\mu$ thick. This system, called by Horridge the giant fibre system (by analogy with the situation in other invertebrates, p. 325), is mainly restricted to the sheets of circular and radial muscle fibres. It is believed to be responsible for the coordination of the swimming beat. The second nerve net is histologically quite distinct, and it is distinct also in its distribution, for it is dispersed over the whole of the epithelium. It is composed of bipolar sensory cells, with bipolar and multipolar cells in the main body of the net, these being smaller, and their fibres more delicate, than those of the other system. This more delicate net is believed to coordinate the feeding response and the spasm.

This functional interpretation of the two nets is based partly upon deductions from the anatomical structure and from the observed behaviour of intact animals, but it is corroborated also by experiments. For example, if the band of circular muscle and its giant fibre net are cut through at the base of each arm, these arms will now beat each at its own rate, independently of the others, whereas the whole animal can still give a properly coordinated spasm. Other evidence for functional independence of the two nets involves the tentaculocysts. These are hollow structures, with a mass of crystals at their tip and including at their base a group of nerve cells that forms a rudimentary ganglion, which is probably connected to both nerve nets. The function of these cells is not fully understood, but it is believed that the impulses which evoke the swimming beat are distributed from them, and are at least to some extent initiated in them. Whatever their precise role, however, it is found that if an arm is removed it will continue to beat in isolation, provided that it still contains its tentaculocyst. If a cut is then made at one side of the latter, in such a position that the nerve fibres passing from the ganglion to the radial muscle are interrupted on that side, only the strip of muscle on the other side, where the nerve fibres are intact, will continue to beat. The whole arm, however, can still be induced to give a feeding response or spasm, indicating that this reaction is mediated independently of the locomotor response.

Evidently the deceptively simple morphological organization of the nerve net of coelenterates permits considerable elaboration of behaviour. We have noted the existence of independent effectors as part of their behaviour mechanism, and we have now seen something of the contribution made by functional specialization within the nerve net. The physiological properties involved, including propagation without decrement, and facilitation, are familiar throughout the Metazoa. The chief peculiarities of the Coelenterata are the absence of a central nervous system, and the comparatively low level of differentiation of their receptors, which would seem to leave them dependent upon a restricted range of information. We shall see later how the removal of these limitations has made possible the greatly expanded field of action of the more advanced invertebrates, but first we must examine the two other major groups that have continued to rely very largely upon the nerve net as the basis of their neural organization.

15–3 ECHINODERMS AND THE NERVE NET

The movements of a starfish, like those of a coelenterate, depend upon the properties of a hydrostatic skeleton, but these properties are expressed in the echinoderm at a much higher level of morphological differentiation, and within a more complex pattern of behaviour. The locomotor steps of the tube-feet of the starfish involve a sequence of three phases: retraction, pointing in the line of advance, and protraction. When the animal is walking (Fig. 15-9), most of its thousand or so feet are so engaged, and the impression that they give is one of considerable disarray, for there is no discernible phase relationship coordinating the movements of these tube-feet into a common rhythmic pattern.

Nevertheless, there is evidence of neural control. The feet show a common direction of movement, for all of the stepping feet, irrespective of the arm to which they belong, point and step in the animal's line of advance (Fig. 15-9). The direction

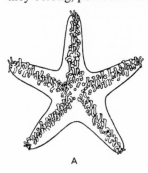

of movement varies from time to time, but at any given moment one arm will be anterior; this is regarded as the leading arm, and its feet will be stepping along the line of its longitudinal axis. Variations in this general pattern of movement are brought about in response to stimulation. These variations may result in changes in the speed of stepping (from 3 to 10 steps per minute in *Asterias rubens*), in changes in behaviour of the individual feet (in connection with feeding, for example), or in changes in the direction of movement. Our problem is to relate this flexible behaviour pattern to neural organization, and in doing this we shall follow the analysis of J. E. Smith.

The nervous system of the starfish is remarkable not only because it retains the form of a nerve net, but also

A

B

Fig. 15-9. Starfish in ventral view, showing (A) the absence of phase relationship between the movement of the tube-feet, but (B) the common direction of movement of the stepping feet. From Smith, 1950. *Symp. Soc. exp. Biol.,* **4,** 196–220.

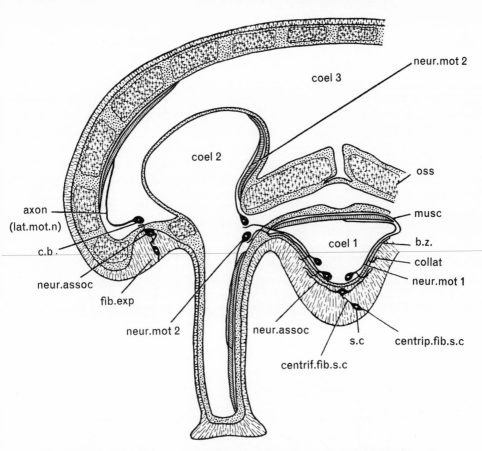

Fig. 15-10. Diagram to show the general anatomy of the nerve tracts within the starfish arm and the pattern of innervation of the muscles lying within the various subdivisions of the coelom. *axon,* axon of motor neuron; *b.z,* boundary zone of connective tissue between the subepithelial nerve plexus of the ectoderm and the coelomic epithelium; *c.b,* cell body of motor neuron; *centrif.fib.s.c,* centrifugal fibre of sense cell; *centrip.fib.s.c,* centripetal fibre of sense cell; *coel 1, 2, 3,* perihaemal water-vascular and perivisceral divisions of the coelom; *collat,* collateral fibre of an axon; *fib.exp,* fibrillar expansion of the subepithelial plexus opposite the point of origin of a motor nerve; *lat.mot.n,* lateral motor nerve; *musc,* muscle; *neur.assoc,* association (internuncial) neurone; *neur.mot 1, neur.mot 2,* motor neurons of the first and second order; *oss,* ossicle; *s.c,* sense cell. From Smith, 1946. *Phil. Trans. R. Soc. B,* **232**, 279–310.

because a major part of it remains in its primitive position within the ectoderm (Fig. 15-10). This ectoderm is composed of epithelial, mucous, and sensory cells. Immediately underlying it is a nerve plexus made up in part of the fibres of multipolar and bipolar nerve cells. Many of these must be association cells, responsible for relaying the sensory input into appropriate pathways. The nerve cells, together with the plexus, are often said to be subepidermal in position. In fact, however, they are strictly intra-epidermal, for they lie among the fibrillar extensions of the other epidermal cells (Fig. 15-11); these run in to meet the layer of mesodermal collagen fibres that marks the inner limit of the ectoderm. This ectodermal plexus is known as the ecto-neural nervous system. Over most of the body wall, and particularly dorsally and laterally, it is very thin, but mid-ventrally along the length of each arm it is markedly thickened to form a V-shaped radial nerve cord; the five cords are continuous centrally with the circumoral nerve ring, which is similarly a thickening of the ectodermal plexus.

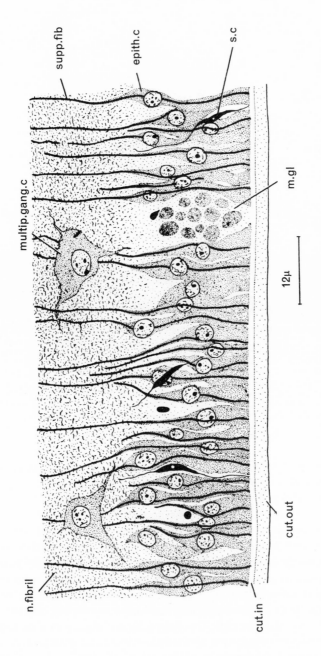

Fig. 15-11. Portion of a longitudinal section through the epithelial and subepithelial layers of the radial nerve cord of a starfish. A composite drawing based on material fixed in Flemming-without-acetic. *cut.in,* inner, and *cut.out,* outer, layer of the cuticle; *epith.c,* epithelial cell; *m.gl,* 'mulberry' gland; *multip.gang.c,* multipolar ganglion cell; *n.fibril,* neurofibrillae of the subepithelial plexus; *s.c.* primary sense cell; *supp.fib,* supporting fibre. From Smith, 1937. *Phil. Trans. R. Soc. B,* **227,** 111–173.

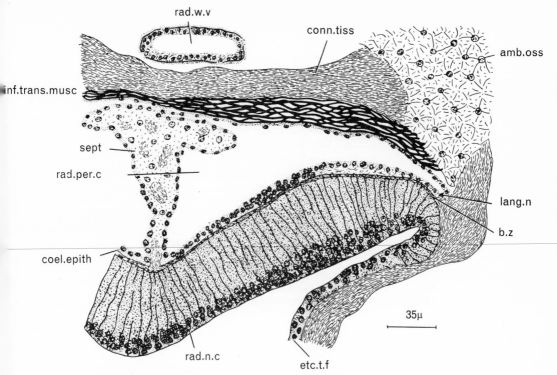

Fig. 15-12. Transverse section of half of the radial cord of *Marthasterias glacialis* showing the innervation of the inferior transverse muscle by Lange's nerve. Fixed corrosive-acetic, stained Mallory's triple stain. *amb.oss*, ambulacral ossicle; *b.z*, boundary zone; *coel.epith*, coelomic epithelium; *conn.tiss*, connective tissue; *ect.t.f*, ectoderm of the tube-foot; *inf.trans.musc*, inferior transverse muscle; *lang.n*, Lange's nerve; *rad.n.c*, radial nerve cord; *rad.per.c*, radial perihaemal canal; *rad.w.v*, radial water vessel; *sept*, septum. From Smith, 1937. *op. cit.*

The ectoneural nervous system as a whole (Fig. 15-10) comprises the ectodermal receptor cells, together with the association pathways that are formed by the nerve cells lying in the plexus, and into which the sensory information is discharged. It is, therefore, a sensory system. The motor nervous system is formed from a separate plexus which is closely associated with the coelomic epithelium, and which is mainly composed of local concentrations of nerve fibres that develop in the neighbourhood of the muscles that are to be innervated. Because of this relationship, and because the locomotion and musculature of the echinoderms differ so much from group to group, the motor nervous system is quite variable in its degree of development, whereas the ectoneural system retains a comparatively constant form throughout the phylum.

In the starfish the motor nervous system is partially represented by the hyponeural nervous system, also known as Lange's nerve. This comprises paired cords of nervous tissue, lying in the wall of the radial perihaemal canal, and distinguished from the coelomic epithelium by their fibrillar appearance (Fig. 15-12). The nerve fibres run transversely to the length of the cords, and innervate the adjacent inferior transverse muscles. Another component of this system is found in the lateral motor nerves (Fig. 15-10), which arise immediately below the ectoneural system and run laterally and aborally to innervate much of the remaining musculature of the arm, including the apical longitudinal muscle. Close to the latter muscle a concentration of this motor plexus forms the apical nerve.

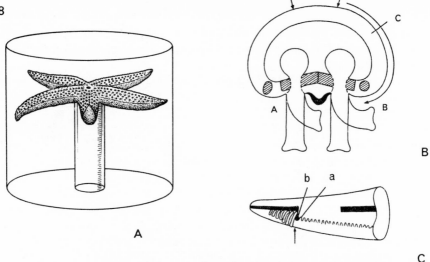

Fig. 15-13. A, position of starfish to show responses of tube-feet. B, effect of tactile stimulus upon underlying tube-feet. C, responses of tube-feet to decremental conduction through the nerve cord; responses are eliminated by removal of a section of the cord. For further explanation see text. Adapted from Smith, 1950. *op. cit.*

Although these two main systems, the ectoneural and the motor systems, are morphologically separable from each other in this way, they come into close conjunction at certain points, notably in the region of the radial nerve cord and at the origins of the lateral motor nerves. At these points fibres running from one system to the other make synaptic connections between the two. Thus nerve impulses originating in the receptors are transmitted to the musculature through the motor system. Despite the plexiform structure of the nervous system, the appropriateness of the response is ensured because the impulses pass through predetermined association pathways. Further regularity is imposed on the routes followed by these impulses because the arms have a pseudo-segmental organization that results from the serial arrangement of the ambulacral and adambulacral ossicles, and their associated tube-feet. In principle, and to mention only part of the communication system (Figs. 15-10 and 15-12), impulses can pass from the radial nerve cord to motor neurones of the hyponeural system, and along the fibres of these to neurones lying at the origins of the lateral motor nerves. From here they are distributed through axons to small groups or complexes of motor neurones which are associated with the various muscles, the last cell in each sequence having an axon that ends on the muscle fibres.

It will be evident from this very brief outline of the neural anatomy of the starfish that its nervous system, still fundamentally a nerve net in character, has carried much further the tendencies already seen in the coelenterates for the establishment of through-conduction pathways. The combination of these two aspects, diffuse conduction and through conduction, is readily demonstrated by simple experimental manipulation of the animal. The results allow us to understand something of how its nervous system is organized in relation to the locomotor requirements of an active animal with a highly differentiated locomotor system.

Smith has shown that the responses of the feet can be conveniently studied by inverting an animal over the open end of a broad glass tube (Fig. 15-13A). If the dorsal surface is now stimulated by pressure with a probe four patterns of response can be seen, resulting from the progressive spread of impulses through the nervous system. The first response, which is reminiscent of those of coelenterates, consists of movements of the pedicellariae and spines, the former opening and closing their valves. The maximum response is shown only in the immediate neighbourhood of the stimulus; even within a distance of 5 mm the movements are slight, and farther away they are altogether absent. The implication is that we are here observing the action of the ectoneural nerve net, transmitting by diffusion through multiple pathways, and restricted in its field of action by the need for facilitation.

Nevertheless, this is not the limit of the effect of the stimulus, for a further response is the extension and bending of the feet that lie immediately underneath the site of the stimulus (Fig. 15–13B). If a short incision is made (at *c*) through the epidermis, and the stimulus applied immediately above it, the response is abolished; this indicates that the excitation from the nerve cord is being propagated along through-conduction pathways that run transversely in the deeper part of the ectoneural plexus. The failure of the excitation to circumvent the small incision shows that there is no spread along the length of the arm, so that the superficial plexus is in this case not involved. The pathways are clearly pseudo-segmental, and correspond to the pseudo-segmentation which, as we have noted, is imposed on the arm by the disposition of the skeletal ossicles.

The third response is lateral protraction of the feet that lie distally and proximally to the point of stimulation. It can be shown that this response depends upon the propagation of impulses through the nerve cord, for if part of this is removed the response is abolished (Fig. 15–13C). The conduction is decremental, as is shown by the way in which the response diminishes with distance from the stimulus; this suggests that chains of neurones may well be involved, although they have not actually been identified.

These three responses are limited to a greater or lesser extent to the neighbourhood of the site of stimulation, but there is one further response which is not limited in this way. Within a few seconds of applying the stimulus all the stepping feet throughout all the arms show an increased rate of stepping, often accompanied by a change in the direction of their movement. This undoubtedly depends upon transmission of impulses along through-conduction pathways in the axial nerve cords and in the nerve ring with which these are connected (Fig. 15–14), for if the cord is cut in any one arm the feet situated distal to the cut no longer respond. Cutting of other parts of the nervous system, however, has no effect.

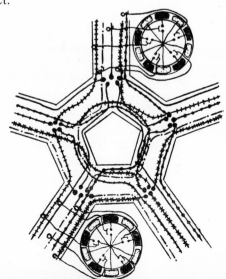

Fig. 15-14. Suggested scheme of relationships of radial nerve cords of starfish with the circumoral nerve ring. A dominant centre at the base of each cord is shown as connecting through the ring with the other radial cords. From Smith, 1950. *op. cit.*

These four types of response clearly result from the spread of excitation first through the ectoneural nerve plexus, next through localized reflex pathways in the arm, and finally through the pathways of the nerve ring and axial cords. As Smith points out, this shows that the nervous system makes a dual contribution to the control of movement. In part this control is peripheral, involving local reflex pathways, while in part it is exerted centrally through the cords and ring. Doubtless the latter contribution depends upon the longitudinal tracts of fibres which pass from one arm to another through the ring (Fig. 15-14). The importance of central control becomes apparent when the starfish is moving normally. As we have seen, one of the arms is then temporarily anterior, and all the tube-feet of all the arms are stepping in the line of movement. Some controlling influence is clearly at work, the source of which can be demonstrated by observing the behaviour of a single arm that has been isolated from the rest of the body. If this arm has no connection at all with any part of the nerve ring it will move predominantly with the base foremost. If, however, it retains even a small piece of the ring, then it will usually move with its tip foremost. This, in conjunction with other observations, is interpreted to mean that there are five nerve centres in the ring, each at the junction of the ring with one of the axial nerve cords, and it is supposed that the discharge of excitation from these centres along the cords confers a polarity upon the arms. The arm which is temporarily anterior is dominant over the other arms, because the nerve centre at its base is dominant over the other four centres.

The balance of central and peripheral control shown by these and many other observations on the behaviour of the starfish is obviously of great adaptive value. The stimuli resulting from the normal contact of the feet with the substratum evoke no localized reflex responses, but probably maintain in the nervous system a general state of activity which in its turn favours continued movement. A brief dorsal stimulus affects only the immediately neighbouring foot, causing a temporary retraction if it is already protracted, and probably saving it from any immediate harm. With prolonged stimulation the central control of movement comes into action in such a way as to bring about the removal of the animal from the source of possible injury. Thus the responses mediated through the nerve net and the through-conduction pathways fulfil the primary requirement of adaptation: the promotion of the survival of the individual.

15–4 HEMICHORDATES AND THE NERVE NET

There is nothing in the organization of the nervous system of the echinoderms, as exemplified in the starfish, that is not foreshadowed in the coelenterates, although differentiation of structure and function has proceeded substantially further in the former group. The third major group that we have mentioned, the Hemichordata, is of particular interest in this connection in that it stands at a level somewhat intermediate between the other two. The link between the Hemichordata and the Echinodermata is a close one, and probably the nervous system of the latter evolved through a stage very much like that found in the hemichordates today. It is the more unfortunate that our understanding of the hemichordate nervous system is still very imperfect. Yet it is at least certain that much, and perhaps all, of it corresponds very closely indeed with the ectoneural component of the echinoderm system.

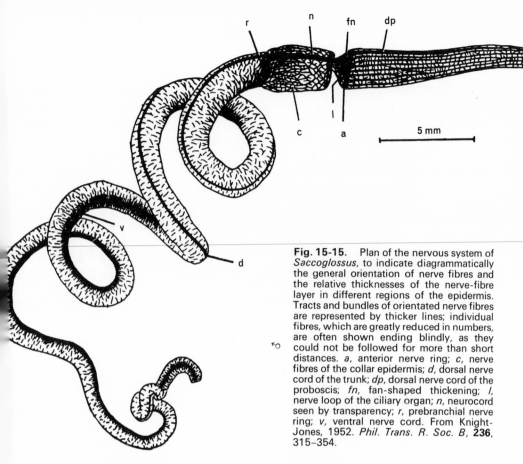

Fig. 15-15. Plan of the nervous system of *Saccoglossus*, to indicate diagrammatically the general orientation of nerve fibres and the relative thicknesses of the nerve-fibre layer in different regions of the epidermis. Tracts and bundles of orientated nerve fibres are represented by thicker lines; individual fibres, which are greatly reduced in numbers, are often shown ending blindly, as they could not be followed for more than short distances. *a*, anterior nerve ring; *c*, nerve fibres of the collar epidermis; *d*, dorsal nerve cord of the trunk; *dp*, dorsal nerve cord of the proboscis; *fn*, fan-shaped thickening; *l*, nerve loop of the ciliary organ; *n*, neurocord seen by transparency; *r*, prebranchial nerve ring; *v*, ventral nerve cord. From Knight-Jones, 1952. *Phil. Trans. R. Soc. B*, **236**, 315–354.

Throughout the body a plexus of nerve fibres lies at the base of the epidermis, interpenetrated by fibrous extensions of the epidermal cells like those in the starfish. Out of this epidermal system, and still forming part of it, there are differentiated through-conduction pathways, formed of fibres that are grouped into longitudinally directed nerve cords (Fig. 15-15). Many of these cords are very small, but two large ones are prominent in the trunk, one mid-dorsal and the other mid-ventral, while there is a prominent mid-dorsal one in the proboscis (Fig. 15-16). Completing this mid-dorsal differentiation there is found in the collar a neurocord, formed by the rolling-up of the epidermal nervous system in the mid-dorsal line. This has often been compared with the hollow spinal cord of the vertebrates, and has been regarded in consequence as one of the truly chordate features of the hemichordates. In fact, however, there is no evidence that it exerts any of the specialized integrative activities of a true central nervous system.

A peculiarity of the hemichordate nervous system is that the cell bodies of the neurones lie entirely outside and above the plexus, with their nuclei at a lower level than those of the epidermal cells. These cell bodies are sometimes clearly identifiable as bipolar neurones, and presumably these correspond to the association cells which, in the starfish, are enclosed within the plexus. The receptor elements of this system are primary sense cells, with distal fibres passing into the plexus.

A puzzling feature of the hemichordates, and one that suggests that the organization of their nervous system is more primitive than that of echinoderms, is the absence

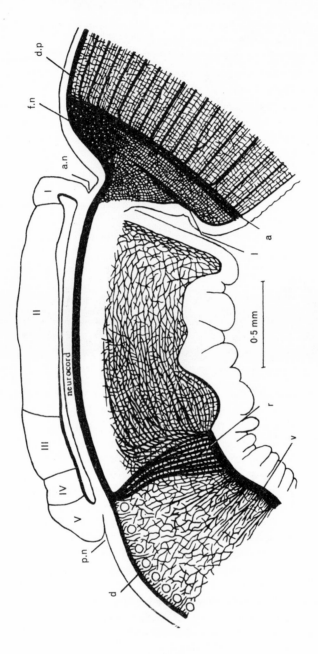

Fig. 15-16. Plan of the nervous system of the collar and adjacent regions of *Saccoglossus*. The dorsal half of the collar is seen in sagittal section, to show the neurocord and the thickness of the epidermal nerve-fibre layer in successive zones of the collar epidermis. The remainder is in surface view to show the arrangement of fibres in the epidermal nerve-fibre layer. Bundles of orientated nerve fibres, represented by thicker lines, are greatly reduced in number for the sake of clarity. *a*, anterior nerve ring; *a.n*, anterior neuropore; *d*, dorsal nerve cord of trunk; *d.p*, dorsal nerve cord of proboscis; *f.n*, fan-shaped thickening of the nerve-fibre layer on the dorsal part of the posterior surface of the proboscis; *l*, nerve loop underlying groove of ciliary organ; *p.n*, posterior neuropore; *r*, prebranchial nerve ring; *v*, ventral nerve cord of trunk. *I–V*, zones of collar epidermis. From Knight-Jones, 1952. *op. cit.*

of any clearly defined motor system corresponding with the coelomic system of the starfish. However, we have seen that the motor system varies in its degree of development in echinoderms in accordance with the degree of muscular activity. The situation in hemichordates may therefore be correlated with the relatively inactive life of these animals. Nevertheless, their reactions certainly demand some innervation of the muscles of the body wall, and it is supposed that this is provided by the passage of individual fibres through the basement membrane, without them being anywhere collected together into nerve tracts.

Just as the nervous system of the starfish is adapted for the needs of an animal that moves over the sea bottom, so that of the hemichordates is adapted for the life of a burrowing animal. For example, burrowing depends upon the passage of peristaltic waves backwards over the body surface, and particularly over the proboscis;

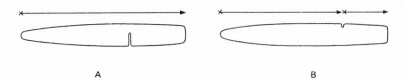

A   B

Fig. 15-17. The propagation of burrowing waves along the proboscis of *Saccoglossus ruber*. Bulges are initiated opposite the points marked with a cross, and travel posteriorly as indicated by the arrows. A, peristalsis is not interrupted by a cut through the ventral half of the proboscis. B, peristalsis is interrupted by a lesion of the dorsal nerve cord; an independent series of waves starts behind the lesion. Adapted from Knight-Jones, 1952. *op. cit.*

these waves can be shown to depend upon the propagation of excitation down the dorsal nerve cord, from the extreme anterior end. If the proboscis is cut through transversely, in such a way that the two portions are connected only by a narrow bridge of tissue containing the dorsal nerve cord, the peristaltic waves will continue to pass without interruption (Fig. 15-17). Conversely, if the dorsal nerve cord is cut out at one point, but the whole of the rest of the proboscis is left undamaged, the waves from the front end will stop at the cut while an entirely independent series will start immediately behind that point. Thus the cord is seen to be a polarized through-conduction pathway, impulses from which are doubtless propagated laterally through the epidermal nerve net. The structure of the proboscis nervous system is thus well adapted for the orderly propagation of impulses evoking peristalsis.

Another characteristic behaviour pattern of the hemichordates is a retreating movement, in which the animal contracts and draws backwards in its burrow. This involves the passage of peristaltic waves forwards from the extreme hind end of the trunk, instead of the backwards-directed passage seen in burrowing. Experiments similar in principle to those already mentioned show that in this case it is the ventral cord of the trunk, but not the dorsal one, which is responsible for the maintenance of the trunk movements. Excitation in the collar is propagated through the neurocord, but in the proboscis it is propagated through the whole nerve net and not, as might perhaps be expected, through the dorsal nerve cord. In contrast to what is found when the burrowing movements are analyzed, cuts through the proboscis will not interrupt the forward progress of the waves, provided that a bridge of epidermal tissue is left. Moreover, this bridge need not in this case include the dorsal nerve cord.

It is thus certain that the regular arrangement of the fibres of the plexus, and the collection of some of them into tracts or cords, is an expression of the establishment of definitely orientated pathways. Moreover, this system, despite its apparent simplicity, has powers of integration which ensure that the animal reacts with the behaviour pattern of a whole organism. For example, if an individual is stimulated mechanically at a point half-way along the body, it may respond with a burrowing reaction, or it may show the retreat movement. But whatever the response it will be a total and integrated one; provided the nervous system is complete, burrowing and retreat behaviour will never occur simultaneously. There is nothing to suggest that the neurocord is particularly active in this regard, or that it functions like the central nervous system of the vertebrates. Presumably this capacity for integration resides in some way in the association cells that must be included among those lying close to the nerve plexus. But to say this is to say little; the source of the influence that welds the separate reflex patterns of animals into an integrated whole remains fascinatingly elusive.

16
Advanced Nervous Systems

16–1 TRENDS IN NEURAL EVOLUTION

As we trace out the history of invertebrate life we see animals developing increasingly complex behaviour patterns, that enable them to exploit their environment with ever-improving efficiency and with an endless variety of means. The nervous system plays a key role in this history, with certain trends in its organization clearly apparent. The primitive nerve net rapidly diminishes in importance, and becomes very difficult indeed to identify, although in some groups at least it still retains significance. In its place there is established a system of nerves, formed of tracts of fibres that convey impulses into and out of a central nervous system, a situation foreshadowed in the development of functionally differentiated tracts and centres within primitive nerve nets.

The particular importance of the central nervous system is that cell bodies, apart from those of the receptor cells, become largely localized within it. Many of these cells are connecting cells: the association cells, internuncial neurones, or inter-neurones as they are variously called. These form links in the reflex pathways, as they do in the plexiform nervous system of echinoderms, and make possible the complex of central pathways and junctions that are the structural basis of advances in integration. Another important feature of the central nervous system, although one not entirely confined to it, is the formation of systems of giant fibres, which we shall consider later. These carry further another tendency that we have already encountered: the formation of through-conduction pathways that improve the efficiency of reactions by increasing the speed of propagation of nerve impulses.

Finally, since freely moving animals usually move in one direction, and consequently are bilaterally symmetrical with the major receptor systems at the anterior end, there is marked specialization at that end of the central nervous system. This, which is part of the process of cephalization that we have already encountered, leads to an increasing domination of the cephalic end of the central nervous system over the remainder of the organism, and thus to the appearance of that morphologically and physiologically complex structure called the brain.

These trends are already present in the Platyhelminthes. A central nervous system with cephalic dominance is well established in this group, despite its lowly status, and we may take this as an indication of the importance of this development for the execution of movement and response in bilaterally symmetrical animals. In the free-living forms there are from 2 to 6 longitudinal nerve cords, which contain nerve cells distributed along their length; these cells are not grouped into ganglia except at the anterior end, where they give rise to a rudimentary brain. The nerve cords are essential for the maintenance of spontaneous movement and for the coordination of responses, as is shown by the fact that isolated pieces of the body will only show these features if they retain some portion of the cords. A peripheral nerve plexus, comparable with the nerve net already considered, is still present in the platyhelminths, but it has become subordinate to the central nervous system; its presence probably explains why an isolated proboscis can show some food-seeking activity even after it has been disconnected from the nerve cords.

Accounts of the functional significance of the brain differ, but on the whole behaviour seems to be incomplete in its absence. In the polyclad *Yungia*, for example, spontaneous and adequately coordinated movement can occur after the brain has been removed, but this movement is undirected. Then again, the triclad *Planaria* can move after the loss of its brain, and can extend its pharynx and carry out swallowing movements, but normal behaviour in response to the presence of food does not occur unless the brain regenerates. Already, then, we can see this organ beginning to exert its dominating influence.

16–2 METAMERIC NERVOUS SYSTEM AND LOCOMOTION IN ANNELIDS

The further development of neural organization can be well studied in the Annelida, particularly in relation to the metamerism which we have seen to be the foundation of their locomotor mechanisms. The central nervous system in these animals is much more compact than in the Platyhelminthes, consisting of two ventral nerve cords which are commonly fused so closely that they often appear as one. The receptors are usually bipolar sense cells, lying peripherally. Within the nerve cords are found the motor neurones and also the association neurones; these are concentrated in the segmental ganglia, which give rise to the segmental nerves that contain the sensory and motor fibres.

This plan lends itself to a good deal of variation. Primitively the two nerve cords remain widely separated, but are connected transversely, thus forming the ladder-like system that is found not only in certain annelids but even in primitive crustaceans such as *Artemia*. Generally speaking, the more primitive the nervous system the closer its relationship with the ectoderm in the adult, although the nerve cords are never intra-epidermal as they are in the echinoderms and hemichordates. These primitive appearances, however, may sometimes be a consequence of secondary simplification of structure, often associated with a small body size and an element of neoteny. This may partly explain the apparently primitive form of nervous system in the archiannelids, for, despite their name, these animals are probably not wholly primitive. Another aspect of variation in metameric nervous systems is the common

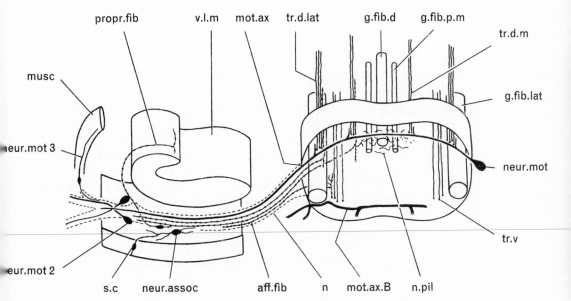

Fig. 16-1. Diagram to show in a generalized form the central and peripheral inter-neural connections of the component neurons of a segmental nerve. *aff.fib,* afferent fibre; *g.fib.d,* dorsal giant fibre; *g.fib.lat,* lateral giant fibre; *g.fib.p.m,* paramedial giant fibre; *mot.ax,* motor axon of dorsal emergence; *mot.ax.B,* motor axon of ventral emergence; *musc,* muscle; *n,* segmental nerve; *n.pil,* neuropile; *neur.assoc,* association neuron of the subepithelial plexus; *neur.mot, neur.mot(2 and 3),* motor neurons of the first, second, and third order; *propr.fib,* proprioceptor fibre; *s.c,* sensory cell; *tr.d.lat,* dorso-lateral fine-fibre longitudinal internuncial tract; *tr.d.m,* dorso-medial tract; *tr.v,* ventral tract; *v.l.m,* ventral longitudinal muscle. From Smith, 1950. *op. cit.*

tendency for fusion of ganglia, particularly in relation to the progress of cephalization. It is, however, more apparent in arthropods than in annelids.

The organization of the metameric nervous system of nereid worms (Fig. 16-1; Fig. 6-5, p. 105) has been analyzed at the structural level in the studies of J. E. Smith, which have been based largely upon the use of methylene blue staining. Bipolar sensory cells are well developed, being particularly numerous on the parapodia (especially on the cirri) and in the ventral body wall. Information from these receptors is conveyed into the central nervous system by afferent fibres running in the segmental nerves, four pairs of which arise from each of the segmental ganglia. Of these nerves, I and IV (Fig. 6-5) carry fibres from receptors on most of the body surface, II from the parapodia, and III from the mechanoreceptors (proprioceptors) of the dorsal and ventral longitudinal muscles.

A remarkable feature of this aspect of neural organization is the disparity between the number of receptor cells in each segment and the number of fibres in each segmental nerve. Smith finds that the number of afferent fibres in each of the four segmental nerves is only 3-4, 6-8, 2, and 6, respectively, yet there are probably not less than 1,000 sensory cells per square millimetre of the body surface alone. This disparity is partly accounted for by the presence of a nerve plexus which lies close below the basement membrane of the epidermis, and which comprises the nerve fibres of multi-polar association cells (Fig. 16-1). Many of the sensory cells discharge into this plexus. From it there arise nerve tracts which pass into the segmental nerves, but the constituent fibres join together so that as the nerves pass inwards there is a continuous reduction in the number of fibres. Not all of the afferent fibres follow exactly this course, however. The proprioceptor fibres, and some of those from the epidermal receptors, pass into the segmental nerves without communicating directly with the plexus at all; nevertheless, the principle of reduction in the number of fibres is unaffected.

The motor fibres of the segmental nerves are even fewer than the sensory fibres, the four nerves of each segment having respectively 1, 3, 1–2, and 4. These fibres, which arise from cell bodies in the segmental ganglia, are more numerous towards the peripheral end of the nerves. Their arrangement thus parallels that of the sensory fibres, and with essentially the same pattern of organization, for the multiplication is effected by the introduction into the motor pathways of intercalary or relay neurones. The more central of these are termed second-order motor neurones, while those that finally supply the muscles are the third-order neurones (Fig. 16–1).

Two conclusions are suggested by this anatomical arrangement. The great preponderance of peripheral fibres in both the sensory and motor pathways may provide for the short-circuiting of the passage of the nerve impulses, so that these do not have to traverse the central nervous system. If this is so (and it is only a suggestion), responses to stimulation can be mediated by local reflexes at the periphery, without involving the central nervous system at all. In addition, the limited connections between the latter and the periphery through the segmental nerves will permit some central integration. Since so few fibres pass to the central nervous system, however, it seems likely that it can only receive broad patterns of information rather than precise detail. The peripheral receptors show much variation in form. This suggests that there must be a good deal of peripheral sensory discrimination, yet from the point of view of the central nervous system much of this information must be wasted. Nevertheless, the importance of central integration is shown by the number of cells that are set aside for this purpose. Since the sensory cells are peripherally situated, and since there are few motor cells, most of the cell bodies in the segmental ganglia must belong to this category.

The mode of action of the metameric nervous system of annelids is conveniently illustrated in locomotion. This involves the interaction of a muscular body wall with an hydrostatic skeleton, and we have already judged that it must depend on the integrative action of a specialized nervous system. Considered from this point of view, two features of locomotion are immediately apparent: the segments can act independently, yet their individual activities are integrated into the unified behaviour of the whole individual. This is seen when a polychaete worm begins to move. The first movement forwards is effected by a stepping action of parapodia situated at about 4-segment intervals from each other. This action begins at the front end of the

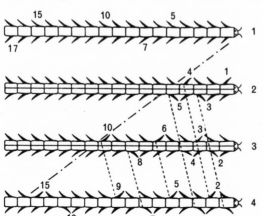

Fig. 16-2.   Diagram showing the start of slow ambulation in *Nereis*. Note the rapid spread of the ambulatory pattern (– · – · –) over the whole body from head to tail, and the movement of this pattern from tail to head at a much slower rate (– – – – –). From Gray, 1939. *J. exp. Biol.*, **16**, 9–17.

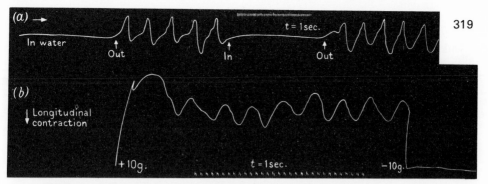

Fig. 16-3. Dependence of the rhythmicity of a decapitated earthworm on longitudinal tension. A, a preparation suspended horizontally in water shows no rhythm; the
rhythm emerges when the preparation is exposed to tension from its own weight by
removal from water to air. B, a preparation freely suspended in water shows no rhythm
but quickly exhibits a rhythm on applying longitudinal tension; it becomes inactive
again as soon as the tension is removed. The records read from left to right. From Gray
and Lissmann, 1938. *J. exp. Biol.*, **15**, 506–517.

body, and spreads rapidly backwards; it is then linked by the movement of the parapodia of the intervening segments, so that the whole of the body becomes involved in
the peristaltic cycle (Fig. 16–2).

The movement of an individual segment is mediated by local (segmental) reflexes; it is because of this that headless worms and short pieces of the body can
exhibit normal locomotor patterns. The integration of these segmental reflexes into
the behaviour pattern of the whole worm is the function of the central nervous
system. This is readily demonstrated by cutting through the nerve cord, but leaving
the animal otherwise intact. The continuity of movement of the whole body is now
interrupted, but the normal locomotor pattern is still shown independently by the
two regions anterior and posterior to the point of section. In this simple way we learn
that the integration of the segments depends upon the propagation of impulses from
segment to segment along the length of the central nervous system.

This phenomenon of central conduction is also readily shown in earthworms.
We can divide one of these animals so that the two portions are left connected by
the ventral nerve cord alone. Peristaltic movements occur in both portions, but these
are completely coordinated with each other, even when there is no possibility of one
portion stimulating the other by pulling upon it. This coordination can only be
attributed to the conduction of excitation through the nerve cord. The importance
of the latter is further shown if isolated pieces of the body, 20 to 40 segments long,
are suspended in a saline bath. The application of gentle tension or touch to such
pieces evokes peristalsis, but only if the nerve cord has been left intact. If it is removed
from these pieces, the response is no longer obtained.

The segmental locomotor reflexes of earthworms, although dependent on central
conduction, are dependent also upon peripheral excitation evoked by the stimulation
of segmental receptors. This is readily demonstrable in intact animals. For example,
a decapitated worm suspended by cotton threads in water shows no peristaltic
rhythm, but this rhythm appears if the worm is removed from the support of the
water into the air (Fig. 16–3). The same result ensues if the animal is subjected to
tension while it is in water; it appears that in both instances the movement is evoked
by the stimulus of stretching. Another important factor is tactile stimulation applied
through the ventral surface. Thus, a suspended earthworm will show peristalsis

while its body is in contact with the substratum, but may cease to do so when it is removed from that contact.

A situation similar in principle, but complicated by a more specialized body form, is seen in the medicinal leech, *Hirudo*. As in the earthworm, terrestrial loco-motion depends upon the passage of waves of muscular contraction, which involve successively the longitudinal and circular muscle layers, with the dorso-ventral muscles remaining inactive. In the intact leech these movements are regulated by excitation arising in the suckers. Fixation of the anterior sucker to the substratum is followed by a wave of contraction of the longitudinal muscles, while activity of the circular muscles follows fixation of the posterior suckers. Yet the suckers are not the only factors, as can be seen if the posterior one is removed, and the anterior one denervated. The resulting preparation can still show normal locomotor movements, but only as long as it is in contact with the ground. The movements cease if the animal is lifted off the ground by passing threads underneath it. Thus the preparation is essentially similar in this respect to an intact earthworm; both require tactile stimula-tion of the ventral surface if they are to move. The intact leech differs from the earth-worm, however, in that its specialized suckers provide time signals for the initiation of the waves of muscular activity.

The leech also differs from the earthworm in being adapted for aquatic as well as terrestrial movement. These two types of movement depend on different patterns of muscular activity, and are evoked by different patterns of stimulation. Aquatic movement involves characteristic up-and-down undulations. During these the dorso-ventral muscles are held in contraction, and the circular muscles are relaxed, while waves of contraction pass rapidly backwards down the longitudinal muscles, alternately dorsally and ventrally. The slow rhythms of terrestrial locomotion are only shown when there is ventral tactile stimulation of the suckers or ventral surface, whereas the rapid rhythms of aquatic locomotion are only shown when that tactile stimulation is removed. Thus an intact leech suspended in water shows long-sustained swimming movements, and so also will the preparation already mentioned, in which the suckers are no longer functional.

Clearly, both peripheral and central neural activity are important in the loco-motion of annelids, but the relative importance of the two factors is not easy to judge from these observations. Some light, however, is shed on this by study of the action potentials in the nerve cord. This shows that, in the earthworm, there is a rhythmic activity in the central nervous system during normal peristalsis which is identical in frequency with that of the muscular contractions. Theoretically, this neural rhythm might be a causal factor in locomotion, arising spontaneously as in the cyclical behaviour of *Arenicola* (pp. 217, 325) and evoking muscular responses which could then be modulated by information from the receptors. This, however, seems not to be so. The isolated nerve cord certainly shows a spontaneous rhythmic activity, but the pattern is often quite different from that of the normal peristaltic rhythm. This lack of correspondence is even clearer in the leech. The nerve cord of this animal shows an electrical rhythm identical with the swimming frequency while it is in normal physiological connection with a body that is displaying swimming movements. If it is removed from the body, however, it shows no such rhythm.

It seems probable that the rhythmic contractions of annelidan muscle depend upon chains of reflexes which are activated by sensory stimulation in the skin or muscles themselves; the excitation is then conducted along the ventral nerve cord by internuncial neurones. The contraction of the muscles in any one segment of the earthworm can apparently be evoked in one or other of two ways: either by excitation transmitted centrally from another segment, or by stimulation of their own stretch receptors by the tension exerted by the next adjacent segment. Gray and Lissmann, in their analysis of this situation, suggest that the stretch reflexes do not operate when the worm is moving over a smooth surface, but become important when the surface is rough, and offers variable resistance to the body surface. In these circumstances both the tactile and the stretch reflexes could cooperate with the conducting role of the central nervous system to produce muscular efforts adjusted to the external conditions. Whether local reflexes, suggested earlier as a possibility in polychaetes (p. 318), play any part at all in this is not clear, but there is no decisive experimental evidence that they do so.

In view of the evident importance of interganglionic conduction throughout the body, one may ask what influence is exerted on locomotion in annelids by the development of specialized ganglia at the anterior end. An earthworm can crawl normally after removal of the supra-pharyngeal (cerebral) ganglia, and can also eat and copulate, but it is restless and unduly active, and its burrowing is less efficient. A nereid without a supra-oesophageal ganglion is similarly over-active, but it does not feed or burrow, it is insensitive to light, and it has a much reduced chemosensitivity. Undoubtedly the nervous connections of these ganglia make them important sensory centres, but these observations show that they also exert an inhibitory control over movement. In this respect they are closely linked with the suboesophageal ganglion, for if this is removed from either earthworms or nereids the animals cease to burrow and become inactive. A somewhat similar effect is seen in the leech, for removal of this ganglion results in loss of muscular tone and a lack of terrestrial movement except in response to strong stimulation.

Probably, then, the cerebral ganglia of annelids exert an inhibitory action on motor centres in the suboesophageal ganglion, but the source of the excitation of the latter remains obscure. Perhaps the function of the peripheral receptors in these animals is not only to initiate specific segmental reflexes but also to establish in the central nervous system a level of excitability adequate to maintain the normal locomotor reflexes. Probably the suboesophageal ganglion, by virtue of its anterior position and its association with the specialized receptor systems, plays a leading role in the excitatory process. In any case we shall see later that these possibilities certainly do not exhaust the importance of the anterior end of the central nervous system in integrative and regulatory processes, for there is good evidence that the cerebral ganglion of annelids secretes hormones, and that many of its cells are concerned in this secretory activity. Thus our interpretation of the results of removing the ganglion must at present be very provisional, and cannot be formulated solely in terms of classical neurophysiology.

Some of the implications of this are relevant to the results of recent experiments on the learning capacity of annelids. These have shown that the cerebral ganglion does not dominate the behaviour of the worms to the same extent that the brain does in animals with more advanced nervous systems. We have mentioned that earthworms can be trained to select one arm of a T-tube when they crawl through it, and this is true also of polychaetes. Nereids, for example, will learn to avoid one arm if they are punished with an electric shock when they select it, and if they are rewarded by being left for some minutes in the dark when they enter the other arm. It has been shown that this acquired behaviour pattern may still persist even after the supra-oesophageal ganglion has been disconnected from the rest of the central nervous system, so that it can have no effect on the worm's choice.

The difficulty in conducting such experiments is that disconnection or removal of the ganglion must often affect the behaviour of the animals by interfering with the inflow of essential information from the cephalic sense organs. Much of this information passes through the ganglion, and is lost to the animal when that ganglion is disconnected. Fortunately the peristomial cirri of nereids provide an exception to this, for they are connected directly with the ventral nerve cord. The retention of the behaviour pattern in the experiment just mentioned depends upon this connection being preserved, so that the animal retains part of its sensory input despite the disconnection of its supra-oesophageal ganglion. Here at least, then, we have evidence that retention of a new behaviour pattern does not require retention of that ganglion. However, it would be wrong to assume that the ganglion plays no part in the learning processes of nereid worms, for training in some types of experiment is more difficult in its absence. Clark summarizes the position by concluding that the supra-oesophageal ganglion is not a unique memory storage centre in polychaetes, although it is involved in some way in learning.

16–3   ASPECTS OF ARTHROPOD BEHAVIOUR

The locomotion of annelids shows a segmented nervous system functioning at a comparatively simple level of organization. To illustrate some of the further potentialities of this type of nervous system we can briefly consider some aspects of arthropodan behaviour. The same principles are operative, for locomotion in these animals continues to depend upon central conduction and segmental reflexes, although these, as is to be expected, are more complex than in annelids. Fortunately, our study of them is greatly aided by the ability of these animals to adapt to experimental interference.

The capacity of the ganglia for independent action is readily demonstrable in cockroaches. An isolated leg of *Periplaneta*, if still connected with its ganglion, will execute a stepping movement when the tarsus is stimulated by traction. The extension of the leg is brought about by the depressor muscle. If, in a suitable preparation, the experimenter arranges for a sudden increase in resistance to the extension, a sudden burst of high-frequency impulses discharges into the muscle, to be followed by a resumption of a steady discharge at a higher rate than before. Normally, this response would serve to overcome the resistance. A similar effect is produced by pressing on the trochanter of the leg, because this stimulates the proprioceptive campaniform sensilla. This response to peripheral stimulation is one means by which coordination of the limbs is effected during walking; movement of an anterior leg will exert a tractive force on a posterior one, which will then respond reflexly to this stimulus. Because of this effect of peripheral excitation, a cockroach will continue to show coordinated walking movements even after its nerve cord has been cut right through in the thorax.

Coordinated movement in this animal is thus possible, at least to some extent, without the participation of the central nervous system. Nevertheless, the transmission of excitation along the nerve cord through the internuncial neurones must also be important in normal conditions. Circumstances doubtless vary in different species. For example, the walking movements of the stick-insect, *Dixippus*, are abolished if the thoracic nerve cord is completely transected. If, however, only one of the two longitudinal commissures is cut, and the other left intact, normal walking is still possible. It follows from this that the central nervous system includes some provision for alternative pathways which can be brought into use when the normal ones are blocked. This is not itself a learning process, for it does not involve the establishment of new associations; yet the existence of multiple pathways may clearly be a factor favourable to the development of learning.

The use of alternative pathways is illustrated also in amputation experiments carried out upon the insect, *Locusta viridissima*. It is possible to alter the normal rhythm of limb movement in this animal by removing a whole limb and even by removing a single foot. Ten Cate concludes from this that the normal sequence of movement cannot be wholly predetermined but must be influenced by particular patterns of reflex stimulation. Other investigators have recorded similar phenomena. Changes in limb coordination are readily produced in a variety of arthropods by selective removal of the appendages. They occur too quickly to be ascribed to the establishment of new neural pathways; they can only result from the use of pre-existing alternative ones. In general terms one can assume that the selection of a particular pathway from among the variety available must depend upon the strength and pattern of the sensory input, and upon the ease of passage through particular central connections. This flexibility is by no means restricted to experimental conditions. On the contrary, we have already noted that locomotor patterns and rhythms normally change during arthropod movement.

This degree of flexibility may seem surprising in nervous systems which, as we have seen in discussing worms, contain so few neurones. The explanation, however, is doubtless to be found in the extensive branching of their processes, and the variety of connections that are thereby made possible. It is, indeed, known that quite complex responses in arthropods are mediated reflexly by very few neurones. For example, a crayfish defends itself in a threatening situation by a characteristic reaction in which the claws and the anterior end of the body are raised; behaviour that would seem to be complex, but which can be evoked in its essentials by stimulation of a single fibre in the circumoesophageal commissure. Then again, the escape reaction, in which the tail is violently flapped, involves many muscles, but these can be brought into action by a single impulse in one of the giant fibres (p. 326). This is not to say that the neural basis of these responses is quite as simple as these observations suggest. During the defence reaction, for example, the animal may turn towards the source of the threat; this will involve the excitation of additional neurones. The escape reaction, too, involves repeated muscular contraction, producing a series of flaps, and it is likely that this prolongation is aided by the muscle receptors. These will be stimulated by the initial flapping, and the impulses that they send into the nerve cord may help to maintain the excitation of the reflex paths; this is known as reinforcement.

What these considerations do suggest is that there need be no hard and fast line between simple reflexes and more complex patterns of instinctive behaviour. These latter may depend upon a chain of reflex pathways, in which each phase is stimulated by the immediately preceding one. For example, the feeding of a decapod crustacean may involve first the seizure of food by the cheliped, then its transfer to the mouth parts, and finally its swallowing if it proves to be acceptable. This sequence of reflex actions can be completed even by a crayfish from which the brain has been removed. Nevertheless, the brain must normally exert some regulatory action, for a brainless animal may burst its stomach by continuing to feed even after that organ has been completely filled.

The pattern of neural pathways involved in such a complex response must be preformed in the ventral nerve cord, with the brain exerting some degree of integration. However, the integrative capacity of the arthropod brain needs to be evaluated in the light of its small size, and free of anthropomorphic preconceptions. For example, the brain of a blowfly has a wet weight of only 0.84 mg, and probably does not contain more than about 100,000 cells. Furthermore, the cell bodies are concentrated around the periphery, where, unlike those of vertebrate brains, they are not well placed to enter into a variety of synaptic connections. These factors, together with the small size of the cells, must limit integration, and thus the perceptual world of the animal is probably less rich than that of a vertebrate.

But regulating centres in arthropods need not always be cerebral ones. An illustration of this is seen in the copulatory behaviour of the male mantis. The last abdominal ganglion of this animal has a copulatory centre that is inhibited by the suboesophageal ganglion until the inhibition is specifically removed. Removal of the brain produces no sexual activity, for it is not responsible for the inhibition. But removal of the suboesophageal ganglion, and hence of its inhibitory centre, results in copulation being carried to completion. This is why, when the female sometimes eats the male, anterior end first, during copulation, the copulatory act itself continues without interruption; she may be 'more deadly than the male', but her action, so far from being inimical to propagation, may actually be said to further it! The world of such animals is a strange one, and difficult for us to penetrate, either by experiment or by intuition. 'Looking at their rigidly armoured bodies', writes Dethier, 'their staring eyes, and their mute performances, one cannot help at times wondering if there is anyone inside.'

Whether there is or not, from such patterns of reflex activity is built up the complex adaptational behaviour that is observed in animals under natural conditions. Current interpretations suggest that these patterns are only manifested when the animal is in a specific state, indicated by the occurrence of the restless activity which is called appetitive behaviour. If, for example, it is hungry, it will search for food; this is appetitive searching, so organized that it tends to lead the animal to those conditions in which food is likely to be found. The essential requirement here is that the animal should encounter specific stimuli (the releasers, mentioned earlier) which are essentially patterns of stimulation to which the animal is adapted to respond. The response is presumably possible because the connections in the central nervous system are so arranged that they are excited by a particular pattern of sensory input. In more abstract terms, the central nervous system is said to possess a releasing mechanism, which, as a result of the stimulation of the releaser, initiates the final step in the behaviour pattern, which is called the consummatory act. When this has occurred, the initial appetitive behaviour disappears. Once the animal has fed, it will no longer search for food. Although, however, the consummatory act is final as regards one particular segment of behaviour, it may yet in its turn constitute the appetitive behaviour for another complex of reactions.

Appetitive behaviour may be very varied in its origins. In one sense it must always be a consequence of some specific physiological state, but this may be determined by external (exogenous) or internal (endogenous) factors. The appetitive behaviour of hunger, for example, may perhaps be directly stimulated by the receptors of the alimentary canal, particularly of those parts that are concerned with the storage of food. Frequently, as with reproductive behaviour, hormones must play a part, and this aspect we shall consider later. In other instances, however, there is increasing evidence that behaviour patterns may arise spontaneously; without, that is, being evoked by specific receptor activity. To say this is no doubt merely to push the cause further back into aspects of physiological organization that have not yet yielded to analysis, but from our present point of view this mode of expression has a meaning; it focuses attention on the possibility of behaviour being initiated by spontaneous activity in the central nervous system.

We have seen an example of this in *Arenicola*, which has a respiratory cycle with a period of about 40 minutes; this is evoked by excitation arising as a spontaneous innate rhythm within the nerve cord, and quite independently of any peripheral stimulation. Similarly, there is a feeding cycle with a period of about 7 minutes; this, it is believed, is regulated by spontaneous excitation arising within the nerve plexus of the wall of the oesophagus. This is an exception to the principle that we have been outlining in this discussion, according to which adaptive reflexes are initiated by stimulation of peripheral receptors. This principle expresses what may be regarded as the classical view of reflex behaviour, and there is no doubt of its wide applicability. Endogenous neural rhythms, however, are certainly widespread in animals. They are seen, for example, in *Periplaneta*, which has a diurnal activity cycle that reaches a maximum of activity shortly after the beginning of darkness. But in this instance the cycle is known to be regulated by stimulation of the ocelli, so that it differs from the purely endogenous rhythm of *Arenicola*. The relative importance of endogenous and exogenous factors in the control of rhythmic activity in animals is a matter of controversy. We can only note here that the demonstration of these rhythms is an example of the way in which invertebrate studies extend our view of animal organization by forcing upon our attention problems of interpretation that are by no means so obvious in the field of vertebrate zoology, although similar principles operate there.

16–4   GIANT NERVE FIBRES

The activity cycles of *Arenicola* are not the only example of a departure by invertebrates from the classical picture of reflex behaviour as being dependent upon internuncial neurones linking afferent and efferent pathways. Another example is seen in the large nerve cells that give rise to so-called giant nerve fibres. These were first described in the central nervous system of crustaceans in 1836, but it was another 25 years before they were seen in annelids. Their nature was at first obscure, for giant fibres, as seen in transverse sections of polychaetes and annelids, look very unlike the expected appearance of nerve fibres. Nevertheless, their nervous character had been well established by 1900, for it became evident that they contained neurofibrillae, that they arose from cell bodies, and that they possessed myelin sheaths which could be blackened by osmic acid. They are now known to be of widespread occurrence, being found, for example, in cestodes, nemerteans, archiannelids, polychaetes, oligochaetes, arthropods, molluscs, and hemichordates. In the squid their diameter may reach 700 μ, as compared with 20 μ for a representative vertebrate nerve fibre.

The pattern of organization of these giant cells shows much variation. To take one familiar example, there are three dorsal giant fibres present in the nerve cord of earthworms, extending throughout the body but divided by septa into segmental units. Each fibre receives processes from several neurones in each segment, so that the fibres are syncytial in structure. In polychaetes, on the other hand, the giant fibres are usually continuous, without septa. They may be unicellular or multicellular, and they may be confined to one segment or extend through a number of segments, and they may or may not be myelinated. Such variation suggests that they have arisen independently many times, and this must surely be the explanation of their distribution in other animal groups. In hemichordates, for example, they form a system peculiar to the group, composed of cells that are variable in size and that are largely restricted to the neurocord. From here they give off giant fibres, some of which run forwards in the dorsal cord of the proboscis, while others run backwards in the ventral cord of the trunk.

If giant neurones have in fact arisen independently on a number of occasions, it is to be expected that they must have a considerable adaptive value. This is indeed so, for they permit exceptionally rapid propagation of nerve impulses. They are particularly concerned in reactions that result in an individual carrying out sudden retreat movements in response to potentially harmful disturbance. In *Lumbricus*, for example, it has been shown by cutting the giant fibres, by studying their development and regeneration, and by recording their action potentials, that these axons conduct the impulses that bring about the rapid end-to-end contractions that form the well-known protective response of this animal.

The exact form of these responses of the earthworm depends upon the position of stimulation. When the anterior end of the earthworm is touched, the head is withdrawn and the tail is anchored, the anchoring being aided by the flattened form of the hind end and by its chaetae being directed forwards. This response, which is an adaptation providing for retreat when the animal is exploring with its anterior end protruded from the burrow, depends on impulses passing backwards along the median giant fibre, which is connected with anterior receptors. If the posterior end is touched when the worm is out of its burrow, the response is different. The head now remains stationary and the tail is pulled forwards, this response being mediated by the lateral giant fibres, which are connected with posterior receptors. Thus the median fibre normally conducts backwards and the lateral ones forwards, but this is a result of their pattern of connections, and not of any limitation in their inherent capacities; in experimental conditions they can be made to conduct in either direction.

Many other examples of the dependence of escape reactions upon giant fibres might be given, but two further illustrations must suffice. In the crayfish there are paired median giant fibres that arise in the brain and extend backwards into the ventral nerve cord. In addition, there are lateral fibres that arise from cell bodies in the ventral ganglia and extend over several segments, and there are also motor fibres that pass out to the periphery from the same segment as that in which their cell bodies are situated. Stimulation of this system evokes the characteristic flapping of the abdomen (p. 323) which draws the animal rapidly backwards, and it also causes movements of the antennae.

Giant fibre systems are well developed in cephalopods, and of these the squid will serve as an example. Here a pair of giant cells in the pedal ganglion region of the brain (p. 331) make synaptic connections with other giant cells, and giant fibres from the latter pass out along the mantle nerves. Within the stellate ganglion these axons synapse with a third set of giant cells, the axons of these leaving the ganglion by a number of nerves to innervate the mantle musculature. The contractile response that results from stimulation of this giant fibre system causes water to be forced out of the mantle cavity so that the animal is propelled rapidly backwards.

All of these giant fibre systems are adaptations ensuring maximum speed of conduction in the mediation of responses that are of particular importance in preserving the life of the animal. They represent, in fact, an extreme manifestation of the selection pressure that has favoured increased efficiency of nerve conduction. We first saw this illustrated in the development of through-conduction pathways in primitive nerve nets. The improvement secured by the development of giant fibres is sufficiently indicated by measurements made in earthworms. These show that the fine fibres conduct at about 0.025 m/sec, the lateral giant fibres at 7 m/sec to 12 m/sec, and the median giant fibre at 17 m/sec to 25 m/sec. The difference is partially due to the reduction or elimination of synaptic barriers in the giant fibre pathway, and partially to the fact that rates of conduction increase with increase in the diameters of the axons. Conduction speed is also improved by the presence of a myelin sheath around the fibre. This latter principle has been used in earthworms, for example, but its exploitation is particularly characteristic of vertebrates, which have not, in consequence, developed the use of giant fibres. Finally, the peripheral connections of the giant fibres often facilitate speed of response. The incoming pathways from the receptors may be short, for example, and in some instances, as in the crayfish, there may be a continuous and uninterrupted pathway between the central cell body and the peripheral musculature.

16–5 MOLLUSCAN NERVOUS SYSTEM

The nervous systems of the Platyhelminthes, Annelida, and Arthropoda show a range of structure from which much can be learned of the factors that have influenced the history of neural organization. It is a comment on the scale of the adaptive radiation of the molluscs that they show a very similar range. Within this single phylum is demonstrated a historical process that culminates, in the cephalopods, in the production of sensory and central nervous mechanisms that demand serious comparison with those of vertebrates as well as with those of arthropods.

The absence of metameric segmentation is a point of obvious difference from the neural organization of the annelids and arthropods, but apart from this there is a very similar trend in the establishment of a ganglionic system controlling local reflexes. The primitive form of the molluscan nervous system (Fig. 16-4) can be judged from its appearance in present-day chitons. Here, as in platyhelminths, there is some centralization, but very little concentration of nerve cells; less, indeed, than in those animals, for there are no cerebral ganglia. Longitudinal nerve cords are present, linked by transverse commissures to form a ladder-like system, with pedal cords running along the foot and pallial cords lying more laterally. These cords link with a ring of nervous tissue encircling the oesophagus, but the only ganglia present are a pair of buccal ganglia, innervated from the ring and concerned with the action of the odontophore. Elsewhere the nerve cells are scattered, in the ring and in the cords.

The subsequent history of this nervous system reflects very clearly the modes of life of the main molluscan groups. It is to be expected that a well-organized central nervous system, capable of a high level of integration and conferring adaptive flexibility upon responses, will only appear when its evolution is promoted by its high selective value. This condition does not occur in the gastropods and lamellibranchs, which, with certain exceptions, are essentially inactive or even sedentary animals, living without a wide range of environmental stimulation. Even when such stimulation does present itself, the invention of the molluscan shell has meant that

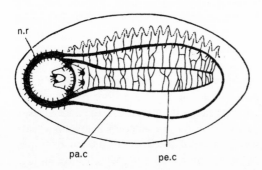

Fig. 16-4. The primitive molluscan nervous system. *n.r,* nerve ring; *pa.c,* pallial nerve cord; *pe.c,* pedal nerve cord. From Morton and Yonge, 1964. *The Physiology of Mollusca,* vol. 1 (Wilbur and Yonge, eds.). Academic Press, New York.

the response is retreat rather than exploration. It is doubtless because of this that the ganglia of these animals are centres of reflexes that involve comparatively restricted sensory and motor areas, and that show only a limited degree of interaction.

In the gastropods a pair of pleural ganglia appears at the anterior end of the pallial cords, while the cords themselves form the visceral loop, bearing a pair of parietal ganglia and a visceral ganglion, which may also be paired. These features are probably the more primitive ones. Later developments involve further concentration of the nerve cells, with a pair of cerebral ganglia appearing in the nerve ring, and a pair of pedal ganglia at the anterior end of the pedal cords; these cords then disappear. Thus arises the typical gastropod ganglionated nerve ring. The torsion of gastropods leads to a twisting of the visceral loop, the original left and right parietal ganglia now forming respectively the subintestinal and supra-intestinal ganglia. The subsequent changes in this visceral loop reflect the complex evolutionary history of the gastropods. The common trend throughout all the higher forms is an increasing concentration of the ganglia, the sub- and supra-intestinal ganglia being drawn into the main nerve ring, with a shortening of the visceral loop. In the Opisthobranchia this process is associated with the reversal of torsion and the untwisting of the visceral loop; in the Pulmonata this does not occur, although little indication of the original twisting of the loop can be seen.

At the structural level of analysis the influence of cephalization upon the gastropod nervous system is sufficiently obvious; no less striking is its virtual absence from the lamellibranchs. These animals have no head, and their mode of life is sedentary and withdrawn. In correlation with this, the nervous system is of a very simple character. It is derivable from the primitive plan that we have outlined above, with cerebral ganglia above the oesophagus, pedal connectives leading from them to the pedal ganglia in the foot, and visceral connectives running back to the visceral ganglia lying under the posterior abductor muscle. Pleural ganglia are associated with the cerebral ones, being completely fused with them except in the protobranchs.

Both in gastropods and lamellibranchs the fields of action of the ganglia are restricted ones, as is demonstrable by conventional experimental procedures. For example, the pedal ganglia of gastropods innervate the foot. If they are removed from *Aplysia* there is an increase of tonus in the foot, and also increased contraction of that region. If, on the other hand, the cerebral ganglia are removed but the pedal ganglia left undisturbed, there is an increase in locomotor activity and increased excitability of the lateral parapodia of the foot. These results suggest that the pedal ganglia inhibit tonic contractions, and that the cerebral ganglia, like the brain of annelids and arthropods, inhibit locomotor activity, in this case by action through the pedal ganglia. The local actions of the latter have been demonstrated by stimulating nerves running inwards to the ganglia from the parapodia. The result is to evoke contractions on the other side, indicating that the ganglia are relay points for reflex responses to stimulation of the foot.

The evidence available from lamellibranchs also indicates localized action of the ganglia. Thus the cerebro-pleural ganglia innervate anterior structures, including the palps, otocysts, osphradia, and the anterior adductor muscle. If these ganglia are removed from *Mytilus*, the foot is still able to creep and also to spin the byssus, being apparently controlled in these activities by the pedal ganglia. The visceral ganglion innervates a large part of the body, including the gills, siphons, pallial sense organs, much of the mantle, and also the posterior adductor muscle. Its removal from *Mytilus* abolishes the opening and closing of the valves which are the animal's response to changes in the conditions of the water.

The simplicity of response of the lamellibranch is correlated with its ability to secure complete protection within the shell, and because of this the regulation of the action of the adductor muscles is of crucial importance. These muscles are of compound structure, being composed of two types of fibre; one of these is striated, and is capable of rapid or phasic contractions, while the other is unstriated, and is responsible for the sustained tonic contractions that maintain closure of the valves. Barnes's description of the regulation of these contractions in *Anodonta* gives a good illustration of the mode of operation of lamellibranch ganglia.

If the animal is maintained in a fixed position, with one valve of its shell attached to a recording lever, it exhibits two rhythms. One of these is a 'slow' rhythm, in which a period of quiescence, with the valves closed, alternates (with frequencies of 3–30 per week) with a period of activity, when the valves gape open. The other rhythm is a 'rapid' one, the adductor muscles showing rapid contractions, followed by slow relaxations, with a frequency of up to 20 per hour. Study of animals from which the cerebro-pleural ganglia have been removed, or of preparations consisting of the posterior adductor muscle and the visceral ganglia, show that the 'slow' rhythm is a function of the unstriated muscle fibres, and that it is jointly controlled by the visceral and cerebro-pleural ganglia. The visceral ganglia produce a tonic contraction, while the cerebro-pleural ones inhibit this at intervals. The 'rapid' rhythm, on the other hand, is a function of the striated muscle fibres, and is controlled entirely by the visceral ganglia, without the participation of the cerebro-pleural ones. Both rhythms are independent of external stimulation, and seem to result from inherent properties of the ganglia concerned, yet they can be modified by stimulation. Thus vibration or rotation of the animal evokes a reflex response in which the tonus of the adductor muscles is relaxed and a new period of activity initiated.

The regulation of the rhythmic contractions of the anterior adductor of *Anodonta* is similar in principle, but this muscle is remote from the visceral ganglia, and probably the cerebro-pleural ganglia alone control both rhythms. This doubtless explains the form of the nervous system of *Pecten*. In this animal, as we have seen, there is a wide departure from the mode of life typical of lamellibranchs. The rapid contractions of the striated fibres of the posterior adductor muscle are in this case responsible for jet propulsion, while the anterior adductor muscle has been lost. In correlation with these changes the visceral ganglia have come to form the largest single component of the nervous system. In an animal which, like all lamellibranchs, is essentially headless, cephalization of the nervous system has no meaning: the cerebro-pleural ganglia are small, and have moved some way backwards.

16–6   NERVOUS SYSTEM AND LEARNING IN CEPHALOPODS

As we have already seen in other contexts, the history of the cephalopods has followed lines very different from those of other molluscs, the fundamental difference lying in their pelagic and predatory mode of life. No doubt they must at one stage have shared a common ancestry with the more sluggish, and more typical, members of the phylum, but of this we know nothing: cephalopod shells occur in Cambrian deposits, so that the independent history of the group must extend over some 500 million years. The only link with past ancestry that we have with us today is *Nautilus*. This animal is described by Anna Bidder as 'odd . . . dumb, and impersonal . . . a *long way* from other living cephalopods'. To judge from its shell, it has probably changed little since Cretaceous times. Its eyes are of simple structure, lacking lens and iris, and it is unlikely that the animal recognizes objects by sight; chemoreception must be altogether more important. Like other cephalopods, its central nervous system shows marked cephalization, but it is still comparatively simple, with only three pairs of lobes connected by commissures to form a ring-shaped complex. With the characteristic specializations of cephalopods setting in so early, there is little profit in seeking in these lobes for precise homologues with the parts of the nervous system of other molluscs. A functional analysis is altogether more revealing, for to this the cephalopods lend themselves very well.

Nautilus has been little studied from this point of view, but the intelligence of the other modern forms, and the ease with which some of them can be maintained in the laboratory, has attracted much attention to them. The sacrifice of their external shell is an index of their commitment to a pelagic life (although the retiring habits of *Octopus* make it an exception in this regard). Associated with this is the speed and freedom of movement of these animals, their well-developed sense of vision, and their remarkable capacity for colour change, to name only some of their outstanding adaptations. No less significant is the complex organization of the central nervous system. This forms a substantial concentration around the oesophagus, and is commonly referred to as the brain.

We may distinguish in the brain of *Octopus* (Fig. 16–5) as many as thirty distinct lobes, each composed of a layer of nerve cell bodies, enclosing a central mass of fibres. Ventral to the oesophagus is a group of suboesophageal lobes which are concerned in motor responses, and which in a very general way recall the ganglia of other molluscs. Direct stimulation with electrodes reveals something of their function. Stimulation of the posterior chromatophore lobe expands the chromatophores of the mantle and funnel; in this instance there seems to be a direct link between the central nervous system and a specific motor response. Stimulation of other parts of the suboesophageal lobes produces motor responses in various parts of the body, such as the arms, funnel, and ink sac, and there is some regional localization of the relevant centres, as indicated in the nomenclature of the lobes. This localization is not, however, as sharply defined as with the chromatophore response.

The responses produced by local stimulation of these centres are isolated sets of muscular contractions, abstracted, as it were, from the complete behaviour patterns of *Octopus*, and showing no sign of the integrations that normally characterize those patterns. The explanation of this is that the supra-oesophageal portion of the brain contains lobes which integrate or organize motor responses, and can therefore be termed higher motor centres. Direct stimulation reveals that the anterior and posterior basal lobes are concerned. Stimulation of the anterior basal lobe evokes movements of the eyes, head, and tentacles, such as are used in feeding; these are sufficiently coordinated to be clearly recognizable as elements of normal behaviour patterns. Similarly, stimulation of the posterior basal lobes produces coordinated respiratory and swimming movements of the fins and funnel, together with the escape reactions mediated by the giant fibre system, and also a variety of visceral responses. In no case are the muscles concerned directly innervated by the basal lobes. The connections of the latter are with the motor centres of the suboesophageal lobes, and it is through these that the integrating action of the basal lobes is exerted.

Naturally direct electrical stimulation is a crude way of testing central nervous function. Not only is the stimulus itself quite abnormal, but the central nervous system is deprived of the sensory inflow from other parts of the body that normally accompanies environmental stimulation, an inflow that includes the feedback of the proprioceptive and other information upon which depends the smooth execution of movements. These limitations can in part be overcome by a study of the effects of brain lesions; results thus obtained are largely in agreement with the conclusions suggested by the stimulation experiments. Removal of the basal lobes seriously interferes with the organization of integrated movements. For example, loss of the anterior basal lobe of one side results in the animal circling continuously with the undamaged side of the brain on the inside of the turn, while loss of the complete supra-oesophageal region of the brain results in the animal swimming backwards. Other experiments have shown that the optic lobes are involved in the maintenance of muscular tone, and that the suboesophageal region of the brain can organize simple reactions, but not the more complex ones that demand widespread integration. In short, the suboesophageal region can be said to include the lower motor centres, while complex integration is carried on in the higher motor centres of the supra-oesophageal region.

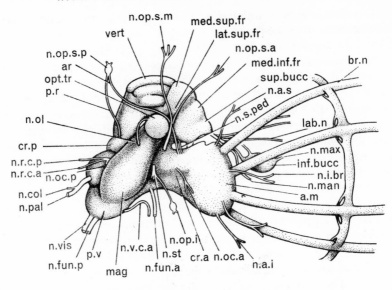

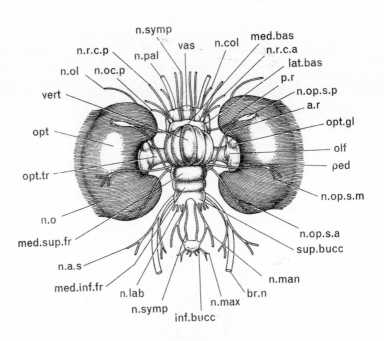

Fig. 16-5. Lateral (*above*) and dorsal (*below*) views of the brain of *Octopus vulgaris*. *a.m*, anterior suboesophageal mass; *br.n*, brachial nerve; *cr.a*, anterior chromatophore lobe; *cr.p*, posterior chromatophore lobe; *inf.bucc*, inferior buccal lobe; *lat.bas*, lateral basal lobe; *lat.sup.fr*, lateral superior frontal lobe; *mag*, magnocellular lobe; *med.bas*, median basal lobe; *med.inf.fr*, median inferior frontal lobe; *med.sup.fr*, median superior frontal lobe; *olf*, olfactory lobe; *opt*, optic lobe; *opt. gl*, optic gland; *p.v*, palliovisceral lobe; *ped*, peduncle lobe; *sup.bucc*, superior buccal lobe; *vert*, vertical lobe; *vas*, vasomotor lobe. Nerves not listed. From Young, 1964. *A Model of the Brain*. Clarendon Press, Oxford.

This, however, leaves unexplained certain areas of the supra-oesophageal region that are called 'silent areas'. If these are removed there is no disturbance of the motor behaviour of the animal, so that they are evidently not concerned with the organization of integrated movements. By analogy with the vertebrate brain we might expect the 'silent areas' to be concerned with memory and learning; extensive experimentation by J. Z. Young, Boycott, Sutherland, and M. J. Wells has shown this to be so, and has suggested important and far-reaching hypotheses regarding the nature of these phenomena in animals in general.

These experiments have exploited the capacity of *Octopus* for the acute visual and tactile discrimination mentioned earlier. The experimental principle, as regards visual discrimination, depends on the use of moving sheets of plastic, cut into well-defined shapes such as circles and rectangles. The animals can be taught to attack one such shape by rewarding them with food, and to avoid others by punishing them with an electric shock. This is the procedure of the classical conditioning experiment. In this instance, to follow Young's analysis, the results show that the nervous system must retain a coded representation of a situation, expressed within some particular set of neural processes, that is stored in the memory of the animal. It may be helpful to draw an analogy with a computer, in which the coded data correspond to the representation of past situations. From this point of view the process of learning is the setting-up of new representations. No animal, however, can afford to depend solely upon this process, for it must be able to survive during the period when the new representations are being established. Accordingly it will also possess to a greater or lesser degree the capacity for making responses that do not have to be learned. This aspect of behaviour, which we have termed instinctive, must also depend upon the presence of representations within the nervous system, but these representations will have been established during embryonic life as a result of the action of the genetic code inherited from the parents.

For all its acuity, the visual discrimination of *Octopus* has marked limitations as regards the shapes that can be distinguished. For example, vertical and horizontal rectangles can be distinguished from each other, but not oblique ones, a limitation that we have seen to be associated with a structural peculiarity of the eye. This and other observations have led to the suggestion that the nervous system operates by computing the ratios between the horizontal and vertical projections of the figures being observed. That some such process is involved is certainly suggested by the marked tendency for horizontal and vertical orientation in the structure of the nervous system. As we have already noted, the retina is organized in this way, and so also are the dendrites of the optic lobes into which the optic nerve fibres discharge. Moreover, the responses depend upon the maintenance of a horizontal orientation of the pupil, through the mediation of the statocysts (p. 290).

These are examples of how modes of response and learning capacities in animals are limited by features of neural organization; a principle that is as significant for the comparative psychologist as it is for the particular species concerned, and that reinforces the lesson that has already been taught us by *Paramecium*. Another illustration is provided by the tacile sense of *Octopus*, as analyzed by M. J. Wells. In this instance association experiments have shown that the animal can distinguish the surface texture of objects seized by its tentacles, but that it differs from man in being unable to distinguish the actual mode of distribution of surface irregularities. All that it can apparently do is to estimate the proportion of the surface that is elevated, or, as we might say, its general roughness.

This is probably connected with another limitation of *Octopus*: it cannot learn to distinguish objects by their weights. This is not because it lacks the proprioceptors upon which we rely for weight estimates; their existence is shown by the animal being able to compensate for the weights of objects when it handles them with its tentacles. The limitation arises because the movements of the tentacles are regulated in local motor centres (axial ganglia) in the arms (Fig. 16-6). It is there that the proprioceptive information is used, so that it does not become available to the brain as a basis for learning. Not only, then, is the animal unable to learn to discriminate by weight:

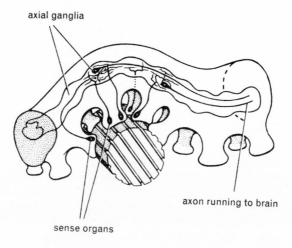

Fig. 16-6.   Diagram of part of the arm of an octopus touching a plastic cylinder. The pathways from the receptors are inferred from physiological and degeneration experiments. After Wells and Wells, from Young, 1964. *A Model of the Brain.* Clarendon Press, Oxford.

lacking proprioceptive information, it cannot judge the position of its mechanoreceptors, and because of this it cannot estimate the surface patterning of an object. Indeed, the consequences of this limitation go even further, for, despite the undoubted intelligence of the animal as measured by its capacity for learning to deal with new environmental situations, it is quite unable to learn to use its tentacles in new manipulative skills.

Wells suggests that this peripheral restriction of proprioceptive information is a consequence of the cephalopods having flexible bodies. Animals with articulated skeletons can readily provide for central monitoring of the positions of the parts of their bodies, since they require information only from relatively few stations. Large animals with flexible bodies would need information from more stations, and the computing of this information would seem to demand brains very much bigger than they actually possess. The decentralization of reflex motor control avoids the need to develop a disproportionately large brain, but at the same time it limits their learning capacities. The activity of the local ganglia in *Octopus* is seen in the way in which the arms of completely brainless animals can carry out movements of seizure and rejection. These presumably depend upon chain reflexes, such as we have encountered in arthropods, and that are here evoked within the individual arm by stimulation of its receptors. Thus the only control that has to be exerted by the computer mechanism of the brain is the signalling to the lower centres of instructions either to attack or to retreat.

As regards the learning process in *Octopus*, there seem to be two partially distinct mechanisms in the brain (Fig. 16-5). One of these, comprising the optic, superior frontal, and vertical lobes, is concerned with visual learning. Information is first transmitted to the optic lobes, and is distributed from there to the superior frontal lobes, and on to the vertical lobes. Anatomical studies show that fibres from the latter pass back to the optic lobes, so that there is a circuit of information through the vertical lobes. A fact of great potential significance is that this circuit makes use of a very large number of cells, the vertical lobes containing some 25 million cells in comparison with the 1 million to 2 million fibres that connect them with the superior frontal lobes. The optic lobes are even richer in cells, each containing some 60 million cells, as compared with 30 million for the whole of the remainder of the nervous system. Undoubtedly the vertical lobes are of great importance in visual learning. If they are removed, the animal substantially loses a previously learned lesson. There are signs, however, if the lesson is retaught, that traces of the old lesson remain in its memory. Such an animal can still learn fresh lessons, but it does so more slowly and less accurately than an intact animal, and only does so at all if the discriminations involved are simple ones.

A suggested interpretation of these facts, argued in detail by Young, is that cells in the optic lobes are pre-set to respond to particular dimensional ratios, and that during the learning process they become conditioned to signal either attack or retreat, according to the information supplied to them. At this stage the conditioning would affect only those cells that are under the direct influence of the receptor system. If the process developed no further the lesson could only be a limited one, for the animal would be unable to generalize from one shape to another closely similar one, or from stimulation of one part of the visual field to another. In fact, however, *Octopus* shows marked powers of generalization, and this, it is argued, could depend upon the activity of the vertical lobes. These, by storing representations, and by distributing excitation back to wider fields of cells in the optic lobes, could extend the area over which conditioning is established.

Force is given to this argument by consideration of the process of tactile learning. The inferior frontal and subfrontal lobes are concerned here. Removal of these regions completely abolishes the capacity to learn by touch. They are separate from the centres concerned with visual learning, yet they are not entirely independent of them, for the two systems overlap in the vertical lobes. Removal of the latter affects tactile learning in essentially the same way as it affects visual learning. This is in accord with the suggestion that the vertical lobes facilitate generalization, yet it must be emphasized that this whole concept of their function is still highly theoretical. In fact, the organization of the subfrontal lobe is much like that of the vertical lobe, and this has led to an alternative suggestion that the latter has no unique function at all, but merely serves as a pool of cells available for the extension of memory. Or again, it may be concerned particularly with representations involving the combination of tactile stimuli with visual ones.

As Young rightly emphasizes, such problems demonstrate our almost total ignorance of the nature of learning, and of the changes that are involved in the conditioning process. It is a measure of this ignorance that the process has tended to be discussed over the years in terms of those particular aspects of neural functioning which were fashionable subjects of research at the time—structural, chemical, or electrical, as the case might be. The current use of the terminology of electronic engineering should be viewed with this in mind. A comparison of neural organization with the organization of computers is immensely helpful in facilitating discussion through a formal and intelligible terminology, but it by no means follows that living organisms actually function in this way.

17
Chemical Coordination

17–1 NEUROHUMOURS

In our review of the general properties of the neurone we saw that it is a cell special-ized to carry out two distinct yet interrelated functions: the propagation of nerve impulses and the manufacture and discharge of secretions. We have so far been considering primarily the first of these, and it is now necessary to consider the second, which is no less important.

The secretory activity of the neurone plays more than one part in the physio-logical organization of animals. The first consequence of this activity to be demon-strated was the production of the substances known as neurohumours. These are necessary because neurones are separated by gaps from the neighbouring cells with which they are in functional relationships. Where the relationship is with another nerve cell, as it is in the reflex pathways that we have been discussing, there is a synapse separating the axon ending of one cell from the dendrite of the next. Where the gap is between a nerve cell and, for example, a muscle fibre, the gap is part of the muscle end-plate; here the axon comes close to the fibre without achieving complete protoplasmic continuity. The conduction of nerve impulses across these points of discontinuity depends upon the production of neurohumours, or, as they are often called, chemical transmitter substances. In general, these are formed in the cell body of the neurone, probably under the influence of the mitochondria and Golgi material. They are then passed down the axon and are stored at the axon terminal; from here they are released on the arrival of nerve impulses, exciting the next cell in the chain of action, neurone or effector cell as the case may be.

Neurohumoral function has been attributed to four substances: acetylcholine, noradrenaline, adrenaline, and 5-hydroxytryptamine. Their action, and the criteria for establishing their function, can best be illustrated by brief reference to acetyl-choline, which acts as a chemical transmitter at the nerve endings of the para-sympathetic nervous system of vertebrates. These endings, which are said to be cholinergic, are shown by electron microscopy to contain small bodies called synaptic vesicles, each with a mean diameter in the range 300Å to 400Å. If the nerve fibre is examined following stimulation some of these vesicles appear empty, as though their contents have been discharged. It is thus supposed that they contain units or 'quanta' of acetylcholine, which are discharged in proportion to the number of nerve impulses arriving at any particular ending.

To maintain a precise relationship between the impulses and their effect the chemical transmitter must be quickly destroyed, otherwise the response could be prolonged out of all proportion to the instruction transmitted through the nerve fibre. With acetylcholine this is ensured by the existence of cholinesterase, an enzyme which rapidly inactivates the transmitter substance. Another essential is that the responding cell shall be highly sensitive to minute quantities of the transmitter substance that excites it. From all of this it is apparent that three conditions must be met before any particular substance can be safely interpreted as a chemical trans- mitter substance. There must be evidence of its storage in the nerve fibres concerned, there must be a very high level of sensitivity to it in the cells that they excite, and there must be some means of rapid inactivation of the substance. It is important to keep these criteria in mind; the presence, and even the wide distribution of certain sub- stances in nervous tissues, cannot in itself be accepted as establishing that these substances are neurohumours.

Of the four substances mentioned, acetylcholine provides the most convincing evidence for neurohumoral action, as far as the invertebrates are concerned. This substance is known to be present in certain protozoans and in all of the main inverte- brate groups, with the exception of sponges, coelenterates, and urochordates. Whether it is physiologically active in this wide range of animals is, however, still very doubtful. The best evidence comes from studies of lamellibranchs. It is known that acetylcholine exerts an inhibitory effect on the heart of *Venus mercenaria*, and it is reasonable to suppose that this effect is a physiological one, and that it is controlled by enzyme action. The inhibition can also be evoked by stimulating the visceral ganglion, and this effect can be enhanced and prolonged by the addition of eserine, which inhibits the action of cholinesterase.

Unfortunately we cannot generalize very far from these observations. Acetyl- choline is present in considerable amounts in the nervous system of decapod crusta- ceans, and it is known that it exerts an excitatory action on the hearts of many crustaceans. Yet convincing evidence that it is a neurohumour is still lacking. The concentrations required to affect the heart are sometimes too high to meet the essential requirement of high sensitivity on the part of the reacting tissue; moreover, it has not yet been clearly established that acetylcholine mediates the transmission of excitation from nerves to skeletal muscle in these animals. The situation in other groups of invertebrates is, in general, no less obscure. The central nervous system of the cockroach, however, has a high concentration of acetylcholine and also a high level of cholinesterase activity, from which Treherne and Smith draw the conclusion that acetylcholine may well be a chemical transmitter in insects. This is a matter of toxicological importance, for certain insecticides are inhibitors of cholinesterase, their action resulting in the accumulation of excess acetylcholine in the animals. The im- portance of precisely understanding the physiological significance of acetylcholine, and, indeed, of other neurohumours, is thus self-evident. As Welsh points out, in- judicious use of insecticides of this type could possibly have a ruinous effect upon aquatic crustaceans, and thereby weaken the food resources of other and commercially important forms.

Noradrenaiine, a catechol amine, acts as a chemical transmitter in vertebrates at the post-ganglionic sympathetic nerve endings, which are in consequence termed adrenergic endings. Together with the closely related adrenaline it is also released from the chromaffin tissue (or medulla) of the mammalian adrenal gland (or its homologue in lower vertebrates) when this is stimulated through its sympathetic nerve supply. These two compounds function as hormones, that can be said, in very general terms, to enhance and prolong the effect of sympathetic stimulation. They are stored in large amounts in the cells of the chromaffin tissue, in the form of granules that react with potassium dichromate or iodate to give a brown oxidation product. This is the so-called chromaffin reaction, from which the medullary tissue of the adrenal gland takes its name. Information regarding the distribution of these two catechol amines in the invertebrates is unfortunately so fragmentary that it is impossible to judge of their possible physiological importance in these animals. The most that can be usefully said here is that chromaffin cells have long been known to be present in the ventral nerve cord of the leech, *Hirudo*. For this reason it has been suspected that adrenergic nerve fibres may exist in annelids, but even this is uncertain.

An indole alkylamine, 5-hydroxytryptamine, is widely distributed in a variety of tissues, including the nervous systems of vertebrates as well as of certain invertebrates. There are reasonable grounds for regarding it as a neurohumour, although the evidence is still very scattered and incomplete. The most convincing evidence is obtained from molluscs, for it exists in the nervous systems of these animals, and can influence their heart beat. It is also known to excite the heart of crustaceans, and to influence the proprioceptors of their legs. The evidence is less complete here than in the molluscs, however, for although a substance resembling 5-hydroxytryptamine is present in the nervous systems of decapods, it is not certain that it actually is that substance. These animals do possess amines that can excite their tissues, but the nature and the precise function of these compounds remains in doubt.

Evidently chemical transmission is an aspect of invertebrate neural organization that needs much further study before useful generalizations can be made about it. On the assumption that the mode of functioning of the neurone will be fundamentally uniform throughout the animal kingdom, we may suspect the occurrence of neurohumoral substances, but we can hardly go much further, except, perhaps, with acetylcholine. Fortunately there is another aspect of neural secretory activity in which the evidence has accumulated much more satisfactorily, and which provides a most striking demonstration of a unified mode of functioning throughout a very wide range of animals, both vertebrate and invertebrate.

17–2 HORMONES AND NEUROHORMONES

On purely etymological grounds it would be reasonable to regard the production of chemical transmitter substances by nerve cells as a process of neurosecretion, and to term the cells neurosecretory cells. It has, indeed, been suggested that all neurones should be so designated, but there is a more widely accepted convention, which we will follow here, that restricts the term neurosecretion to a different type of neural activity. This convention regards the 'ordinary' or 'typical' neurone (the *neurone banale* of French endocrinologists) as concerned with the propagation of nerve impulses and with the secretion of the chemical transmitter substances required for the transmission of the excitatory state from a neurone to another cell. As we have emphasized, this concept is based primarily upon vertebrate studies, but is thought likely to apply also to invertebrate nervous systems. It is now very well established that in addition to these 'ordinary' neurons there is a second type (Fig. 17–1) that differs from them in containing a secretory product that is readily stainable and that can be seen with the light microscope. It is referred to as a neurosecretion. This

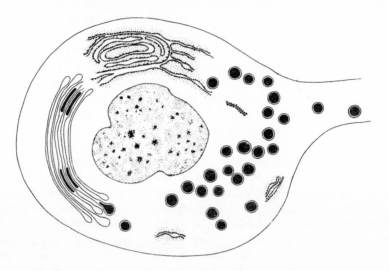

Fig. 17-1. Diagram based on electron micrographs of neurosecretory cells of the supra-oesophageal ganglion of *Lumbricus terrestris* illustrating formation of granules. The antecedents of the granules are presumably synthesized in the ergastoplasm (above the nucleus) from where they are transferred to the Golgi apparatus. Lying between the lamellae, the product becomes visible as an electron-dense substance which eventually fills Golgi vesicles (to the left of the nucleus). Next, the granules leave the Golgi lamellae which furnish the membranes of the neurosecretory granules (below the nucleus). They accumulate in the intercisternal space of the ergastoplasm which becomes disorganized. Eventually the granules are carried off along the axon of the cell (to the right of the nucleus). From Scharrer and Brown, 1962. *Gen. & compar. Endocr.*, **2**, 1–3.

material, like the neurohumours, arises in the cell body, passes down the axon, and is released from the nerve endings. The fundamental difference is that it is not restricted to local and transitory action. Instead it passes into the blood stream and circulates round the body, to produce specific physiological effects at points that may be remote from the region of its release. The cells producing this substance are customarily referred to as neurosecretory cells; their function is the secretion of neurohormones, which form part of the endocrine secretion of the body.

So important is this concept that we must examine some of its implications further before considering specific illustrations of it. First, it must be emphasized that the mere existence of stainable material within a neurone does not justify regarding it as a neurosecretory cell. Such material may consist of inert metabolic products, such as lipofuscin granules, that would certainly be unable to exert specific effects upon other tissues. The function of the product is, therefore, an essential criterion of its status as a true neurosecretion. To put the matter in a formal way, we can say that the term is applicable only when it can be shown that the products are acting in a manner characteristic of the particular group of secretory products that we call hormones.

We have so far considered coordination and integration as being the field of action of the nervous system, and as being mediated by the propagation of nerve impulses. Yet we have seen also that the body fluids, and more particularly the blood systems, provide communication systems by which the products of digestion and metabolism are transmitted. It is perhaps not surprising, then, that these fluids are also used for the transmission of chemical substances that act in conjunction with the nervous system to convey information and to promote integration. Sometimes these substances may themselves be the by-products of metabolism. A well-known example of this is the way in which carbon dioxide acts in vertebrates to regulate the respiratory centre; we have seen that it also acts in a similar way in certain insects. Many of these substances, however, are specialized secretory products, and it is these that are termed hormones. According to the classical definition, based initially upon studies of vertebrate physiology, hormones are substances that are formed in particular regions of the body, usually in specialized glands, and that are discharged into the blood stream. This process is called internal or endocrine secretion, and the glands are termed endocrine glands. After the discharge of these substances, they are transmitted in the blood stream to other parts of the body, where they produce specific regulatory effects. The term hormone is derived from the Greek *hormaein* (to impel or arouse to activity), and thus refers only to the regulatory effect. In practice, however, the concept of action at a distance, with the substance forming part of the communication system of the body, is an essential part of the full definition.

Endocrine glands were originally conceived as being formed of epithelial secretory tissue. The importance of the concept of neurosecretion, as defined above, is that it extends endocrine activity to the nervous system, thereby bringing into close association two modes of coordination, chemical and neural, that were earlier regarded as distinct. It is thus all the more important that the hormonal character of the products of supposed neurosecretory cells should be clearly established; yet this may present great difficulties. In vertebrate studies it has often been possible to achieve chemical characterization and even synthesis of hormones, and, in consequence, to define very precisely their physiological effects. The small size of many invertebrates is a serious obstacle to such success, and the evidence has often to be secured by indirect methods. These include the extirpation of supposed endocrine tissue, the injection of extracts of it, and histological and cytological study designed to establish changes in the appearance of the animal's cells that can be correlated with physiological changes in the body. It is here that the electron microscope has proved of the greatest value, particularly with neurosecretory cells. In these it has been shown that the material visible with the light microscope is composed of elementary granules having a diameter from about 1,000Å to 3,000Å. These form the ultrastructural basis of the visible neurosecretion; it is generally agreed that the stainable material seen with the light microscope is a carrier substance, formed by the aggregation of these granules, and providing the means by which the hormonal molecules are transported through the neurosecretory cell.

Neurosecretion, then, is a specialized activity of neurones that are carrying out a type of secretory process distinct from the neurohumoral secretion of the 'ordinary' neurone. Neurohumours themselves are distinct from hormones, because they are acting locally instead of at a distance. In this respect, it may be noted, the noradrenaline of vertebrates acts both as a neurohumour and as a hormone, but this is a very special and perhaps unique case. On this interpretation, neurosecretory cells can be thought of as being derived by specialization from 'ordinary' nerve cells, and this is probably the most widely held view. (There are those, however, who would regard them as being entirely distinct in their evolutionary origin, presumably from the unspecialized surface epithelia of very simple Metazoa.) It is not clear whether this specialization has resulted in the loss by the neurosecretory cell of the capacity of 'ordinary' neurones to propagate impulses. It is believed that neurosecretory axons are commonly accompanied by the axons of 'ordinary' neurones, and that impulses transmitted through these may be responsible for evoking the discharge of the neurosecretion from the axon endings of the neurosecretory cell. There is also some evidence, however, that the latter may itself be able to transmit impulses, and that perhaps these may evoke release of secretion from the same fibre that is conveying them. It may well be that both possibilities occur.

The release of the neurosecretory product, whatever the mechanisms that evoke it, is in itself an important and characteristic aspect of the functioning of the neurosecretory cell. Unlike the 'ordinary' neurones, these cells do not usually end in synaptic connection with neurones or effector cells, although it is now becoming apparent that there are exceptions to this generalization. Their axon endings are typically in close physical relationship with blood vessels, the result being the formation of compound structures called neurohaemal organs. These organs are the storage and release centres of the neurosecretory system. It is probable that the neurosecretory product is always stored there within the axon bulbs, for there is no convincing evidence for the existence of granular neurosecretory material within the blood vessels. Presumably the secretory product is released from the granules as hormonal molecules that diffuse through the membranes into the blood stream.

17–3   ENDOCRINE REGULATION IN CRUSTACEANS

Crustaceans and cephalopods share with many fish, amphibians, and reptiles a remarkable capacity for changing the pattern and intensity of their colouring. In considering this phenomenon we must first distinguish between morphological colour change, which depends upon alterations in the total amount of pigment, and physiological colour change, which depends upon the movement of pigment granules within specialized cells called chromatophores. We are not concerned here with morphological change, nor shall we deal with the physiological change in cephalopods, for in these particular animals the effector cells are unique in being controlled by extrinsic muscle fibres. The chromatophores of crustaceans and vertebrates are cells with branched processes; pigment granules are present in them, and these can either be concentrated in the centre of the cell, giving a minimum display of colour, or dispersed through the cell body and its processes, giving a maximum display. The pigments are of more than one colour; black, red, or yellow, for example. This creates possibilities of elaborate patterns, but at the same time requires correspondingly elaborate regulation. Usually any one chromatophore will contain only one type of pigment, but several cells with different pigments may often be united in crustaceans to form syncytial complexes called chromatosomes.

It is usually assumed that physiological colour change is of adaptive value to the animals concerned, and this is probably so, although the nature of the adaptation takes many forms. Colour change may, for example, be a response to the colour of the background, or to the intensity of illumination. There may be a diurnal rhythm of change, which is possibly sometimes of thermoregulatory advantage, as in the fiddler crab, *Uca*, in which black pigment becomes concentrated when the temperature rises.

Whatever may be the adaptive significance of colour change in crustaceans, there is a fundamental uniformity in the means by which it is controlled, for it is under the influence of neurohormones secreted by a complex neurosecretory system. The vertebrates differ in this respect. In cyclostomes, fish, amphibia, and reptiles a hormone (melanocyte-stimulating hormone, MSH) certainly plays a part, but it is not neurosecretory in origin; it arises in the epithelial secretory tissue of the pars intermedia of the pituitary gland. In teleost fish other hormones may also be involved; their origin, if they exist at all, is uncertain, but they are not neurosecretory products. Further, in teleosts and reptiles, and perhaps also in selachian fish, the nervous system directly innervates the chromatophores, so that these are under combined nervous and endocrine control. This is certainly not so in crustaceans, which have no innervation of their chromatophores. There are thus differences between crustaceans and vertebrates in their mechanisms of colour control. The differences, which reflect the independent origin of the phenomenon in the two groups, are discussed further below.

The key to understanding the crustacean mechanism was contained in a discovery made in the 1870s by Pouchet, who found that the colour responses of shrimps to background conditions were eliminated if their eye stalks were removed. The significance of this was not apparent at the time. The observation suggested that colour change in these animals was controlled by the nervous system after this had been activated by the visual receptors of the eye stalk, and not until 1928 was it shown that chromatophores of blinded shrimps would respond to injections of eye stalk extracts. This indicated that there might be endocrine tissue in the eye stalk, regulating colour change through its hormonal secretion. This interpretation has since been amply confirmed by a wide range of evidence.

Within the eye stalk (Fig. 17–2) is a brain centre, the medulla terminalis, distally to which lie three optic centres, the medulla interna, the medulla externa, and the lamina ganglionaris. Clusters of neurosecretory cells exist in this nervous tissue, the principal one being a group called the medulla terminalis X organ. There is also a sensory pore or sensory papilla X organ. This is so called because it is separate from the other groups of cells, and is typically associated with a sensory pore or papilla, which seems from its histological structure to be in part sensory and in part neurosecretory. Undoubtedly this neurosecretory system is very complex both in its structure and its function, and we know it is concerned in the regulation of much more than colour change. Irrespective of the functions of the various types of neurosecretory cells, however, they share a final common path in that their fibres end within the eye stalk in a neurohaemal organ called the sinus gland. The axon terminals within this organ contain electron-dense granules, 1,000Å to 3,000Å in size, of the general type that we have already mentioned; they are the product of the neurosecretory cells, trans-

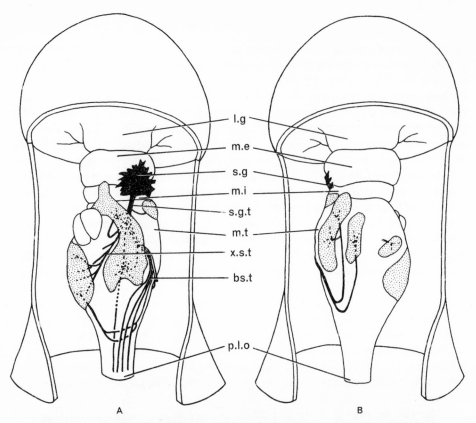

Fig. 17-2. The eye stalk neurosecretory system of the crayfish *Orconectes virilis*. A, dorsal view of the right eye stalk; B, ventral view. Stippled areas indicate regions in which neurosecretory cells occur. The principal neurosecretory fibre tracts to the sinus glands are shown. *bs.t*, brain-sinus gland tract; *l.g*, lamina ganglionaris, first optic ganglion of the eye stalk; *m.e*, medulla externa; *m.i*, medulla interna; *m.t*, medulla terminalis; *p.l.o*, optic lobe peduncle; *s.g*, sinus gland; *s.g.t*, sinus gland tract; *x.s.t*, tract from medulla terminalis X-organ to sinus gland. After Bliss, from Charniaux-Cotton and Kleinholz, 1964. *The Hormones*, vol. IV (Pincus et al., eds.). Academic Press, New York.

mitted to the gland along their fibres. The discharge of the secretion into the blood stream is probably brought about by nerve impulses initially evoked by stimulation of the appropriate receptors. This discharge is facilitated by the close association of the sinus gland with a blood sinus, an association from which it derives its name. The term 'gland', however, is a misnomer; it was given to the organ before the phenomenon of neurosecretion had been defined, and when the secretion visible within the organ was presumed to arise there.

The recognition, from 1951 onwards, of the importance of neurosecretion in the control of crustacean colour change led at first to emphasis being placed upon the role of the X organ and sinus gland complex. But we have already noted that crustaceans possess several types of chromatophore. Not only do these differ in the pigment that they contain, but there is also evidence that some at least of these types can exhibit independent responses. Out of these observations has grown what may be termed the multiple-hormone hypothesis of colour control. According to this the responses depend upon a number of hormones, acting to some extent independently of each other and capable of evoking individual responses from particular types of chromatophore. Associated with this has been the demonstration that neurosecretory cells exist in parts of the central nervous system other than the centres of the eye stalk. One region of particular importance is the tritocerebrum, and the tritocerebral commissure which is anatomically derived from it. Neurosecretory fibres, arising in the tritocerebrum, run to the commissure, which they leave in the post-commissure nerves. At one point on these nerves the surrounding membrane, the epineurium, is enlarged to form an epineural plate, or post-commissure organ. This structure, which contains many neurosecretory droplets, is thought to be a neurohaemal organ, similar in function to the sinus gland. The injection of extracts of this region evokes responses in particular types of chromatophore. It is believed that several hormones are concerned, and that these differ from the hormones released from the sinus gland.

Undoubtedly the phenomenon of colour change in crustaceans presents a well-established demonstration of the importance of neurosecretion in regulating adaptive responses. But what is particularly striking is the wide distribution of neurosecretory cells in the crustacean nervous system. They are by no means restricted to the sites already mentioned. Moreover, such diverse types exist that it would seem improbable that they should only regulate the behaviour of chromatophores. There is, in fact, ample evidence that crustacean neurosecretions regulate a wide range of physiological activities.

We have already mentioned the adaptive significance of the movements of the pigments of the compound eye. In the eye of *Palaemonetes vulgaris* (Fig. 17-3) these pigments comprise a distal pigment, situated in distal pigment cells; a proximal pigment, situated in the retinular cells; and a white reflecting pigment, situated in tapetal cells that lie between the proximal ends of the ommatidia. In bright light the distal and proximal pigments screen the sides of the rhabdome so that the ommatidium is stimulated mainly by light entering along its axis. This is the light-adapted condition (p. 286), giving maximum visual acuity. In darkness the pigments move into the dark-adapted condition; the rhabdome is unscreened so that the ommatidium is stimulated by light entering from a larger source, while the reflecting pigment is so situated that it scatters incident light and still further increases the stimulation of the rhabdome. Visual acuity is less in this condition, but maximum use is made of the available light rays.

These pigment movements are in part under hormonal control, as can be shown by injecting extracts of eye stalks into dark-adapted *Palaemonetes*. The result of this is that the distal and the reflecting pigments move into the light-adapted condition. Further and convincing evidence is that the distal pigment in *Palaemon* (*Leander*) will pass permanently into the dark-adapted condition if the sinus glands are extirpated, even though the eyes are left quite undamaged. Curiously enough, the reflecting pigment is unaffected by this exirpation. However, we may conclude that some of these pigment movements (certainly those of the distal pigment, and probably those of the reflecting pigment) are regulated by a neurohormone released from the sinus gland. The hormone is known to be secreted within the eye stalk, exactly like some of the chromactivating secretions, for active extracts can be obtained from various parts of the nervous tissue of the stalk, as well as from the sinus gland itself. There is, therefore, some considerable similarity in the mechanisms regulating these two categories of pigment movement. Nevertheless, there are aspects of retinal pigment migration that still remain unexplained. It is not clear how the position of the proximal pigment

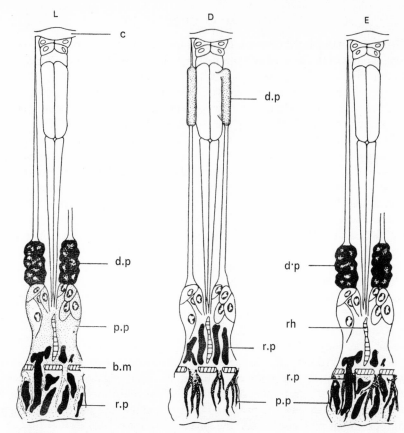

Fig. 17-3. Ommatidia from the eyes of *Palaemonetes vulgaris,* showing the general structure and the position of the retinal pigments under various conditions. L, from an eye in the light condition; D, from a dark-adapted eye; E, from the eye of an animal which, after adaptation to darkness, was injected with eye stalk extract prepared from light-adapted prawns. *c*, cornea; *d.p*, distal pigment; *p.p*, proximal pigment; *b.m*, basement membrane; *r.p*, reflecting pigment; *rh*, rhabdom. From Kleinholz, 1936. *Biol. Bull. mar. biol. Lab., Woods Hole,* **70**, 159–184.

is regulated, for example, nor is it certain that dark adaptation is effected hormonally, although there is some evidence suggesting that a separate dark-adapting hormone may exist.

The regulation of pigment movements is a very specialized and limited aspect of the physiology of crustaceans. Emphasis upon colour change in accounts of crustacean endocrinology is a result of the historical accident that, being a conspicuous feature of their behaviour, it has for a long time attracted attention, and has lent itself well to experimental analysis. However, considering the wide range of activities that are controlled by hormonal action in the vertebrates, and considering the complexity of crustacean organization, we might reasonably expect to find hormonal mechanisms fulfilling a variety of functions in crustaceans. Information here is still very limited, but at least there is good evidence that the eye stalks have an important influence on moulting.

The interval (or intermoult) between one moult and the next is characteristic for particular species, but varies a great deal from one species to another. It may, for example, be a long interval in species that have a seasonal moult, but a short one in those that moult frequently during the year. Evidence for hormonal control can be

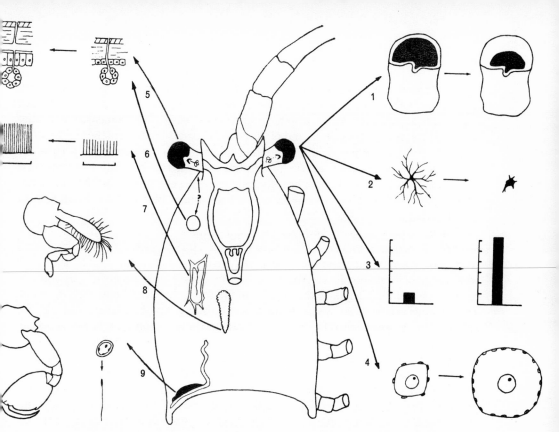

Fig. 17-4. Hormonal functions in crustaceans. On the right side *1–4* represent hormones from the eye stalk; on the left, *5–9* represent eye stalk and other endocrine effects. *1*, light-adapting distal retinal pigment hormone; *2*, chromatophorotropins; *3*, hyperglycaemic hormone; *4*, eye stalk ablation results in ovarian growth, through precocious vitellogenesis. *5*, moult-inhibiting hormone of the eye stalk, probably acting normally on the Y gland; *6*, the Y gland, from which is secreted a moult hormone; *7*, the pericardial organ, extracts of which accelerate the heart rate; *8*, ovarian hormones regulating female secondary sexual characters; *9*, androgenic gland of male, regulating spermatogenesis and secondary sex characters in male. From Charniaux-Cotton and Kleinholz, 1964. *op. cit.*

obtained by removing both eye stalks from decapods during the intermoult; the result of this is to accelerate the onset of the next moult. This acceleration is abolished if sinus glands are implanted into these stalkless animals, from which it is inferred that these glands contain a moult-inhibiting hormone. As with certain of the chrom-activating hormones, the moult-inhibiting hormone is secreted by the medulla terminalis X organ, and released by the sinus gland. The existence of this relationship has been well established by experiments in which sinus glands and appropriate parts of the nervous tissue of the eye stalks have been removed and/or implanted.

Other aspects of crustacean metabolism may well be under hormonal control, but the evidence is still very incomplete and can sometimes be interpreted in more than one way. For example, the uptake of water, which is an important aspect of moulting, may be hormonally regulated, as may be calcium metabolism, also closely involved in moulting. Nitrogen and carbohydrate metabolism are also thought to be influenced by hormones. All of these suggestions are plausible, and have some experimental evidence to support them, particularly as regards the involvement of the sinus gland system and the eye stalk. The difficulty in dealing with them critically is simply that too little is known at present of crustacean physiology, of the biochemical pathways in these animals, and of the interaction of the supposed hormones with each other. In particular, the existence of the Y organ, to be mentioned below, is a complicating factor. Those who have some knowledge of the immense complexity of vertebrate endocrine systems, and of the array of experimental evidence upon which their interpretation is based, will be content to wait for comparable advances in our knowledge of crustaceans before attempting to generalize about the endocrine systems of these animals. It must be sufficient now to accept the undoubted and fundamental importance of neurohormones as a component part of their machinery of coordination (Fig. 17–4).

In crustaceans, as in vertebrates, the hormones are not exclusively neurosecretory in origin. Some arise from epithelial secretory tissues, although these seem to play only a minor part in crustacean endocrine systems, as compared with their wide range of functions in vertebrate ones. One source of these hormones is the Y organ, a pair of glands lying either in the antennary or the second maxillary segment. These glands are believed to secrete the true moulting hormone of these animals; the action of the hormone secreted by the X organ and sinus complex, referred to above, is to inhibit the release of the moulting hormone from the Y organ. The evidence for this rests upon various extirpation and implantation experiments. Thus removal of the Y organ from *Carcinus* during the intermoult or during the preparatory stage of moulting will prevent the moult from taking place. The inhibition is a permanent one, provided that the animals receive no further treatment. If, however, Y organs are implanted into them the moulting cycle is resumed. Physiological relationships between the X organ and sinus gland complex and the Y organ are suggested by the results of experiments in which both the Y organ and the sinus gland were extirpated: this treatment prevents moulting, whereas removal of the sinus gland alone, with the Y organ remaining in position, produces the acceleration of moult to which we have already referred.

Another aspect of crustacean endocrinology in which neurosecretion is not involved is the hormonal regulation of sexual differentiation. The situation in females has not yet been very thoroughly explored, but there is evidence that in females of *Orchestia* a hormone secreted by the ovary controls a permanent secondary sexual character, the presence of oostegites, and a temporary one, the presence of ovigerous hairs on the oostegites. Removal of the ovaries leads to loss of the hairs, but these reappear in the castrated females if ovarian tissue is implanted into them. The production of sex hormones by the gonads is a familiar feature of vertebrate sexual organization, but the situation in the males of higher crustaceans is quite different from that in male vertebrates, where the male hormone is secreted by interstitial tissue in the testes. The male hormone of crustaceans is secreted by the androgenic glands (Fig. 17–5), which are entirely independent of the gonads, being attached to the hinder end of the vasa deferentia (except in isopods, where they lie more anteriorly, and may even be attached to the testes).

The hormone of the androgenic gland is responsible for the differentiation and maintenance of the testes and also of the secondary sexual characters. If the androgenic glands are removed from males, and the appendages also removed, the animal regenerates sexually undifferentiated limbs, while the testes may transform into ovaries. Conversely, implantation of androgenic glands into females results in the ovaries becoming transformed into testes, while the appendages become masculin-

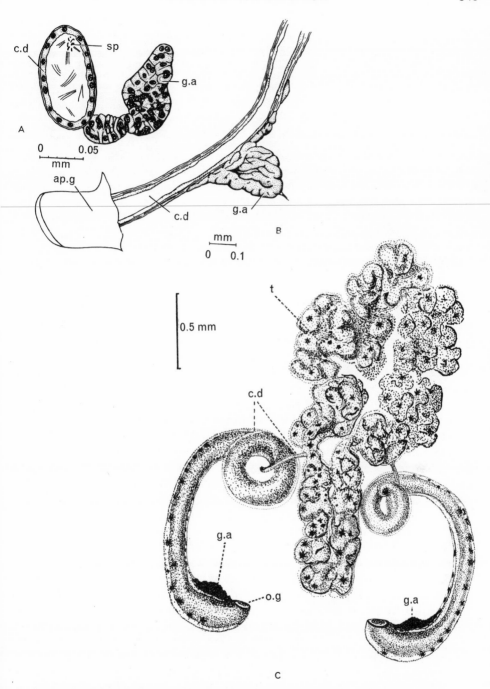

Fig. 17-5. Androgenic gland of *Orchestia gammarella*. A, transverse section; B, appearance of fresh gland. *ap.g*, genital apophysis; *g.a*, androgenic gland; *c.d*, genital duct; *sp*, spermatozoids. From Charniaux-Cotton, 1957. *Annls Sci. nat., Zool., 11 sér.*, **19**, 411–560. C, reproductive system and androgenic gland of a male *Palaemon serratus*. *cd*, genital duct; *g.a*, androgenic gland; *o.g*, genital opening; *t*, testis. Charniaux-Cotton and Huguet, unpublished.

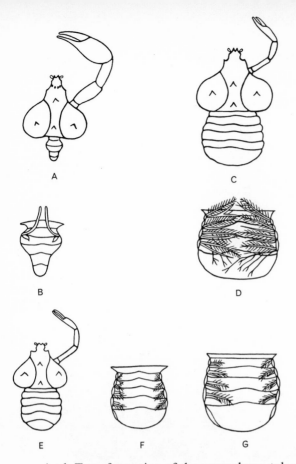

Fig. 17-6. The crab *Inachus*. A, normal male with short small abdomen and broad claw; B, male abdomen without pleopods from beneath; C, normal female with broad abdomen and small claw; D, female abdomen from beneath with hairy pleopods; E, sacculinized male with female characters (small claw and broad abdomen); F, abdomen of sacculinized male from beneath with pleopods; G, abdomen of sacculinized female. After Smith. From Hanstrøm, 1939. *Hormones in Invertebrates*. Clarendon Press, Oxford.

ized. Transformation of the appendages takes place even if the ovaries are removed from the females before the implantation of the androgenic glands, which shows that the male hormone acts directly on the limbs and not through the transforming gonad.

The sexual endocrinology of crustaceans is very remarkable, and could not have been predicted by arguing from analogy with the vertebrates. Indeed, it is precisely because of this that certain well-known examples of intersexuality in crustaceans proved impossible to interpret satisfactorily until this endocrinological mechanism had been unravelled. Particularly is this true of parasitic castration, a phenomenon in which males become feminized when they are parasitized by rhizocephalan cirripedes or by epicaridian isopods (Fig. 17–6). The widespread nature of the effect which in crabs, for example, involves changes in the shape of the abdomen and in the development and form of the appendages, is clearly suggestive of some endocrine disturbance. For a long time it was supposed that this disturbance was associated with the destructive action that the parasites were known to have on the gonads. By analogy with vertebrates, it seemed reasonable to assume that destruction of the testes resulted in a reduced output of male sex hormone, and a consequent reduction of male differentiation. There was always difficulty in accepting this view, however, for there was no close correlation between the degree of gonadal destruction and the degree of masculinization. The discovery in 1954 of the androgenic gland resolved this particular problem, for it was then apparent that parasitic castration resulted from the destruction of that gland by the parasites. There could be no better illustration of the danger of pressing too far an argument by analogy, when the groups concerned are as widely separated as are the crustaceans and the vertebrates.

17–4 ENDOCRINE REGULATION IN INSECTS

Studies of hormonal coordination in insects have largely centred around moulting and growth, which are regulated by neurosecretory mechanisms bearing remarkable resemblances to those of crustaceans. Here again we are concerned with neurosecretory cells in the central nervous system. An important assemblage of these is found in the median region, or pars intercerebralis, of the protocerebrum, where they commonly form four groups, two medial and two lateral. We may compare these cells with those of the ganglionic X organ of the crustacean eye stalk. Like the latter, they are connected with a neurohaemal organ, which in this instance is formed by the corpora cardiaca, a pair of bodies lying behind the brain and close to the aorta (Figs. 17–7 and 17–8). The corpora cardiaca are comparable, therefore, with the sinus gland, but they are probably more complex in function than the latter organ. They

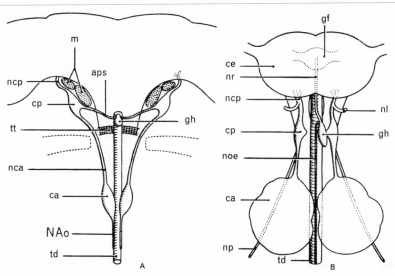

Fig. 17–7. (Above) Retro-cerebral complex in A, the psyllid *Homotoma ficus*, and B, the coccid *Pulvinaria mesembryanthemi*. *aps,* paracardiosympathetic anastomosis; *ca,* corpora allata; *ce,* brain; *cp,* corpora paracardiaca; *gf,* frontal ganglion; *gh,* hypocerebral ganglion; *nao,* aortic nerves; *nca, ncp,* nerves to corpora allata and paracardiaca; *noe,* oesophageal nerve; *np,* posterior nerve; *nr,* recurrent nerve; *td,* gut; *tt,* tentorium. From Grassé, 1951. *Traité de Zoologie,* vol. 10, fasc. 2. Masson, Paris.

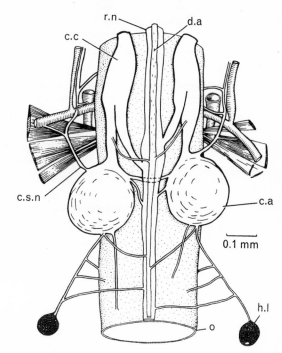

Fig. 17–8. (Right) The corpora cardiaca, corpora allata, and their nervous connections in the cockroach, *Periplaneta americana*. *c.a,* corpus allatum; *c.c,* corpus cardiacum; *c.s.n,* corpus allatum-suboesophageal ganglion nerve (enlarged); *d.a,* dorsal aorta; *h.l,* head lobes; *o,* oesophagus; *r.n,* recurrent nerve. From Harker, 1960. *Cold Spring Harb. Symp. quant. Biol.,* **25,** 279–287.

are composed in part of neurosecretory nerve endings, but in addition they contain cells, some of which are probably themselves neurosecretory. However, it is certain that neurosecretion formed in the pars intercerebralis passes down axons into the corpora cardiaca; there it is stored and eventually released, perhaps after further processing by the secretory activity of the cells of the corpora.

It is probable that different brain hormones with diverse effects are secreted in the neurosecretory cells of the pars intercerebralis. The most closely studied is the pro-thoracotropic effect, which is attributed to a prothoracotropic hormone. This is so called because it activates a pair of glands called the prothoracic glands (*trope*, turn, i.e. towards). The relationship is best understood by considering the sequence of events that is believed to determine moulting in the larva of hemimetabolous bug, *Rhodnius*, the suitability of which for experimental study has been brilliantly exploited by Wigglesworth.

The initial stimulus to moult in this animal is the stretching of the wall of the alimentary canal by the single large meal which the larva takes in each instar. As a result of this stimulation, nerve impulses are transmitted to the brain and promote the secretion of the prothoracotropic hormone and its release from the corpora cardiaca. This hormone then stimulates the prothoracic glands, changing the appearance of the nuclei and cytoplasm of their cells; these changes culminate in the release of another hormone, the prothoracic gland hormone, or ecdysone. This hormone actually initiates the complex of metabolic processes that constitute moulting. Ecdysone merits its independent name; it is at present unique among insect hormones in that it has been crystallized, and its chemical composition determined. It proves to be a steroid, with the empirical formula $C_{27}H_{44}O_6$, a finding of particular interest because steroid hormones play a major part in the endocrine systems of vertebrates. The gonadial sex hormones of vertebrates are steroids, and so also are the hormones of the adrenal cortex, which regulate ion and water exchanges and certain other aspects of metabolism. Moreover, the prothoracotropic hormone of insects may be a sterol. Here, then, are examples of the biochemical potentialities of the sterol ring structure being exploited independently in arthropods and vertebrates.

Rhodnius passes through five larval (nymphal) instars during its growth and development. The moult at the end of the fifth instar also involves metamorphosis into the adult stage, with the formation of wings and the complete reproductive equipment. This does not mean, however, that the larval moults involve no more than simple increase in size, with all morphological transformation confined to the metamorphic moult. On the contrary, the wing lobes of *Rhodnius* show some relative increase in size during the earlier larval instars, and the reproductive organs undergo some differentiation. Nevertheless, so much transformation takes place at metamorphosis that there is clearly some major difference in the factors that influence this moult as compared with those influencing the earlier non-metamorphic ones. This difference lies in the functioning of an epithelial (non-neurosecretory) endocrine gland, the corpus allatum. This gland, which develops from the ectoderm, lies close to the corpora cardiaca. It is innervated by the nerve supply of the corpora cardiaca, and it appears to receive neurosecretory products from them. Possibly, then, the corpus allatum can be stimulated by neurosecretory fibres from the pars intercerebralis.

The corpus allatum secretes a hormone, called the juvenile hormone, which is believed to arise initially within the cell nuclei and to be processed further in the cytoplasm of the gland cells. In simple terms this hormone can be thought of as inhibiting metamorphic change. While it is circulating, the moult evoked by ecdysone will be a larval moult. It is not, however, present during the last larval moult, and its absence makes possible the drastic morphological changes of metamorphosis. We have seen, however, that some advance towards the adult form can be detected at the earlier moults, and this in itself shows that we are stating the role of the juvenile hormone in over-simple terms. To obtain a closer approximation to the truth it is helpful to adopt an analysis that has been developed by Wigglesworth.

According to this the developing insect is thought of as having the capacity for existing in either larval or adult form. The particular form that it assumes depends upon whether at any given stage it is under the influence of the genes that determine larval structure, or of those that determine adult structure. On this view the function of the juvenile hormone is to maintain the activity of the genes that determine larval form. In the absence of this hormone at the end of larval life these genes can no longer be active, and those determining adult form can exert their effect. There would probably be general agreement on this aspect of the interpretation. What is less clear is what determines the small degree of differentiation that does actually occur at the larval moults. One view ascribes this to a continuing fall in the amount of juvenile hormone released, which consequently allows the expression of some degree of adult form. Another suggests that it is determined by the pattern of release of prothoracotropic hormone, variations in the amount of juvenile hormone having no influence upon the result. For our present purposes, however, we can disregard this particular problem, for it does not affect the validity of the fundamental principles of moulting and metamorphosis that we have briefly outlined.

These principles could not have been established without prolonged experimentation, involving the application of exceedingly elegant techniques to animals that fortunately have the capacity for surviving drastic surgical treatment. Examples of these are parabiosis experiments in which two decapitated *Rhodnius* are joined together by their cut surfaces. If an animal is decapitated one or two days after its meal it will not moult, but it will do so if decapitation is delayed until a critical period of several days has elapsed. This is because the brain hormone has to exert its action upon the prothoracic glands for several days before the glands can come into full secretory activity, and release adequate amounts of ecdysone. The presence of the latter in the blood can be demonstrated by uniting in parabiosis two decapitated larvae, one of which has been decapitated before the critical period and the other after that period. Both will moult, although the former would not have done so had it been left in isolation. The result is ascribable to the fact that the united animals have a common circulation and a common share of ecdysone derived from the larva that was decapitated after the critical period.

The influence of the juvenile hormone can be similarly demonstrated by parabiotic union of a first-stage larva, decapitated before the critical stage, with a moulting fifth-stage one (Fig. 17–9). The latter undergoes metamorphosis, as is to be expected, but so also does the first-stage larva, so that this becomes a small and precocious adult. This is because it is under the influence of the ecdysone of the moulting animal, and has no source of juvenile hormone to permit the expression of larval structures. Conversely, a fourth-stage larva, decapitated after the critical stage, can be united with a fifth-stage one that has been decapitated before the critical stage. The fifth-

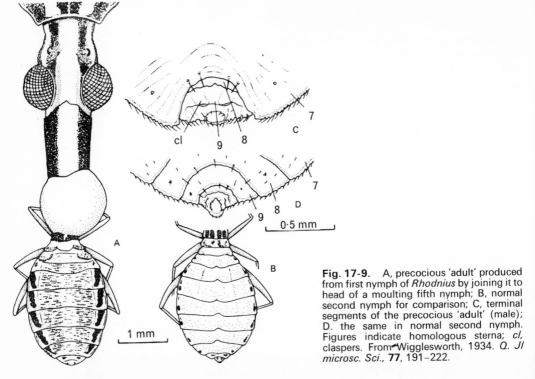

Fig. 17-9. A, precocious 'adult' produced from first nymph of *Rhodnius* by joining it to head of a moulting fifth nymph; B, normal second nymph for comparison; C, terminal segments of the precocious 'adult' (male); D, the same in normal second nymph. Figures indicate homologous sterna; *cl,* claspers. From Wigglesworth, 1934. *Q. Jl microsc. Sci.,* **77**, 191–222.

stage larva should metamorphose when it moults, but does not, in fact, do so, because both juvenile hormone and ecdysone from the fourth-stage larva are circulating in its body.

These and other experiments have provided an extensive and wholly convincing demonstration of the hormonal regulation of growth, moulting, and metamorphosis in *Rhodnius*, but this is only one species in a class that includes more species than all the remainder of the animal kingdom (Fig. 1–2, p. 5). The number of other species that have been critically investigated from this point of view is small indeed; it is said to amount to less than 0.01 % of the total number of insect species. Yet we can be confident that the fundamental principles are of wide applicability in the group, for they depend upon the secretory activity of organs that are common features of insect organization. At the same time, much variation is likely in the precise way in which these principles operate in any particular species.

One aspect of this variation concerns the relationship between the prothoraco-tropic hormone and the prothoracic gland. In *Rhodnius* this is determined by the output of the hormone that is evoked by the stimulus of ingestion. But the locust, for example, feeds continuously during its larval instars, yet the prothoracic (thoracic) gland only produces ecdysone at the time appropriate for evoking moulting. One explanation of this, put forward by Clarke and Langley, is that in this animal the brain secrets its hormone continuously, and that this is continuously released from the corpora cardiaca. The stimulus for production and release is thought to be distension of the pharyngeal wall by feeding, or, at ecdysis, by the swallowing of air. During the larval instar the released neurosecretion is used in normal growth and metabolism, and its concentration does not rise sufficiently high to stimulate the prothoracic glands. Near the time of ecdysis the animal ceases to feed, so that these metabolic processes decline. In consequence there is a diminished demand for the brain hormone, which now reaches a concentration high enough to stimulate the prothoracic glands, thus initiating the moult. This hypothesis awaits further experimental exploration, but in the meantime it provides a good example of the flexible way in which the principles of insect endocrinology can be applied.

Another illustration is given by the giant American silkworm moth, *Hyalophora* (*Platysamia*) *cecropia*. This passes during its holometabolous life history through a diapause, a specialized condition of arrested development. This is a well-known phenomenon among insects, usually interpretable as an adaptation favouring survival during adverse environmental conditions. Diapause in this species sets in at the beginning of the pupal instar and persists during the winter. It results from the brain being inactive; not only does the brain secrete no prothoracotropic hormone, but if microelectrodes are inserted into it it is found to be electrically silent, showing a lack of spontaneous activity. The end of diapause, and the initiation of adult development, require the renewal of activity in the brain, and the resumption of neurosecretion. This will only occur if the pupa is chilled for some 10 weeks at a temperature of 3 °C to 5 °C. Without this chilling (if, for example, the pupa is maintained at normal room temperature) diapause cannot end. This analysis, like that of moulting and metamorphosis in *Rhodnius*, is well substantiated by experimental analysis. For example, pupae from which the brains have been removed cannot metamorphose. But a long chain of such pupae, united in parabiosis, can be induced to metamorphose if a chilled (activated) brain is implanted into the most anterior member of the chain. This is because their prothoracic glands can now be activated by the prothoracotropic hormone that diffuses through the chain from the activated implant. The action of these glands is well seen in the responses of isolated abdomens. These lack the glands, and could never normally metamorphose, although they can survive for long periods if they are attached by their cut surfaces to cover-slips. If prothoracic glands from activated pupae are implanted into such abdomens they are able to metamorphose under the influence of the ecdysone released from the implants; indeed, they may even survive to lay eggs!

We have referred here only to the control of moulting and metamorphosis in insects because it is these aspects of insect endocrinology that are at present best understood. But as with crustaceans, the concentration of research upon one particular aspect is a consequence of historical accident and of experimental convenience. There is no reason to doubt that hormones must regulate a wide range of physiological activity in insects; indeed, this surely follows from the evident fact that moulting and metamorphosis themselves involve a diversity of morphogenetic and metabolic changes. It is reasonable to suppose that the pars intercerebralis secretes a number of hormones with differing effects. As just one illustration of this possibility, it has been suggested that the differentiation of supplementary reproductives in termites (p. 468) may be regulated by such a hormone. There is evidence, too, that the synthesis of proteolytic enzymes in the alimentary tract of *Calliphora* is influenced by a neurosecretion from the brain.

Similar considerations apply to the corpora allata, which are certainly not always restricted in their action to the encouragement of the expression of larval characters. In some insects they resume activity in the adult; this is so, for example, in *Rhodnius*, where they are essential for the production of ripe eggs. In other insects they influence the activity of the accessory reproductive glands, but whether these and other effects attributed to the corpora allata are mediated by one hormone or by several is still unknown. Clearly, however, this gland has some influence upon sexual activity. Yet there is here an important difference between crustaceans and insects. In the former group, as in vertebrates, sex hormones have a far-reaching effect upon sexual differentiation, but in insects this is not so. In these animals the sex chromosome mechanism determines the sexual pattern of all parts of the body, and cannot be overridden by hormones from implanted tissues as it can in crustaceans and vertebrates. That the two latter groups should resemble each other closely in this principle of organization, and that crustaceans should differ so markedly from insects, is one of several aspects of arthropodan endocrinology that raises interesting questions of homology and analogy in the organization of endocrine systems. These, however, will be more easily discussed when we have considered the situation in other invertebrate groups.

17–5 ENDOCRINE REGULATION IN ANNELIDS

The annelids are the only other group of invertebrates in which the study of hormonal regulation now allows some tentative generalization. The evidence partly hinges on the existence of neurosecretory cells in their cerebral ganglia. Four types of such cells were at one time thought to exist in *Nereis*, three types in the earthworm, and three in the leech *Theromyzon rude*. The evidence for this rested initially on the presence within these cells of stainable material visible with the light microscope; but this evidence, as we have explained, can be deceptive, and we cannot regard such material as neurosecretory unless there is independent confirmation. It now seems probable that not all of these cells are neurosecretory. Some of the inclusions in the leech were subsequently shown to be giant mitochondria, and it has been said that only one of the four types in *Nereis* is unequivocally neurosecretory. Nevertheless, if we confine ourselves to evidence that has been critically examined and experimentally confirmed we can still safely say that neurosecretory regulation is well established in annelids.

The production of neurosecretory hormones is associated in crustaceans and insects with the presence of neurohaemal organs that act as centres for storage and release. These have therefore been looked for in worms, although it does not follow that they must necessarily be present. Even in insects there is evidence that the brain secretion may sometimes pass directly into the blood stream, and there is no reason why this should not occur in annelids. On the other hand, there is at the base of the cerebral ganglion of *Nephtys* a vascular structure, referred to as the cerebrovascular complex (Fig. 17–10), to which run neurosecretory fibres. Neurosecretory material can be detected in the vessels of this complex, so that it may be a neurohaemal organ, although apparently a very simple one. It is clear, however, that we must rely primarily upon experimental studies to establish the occurrence of neurohormonal regulation.

Part of this evidence comes from studies of growth and regeneration in nereids. These worms grow rapidly when they are young, with proliferation of new segments. Later the growth rate declines, until increase in length comes to depend mainly on the enlargement of already existing segments. This reduction in growth rate is accompanied by a parallel decline in regenerative capacity, which suggests that both processes may be controlled by the same regulating factor. Theoretically this factor might be no more than the ageing of the tissues, but in fact this is not the correct explanation. On the contrary, there is good evidence that the occurrence of both growth and regeneration depends upon a neurohormone produced by the cerebral ganglion, and that their decline results from a reduction in this secretion.

Part of the conventional definition of a neurosecretion is that it should be visible in preparations that have been suitably fixed and stained, but this condition is unfortunately not satisfied in immature and normally growing worms. Although the hormone is believed to be present in small quantities, there is no visible sign of a neurosecretory product in the ganglion cells. Secretory material does, however,

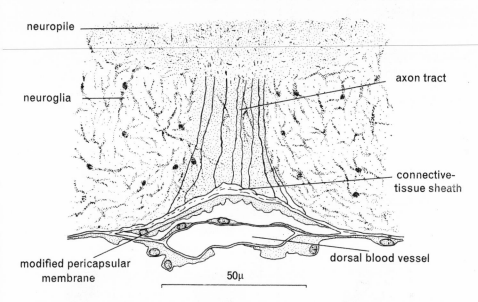

neuropile

axon tract

neuroglia

connective-tissue sheath

modified pericapsular membrane

50μ

dorsal blood vessel

Fig. 17-10. The cerebro-vascular complex of *Nephtys californiensis*. The area illustrated is the lower part of the brain. From Clark, 1959. *Zool. Jb. Abt. Allg. Zool. Physiol.,* **68**, 395–424.

become visible when the cells are stimulated to increased activity, as happens when some of the posterior segments of an immature worm are amputated. The operation is followed by regeneration of the lost segments, and, prior to this, by the appearance of visible secretion in some of the ganglion cells. This secretion increases to a maximum on the third day after the amputation. Histological observations show that it is then gradually released into the blood stream, so that by the fifth day the ganglion cells again contain very little of it.

These visible changes are believed to reflect storage and release of the hormone, for experimental analysis shows a close correlation between the histological evidence and regeneration (Fig. 17-11). For one thing, if the worm is decerebrated (i.e. cerebral ganglion removed) at the time of the amputation, regeneration will not take place. The decerebrate worm can, however, be made to regenerate by implanting into it a cerebral ganglion taken from another worm three days after that worm has itself had some segments amputated. But the time interval is critical; if the implant is taken from the donor worm five days after the amputation, it will not evoke regeneration in the recipient. The inference is that after three days it contains sufficient hormone to evoke

358

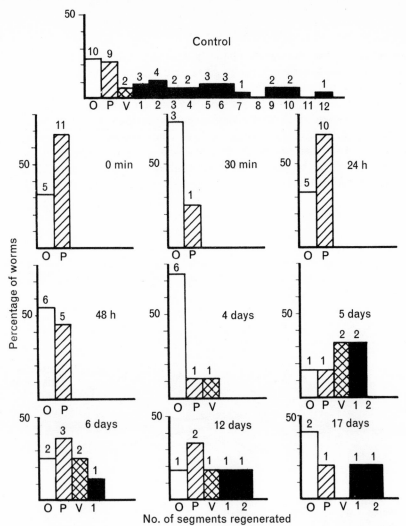

Fig. 17-11. Effect upon regeneration of extirpation of the supraoesophageal ganglion at various times after amputation of the posterior segments of *Nereis diversicolor*. *Controls:* ganglion intact throughout. *O,* no regeneration; *P,* pygidium regenerated; *V,* vascularized pygidium regenerated; the succeeding numbers indicate the number of segments proliferated. The number of worms represented by each block is indicated above the block. From Clark and Evans, 1961. *J. Embryol. exp. Morph.,* **9,** 97–105.

regeneration, but has discharged it after five days. This is in precise accord with the histological evidence. Further, even a decerebrate worm can regenerate provided that its ganglion is not removed until five days after the amputation. This suggests that by this time adequate amounts of the hormone will have been released from the ganglion into the circulation, so that the continued presence of the ganglion is not necessary.

Growth and regeneration are not the only aspects of nereid development that are subject to hormonal regulation. This extends also to sexual maturation, as is particularly well illustrated by the phenomenon of epitoky. In some species of nereids sexual maturity is accompanied by various somatic changes (Fig. 17-12) which include enlargement of the parapodia, development of a different type of chaeta, and histolytic changes in the body musculature (Figs. 17-13, 17-14). The changes are confined to a particular part of the body, termed the epitoke; as a result of them, the worm undergoes a transformation or metamorphosis into the heteronereid phase, which is adapted for sexual swarming.

If the cerebral ganglion is removed from individuals when they are at an appropriate stage of development, but are not yet sexually mature, they will undergo precocious metamorphosis into the heteronereid. The conclusion is that the cerebral ganglion of sexually immature worms secretes a hormone that inhibits epitoky. This is confirmed by the demonstration that the premature epitoky of decerebrate nereids can be prevented by the implantation of cerebral ganglia from immature worms. On the other hand, implanted ganglia are unable to prevent such precocious epitoky if they have been taken from nereids that are themselves in the heteronereid phase. It follows from all this evidence that the attainment of full sexual maturity in nereids requires the withdrawal of an inhibitory cerebral hormone. The hormone is neither sex-specific nor species-specific, and is present even in nereids that do not have a heteronereid phase in their reproductive cycle. Ganglia from immature individuals of *Nereis diversicolor*, a non-epitokous form, can thus inhibit precocious epitoky in decerebrate individuals of epitokous species.

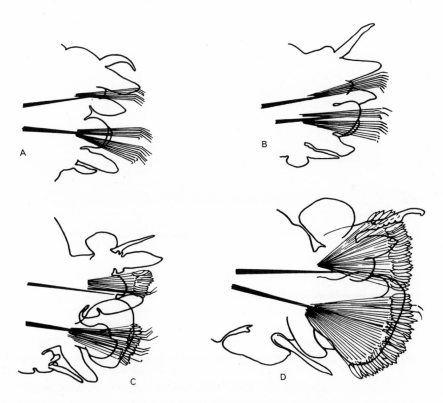

Fig. 17-12. Modification of the parapodia of *Perinereis cultrifera* at metamorphosis (Bauchot-Boutin and Bobin, 1954). A, parapodium of the immature worm. B, enlargement of the parapodial lamellae and ventral cirrus at an early stage in metamorphosis; some nereid chaetae have been shed, but the heteronereid chaetae have not yet erupted at the surface. C, appearance of the heteronereid chaetae and continued shedding of nereid chaetae; further enlargement of parapodial lamellae. D, parapodium of male heteronereid, a few nereid chaetae remain to be shed. From Clark, 1961. *Biol. Rev.*, **36**, 199–236. Used by courtesy of the Cambridge Philosophical Society.

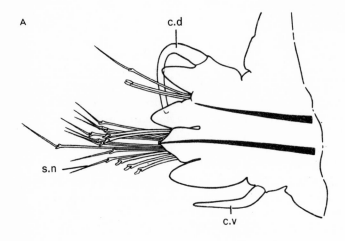

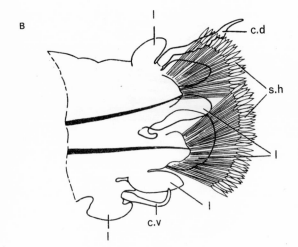

Fig. 17-13. A, atokous parapodium of *Nereis pelagica*, from the middle region of the body. B, parapodium of an experimentally produced heteronereis of *N. pelagica*, from the same region. *c.d*, dorsal cirrus; *c.v*, ventral cirrus; *l*, parapodial lamellae; *s.h*, heteronereid chaetae; *s.n*, nereid chaetae. From Durchon, 1960. *Bull. Soc. zool. Fr.*, **85**, 275–301.

The likely explanation of this is that the hormone inhibits sexual maturation as a whole, regardless of whether or not this involves the heteronereid transformation, and a study of oocyte maturation in *N. diversicolor* has provided evidence that this is so. The oocytes at first grow slowly, after their proliferation into the coelom; later they pass into a phase of rapid enlargement, and then complete their maturation in a final phase of slow growth. Removal of the cerebral ganglion during the initial phase of slow growth evokes a precocious assumption of the rapid growth phase (Fig. 17-15). Presumably, therefore, the slow growth is an expression of the action of the inhibitory cerebral hormone. The normal onset of the rapid growth phase can be ascribed to a decline in secretory activity in the cerebral ganglion, and a consequent fall in the concentration of circulating hormone. This, of course, is precisely comparable with the suggested mode of regulation of epitoky, which thus appears as one special aspect of sexual maturation. It has been observed that a continued, although small, amount of secretion is necessary for the completion of normal maturation of

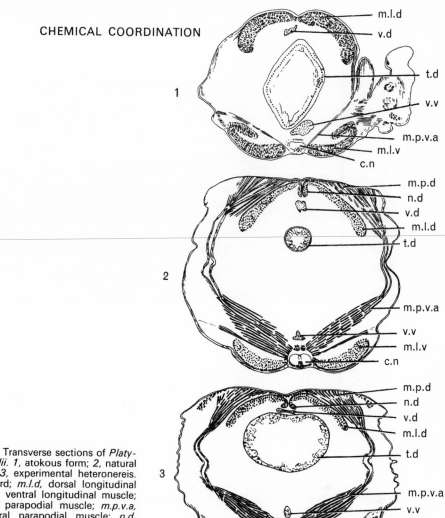

Fig. 17-14. Transverse sections of *Platy-nereis dumerilii*. *1*, atokous form; *2*, natural heteronereis; *3*, experimental heteronereis. *c.n*, nerve cord; *m.l.d*, dorsal longitudinal muscle; *m.l.v*, ventral longitudinal muscle; *m.p.d*, dorsal parapodial muscle; *m.p.v.a*, anterior ventral parapodial muscle; *n.d*, dorsal neoformation; *t.d*, intestine; *v.d*, dorsal vessel; *v.v*, ventral vessel. From Durchon, 1960. *op. cit.*

the eggs; after complete decerebration they do not, despite their accelerated growth, reach full size, while their yolk deposition is abnormal.

Successful fertilization obviously demands that individuals of both sexes must come together when they are sexually mature. This may be effected very simply, as it is in the non-epitokous *Nereis diversicolor* (see Fig. 18-6), where the male enters the burrow of the female. Alternatively, this species may spawn on the surface of the substratum. The epitoky of other nereids (and also of many syllids) is a more sophisticated device for securing the same end, for it enables the two sexes to swim freely to the surface, the males often arriving first and emitting their sperm when joined by the females.

A further condition for success is that adequately large numbers of individuals shall become sexually mature at the same time. Adaptations to secure this, in conjunction with swarming, have been evolved independently in eunicid polychaetes as well as in the nereids and syllids. The Eunicidae include the palolo worms, well

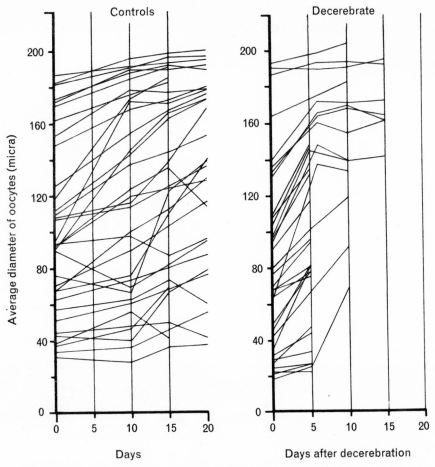

Fig. 17-15. Growth of oocytes in intact and decerebrate worms. *Left*, intact animals; *right*, animals decerebrated immediately after the initial determination of the average oocyte diameter. From Clark and Ruston, 1963. *Gen. & compar. Endocr.*, **3**, 529–541.

known as examples of the correlation of spawning with phases of the lunar cycle. *Eunice viridis*, of Fijian and Samoan waters, and *E. fucata*, of the Dry Tortugas, are illustrations of this. The hind parts of these animals contain the ripe germ cells, and these parts are released, while the anterior ends remain behind and presumably regenerate the lost segments. In principle, however, the process is an epitokous one, similar to that found in swarming nereids and syllids (see also p. 381). The three groups thus show very clearly how natural selection, acting on common potentialities, can lead to the parallel yet independent evolution of similar adaptive mechanisms. In this particular instance, however, an important unifying influence is the capacity of these worms for the neurosecretory regulation of sexual maturation.

It is now known that this regulation operates in conjunction with an environmental factor that brings about a more or less simultaneous reduction of neurosecretory activity in the cerebral ganglia of separate individuals of a population. Not surprisingly, in view of the lunar periodicity that is a feature of the process, this factor proves to be the cyclical fluctuation in the intensity of moonlight. Evidence that the worms can respond to the weak light of the moon comes from studies of *Eunice fucata*. Immature individuals are photonegative to light of greater intensity than

0.01 foot-candles, which means that they are confined to burrows at the full moon. The epitokal regions of mature worms, by contrast, are photopositive at intensities above 0.005 foot-candles, which means that they are stimulated to swarm at the quarter moon.

The way in which the lunar cycle becomes related to the maturation process of polychaetes is best understood in *Platynereis dumerilii*, a worm that has a spawning maximum around the phase of the new moon. Hauenschild has shown that sexual maturation can be artificially induced in this species by exposing individuals to varying photoperiods corresponding to those of the lunar cycle, always provided that the worms have reached a certain critical stage of development. They will swarm over a number of days, but with a peak at 17 days after the start of the reduction of the photoperiod. It is thus supposed that this reduction initiates the decline in production of the cerebral hormone which is a necessary condition for the attainment of sexual maturity. Confirmatory evidence for this has been obtained by ultraviolet irradiation of the cerebral ganglion. The radiation damage results in a reduced production of the hormone, and this, too, is followed by precocious sexual maturation with a peak at around 17 days after the onset of the treatment. The agreement in the timespan in the two types of experiment provides good grounds for believing that in natural conditions the decline in lunar photoperiod can evoke sexual maturation and so bring about the phenomenon of lunar periodicity of spawning.

There is also evidence that cycles of lunar photoperiodicity can be imprinted on worms, so that the effect of the cycles is manifested after an interval of time. For example, individuals of *P. dumerilii* can be induced to spawn synchronously by exposure in the laboratory to appropriate cycles of photoperiod. This response may be shown even if the treatment is terminated before sexual maturity, and constant illumination substituted for the changing photoperiod. In such circumstances, synchronous spawning may occur after exposure to continuous illumination for up to three months following the end of the treatment.

Thus growth, regeneration, and sexual reproduction are all under neurohormonal regulation in polychaetes. The same region of the cerebral ganglion is thought to be concerned in each case, but it is uncertain whether more than one hormone is involved. It may be that there is a growth and regeneration hormone, distinct from the inhibitory hormone, but even so there must be some relationship between them, for there is a parallel decline in their rates of output. No doubt this degree of coordination is adaptively advantageous, for it prevents competition between the metabolic demands of growth and those of sexual reproduction. The situation is analogous to the alternation of budding and sexual reproduction that is found, for example, in many ascidians (p. 452). However, our present information is still too fragmentary to justify much generalization about polychaete endocrinology, and we certainly cannot assume that hormonal mechanisms will be uniform throughout the group. The scope for variation is illustrated by the syllid worms. Their reproductive maturation is hormonally regulated, but the secretion is believed to originate in the proventriculus (Fig. 17-16), the cerebral ganglion not being involved. *Arenicola marina* is another illustration of this variability. Both the ripening and the spawning of the eggs of this lugworm are controlled by a hormone that is probably secreted by the cerebral ganglion. But in contrast to the situation in *Nereis*, this hormone is an excitatory one, present when breeding is imminent, and absent at other times.

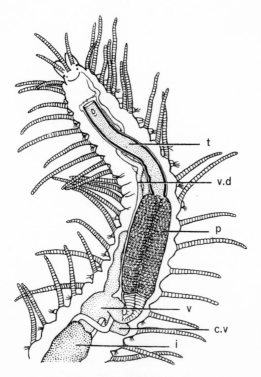

Fig. 17-16.   Pharyngeal region of *Syllis amica.*
c.v, ventricular caecum; *i,* intestine; *p,* proventriculus; *t,* proboscis; *v,* ventriculus; *v.d,* dorsal
vessel. From Durchon, 1960. *op. cit.*

   Looking more widely at the annelids, however, there do appear to be common
principles operating in polychaetes and oligochaetes. Earthworms (*Lumbricus,
Allolobophora*) can regenerate missing posterior segments, and, as in nereids, this
regeneration is prevented by removal of the cerebral ganglia. But it seems that the
presence of the suboesophageal ganglion is also essential, although this may be a
consequence of the vascular arrangement referred to below.
   As regards reproduction, there is an obvious difference between the organization
of the two groups in that oligochaetes are hermaphrodite and possess, in the ventral
glands and clitellum, important secondary sex characters. It has long been known
from castration experiments that the development of these characters is independent
of the gonads, and there is now evidence, from studies of *Eisenia foetida*, that this
development is regulated by a neurosecretory product of the brain. Removal of this
organ, together with the circumoesophageal connectives and the suboesophageal
ganglion, results in a reduction in size, a disappearance of the secondary sex characters, and cessation of egg laying, together with interference with the maturation of
both ova and sperm. Within 4 to 7 weeks the normal reproductive condition is, however, restored, correlated with a regeneration of the nervous system and a restoration
of neurosecretory cells. Probably the cells concerned are situated, like those of
polychaetes, in the cerebral ganglia. Their product is discharged into blood vessels
that run along the circumpharyngeal connectives to the suboesophageal ganglion;
it is because of the interference with these vessels that removal of those regions also
inhibits reproduction.

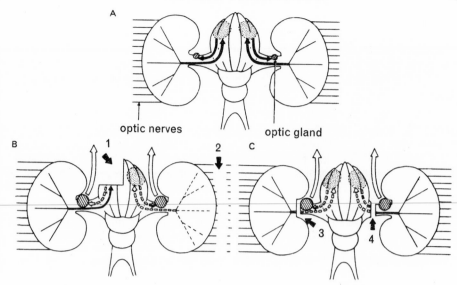

optic nerves   optic gland

Fig. 17-17. The mechanism of hormonal control of gonad maturation in *Octopus*. A, situation in an immature, unoperated *Octopus*, where secretion by the optic glands is held in check by an inhibitory nerve supply. B, two operations that cause the optic glands to secrete a product causing the gonad to enlarge, being (*1*) removal of the source of the inhibitory nerve supply, and (*2*) optic nerve section. C, further operations having the same effect upon the gonads, thus eliminating the possibility that there is also an excitatory innervation, being (*3*) optic lobe removal and (*4*) optic tract section. From Wells and Wells, 1959. *J. exp. Biol.*, **36**, 1–33.

17–6 EVOLUTION OF ENDOCRINE SYSTEMS

Evidence of hormonal regulation in other groups than those so far mentioned is very fragmentary. Supposed neurosecretory cells have been described in a wide range of invertebrates, but the evidence for their hormonal function is often incomplete. In any case it is not to be supposed that invertebrate hormonal mechanisms must always be exclusively or predominantly neurosecretory ones. This is well illustrated in *Octopus*, in which the maturation of the gonads is under the control of the optic glands, situated on the optic stalks (Fig. 17-17). The onset of sexual maturity is marked by the enlargement of these glands and the discharge from them of a gonado-tropic secretion, which evokes enlargement and maturation of the ovaries or testes. The activity of the optic glands is repressed in the immature animal by inhibitory nerve fibres, the source of this inhibition being in the subpedunculate lobes of the supra-oesophageal region of the brain. This can be shown by appropriate lesion experiments (Fig. 17–17). For example, removal of the source of the inhibition leads to enlargement of the optic gland on that side; so also does optic nerve section, optic lobe removal, and optic tract section. Here, then, control of the maturation of the gonads is operating through the optic receptors and neural pathways, with no participation of neurosecretory mechanisms.

Nevertheless, the secretion of neurohormones is well established in annelids, crustaceans, and insects; so much so that epithelial endocrine tissues are still unknown in annelids, and are of subsidiary importance in the other two groups. It seems very likely that the early evolution of endocrine systems largely depended upon the secretory capacity of the nerve cell, and this development may even have antedated the appearance of epithelial endocrine glands. It must be admitted, however, that if this is so it is surprising that there is so little evidence for the existence of neurosecretory phenomena in flatworms. That some diffusion of regulatory substances may occur in these animals is suggested by the report that if the anterior third of an individual of the sexual strain of a planarian, *Dugesia tigrina*, is grafted onto the posterior two thirds of an individual of a non-sexual strain, it will induce the appearance of testes and copulatory organs in the latter. It has been said, too, that regeneration of ocelli in *Polycelis nigra* can be induced by extracts of the cerebral ganglion; it is not clear, however, that this effect is a specific one, for homogenates of chick embryos can also do this. While, then, supposed neurosecretory cells are present in the brain of these animals, their true nature and function remain to be defined.

On the other hand, neurosecretory phenomena are clearly a feature of the great annelid–arthropod assemblage, not only in the groups already mentioned, but probably in others also, for there are plausible accounts of neurosecretory pathways in myriapods and arachnids. It is of great interest to find that in this respect the annelids and arthropods resemble the vertebrates. A feature of the latter animals is the existence of neurosecretory cells in the hypothalamus, discharging their products along nerve fibres into the pars nervosa of the pituitary gland, which serves as the neurohaemal organ of the system. Epithelial endocrine glands seem to be much more important in vertebrates than they do in the invertebrates, yet the functions of the hypothalamic neurosecretory system undoubtedly include the regulatory control of many of those epithelial glands.

Much has naturally been made of the remarkable anatomical similarity shown by the X organ and sinus gland complex, the pars intercerebralis and corpora cardiaca complex, and the hypothalamus and pars nervosa complex. Yet this similarity is to be expected. What is common to all of these systems is the neurosecretory cell itself. Given this, the anatomical relationships necessarily follow, for they become essential for efficient organization of secretion, storage, and release. We are dealing, therefore, with convergent evolution, resulting from the existence in unrelated groups of a common principle of secretion. It is impossible to say in our present state of knowledge whether this principle has itself been developed independently in the several groups, but there is no good reason why it should not have been. We have seen that there are two views of the origin of neurosecretory cells. One is that they were elaborated from neurones, as a development of their inherent secretory capacity shown in their production of chemical transmitter substances. The other is that they evolved, independently of neurones, from primitive ectoderm cells, in this case developing further, like the neurones themselves, the fundamental secretory capacity of the ectoderm. The first view is perhaps the more plausible. But whichever is correct, the sequence of events might well have occurred independently in more than one evolutionary line, the common starting point being no more than a capacity for secretion in primitive epithelia.

There is, of course, a high proportion of speculation in this argument, and further clarification must await further research. Putting this speculation on one side, however, it is still evident that the neurosecretory systems of vertebrates, on the one hand, and those of arthropods, on the other, must have resulted from convergent evolution. How far this also applies within the arthropods themselves is more difficult to judge, but it will be recalled that convergence must have played an important part in the evolution of these animals. The X organ and sinus gland, and the pars intercerebralis and corpora cardiaca complexes are sufficiently dissimilar in their anatomical relationships to suggest that they, too, could be a product of convergent evolution. More than this we cannot say.

As regards the epithelial glands, attention has often been drawn to the similarity, both morphological and functional, of the prothoracic gland of insects and the Y organ of crustaceans, and this has led to enquiries into the possible identity of their hormones. Extracts of *Crangon* and of *Astacus* have, in fact, yielded material capable of inducing puparium formation in the blowfly larva. This is a standard test for ecdysone, so that there is a suspicion that the crustacean extracts may actually contain that substance. It must be emphasized, however, that there is no chemical evidence for this identity. Moreover, these interchanges operate in only one direction; ecdysone obtained from insects has not been shown to produce moulting in crustaceans. It will be appreciated that the mode of control exerted by the Y organ differs from that exerted by the prothoracic gland; the former inhibits moulting, while the latter evokes it. This, however, would not in itself be an argument against the identity of their products.

One of the unresolved problems of endocrinology, vertebrate as well as invertebrate, is the mode of action of hormones, although there is a growing belief that at least some of them may act directly on the nucleus. In particular, there is evidence that ecdysone may influence the growth and development of insects by activating specific regions of the chromosomes; in this way it could direct the metabolism of the cells so as to favour specific biosynthetic pathways. It is certain, however, that the response produced by a particular hormone depends not only upon the hormone, but also upon the specialization of the tissues with which it reacts. The same hormone, in other words, can produce very different effects in different species, simply as a result of divergent specialization of the tissues which it is stimulating. The complexity of the problems of the evolution of endocrine systems should be sufficiently obvious from these brief considerations. Discussion of these problems can point the way to further investigations; it cannot yet answer our questions.

17–7 SOME WIDER IMPLICATIONS OF CHEMICAL COORDINATION

Chemical communication systems not only provide for regulation within the body of an individual animal. They also coordinate the activities of individuals of the same species, while they further play important parts in maintaining and regulating relationships between more than one species. Such uses may well have provided the earliest forms of chemical communication, for they are arguably an inevitable result of the release of metabolic products from the animal body. These must to some extent affect neighbouring individuals, and, if the relationship proved beneficial, it is to be expected that it would be improved by the agency of natural selection; the products would be further elaborated, and sensitivity to them would be enhanced.

Examples of this are to be seen in the regulation of spawning. The interaction of lunar periodicity and the neurosecretory activity of the cerebral ganglion of certain polychaetes is one means of securing this, but it does not exclude the possibility that chemical signals may be exchanged between the swarming animals. An example of such signalling in polychaetes is seen in *Nereis succinea*; a secretion from the mature eggs and the gravid females induces the males to spawn, the presence of sperm then inducing the females to spawn. An example from another group of animals is the spawning of female oysters, which is evoked by some substance present in the sperm and testes of the males. In this instance a chain reaction develops, for spawning of the females then induces spawning of other males, which in their turn stimulate other females. Substances like this, released by one sex and stimulating the other sex to reproductive activity, have been called gamones.

Our knowledge of this type of chemical communication system is often fragmentary and incomplete, but certain highly sophisticated examples have been studied in some detail. Among these are the sex attractants of insects, substances that may well be widespread in this group. The readiness with which a single female moth can attract males over very large distances is an indication of the extraordinary sensitivity of these communicating systems; a sensitivity that has been amply confirmed in certain instances by the isolation of the compound concerned. This isolation makes possible the use of biological assays, which may involve observing the behaviour of a male insect, or recording the activity of its antennal nerve, when its receptors are stimulated.

One of these compounds has been called bombykol. This substance, the sex attractant of *Bombyx mori*, has been chemically identified as a result of extracting no less than 500,000 scent glands from virgin females; it is known to be a 16-carbon doubly unsaturated alcohol, hexadeca-10,12-dien-1-ol. As so often with biologically active molecules, the sensitivity of reaction to the substance depends closely upon its molecular configuration. The native substance, which has been shown to be the 10-*trans*-12-*cis* isomer, is active on males in concentrations as low as 10^{-3} μg/ml, yet 1 μg/ml is needed to elicit a response with the *trans, trans* isomer. Butenandt, who has been responsible for much of this remarkable analysis, has calculated that a male *Bombyx* can be stimulated by the arrival at its antenna of a single molecule of bombykol, or at most a very few. This sensitivity is certainly not unique. The female cockroach, *Periplaneta americana*, secretes a sex attractant that has been identified as 2,2-dimethyl-3-isopropylidene cyclopropyl proprionate; quantities of less than 10^{-14} μg can evoke a response from the male.

Substances acting as specialized agents in external chemical transmission extend the classical principles of endocrinology, which were elaborated in relation to internal communication. The novelty in the type of communication that we are now considering is primarily the external transmission; the adaptation of chemical substances to the stimulation of specific receptors is no different in principle from the adaptation of hormones to the stimulation of specific internal tissues. Indeed, this situation shows very clearly that endocrine systems, in the classical sense of the term, are part of a much wider system of chemical relationships; a system that is concerned in a diversity of ways with the regulation of living processes. Because of this, substances such as sex attractants, transmitted externally and exerting specific effects at a distance, have been called ectohormones. An alternative term is pheromone, derived, by mutilation, from the Greek roots *pherein* (to bear) and *hormaein* (to excite).

We shall see in due course that chemical transmission is very important in coordinating the life of social insects. One example that has been particularly well studied is the queen substance of bees (p. 459), a substance that, by virtue of its specific constitution and the high sensitivity that members of the colony show towards it, merits also the designation of ectohormone. The principle of chemical regulation is also operative in ants and termites, although its basis is less well understood. The term sociohormone is sometimes used for chemical substances that function in social communities in this way, but a separate term is hardly necessary, if we accept that they are part of the general pattern of chemical communication that we have outlined. Also included within this concept are the substances secreted by social insects to serve as markers enabling other members of the colony to follow their trails. It is not difficult to visualize such substances evolving from metabolic products, and we can assume that there is unlikely to be a sharp boundary between the latter and highly sophisticated secretions like queen substance, with their more specialized effects.

Finally, and in further illustration of the wide range of action of chemical communication, there are the substances that promote and regulate relationships between individuals of different species. It has been suggested by Lucas that the excretion of metabolities may provide pervasive and subtle means of regulating the interspecific relationships within plant and animal communities. This is particularly likely in aquatic communities, where water allows the ready exchange of materials to regulate behaviour and reproduction, and hence the population structure of the communities. This principle is certainly important in maintaining such specialized interspecific relationships as symbiosis and parasitism, where chemical communication is one of the devices by which partners are brought into association. This, too, we shall refer to later. No doubt this must often result from one species having 'captured' and turned to its own end some metabolic product of the partner species. One very remarkable example of this is provided by certain flagellate protozoans that are symbiotic in the intestine of the wood roach *Cryptocercus*. The gametogenesis of these protozoans is believed to be a direct response to the ecdysone secreted by their host, which means that there is here an adaptation to what is itself a highly specialized hormonal secretion. It has been suggested that the response of the symbiotes may be to chemical changes set up in the intestine by the hormone, rather than directly to the hormone itself; even so this would still remain a striking demonstration of the possibility of the reproduction of one species being chemically regulated by another.

18

Patterns of Reproduction

18–1 PROTOZOAN LIFE CYCLES

The replication that is a fundamental property of living organisms is expressed in two forms in the life cycles of animals: asexual reproduction and sexual reproduction. Of these, the asexual type is in a sense the simpler; it involves no more than the equal partitioning of the genetic material between two daughter organisms, with a correlated division of the associated soma, and it normally depends upon mitotic division of the chromosomes. The essential feature of sexual reproduction is the formation of gametes, which fuse in pairs during syngamy, the fusion products being zygotes. A reduction of chromosome number is needed at some stage of the life cycle to compensate for the doubling that occurs at syngamy. This reduction is provided for by meiosis, which can be interpreted as a specialized derivative of mitosis.

In the Metazoa meiosis takes place during the maturation of the gametes. It does not necessarily occur at the corresponding stage of the life cycle of the Protozoa, but in some of these animals it certainly does so. It is then known as gametic meiosis, which is found, for example, in foraminiferans, *Monocystis*, and *Plasmodium* (malaria parasite). Alternatively, meiosis may occur during one of the early divisions of the zygote; examples of this, which is known as zygotic meiosis, are seen in coccidians and in many gregarines. The species concerned are necessarily haploid during their adult, or trophic, stage. Here, as we have already noted in another context (p. 21), there are differences between the nuclear processes of Protozoa and Metazoa. They are not, however, fundamental, and there is no doubt of the essential similarity of the sexual processes of the two groups.

This similarity is not surprising, for the sexual processes of animals as a whole are fundamentally similar to those of plants. It seems likely, therefore, that sexual reproduction appeared at a very early stage of evolution, and that animals and plants inherited their characteristic features from a remote common ancestry. There is good reason why this should be so. The sexual method of reproduction confers an important advantage in ensuring, through meiosis and syngamy, the recombination of genes and the variation that follows from it. Without it, the only source of genetic variability would lie in mutation, and the amount of this would be insufficient to provide a basis for the establishment of new and more effective patterns of organization through the action of natural selection.

Such peculiarities as we find in the sexual processes of Protozoa are in part an inevitable consequence of the small size of these organisms. Because of this, syngamy may take place between fully developed organisms, without their prior division; they are then known as hologametes. Exceptionally, the syngamy may involve nuclei alone, these forming and fusing within a single undivided organism in the process called autogamy (p. 376). Gametes more akin to those of Metazoa may be formed by division of whole organisms, in which case they are known as merogametes. These may be similar in general appearance (isogametes) or markedly dissimilar (aniso-gametes), but even when gametes look similar there may be some physiological differentiation between them. This differentiation becomes apparent when they are unable to unite indiscriminately. They may then be divisible into two groups such that members of one group will fuse only with members of the other group; these two groups may then be thought of as representing two 'sexes'. It is, in fact, likely that the origin of sexual differentiation lay in the establishment of divergent physiological properties between two categories of gametes. These properties, which could well have increased the efficiency of syngamy, may later have been expressed in morphologically visible terms, leading to the division of labour between two types of gamete that is so familiar in the Metazoa. This in its turn would have led to the correlated differentiation of the adults into two sexes, divergently specialized for the production of the two types of gamete.

Although sexual reproduction may thus be thought of as a fundamental property of the Protozoa, these animals make extensive use of the asexual method, and many of them probably reproduce exclusively in this way. This is doubtless because asexual fission provides for a rapid increase in number, and for the efficient exploitation of localized sources of food. An illustration of this is seen in the rapid build-up of a parasitic infection that often follows when an infective stage has gained entry into a host. For the reasons given above, however, we must regard the absence of sexual reproduction in certain protozoan life cycles as a secondary specialization, analogous to the biochemical regression that we have noted elsewhere. This absence is particularly characteristic of the Mastigophora. In this group asexual reproduction (typically by longitudinal binary fission) is universal, but there has been a widespread loss of sexual reproduction. Where the latter does persist it is sometimes found in the more specialized forms. Thus the only euglenid that is believed to reproduce sexually is the specialized Scytomonas (Copromonas), and this mode of reproduction is also found in the highly specialized hypermastigine flagellates that live symbiotically in the alimentary tract of the wood-eating cockroach, Cryptocercus. We have seen that in these symbionts the life cycle is correlated with the moulting cycle of the host. One other example is Noctiluca (Fig. 18-1), the aberrant dinoflagellate which is the only member of its group known to reproduce sexually; uniflagellate isogametes are formed, the parent dying after they have been released.

Finally, sexual development remains well established in the Phytomonadina (Volvocina), which include many familiar holophytic forms. In Chlamydomonas repeated division gives rise to small merogametes which are either isogametes or anisogametes; they fuse in pairs to form zygotes which pass into resting stages within a thick wall. Particularly notable in this group are the colonial forms (p. 443). Sexual reproduction is universal in these colonies, and ranges from isogamous hologamy to an extreme of anisogamy that resembles the differentiation of ova and sperm in Metazoa. *Gonium* illustrates the simplest situation, the members of the colony becoming free and acting as isogametes. *Eudorina, Pleodorina*, and *Volvox* illustrate the other extreme, with a marked division of labour in which some individuals enlarge without division to form macrogametes (or ova) while others produce biflagellate microgametes (or sperm) by repeated division. The group has long been used to illustrate

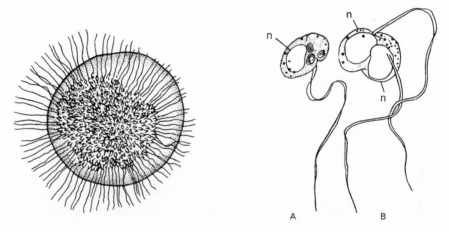

Fig. 18-1. *Left, Noctiluca:* gametogenesis. × 75. The relative size of the 'swarmers' at the oral pole is exaggerated. *Right*, living 'swarmers'. A, single gamete; B, syngamy. *n*, nucleus. From Mackinnon and Hawes, 1961. *An Introduction to the Study of Protozoa.* Clarendon Press, Oxford.

the principle that we have mentioned above, of the evolution of sex by the progressive modification of gametes, although this does not mean, of course, that the particular genera concerned represent a continuous evolutionary series.

The Mastigophora are not alone among Protozoa in showing extensive loss of sexual reproduction. This condition is found also in the Sarcodina, where it is particularly characteristic of the Order Amoebina. Thus the life history of *Amoeba proteus* consists of a sequence of growth and binary fission. In constant conditions this follows a very regular pattern, with a division at perhaps every 24 hours at a temperature of 23 °C. This species has been said to form protective cysts, but it is far from certain that it actually does so; it may be that the capacity for encystment, like the capacity for sexual reproduction, has been lost in *Amoeba proteus*, and that growth and fission are the only events of its life history.

This is not necessarily true of all the free-living Amoebina, and it certainly does not apply to the entozoic *Entamoebidae*. Most of these produce cysts that are of high adaptive value in that they serve for the transmission from host to host that is essential for such forms. An example is *Entamoeba histolytica*, found in the intestine of man and other primates, and also in the rat; it is frequently harmless, but sometimes it invades the gut wall and sets up the symptoms of amoebic dysentery. This organism is transmitted in the form of spherical cysts, containing four nuclei, and entering another host as a result of ingestion. Within the intestine a quadrinucleate amoeba emerges and divides to form eventually eight uninucleate organisms. *Entamoeba gingivalis* is an exception to this type of cycle, in that, like *Amoeba proteus*, it has lost the capacity for encystment. This is presumably correlated with its habitat, which is the human mouth, and particularly the gums; this mode of life readily allows transmission by personal contact between hosts.

The loss of sexual reproduction in the Amoebina is by no means characteristic of all the Sarcodina. It is retained in the Foraminifera and the Heliozoa, the foraminiferan *Elphidium* (*Polystomella*) being an example of a sarcodinan in which there is a regular alternation of asexual and sexual generations. The small zygote gives rise to the asexual stage (agamont), often referred to as the microspheric stage because the first chamber of the spirally coiled shell is a small one. Its nuclear division begins early, so that the microspheric form is multinucleate. Eventually it divides asexually to form a number of amoebulae, each of which secretes a shell of which the first chamber is large; the resulting organism (gamont) is often called the megalospheric stage for this reason. In due course it divides to form a number of biflagellate gametes; the fusion of these completes the life cycle.

It will be apparent that protozoan life cycles provide a basis for close adaptation to changes in the environment. Growth is a reflection of the nutrient value of the surrounding medium, and encystment clearly provides a means of withstanding adverse conditions, although the factors evoking it are often not understood. This relationship between modes of reproduction and environmental conditions is particularly well shown in the complex life cycles of parasitic Protozoa. As we have suggested above, an asexual phase, following invasion of a new host, makes it possible to exploit, through multiple fission, the nutrient qualities of the environment, and to establish a firm hold upon the host. Not all parasites, however, take advantage of this possibility, and in some life cycles greater emphasis is placed upon the other essential requirement: the ensuring of transmission.

In *Entamoeba* the procedure is a simple one, and is dependent only upon encystment and a small degree of asexual reproduction. In many other forms, however, and notably in the Sporozoa, an alternation of sexual and asexual generations is found, resembling in principle that of the free-living *Elphidium*. This alternation operates according to more than one pattern. In *Monocystis* the adult trophozoites become gamonts, which encyst in pairs and give rise to numerous gametes. Those produced by one individual fuse with those from the other to form zygotes, each of which develops a spore coat that provides protection during transmission. Within this coat the zygote divides to form 8 sporozoites. As in many other gregarines, this is the only asexual stage. The sporozoites grow into adult trophozoites which pass into the gamont stage without dividing; such gregarine infections thus tend to be light ones.

Coccidians, which have probably evolved from gregarines (p. 501), differ from the latter in being typically intracellular, and in undergoing extensive asexual multiplication before the adult becomes a gamont. This multiplication is termed schizogony, the adult at this stage being called a schizont. In Haemosporidia, such as *Plasmodium* (the malaria parasite), this alternation of asexual and sexual phases has become part of the adaptation to transmission through an invertebrate (arthropod) vector from one vertebrate host to another. Sexual individuals (gametocytes) are formed in the vertebrate host, but the production of gametes, together with fertilization, is now specifically evoked by the change of environment resulting from passage into the vector. This change can be artificially simulated by drawing off some blood from the infected host. In this type of cycle the zygotes are unprotected and motile, because the products of their fission are transmitted directly into the vertebrate host from the invertebrate one, and do not, therefore, have to resist adverse conditions in the external environment.

Schizogony is thus a valuable feature of parasitic life cycles, but its absence in many gregarines is not necessarily to be regarded as primitive. Certain gregarines that live in marine invertebrates do, in fact, show schizogony in what is now thought to be a primitive form. An example is *Selenidium mesnili*, from the intestine of the tubicolous polychaete *Myxicola infundibulum*. This gregarine reproduces by schizogony during an intracellular phase, the eventual association of the gamonts taking place in the gut lumen. Apparently most gregarines have secondarily lost this schizogonic stage. Certain specialized forms that live in insects, however, seem to have re-acquired it.

The protozoan cycles so far mentioned, based upon various combinations of asexual reproduction, sexual reproduction, and the formation of protective cysts, conform to principles that seem to be common to the Mastigophora, Sarcodina, and Sporozoa. The members of the remaining major group, the Ciliata, stand somewhat apart from these, as they do in so many aspects of their highly specialized organization. Sexual processes are a well-known characteristic of the class, but they are of a highly distinctive nature, and are at first sight not easily compared with those of the other Protozoa, nor, indeed, with those of Metazoa. They have been most closely studied in *Paramecium*, to which we shall here mainly refer.

Asexual reproduction is the only means of multiplication possessed by ciliates. It takes the form of a highly characteristic binary fission, differing from that of flagellates in that the division is transverse, separating an anterior half from a posterior one. Since the macronucleus divides by amitosis, and the micronucleus by mitosis, each half starts at once with a full nuclear equipment. In other respects the two daughter forms are at first different from each other, the feeding structures, for example, passing to one of them so that the other has to develop new ones; these, it is said, are formed at least in part by budding from the old structures. The process of fission, which may last for about 30 minutes, takes place regularly under healthy culture conditions, perhaps as often as three times in 24 hours. So far, then, the life cycle is straightforward; growth and fission alone are involved, for cysts are believed not to be formed in this genus. This does not, however, constitute the whole of the life cycle, which is greatly complicated by the occurrence of sexual processes that seem to be essential if the stock is to remain viable. These processes are of three kinds, called conjugation, autogamy, and cytogamy; they have been intensively studied in recent years, particularly by Sonneborn, in whose hands they have provided material for far reaching genetic investigations.

Conjugation in *Paramecium aurelia* (Fig. 18–2) will take place when cultures are subjected to certain defined conditions, including some degree of starvation, and maintenance at certain levels of temperature and illumination. It involves the association of the animals in pairs, but this association is not a random one; it can take place only within limits which themselves indicate the high level of speciali-

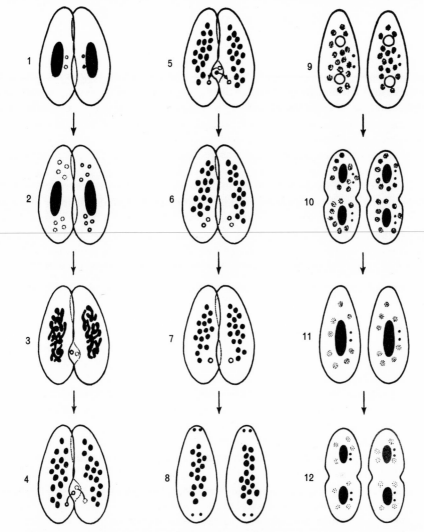

Fig. 18-2. Nuclear changes at conjugation in *Paramecium aurelia*. *1*, two parental animals, each with one macronucleus and two diploid micronuclei. *2*, formation of 8 haploid nuclei from the micronuclei in each conjugant. *3*, 7 nuclei in each conjugant disappear; the remaining haploid nuclei pass into the paroral cones; macronucleus breaks up. *4*, the nuclei in the paroral cones divide mitotically, forming 'male' and 'female' gamete nuclei. The 'female' gamete nuclei pass back into the interior of the parental animals. *5–7*, fusion of 'male' and 'female' gamete nuclei from opposite mates. *8*, each fusion nucleus divides twice, mitotically. *9*, two products of each fusion nucleus differentiate into macronuclear rudiments (white circles); the other two into new micronuclei. *10–12*, return to normal state of one macronucleus and two micronuclei per animal; fragments of old macronucleus gradually lost. From Beales, 1954. *The Genetics of Paramecium aurelia*. Cambridge University Press, London.

zation involved. Within the species there is much physiological variation, the basis of which, according to Sonneborn, can be interpreted as being the existence of separate varieties and mating types. Each variety (nine of these have been identified in *P. aurelia*) includes two mating types, and conjugation can only take place between individuals belonging to the same variety but to opposite types. If the two different types of the same variety are mixed under suitable conditions, the animals first clump together in large groups, but within an hour they begin to separate and then conjugate in pairs, first by attachment at their anterior ends, and later in the region of their oral surfaces.

There follows a series of nuclear changes, which involve the fragmentation of the macronuclei and the division of each of the micronuclei (two of which are present in each individual of this species) into four. Seven of these daughter nuclei disappear, while the eighth, lying now in a protuberance of the oral surface called the paroral cone, divides again. It is believed that meiosis occurs during the first two micro-nuclear divisions; thus the nucleus in the paroral cone is already haploid, and its division is mitotic. The haploid phase, however, is only a brief one. One of the two nuclei in the paroral cone in each individual passes back into the general cytoplasm; this nucleus now remains stationary, and is regarded as the female nucleus. The other is regarded as the male nucleus, for it crosses over into the other conjugant and fuses there with the female one. The process is reciprocal, the two partners exchanging their male nuclei. The conjugants now separate as ex-conjugants and undergo fission so that each gives rise to four daughters; during this the old macronuclei finally disappear. Meanwhile the fusion nuclei divide and their products diverge in size so that each daughter comes to contain the normal complement of two micronuclei and one macronucleus. All the surviving nuclei are thus derived from the original fusion nucleus of the ex-conjugant parent.

The significance of conjugation, which has been much debated, cannot be evaluated without considering autogamy and cytogamy. Autogamy includes a nuclear reorganization. This is similar in principle to that resulting from conjugation, but differs in that it is not accompanied by conjugation, so that only one individual is involved. Cultures of *P. aurelia* undergo autogamy when they have been well fed for a time and then starved. Nuclear changes take place identical to those occurring in a conjugant, down to the movement of a nucleus into the paroral cone and its division. Then, however, these two daughter nuclei fuse to form the fusion nucleus; from this a new nuclear equipment is formed, the old macronucleus having broken down. Cytogamy, less easy to demonstrate and perhaps less frequent in its occurrence, involves a pairing of animals as in conjugation. It differs from the latter process, how-ever, in that no exchange of nuclei takes place; instead, the fusion nucleus is formed from two nuclei within the same animal, essentially as in autogamy.

The sexual nature of these processes is clear, since it involves the fusion of two haploid nuclei that can be compared with male and female gametes. Whether the individuals are sexually differentiated, however, is less easy to assess. The varieties into which they are divisible are possibly comparable with physiological species; not only are they unable to effect cross-conjugation, but they differ also in certain characters, such as the duration of conjugation and the conditions in which it will be initiated. The existence of mating types within each variety cannot, however, be regarded as a sexual differentiation into male and female groups, for each type pro-vides both male and female nuclei. It thus seems more acceptable to regard the indivi-duals as hermaphrodites that are capable both of self-fertilization and cross-fertilization. This means that the differentiation of mating types must be regarded as one of the many specialized characteristics of the ciliates.

Quite apart from this difficulty of relating the sexual processes of ciliates to those of other animals, there remains the even greater problem of the significance of the processes for the ciliates themselves. Two contrasting views have been much discussed.

One is that if cultures are prevented from conjugating they gradually decrease in vitality, this being shown in a decline in their rate of binary fission. Eventually such cultures are thought to die out, a result that has been compared with the senescence of the body (soma) of a metazoan. A contrasting view is that vitality does not decrease if the culture conditions are maintained with sufficient care. According to this interpretation, cultures can divide and survive indefinitely, even without conjugation. This view, however, was developed before the occurrence of autogamy had been established. It now seems likely that autogamy is taking place when cultures survive in the absence of conjugation.

Probably, therefore, we can accept that conjugation or autogamy do provide some rejuvenating effect, but it remains uncertain what that effect may be. If conjugation were the only process involved we could ascribe its benefits to the gene recombination that must result from the syngamy of the haploid male and female nuclei. In autogamy, however, this recombination takes place only once, at the first act of autogamy. Thereafter the nuclei of any given individual must necessarily be homozygotic; no further recombination can therefore take place, except for an occasional mutation. Similar considerations apply to the suggestion that benefits may result from an exchange of cytoplasm. Probably this exchange does sometimes occur during conjugation, but it clearly plays no part in autogamy.

One possible explanation of the rejuvenation is that the old macronucleus becomes in some way degenerate or ineffective, and that the nuclear reorganization provides for its replacement. Here it is of great interest that individuals emerging from either conjugation or autogamy may sometimes replace their macronuclei from one of the small fragments of the old macronucleus instead of from one of the micronuclear products. Studies of such animals have revealed that the macronucleus determines the phenotype of *Paramecium*; this follows from the fact that individuals in which a macronucleus of one genotype is combined with micronuclei of another genotype will show the phenotype of the macronucleus. Further, since a fully functional macronucleus can regenerate from a macronuclear fragment representing no more than one-fortieth of the complete nucleus, it follows that the complete macronucleus must contain 40 or more sets of genes. This suggests that during the normal repeated binary fission of *Paramecium* the macronuclei may eventually accumulate sets of genes that are unbalanced because of inequalities in the amitotic divisions of these nuclei (p. 23). A situation could thus arise in which replacement of the effete macronucleus by a new and properly balanced one might be the only way of ensuring adequate maintenance of the phenotype. This, however, is supposition. Sonneborn himself concludes that there is no wholly adequate explanation of the rejuvenating effect of sexual processes in *Paramecium*.

18–2 ASEXUAL REPRODUCTION AND POLYCHAETE LIFE CYCLES

The value of asexual reproduction in providing for rapid increase in numbers, and for efficient exploitation of localized sources of food, is evident enough in the Protozoa. Rotifers and aphids behave in an analogous way, by producing entirely female generations with parthenogenetic eggs, but rapid and truly asexual reproduction is scarcely found in the Metazoa, especially when they have gained some degree of size and complexity of differentiation. Asexual reproduction, when it does occur

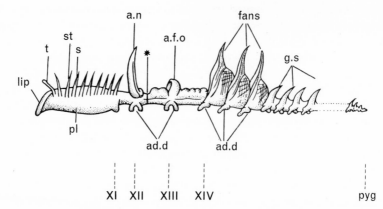

Fig. 18-3. Diagram of *Chaetopterus*. *a.f.o,* accessory feeding organ; *a.n,* aliform notopodia; *∗,* autotomy level; *g.s,* genital segments; *pl,* plastron; *pyg,* pygidium; *s,* stout setae; *st,* setigerous segment; *t,* tentacle; *xi–xiv,* segment numbers. From Berrill, 1928. *J. mar. biol. Ass. U.K.,* **15**, 151–158.

in these animals, takes the form of budding or fragmentation; processes that involve both growth and the regeneration of missing parts, and that draw heavily upon the nutritive resources of the organisms. It is particularly characteristic of the Coelenterata, and fresh-water rhabdocoels and triclads, certain polychaetes and oligochaetes, and the Urochordata. These groups would be considered as being lower invertebrates, but evolutionary status is not the only factor that is concerned. A. E. Needham has pointed out that while both regeneration and asexual reproduction can be regarded as primitive properties of organisms, their distribution in the animal kingdom as a whole is consistent with the view that they have been selected in certain groups because of their high adaptive value.

It is easier to appreciate the essentially primitive nature of regeneration in view of what we now know of the rapid and continuous exchange of materials between the organism and its environment. Not only is there replacement of the molecules lost in the wear and tear of physiological processes; radioisotope studies show that even those components of the body that seem superficially to be stable are in fact being constantly renewed. Because of this we cannot clearly distinguish between the replacement of lost parts, that we call regeneration, and the processes of normal metabolism. Rather must we suppose that regeneration has simply been brought into special prominence under the influence of natural selection, where conditions make it advantageous and the level of organization of the animal allows it to be practicable.

Similarly, we can view asexual reproduction in the Metazoa as being, in its simplest form, an extension of normal growth. This is most evident in the Coelenterata, where it is manifested in the budding that is the basis of colony formation. This, as we shall see later, carries a substantial adaptive advantage. In worms, with their higher level of differentiation, asexual reproduction is more complex, usually involving fragmentation of the body and subsequent regeneration of the missing parts. The close correlation between regeneration and asexual reproduction is, indeed, particularly well shown in these animals, for they display a wide spectrum of phenomena that range from the straightforward replacement of a damaged part to specialized acts of fission that are closely correlated with sexual reproductive processes. The damaging by a predator of part of an elongated body must be a common hazard for them; considerable survival value must consequently attach to the ability to shed the damaged part (a process called autotomy) and then to replace it. This ability is found, for example, in *Chaetopterus* (Fig. 18-3). If the anterior end of this animal is pulled, as it might well be by a predator, a contraction of the circular muscle occurs between segments 12 and 13, and the body breaks into two pieces at that point. Berrill points out that this autotomy, which is followed by regeneration, results in the reproductive and current-producing regions being preserved at the expense of the possibly less valuable head region. Such are the regenerative powers of this animal that a complete worm can be regenerated from a single isolated segment (Fig. 18-4). The anterior and posterior surfaces of this will grow and differentiate until the normal number of segments has been replaced, the initial segment thus coming to occupy once again its correct position in the body. The only limit in this process is that regeneration of the anterior part of the animal can only take place from segment 14 forwards; posterior regeneration, however, can be successfully completed by any segment.

Autotomy and regeneration could clearly provide, in suitable circumstances, for reproduction as well as replacement, and well-known examples of this exist. The syllid polychaetes are particularly notable for this, fragmentation (stolonization) of their bodies being associated with a highly specialized organization of their segments. Autotomy takes place in *Autolytus*, for example, if it is placed in dilute sea water, the fragmentation being brought about by very strong contractions of the longitudinal musculature. The breaking points are predetermined by the position of specialized septa, the positions of which are indicated by white transverse lines.

In natural conditions the anterior and posterior pieces of the syllid may regenerate respectively the missing tail and head (Fig. 18-5A, B); this regeneration may actually precede the fragmentation (Fig. 18-5C), and may be accompanied by pygidial budding (Fig. 18-5D). In some instances the level at which the head is differentiated is predetermined. Thus, in *Autolytus edwardsi* a new head forms in a segment situated within 16–22 segments from the hind end; more heads then appear in front of it, so that a chain of individuals or zooids is formed. As many as 29 such individuals have been observed in *Myrianida*, all for a time attached to the parent stock. In *Autolytus pictus* the new head is said always to appear on the anterior half of the fourteenth segment from the anterior end. If the worm is cut into two through the anterior half of its thirteenth segment it will regenerate a new head at the anterior cut surface, but another will also differentiate on the anterior part of segment 14. Here it would seem that segment 14 is inherently specialized for head production; in classical embryological terminology, this

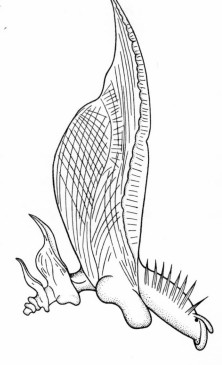

Fig. 18-4. Anterior and posterior regeneration in *Chaetopterus* from (fan) segment 14. From Berrill, 1928. *op. cit.*

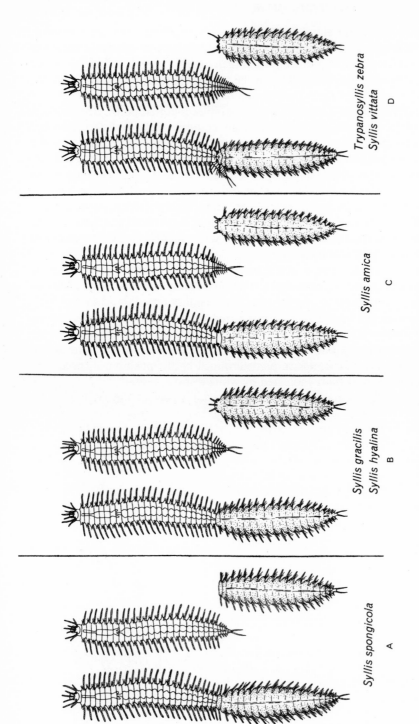

Fig. 18-5. Different types of stolonization in syllid polychaetes, ranging from simple fission on the extreme left to stolonization with pygidial budding on the extreme right. Note the different stages at which the head may differentiate. From Durchon, 1960. *op. cit.*

A — *Syllis spongicola*

B — *Syllis gracilis*
Syllis hyalina

C — *Syllis amica*

D — *Trypanosyllis zebra*
Syllis vittata

segment is a presumptive head. One other example of the highly specialized budding of syllids may be mentioned, from among many. In *Syllis ramosa*, which is commensal within a siliceous sponge, lateral buds grow out tail-first from various segments. Some of these buds then produce secondary lateral buds before they separate from the parent.

Budding carried to this level of specialization provides scope for a significant degree of multiplication, and even more striking results are possible on theoretical grounds. Thus there are species of the nemertine *Lineus* with a capacity for regeneration so well developed that, according to one calculation, as many as 200,000 individuals could be formed out of the fragments of one parent. Even at the higher level of organization of oligochaetes, a species of *Nais* (*N. paraguayensis*) is theoretically capable of producing 15,000 individuals in 2 months. We need not suppose that this potentiality is ever realized in practice. As we have seen, there are limits to the efficacy of asexual reproduction for increasing numbers, and it is thus significant that in one of its most specialized manifestations it is closely associated with sexual reproduction. This is the situation that we have already encountered in certain polychaetes, where fission, in conjunction with epitoky, ensures a successful completion of external fertilization.

The epitokes (Fig. 18-6) of nereids (heteronereids) are simply the intact bottom-dwelling individuals that have become transformed into free-swimming swarmers, and this is true also of certain syllids, such as *Odontosyllis*. Events in this latter family, however, take a variety of courses, sexual reproduction often being associated with the budding and fragmentation processes mentioned above. Sometimes, as in *Syllis*

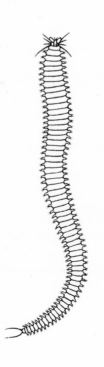

Fig. 18-6. Modes of reproduction in the nereid polychaetes. *Left,* without epitoky (e.g. *Nereis diversicolor*); *middle,* median epitoky (e.g. *Perinereis marionii*); *right,* median and posterior epitoky (e.g. *N. pelagica; Platynereis dumerilii*). From Durchon, 1960. *op. cit.*

hyalina, it is the hind region which becomes separate as a group of sexually mature segments. Here the separated pieces does not develop a head, doubtless because its independent life is a brief one, concerned only with swarming. In other instances a head may be formed, but it remains incomplete, lacking pharynx and jaws. In *Myrianida* and *Autolytus* chains of zooids are formed by asexual reproduction, the zooids breaking off as sexually mature individuals. The zooids of *Myrianida* do not produce their germ cells until after they have attained some size, so that there is here a true alternation of generations, the founding parent of the chain functioning as the asexual phase.

18–3   UNITY IN THE EARLY DEVELOPMENT OF METAZOA

Sexual reproduction in the Metazoa usually involves the fusion of two highly specialized gametes, the sperm and the ovum. These show a division of labour that, as we have seen, is closely paralleled in the sexual reproduction of many protozoans. The specialization of the sperm is sufficiently obvious from the way in which it is adapted for locomotion and for the conveying of genetic material in a concentrated form. The specialization of the ovum is less obvious, apart from the fact that it is often an unusually large cell, heavily loaded with food reserves. Its true nature was a matter for controversy long before the occurrence of syngamy had been observed, or the events of sexual reproduction understood. During the seventeenth and eighteenth centuries it was supposed by some that the future organism was preformed in the egg, and that its development involved the unfolding of a structure that was already established within it. This was the preformation theory of animal development. Opposed to it was the epigenesis theory; according to this there was no preformed structure within the egg, development consisting instead of the progressive laying-down of new organization.

There was an inherent absurdity in the classical preformation theory, for it implied that the first females must have contained the rudiments of all subsequent generations. Apart from this, however, the advances in the techniques of microscopy during the nineteenth century seemed in any case to favour the epigenesis theory, for they failed to reveal any signs of preformed embryos in eggs. Yet towards the close of the century the controversy was re-opened, or developed in new terms, as a consequence of the application of the experimental method to embryological problems. This led to the demonstration that in certain circumstances a complete embryo can develop either from an isolated part of an egg, or from parts of the whole of two eggs that have been artificially fused together. For example, it is possible to separate the blastomeres of the 2- and 4-cell stage of the cleaving egg of sea-urchins, and to show that any one of these blastomeres can continue to cleave on its own and to develop into a larva that is unusually small but that is in other respects normal. Conversely, if two sea-urchin eggs are removed from their membranes and brought carefully together they may sometimes fuse and give rise to a single larva of abnormally large size. Such results suggested on first analysis that the egg in these early stages must be free of any regional differentiation, and that its subsequent development must be truly epigenetic. Capacities for future differentiation seemed to be distributed equally throughout the egg, which could thus be described as an equipotential system, any one part of which contained a share of all the properties of the whole. During normal development, one such part would form only part of the embryo, but under abnormal conditions it could give rise to the whole embryo. Eggs behaving in this way were referred to as regulation eggs.

Other eggs, however, proved to have different properties. As an example, the unfertilized egg of an ascidian contains in its cytoplasm three zones, each with a characteristic pigmentation. This egg has a polar axis, at one pole of which, the animal pole, is a zone of clear cytoplasm, the ectoplasm. Around the surface of the egg is a thin layer of mesoplasm, while the rest of the cell, including the other (vegetative) pole, consists of endoplasm.

Fertilization of this egg is followed by streaming movements in the cytoplasm that redistribute these zones. The ectoplasm and endoplasm come to lie respectively in the animal and vegetative regions; meanwhile the mesoplasm forms a yellow crescent in the future ventral region, and a new zone, the grey crescent, forms opposite to it in the future dorsal region. Not only has the fertilized egg now a bilateral symmetry; it has also a regionally differentiated organization, for the four zones already differ in their developmental potencies. These zones become confined to particular groups of cells during subsequent cleavage and gastrulation, and the fates of these cells are determined in particular ways. Those containing the ectoplasm produce the ectoderm, those containing the endoplasm produce the alimentary tract, those containing the yellow crescent produce mesoderm, and those containing the grey crescent produce the central nervous system and the notochord. As a result, isolated blastomeres will give rise to little more than those structures which they would normally have produced had they remained in their correct positions. In other words, such an egg behaves like a mosaic of parts, each of which has its own independent properties. Regulation appears impossible, so that eggs behaving in this way have been termed mosaic eggs.

We now know that this distinction between regulation and mosaic eggs is a false one as far as the fundamental mechanisms of development are concerned, although it retains a certain descriptive value. The falsity can be demonstrated in experiments involving the separation of the blastomeres of the sea-urchin. If these are separated later than the 4-cell stage, after the first transverse cleavage furrow has formed, it becomes evident that the developmental potencies are already distributed differentially along a polar axis (Fig. 18–7). For example, one half (the animal half) of the cleaving egg will give rise to a larva with a large apical tuft but no alimentary tract, while the opposite (vegetative) half produces a larva with an alimentary tract and skeletal structures, but with no apical tuft or ciliary band. Some form of polar differentiation is, in fact, common in eggs; it is determined in part, perhaps, by their position of attachment within the ovary and by the way in which the nutritive reserves are deposited. It is believed that in the particular case of the sea-urchin there are two interlinked patterns of differentiation in the unfertilized egg. One is the gradient of potencies distributed along the polar axis. The other is a pattern of differentiation lying in the superficial layer, or cortex; this, it is supposed, forms with the polar axis a system of coordinates that controls the progressive further differentiation of the cleaving egg.

This initial pattern may be invisible, as also may be the more complex patterns that grow out of it. Its expression in colour, as in the ascidian, is thus accidental and irrelevant, as far as the fundamental mechanism of differentiation is concerned. This

384

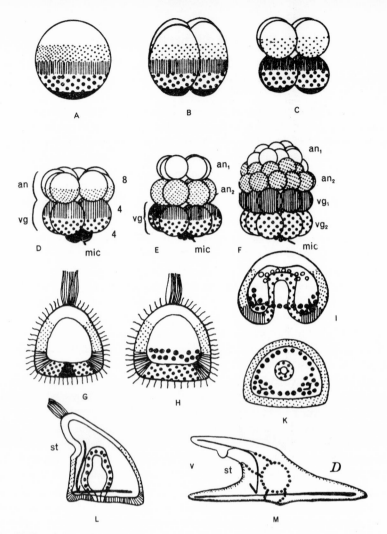

Fig. 18-7. Schematic representation of the larval development in the sea-urchin, to show the primitive position of the materials destined to each region. A–F, cleavage; G–M, gastrulation and establishment of some larval characteristics. *Black*, micromeres; *coarse dotting*, entoblast, secondary mesenchyme, and coelomic material localized in vg$_2$ during the 64-cell stage (F); *vertical hatching, light stippling*, and *white*, ectoblastic areas respectively located in vg$_1$, an$_2$, and an$_1$ during the 64-cell stage (F); *d*, dorsal; *v*, ventral; *st*, stomodaeum. Modified after Hörstadius, from Dalcq, 1938. *Form and Causality in Early Development.* Cambridge University Press, London.

differentiation is essentially chemical, and it is therefore referred to as chemodifferentiation. It is a necessary part of all early development, and the differences between regulation and mosaic eggs lie simply in the rate of differentiation and its relationship to the main axes of the embryo. In the ascidian it sets in early, and in the sea-urchin somewhat later, yet it is clearly not absent from the latter. The regulative capacities of the first four blastomeres of the sea-urchin are not a result of the absence of chemodifferentiation. They are a consequence of chemodifferentiation being distributed in such a way that each of those blastomeres has a share of all the potencies that have at that stage been defined. If the first cleavage furrow of the sea-urchin had happened to be transverse instead of meridional, the egg would presumably have been regarded from the beginning as mosaic in type.

The experimental analysis of early development therefore reveals an underlying unity in the modes of development of metazoan eggs. Yet it is none the less possible to distinguish, at a different level of analysis, certain patterns that are of the greatest value in helping us to understand the history and relationships of some of the main invertebrate groups. To judge the validity of this proposition, however, we must first examine how far embryological data are in general a reliable guide to phylogenetic history.

18–4 EMBRYOLOGY AND PHYLOGENY: THE ORIGIN OF METAZOA

Belief in the phylogenetic value of embryological evidence may be said to stem from the enunciation by von Baer, in 1828, of four fundamental principles, which have been restated and discussed in contemporary terms by de Beer. In essence, these principles state that the general characters of an animal (those that it shares with members of other groups) develop before the special ones that are peculiar to it. As a corollary of this, we find that animals resemble others more closely in the earlier stages of their development than they do in the later ones. In the early nineteenth century these principles carried no evolutionary implications. Following the publication of the *Origin of Species*, however, it was appreciated that embryological resemblances could be interpreted as evidence of common ancestry, indicative of the common ground plan of organization from which the specialized forms of today had diverged.

This point of view was elaborated by Haeckel into the biogenetic law, or the theory of recapitulation, according to which an individual passed through its ancestral history during its early development. This interpretation of embryology no longer commands assent. The reasons for this cannot be fully discussed here, but essentially they rest upon the recognition that adaptive evolution is grounded upon mutations and their recombination in sexual reproduction, and that new characters are therefore products of the complete ontogeny of individuals, and are not merely added on to the end of ancestral ontogenies. Early stages of embryology, therefore, are not a summary of past history, compressed by the addition of new characters in later stages of embryology. What they show us are the foundations upon which later specialization has been based; foundations that have often changed little because they have not been subject to adaptational modification.

Nevertheless, the interpretation of embryological data is not so straightforward as this may suggest. The major difficulty is that adaptive modification is by no means confined to the adult. The early stages of development, too, can undergo adaptive change, giving rise to characters that have been evolved in relation to special requirements of embryonic or larval life. These are called caenogenetic characters, in contrast to palingenetic ones, which are adaptations of the adult. Caenogenesis may thus seriously disturb the phylogenetic value of embryological evidence, and this is another reason for rejecting the over-simple concept of the recapitulation theory. Because of this, the comparative embryologist, just as much as the comparative anatomist, has to base his judgments upon a careful assessment of what is primitive and what is specialized in any particular situation. Moreover, for the same reason, it is unwise to interpret embryological data in isolation. Estimates of phylogenetic

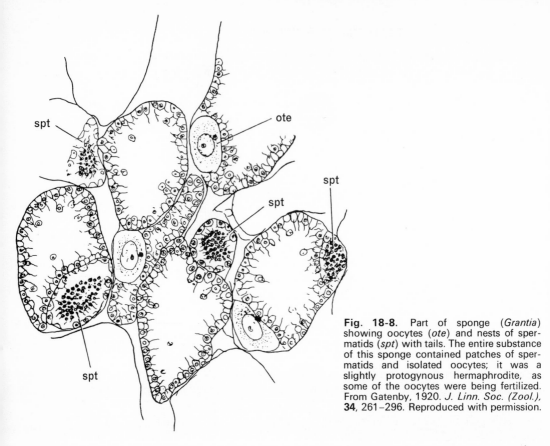

Fig. 18-8. Part of sponge (*Grantia*) showing oocytes (*ote*) and nests of spermatids (*spt*) with tails. The entire substance of this sponge contained patches of spermatids and isolated oocytes; it was a slightly protogynous hermaphrodite, as some of the oocytes were being fertilized. From Gatenby, 1920. *J. Linn. Soc. (Zool.),* **34**, 261–296. Reproduced with permission.

relationships need to consider all the evidence available from the form and function of the adult as well as of the young stages. Yet, given this cautious approach, the evidence of embryology will often be the surest guide to phylogeny, since the earliest stages of development seem to be generally more stable than the later ones.

Consider the problem of the evolutionary origin of the Metazoa, and the bearing upon this of the mode of development of the Porifera and the Coelenterata. The sexual reproduction of the sponges involves the formation of sperm and ova (Fig. 18-8). These resemble the corresponding gametes of Metazoa so closely that the principle of division of labour that they embody was probably established before these groups originated from their protozoan ancestors. Indeed, we have seen already that this principle is operative in certain Protozoa at the present day. In other respects, however, the sponges behave in ways peculiar to themselves. For example, the developing oocyte moves like the amoebocytes which are common in the sponge body, and it grows by engulfing other cells, or by receiving nutriment from them. It is a sign of the low level of organization in the sponge body that these oocytes may sometimes arise by transformation of choanocytes, as also may the sperm; indeed, entire flagellated chambers are said to transform into nests of sperm. Yet another peculiarity is the way in which the sperm first enter choanocytes (Fig. 18-9) or wandering amoebocytes, which then transmit them to the ova.

This is so individual a picture that we may reasonably suspect that sponges diverged very early from the main metazoan stem, or, as we have suggested elsewhere, had an origin entirely independent of the Metazoa. This conclusion is borne out by

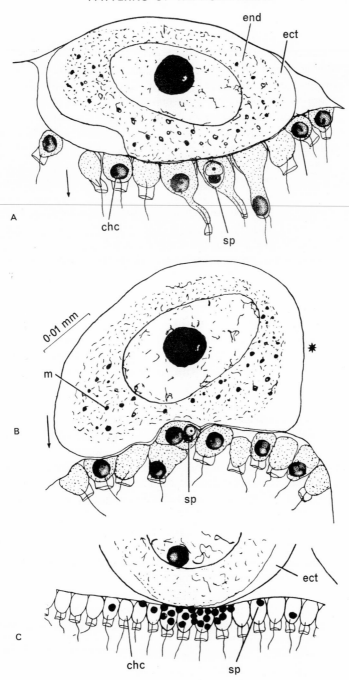

Fig. 18-9. A, B, two stages in the fertilization of *Grantia*; in A the spermatozoon (*sp*) has just entered a collar cell; in B the collar cell has lost its collar and is sinking below its fellows. C, part of an oocyte and the covering wall of collar cells (*chc*). The black dots represent the comparative positions of 25 spermatozoa in that number of cases examined in the stage drawn in B. *ect*, ectoplasmic, and *end*, endoplasmic regions of oocyte; *m*, mitochondria. From Gatenby, 1920. *op. cit.* Reproduced with permission.

the course of later development. In some Calcarea the fertilized egg develops first into a stomoblastula. This is composed in part of non-flagellated cells surrounding a mouth, and in part of flagellated cells which have their flagella directed inwards towards the blastocoel. Later the stomoblastula undergoes a process called inversion, in which it turns itself out so that the flagella are directed towards the outside. Thus it becomes the amphiblastula, which is the characteristic larva of the Calcarea. This larva, having completed its development within the maternal mesenchyme, passes to the outside through the canal system as a hollow structure, one half being composed of slender flagellated cells and the other of larger unflagellated ones. The flagellated hemisphere is anterior during swimming, and would thus seem to correspond with the animal hemisphere of a metazoan gastrula, but this interpretation is belied by subsequent events. Soon the flagellated cells become covered over by the non-flagellated ones. The latter then produce the dermal epithelium, together with the porocytes and scleroblasts (which secrete the major part of the spicules), while the flagellated cells become the choanocytes and produce also the amoebocytes.

This transformation of the amphiblastula, which takes place within a few hours or days of the initiation of swimming, is a simple example of metamorphosis (p. 402) which in this instance may be regarded as reversing the inversion that took place at the stomoblastula stage. Sometimes the flagellated cells may pass inwards by a form of invagination, giving rise to a gastrula-like structure with a blastopore. Sometimes they pass inwards to form a solid core, the larva being known at this stage as a parenchymula. From the morphological point of view both types of transformation give rise to stages that are comparable with stages of metazoan development, but the unexpected fates of the two main types of cell have no parallel in the Metazoa. There is no evidence that this is a consequence of any secondary modification of a type of development that was originally metazoan in character, so that here again, as with the peculiarities of the history of the germ cells, we conclude that the Porifera must have followed a line of evolution independent of the main metazoan one.

With the Coelenterata and Ctenophora we pass to animals that are truly metazoan (or eumetazoan, as they are sometimes called). The mutual relationships of coelenterates and ctenophores are, however, decidedly uncertain. They have much the same grade of diploblastic organization, but they differ in many characters, and not least in their sexual development. Cleavage in the coelenterates is indeterminate and of a generally unspecialized nature, whereas that of ctenophores is very highly specialized, and is, indeed, one of the classical illustrations of determinate and mosaic development. Probably the ctenophores are best regarded as an early offshoot of the coelenterate stem, and one which subsequently pursued an entirely independent line of evolution. The coelenterates themselves can be more easily related with higher metazoans, since they have preserved more of what is usually visualized as the primitive equipment of the Metazoa (but see below, p. 390). For this reason the course of their development has a wider significance.

Cleavage in coelenterates usually leads to the formation of a hollow blastula, which may be set free as a simple ciliated larva in those species in which the ova develop outside the body. Subsequently this larva becomes a solid structure as a result of the passage of cells into the central cavity. These cells constitute the endoderm while those on the outside form the ectoderm. This stage is the planula larva, which is the earliest free-swimming stage in those many hydroid species in which the ova develop within gonophores. This larva, despite its lack of mouth and enteron, has something of the characteristic cellular differentiation of the phylum, with nematocysts, muscle processes, and sensory, nervous, and secretory elements. After a brief free-swimming existence, ranging from some hours to a few days, the endoderm cells become arranged to form the lining of a coelenteron. The organism now settles on a suitable surface, develops a mouth and tentacles, and gives rise to the first hydranth of a new colony.

Even within such a simple course of events there is room for variation in detail. One example of this is seen in *Tubularia*, where the planula stage remains within the gonophore (Fig. 4-4, p. 59) to develop into the actinula larva. This larva has the form of a polyp, but lacks the stalk of the fully formed individual. It leaves the parent, but soon attaches to the substratum after a period of creeping; it then completes its growth into a typical polyp. This variation is a trivial one, which does not modify the general pattern of hydrozoan development. What is of wider interest from the standpoint of phylogenetic speculation is that the endoderm originates differently in the hydrozoans and certain scyphozoans and anthozoans. In the Hydrozoa it is formed by proliferation of cells into the central cavity of the blastula, whereas in the latter two groups it may be formed by invagination.

The importance of this difference derives from Haeckel's blastaea–gastraea theory of the origin of Metazoa. Arguing from his recapitulation theory, and from the frequent existence of a blastula stage in metazoan development, he believed that the earliest Metazoa had the form of a hollow blastula. This, it was supposed, could probably have originated as colonies of protozoans, such as are seen today in the Volvocinae. Haeckel further suggested that these hollow, single-layered organisms later developed a two-layered structure by invagination. He thus regarded the formation of a gastrula by invagination in many metazoans as a persistent ancestral stage, corresponding to a coelenterate-like level of evolution. On this view, one would expect to find invaginate gastrulae in coelenterates, for these are envisaged as comparatively primitive forms in which development has been little modified. The fact that invagination does not occur in hydrozoan development is thus an obstacle to the acceptance of Haeckel's theory, unless one is to suppose that invagination has been secondarily discarded in this group. More serious, however, is the general abandonment of the fundamental principle of recapitulation upon which the blastaea-gastraea theory is based.

Nevertheless, Haeckel's concept of the origin of Metazoa has been revived in a modified form by Jägersten. Starting, as did Haeckel, with a blastula stage, he suggests that this began to move over the substratum instead of swimming at the surface, and that invagination into a diploblastic gastrula stage was promoted as a result of the body arching over food material to engulf it. Haeckel's theory supposed that the gastrula evolved while the organism retained its free-swimming habit, and it is admittedly difficult to see the advantage that would have been gained by this development. Jägersten's theory avoids this difficulty, although, like Haeckel's, it makes it necessary to assume that gastrulation by invagination has been secondarily lost in many coelenterates, and particularly in the Hydrozoa.

An alternative theory, and one that avoids this latter difficulty, is the planula-acoeloid theory, first suggested by Metschnikoff. This view, which has been cogently supported by Hyman, among others, supposes that the diploblastic stage of evolution was reached from a hollow blastula by the immigration of cells, just as occurs today in hydrozoan development. The resulting planula-like stage is visualized as feeding by phagocytosis, so that the development of mouth and enteron was at first unnecessary. The Coelenterata are visualized as developing from this stage as a consequence of the planula evolving, through a transitional actinula-like organism, into a medusa, specialized for locomotion and for the distribution of the germ cells. Colonial organization, with its alternation of generations, could have resulted from the actinula settling on the substratum and budding before the medusa stage. Further, a planula-like stage, creeping over the substratum and feeding by phagocytosis, could conceivably have been the origin of the acoelous platyhelminths, which, as we have seen, still rely largely upon phagocytosis for feeding. From these would then have evolved the higher platyhelminths, together with the vast range of forms that, as we shall argue below, constitute the assemblage called the Protostomia.

The planula–acoeloid theory may fit the facts in a comparatively simple way, but this does not necessarily make it correct. There remains, indeed, an entirely different way of interpreting them. This, which may be called the ciliate–acoeloid theory, has been particularly developed by Hadži. The full implications of this theory, and the wealth of argument with which he supports it, go beyond the scope of our present discussion. It must suffice to say that it is based on the belief that metazoans did not evolve from colonial aggregations of protozoans; instead, they are supposed to have arisen from ciliated protozoans by multiplication of their nuclei in the manner seen in the polymastigine and hypermastigine flagellates (cf. Fig. 23-1, p. 484). This would have been followed by gradual cellularization of the body.

The feature of Hadži's theory that has attracted most attention and controversy, however, is his further supposition that this cellularization would have given rise not to coelenterates but to acoelous platyhelminths. The triploblastic structure of these latter animals is thus regarded as primitive, arising not by invagination and cell immigration, but by the subdivision of a continuous body. A further and fundamental corollary is that the Coelenterata are not primitive metazoans, but are secondarily derived from platyhelminths. Thus the subdivision of the animal kingdom into two levels of organization, the diploblastic and the triploblastic, breaks down. Indeed, Hadži goes further than this. He regards the Anthozoa as the earliest of the coelenterates, deriving them from rhabdocoel platyhelminths. The latter have cephalic tentacles, a simple nerve net, and an alimentary tract with some tendency towards folding, and in these respects they show coelenterate features. Moreover, the bilateral symmetry of the Anthozoa can be held to mark their derivation from freely moving ancestors, although we have seen earlier (p. 66) that an alternative explanation of this is possible.

A final feature of Hadži's theory is that the whole of the Metazoa are monophyletic. This view, however, is not easy to maintain unless embryological data are ignored or dismissed as relatively unimportant. We shall suggest below that if we view the life history of individual groups as a whole, and take their embryological development and larval organization into full account, there are good grounds for recognizing a fundamental division of at least the greater part of the invertebrates into two main assemblages. The coelenterates admittedly remain outside these, but whether as a basal stock, or as a secondary derivative of platyhelminths, is not easy to decide. Undoubtedly the latter interpretation raises serious difficulties. In our discussion of the hydrostatic skeleton we showed that the organization of the platyhelminth body was more complex and better suited for movement than is that of coelenterates. It is not easy to see why these advantages should have been abandoned. Nor is it easy to see why coelenterates should have also abandoned the advantage of a central nervous system in favour of exclusive reliance upon a nerve net. Other difficulties could also be mentioned. The complete lack of any trace of spiral cleavage in coelenterates, for example, is understandable if they preceded the platyhelminths, but surprising if they were derived from them; although it might perhaps be held that this derivation took place at a very early phylogenetic stage, before spiral cleavage had become established. A discussion of these and other aspects of Hadži's views must, however, be looked for elsewhere. Rees focuses a vigorous attack upon them, asserting that they have received an unwarranted amount of publicity, that they require too many assumptions, and that many of the arguments are reversible.

It is fair to add that the theory of the derivation of metazoans from a volvocine type of colonial organization also has its difficulties. For example, the coelenterates are carnivorous and are predominantly marine, whereas the volvocids are freshwater phototrophs. The derivation of coelenterates by cellularization of multinucleate ciliates has its attractions from this point of view, and could presumably be accepted without necessarily adopting the view that coelenterates are secondary derivatives of platyhelminths. There is a point, however, at which discussions along these lines lose touch with reality. We are considering events that may have occurred in the remote past, in conditions that no longer obtain, and affecting organisms that no longer exist. The volvocine series of flagellates affords no more than a suggestion of one possible route of origin of metazoans. Even if we accept that a colonial origin of the Metazoa is likely it does not follow that the ancestral types resembled *Volvox*, or, indeed, that they were necessarily phototrophic. But Hardy has argued that they may well have been so, for that would have solved the very real difficulty of how nutrition was carried on while the gap between protozoan and metazoan organization was being bridged. Metazoa may have evolved from early metaphyta, which developed pocket-like invaginations in which small organisms might collect and perish, to provide nutritive products within the cavity. The water plant *Utricularia* catches small crustaceans in such pockets, and the sundew puts tentacles to similar use. Admittedly these are specialized organisms, yet analogous adaptations might conceivably have developed at earlier stages of evolution.

There is surely much truth in Hyman's observation that 'anything said on these questions lies in the realm of fantasy'. But this is not a reason for declining to discuss a problem that must always be of compelling interest to biologists, and that provides a valuable exercise in the application of biological principles. It is, however, a reason for not pursuing in too much detail an analysis of questions to which we cannot hope to obtain a final answer because essential data are forever lost to us. We may pass instead to a more decisive field of analysis, and consider certain embryological evidence that bears on the problem of the history and relationships of some of the higher invertebrate groups.

18–5 PROTOSTOMIA AND DEUTEROSTOMIA

One fact of fundamental importance is that the polyclad platyhelminths, the nemertines, the annelids, and the molluscs share a common characteristic in the possession of highly mosaic eggs that undergo a specialized form of cleavage called spiral cleavage (Figs. 18–10, 18–11). The distinguishing feature of this is that during the third and subsequent cleavages the mitotic spindles are orientated nearly vertically, but at an angle to the polar axis, the displacement from the vertical being alternately to one side of the axis or to the other. The first two cleavage furrows are meridional, and produce four large blastomeres (macromeres), distinguished by convention as the A, B, C, and D blastomeres. The third furrow is latitudinal, and separates four small blastomeres (micromeres) from four macromeres. These first micromeres (1a, 1b, 1c, 1d) are called the first quartet of micromeres. The orientation of the spindles results in each of the four cells of this quartet being displaced to one side of its corresponding macromere (1A, 1B, 1C, 1D), the displacement being clockwise as viewed from the animal pole, in all four of the phyla concerned. (A well-known exception to this, however, is a variety of the pond-snail *Lymnea*. In this variety the first quartet is budded off in an anticlockwise direction and the symmetry of the whole animal is correspondingly reversed, so that the shell coils sinistrally, instead of dextrally as in most gastropods.)

At the next cleavage, in which the displacement is anticlockwise, the macromeres give off a second quartet of micromeres (2a, 2b, 2c, 2d), and are then termed the 2A, 2B, 2C, and 2D macromeres. At the same time the first quartet of micromeres divides to form two daughter quartets. The component cells of these are designated as shown; for example, the cells formed by the division of 1a are lettered $1a^1$ and $1a^2$,

Fig. 18-10. Early stages in the spiral cleavage of the gastropod *Trochus*. A, B, 4-cell stages from upper pole; C, 8-cell stage, first micromere quartet; D, 12-cell stage, transitional to 16-cell, second quartet just formed; E, 20-cell stage (transitional to 32-cell), from upper pole, third quartet formed; F, 36-cell stage from upper pole; showing apical rosette (*r*), trochoblasts (*t*), and all the blastomeres of the first two quartets (28 cells). From Wilson, 1928. *The Cell* (3rd ed.). Macmillan, New York.

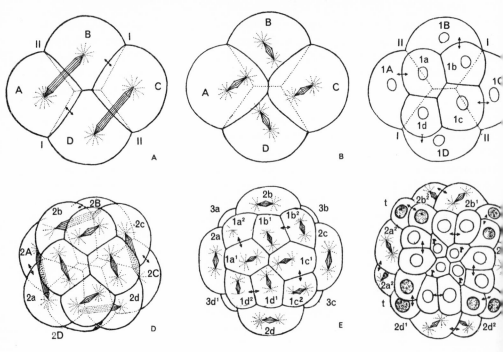

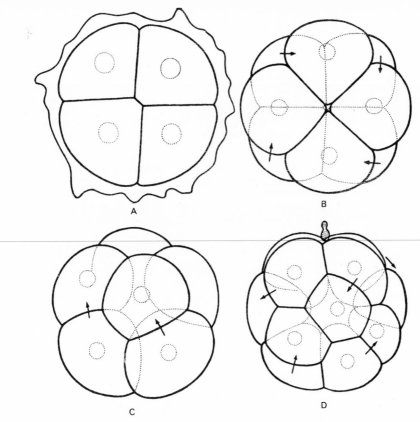

Fig. 18-11. Cleavage of *Polygordius*, from life. A, 4-cell stage, from above; B, corresponding view of 8-cell stage; C, side view of the same; D, 16-cell stage from the side. From Wilson, 1928. *op. cit.*

the former being the one lying nearer to the animal pole. The same pattern of cleavage is continued, with successive divisions of macromeres and micromeres, to build up a blastula in which the division products have been alternately displaced clockwise and anticlockwise. As a result, the shortest line that can be drawn from one pole to the other without cutting through the sides of any cell is a spiral, and it is this that gives spiral cleavage its name.

Spiral cleavage is mosaic development in classical terminology, for by the time that the 32-cell stage has been reached the fates of the blastomeres are fixed (Figs. 18–12, 18–13). It is impossible to follow their history here in detail. In summary, the macromeres, together with 4a, 4b, and 4c, form endoderm, the first three quartets of micromeres give rise to the ectoderm and its derivatives, while 4d, in annelids and molluscs, forms two cells called the teloblasts, from which are proliferated two mesoderm bands. These bands form the coelomic mesoderm, which comprises all of the mesoderm, apart from larval mesoderm formed from the ectoderm and known as ectomesoderm. At one time it was supposed that the fate of the different blastomeres depended upon the orderly segregation among them of invisible substances called organ-forming substances; these were thought to provide essential material for the development of the various tissues and organs. The course of events, however, is not as simple as this. No doubt determining materials of one sort or another do accumulate during the progress of chemodifferentiation, but these materials are probably

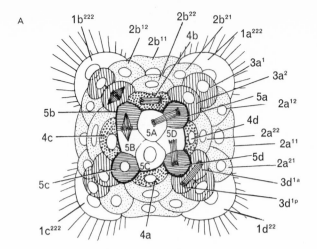

A

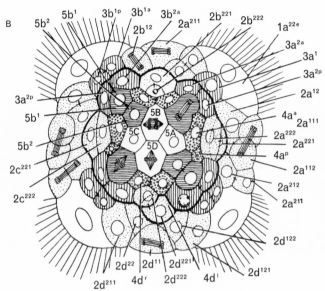

B

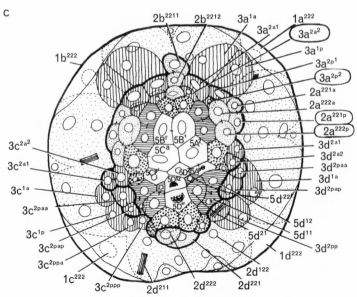

C

Fig. 18-12. (Left) Three stages in the segmentation of the lower or vegetative surface of the egg of *Polygordius*. A, about 76 cells. B, about 112 cells. C, later stage in which a mass of rapidly dividing cells at the lower pole is sharply distinguished from an outer zone of clear cells. The heavy black line surrounds the cells which later will take part in the process of invagination and the formation of the lips of the blastopore. The cells belonging to the second quartet are dotted, those belonging to the third quartet are marked by vertical lines. The cells belonging to the fourth quartet are marked by little circles, those belonging to the fifth quartet by horizontal lines. The residual macromeres, and those belonging to the first quartet, are left white. The names of the cells which form the larval mesoderm are surrounded by circles. From MacBride, 1914. *Text-book of Embryology*, vol. 1: *The Invertebrata*. Macmillan, London.

Fig. 18-13. (Below) Four views of the vegetative pole of the developing egg of *Polygordius* to show the processes of gastrulation and of formation and closure of the blastopore. A, stage with blastopore shaped like a figure of eight; B, stage where blastopore has become divided into primitive mouth and primitive anus. The arrows show the direction of rotation of the cells $3c^{2paa}$ and $3d^{2paa}$. C, stage in which primitive anus is closed. D, stage in which telotroch and metatroch are formed, and in which stomodaeal cells have become invaginated. The different quartets are distinguished as in Fig. 18-12. *a*, position where the permanent anus breaks through; *a.n*, protonephridium; *blp*, blastopore; *l.a*, larval anus; *m*, mouth; *m.tr*, metatroch; *p.a*, primitive anus; *t.b*, trunk blastema; *t.tr*, telotroch. From MacBride, 1914. *op. cit.*

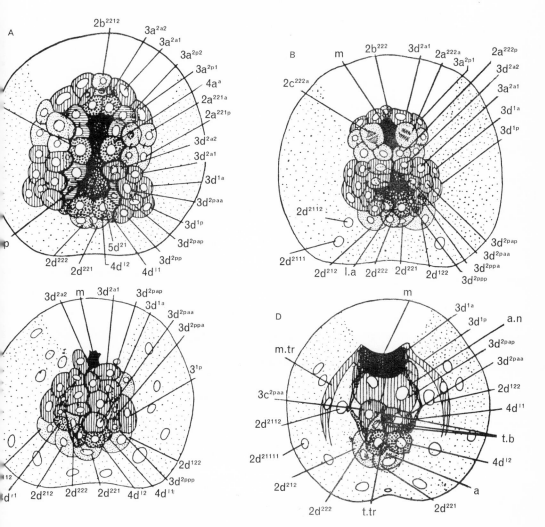

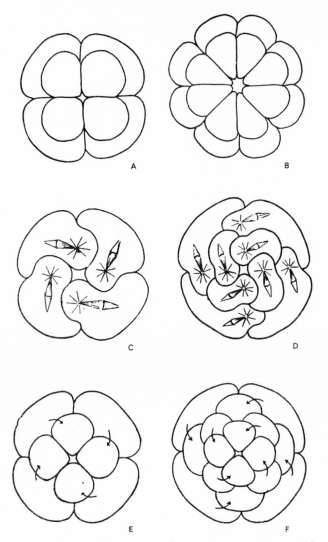

Fig. 18-14. Comparison of spiral and radial cleavage. A, B, 8- and 16-cell stages, radial type; C, D, 3rd and 4th cleavages, spiral type; E, F, 8- and 16-cell stages, spiral type. From Richards, 1931. *Outline of Comparative Embryology*. Wiley, New York.

complex regulators of cell metabolism, and they may well have influences extending beyond their own immediate site. These are issues that we cannot consider here. Our present concern is with the visible cleavage pattern that segregates the differentiating regions, for this pattern is so very specialized and characteristic that it is most unlikely to have been evolved independently in unrelated groups. Provisionally, therefore, we can take this as evidence that the groups showing spiral cleavage are phylogenetically related, and we can search for further evidence to support this conclusion.

One suggestion that has been increasingly supported is that most invertebrates, together also with the Chordata, but excluding the radially symmetrical Coelenterata and Ctenophora, can be assigned to one or other of two large assemblages, the

Protostomia and the Deuterostomia. The major groups included within the Protostomia are the Platyhelminthes, Nemertinea, Annelida, Arthropoda, and Mollusca. Spiral cleavage occurs in all of them, except the arthropods, while in the arthropods as well as in the others the mesoderm develops by cell proliferation. The coelom thus arises as a schizocoel, by splitting of the mesoderm layer. Further, the mouth forms directly from the blastopore (Fig. 18-13), or in the region where the blastopore closes, and it is for this reason that the term Protostomia has been introduced for this assemblage. Finally, in those forms that show indirect development (that have, in other words, a larval stage) the larva is often of the type called the trochophore, or can be interpreted as having a structure closely related to it. Again the exception is provided by the Arthropoda, in which group there is no sign at all of a trochophore larva, despite the indirect development of many members, and notably of the crustaceans. There can be no doubt, however, of the close relationship of the annelid and arthropod plans of structure, even though we lack evidence for a common origin of the two groups as we see them today. As regards arthropodan embryology, we can only suppose that the specialized course of events that we have termed arthropodization has involved a modification of development so extreme that embryological links with other groups have been largely lost.

The Deuterostomia are envisaged as comprising the Echinodermata, Pogonophora, Hemichordata, and Chordata (including the two protochordate groups, the Urochordata and the Cephalochordata). In echinoderms, where deuterostome characters are easiest to appreciate, there is no sign of spiral cleavage; instead, a simple pattern of meridional and latitudinal furrows (radial cleavage, Fig. 18-14) leads to the formation of a hollow blastula. After gastrulation the anus typically forms from the blastopore, or at the region where the blastopore closes, but the mouth is a new formation, from which feature is derived the term Deuterostomia (*deuteros*, second). After the proliferation of mesenchyme, the coelom forms from outgrowths of the enteron (Fig. 18-15), so that it is an enterocoel instead of a schizocoel. Finally, indirect development involves the formation of a dipleurula larva, or other types of larvae derivable from it. The organization of these larvae, and particularly the pattern of their ciliation, is fundamentally different from that of the trochophore.

These, it must be emphasized, are the fundamental and typical characteristics of echinoderm development, from which individual species may secondarily diverge. These divergences do not in themselves affect our interpretation, for they are so obviously of a secondary nature. Greater difficulties admittedly arise when we consider the other deuterostomes, but these, too, can be attributed to extreme and divergent specialization, in this case affecting all the members of particular groups.

It is at least certain that none of them shows spiral cleavage, but the development of the mesoderm is greatly diversified. In the Cephalochordata the coelom is clearly enterocoelic. In the Hemichordata its mode of origin varies, while in the Urochordata it is reduced, and even its existence is a matter of opinion. In the vertebrates it arises as a schizocoel; in the highly specialized development of the chick, for example, the future mesoderm moves in from the primitive streak without having any direct relationship with the endoderm. As for the larvae, the development of the Pogonophora is direct, the larval stage having been secondarily suppressed. In the Hemichordata, however, there is a tornaria larva that closely resembles the dipleurula,

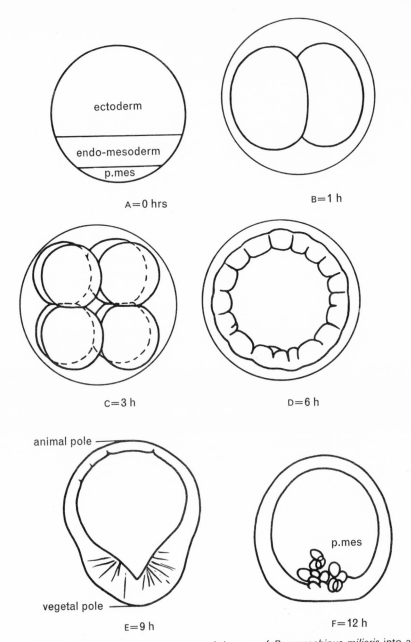

Fig. 18-15. Stages in the development of the egg of *Psammechinus miliaris* into a pluteus larva. A, eggs with the main presumptive regions of the larva indicated. B, 2-cell stage. C, 8-cell stage. D, blastula before hatching. E, blastula shortly after hatching. F, release of mesenchyme. G, mesenchyme blastula at the outset of gastrulation. H, profile of early gastrula, at the end of primary invagination, showing the beginning of dorsoventrality, the ring of primary mesenchyme, and one of the two ventral branches from this ring. I, gastrula at the onset of the second phase of invagination, showing pseudopodial activity at the tip of the archenteron rudiment, further flattening of the ectoderm, and appearance of thickening at the animal pole. J, gastrula at the end of invagination, showing release of secondary mesenchyme from the archenteron tip, early skeletal formation, and further flattening of the ventral side. K, gastrula after oral contact has formed, and the beginning of subdivision of the gut; note the oral invagination (stomodaeum rudiment). L, early pluteus in ventral view, showing the paired coelom formed from the archenteron tip, stronger subdivision of the gut, and further growth of the skeleton. M, later stage of the pluteus development where the mouth has opened, and one of the coelomic sacs has been extended to form the primary pore canal which later opens at the primary madreporic pore (in this case it is the right coelom, but normally the left); the skeleton has extended the ectoderm. From Gustafson and Wolpert, 1963. *Int. Rev. Cytol.*, **15**, 139–214.

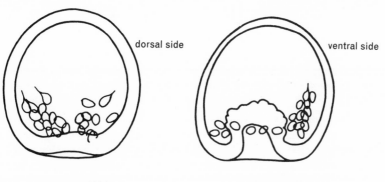

dorsal side   ventral side

G = 14 h   H = 16 h

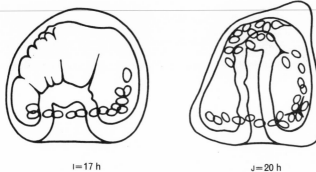

I = 17 h   J = 20 h

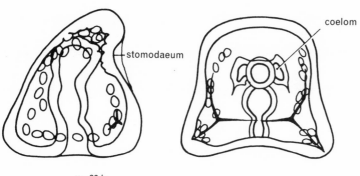

— stomodaeum   coelom

K = 23 h   L = 32 h

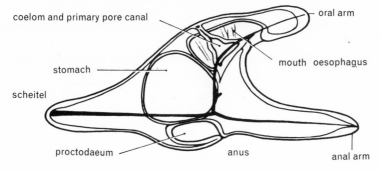

coelom and primary pore canal   oral arm

stomach   mouth oesophagus

scheitel

proctodaeum   anus   anal arm

M = 48 h

and that therefore provides good evidence for the close relationship of this group with echinoderms. The development of the protochordates is also indirect, but here the larvae are highly specialized and show no obvious relationship with those of hemi-chordates and echinoderms; they present a separate problem that we shall discuss later.

Evidently, then, the patterns of development within the Deuterostomia are far from homogeneous, and, exactly as with the arthropods, embryology here provides us with only a partial picture of phylogenetic relationships. Nevertheless, it can be argued that the concept of the Protostomia and the Deuterostomia is a sound one, for it takes its support from other considerations as well as from the purely develop-mental ones with which we are here concerned (p. 85). What is particularly convinc-ing is that within each of the two assemblages we can distinguish characteristic and coherent evolutionary trends. These suggest that the members of each assemblage have inherited from a common ancestry a common stock of genetic potentialities. The trends associated in the Protostomia with the history of the coelom, of metamer-ism, and of the nervous system are one illustration of this. Another is seen in the history of the ciliary feeding mechanisms of the Deuterostomia.

19
Larval Forms

19–1 MODES OF LARVAL DEVELOPMENT

The history of the eggs and embryos produced by sexual reproduction reveals many different patterns of development and life cycle. One variable factor is the degree of protection given to these stages. Here a primary distinction is often made between oviparity, with the parent releasing the eggs or at least the early cleavage stages, and viviparity, which, in its most complete form, involves the retention of the young stages and their eventual release as juveniles that resemble the adults except in their size and sexual immaturity. This distinction, however, is something of a simplification, for between the two extremes there lies a wide range of conditions affording variable degrees of protection. The eggs may be shed singly, for example, or grouped in gelatinous masses, or protective capsules. Those of aquatic forms may be left to float freely in the upper layers of the water or at the sea bottom, or they may be attached to the substratum. We might suppose that each mode of dealing with the eggs would have its own advantages and disadvantages, and would somehow be correlated with the particular way of life of the species concerned, but it is often difficult to find any clear-cut evidence of this.

J. E. Smith has mentioned a number of examples illustrating this difficulty. Of three common shore-dwelling nemerteans, which might be expected to show similar life histories, *Amphiporus lactifloreus* hatches its young in a crawling stage, *Lineus ruber* has a short free-swimming phase, while *Cephalothrix* has larvae that may live in the plankton for two or more weeks. Shore-dwelling gastropods, to take only one other set of examples, show a variation of pattern that has no obvious explanation. *Littorina littorea* has larvae that live for four weeks or more in the plankton. *L. littoralis* and *Nucella* have a direct development in egg capsules, while *L. rudis* and *Hydrobia jenkinsi* are viviparous. These are all abundant animals, and there is no indication that the maintenance of their populations is influenced by the differences in their modes of development. It might be thought that species lying highest on the shore would stand in most need of the protective advantage of viviparity, but there is no evidence even of this. *L. rudis*, which is covered by most tides, is viviparous, whereas *L. neritoides*, occupying the splash zone and only rarely wetted, relies on a planktonic larva for its survival.

The difference between direct and indirect development is a familiar feature of life histories. In the former the adult stage is attained by progressive growth and differentiation, whereas in the latter there is a larval stage, differing both in its structure and its habit from the adult, and acquiring adult form through a radical and sometimes sudden metamorphosis. Three main types of these larvae can be distinguished. There is firstly the lecithotrophic larva, so called because it feeds exclusively upon the yolk originally laid down in the egg, and does not, therefore, take any food from external sources. Nevertheless, such larvae may have a long period of life in the plankton, being carried along largely by currents. Thorson estimates that they form about 10% of the species of temperate and tropical seas that have pelagic larvae. They appear to be absent from arctic waters.

A far commoner type of larva is the planktotrophic larva, so called because the yolk reserves of the egg are soon exhausted, and the organism has to feed on plankton. Such larvae are usually well adapted for prolonged movement, swimming actively for 2-4 weeks in summer months and perhaps for as long as 3 months during the winter. They are estimated to occur in the life cycle of 55% to 65% of marine species in boreal seas, and 80% to 85% of those living in tropical waters. As with the lecithotrophic type, they are hardly represented in arctic species, nor in those that inhabit abyssal waters.

Finally, there are other planktotrophic larvae with only a short period of free-swimming life, amounting to a matter of hours or at most to a very few days. These are estimated to be produced by about 5% of marine invertebrate species, from the arctic to the tropics.

We shall consider later the significance of larval life, but we can distinguish three fundamentally important aspects of it now. There is firstly the need for the delicate young organism to grow in conditions which satisfy its special requirements, and which avoid unnecessary competition with the adult. Secondly, there is the need to provide for dispersal of the species, and thus to avoid over-crowding. Finally, there is the need to select a habitat that is suited to the requirements of the adult. Because of these varied functions larvae often become very highly specialized, and all of them undergo some degree of metamorphosis. It is impossible here to attempt a comprehensive review of the rich diversity of ways in which larvae fulfil the requirements of their species. It must be sufficient to illustrate the general principles by reference to some of the more familiar types.

19–2 SOME PROTOSTOME LARVAE

The trochophore larva (Fig. 19-1), formerly known as Loven's larva, after the Swedish priest and naturalist who discovered it in 1840, is exemplified in the larva of certain species of the archiannelid *Polygordius*. It is approximately biconical in shape, with a ciliated band extending around its equator. This band, which is one of the distinguishing features of the trochophore, is mainly responsible for locomotion. Two other ciliated bands, the metatroch and paratroch, may be present below it, the paratroch surrounding the anus. Another characteristic feature is the arrangement of the alimentary canal. This opens at the mouth, which lies below the equator on the future ventral surface; the anus is at the lower pole, or future hind end. The alimentary canal lies within the body cavity, which is a blastocoel. This cavity contains also a pair of mesoderm bands, developed from the teloblasts, and a pair of protonephridia, together with muscle fibres and mesenchyme cells which represent the ectomesoderm.

The receptors and nervous system are of some complexity; a significant fact in view of what we shall later see of the complex behaviour of this and similar larvae in

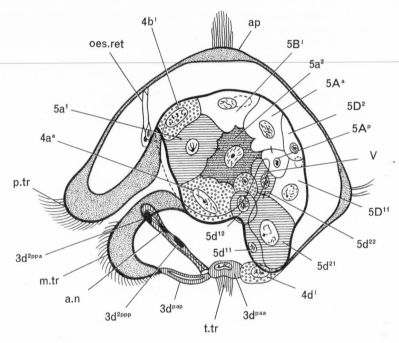

Fig. 19-1.   Optical section of young trochophore of *Polygordius* after gastrulation is complete. *ap,* apical plate; *oes.ret,* oesophageal retractors; *p.tr,* prototroch; *v,* valve. For other lettering, see Figs. 18-12 and 18-13. Adapted from MacBride, 1914. *op. cit.*

general. At the apical pole is an area of thickened ectoderm, the apical plate, which bears a tuft of supposedly sensory cilia. Beneath the plate is a ganglion, from which extend radial nerves. These are united by one or more delicate nerve rings, the chief one being associated with the prototroch. Statocysts and eye spots are often present towards the apical pole, while other parts of the ectoderm may well be sensory.

The need for metamorphosis is evident in the trochophore larvae of archiannelids and polychaetes, for these larvae, unlike the adult worms, are unsegmented organisms. In its simplest form the metamorphosis of the trochophore involves the backward growth of the lower pole, which thus becomes recognizable as the hind end. Immediately in front of the anus is a growth zone from which segments arise, as they continue to do in the adult. The lower half of the larva becomes incorporated into this segmented region, while the upper half becomes the prostomium. Such is the course of events in certain species of *Polygordius* and in many polychaetes (Fig. 19-2). Comparison with a range of polychaete species, however, immediately

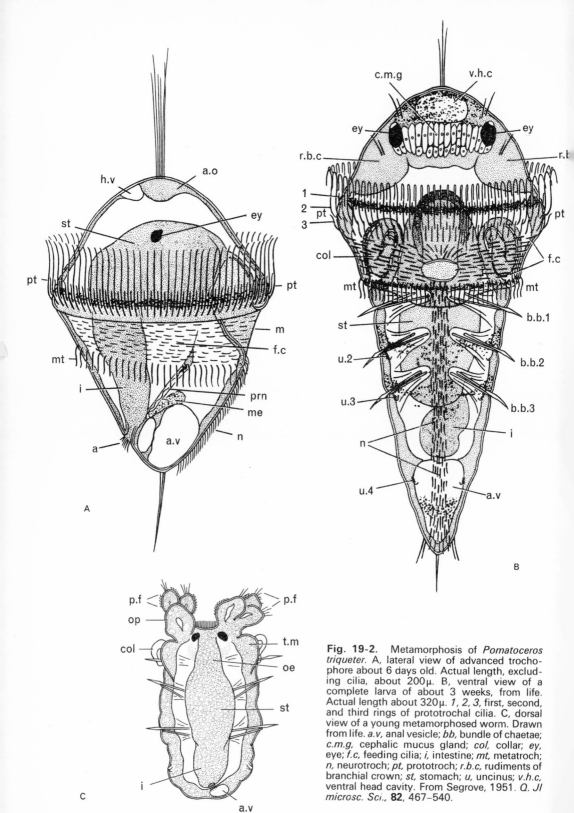

Fig. 19-2. Metamorphosis of *Pomatoceros triqueter.* A, lateral view of advanced trochophore about 6 days old. Actual length, excluding cilia, about 200μ. B, ventral view of a complete larva of about 3 weeks, from life. Actual length about 320μ. *1, 2, 3,* first, second, and third rings of prototrochal cilia. C, dorsal view of a young metamorphosed worm. Drawn from life. *a.v,* anal vesicle; *bb,* bundle of chaetae; *c.m.g,* cephalic mucus gland; *col,* collar; *ey,* eye; *f.c,* feeding cilia; *i,* intestine; *mt,* metatroch; *n,* neurotroch; *pt,* prototroch; *r.b.c,* rudiments of branchial crown; *st,* stomach; *u,* uncinus; *v.h.c,* ventral head cavity. From Segrove, 1951. *Q. Jl microsc. Sci.,* **82**, 467–540.

reveals the plasticity of larval forms and of their metamorphoses. Larvae, in fact, have their own history of specialization, which may run quite independently of that of the corresponding adults; this, as we shall see, is a principle of fundamental evolutionary importance.

Within a range of organization that is still essentially that of the trochophore there is much variation in the arrangement of the ciliary bands. Thus the prototroch may be lost, and the ciliated bands confined to the mesotroch (mesotrochous larva) or paratroch (telotrochous), or represented by a series of bands (polytrochous). Alternatively, the larva may be released in a stage of development less advanced than that of the trochophore; this happens in *Nereis diversicolor*, the larva of which lacks mouth and anus, and has been called a protrochophore larva. Conversely, the larva may persist for some time at a stage more advanced than that of the trochophore. An example is the nectochaetous larva, in which the posterior (lower) half of the larva is metamerically segmented, with parapodia and chaetae. Such a larva is well able to swim (as its name implies), and these stages of development are common in the plankton; in some circumstances, however, they creep over the substratum, a mode of life for which the trochophore is obviously unsuited.

The nectochaetous stage shows the larva developing appreciably towards the adult stage without necessarily losing its capacity for planktonic life and hence for dispersal of the species. Its increased size and weight must reduce the efficiency of its cilia as locomotor structures, but the muscular parapodia to some extent assume this function, aided by the often considerable length of the very slender chaetae, which help to support the organism in the water. A possible advantage of this combination of greater size and increased freedom of movement is suggested by Garstang's verses. Having written of the trochophore of *Phyllodoce*, he goes on:

> In this way fares *Phyllodoce*, but *Nereis* can beat her:
> She gives each egg some extra yolk to hatch as *Nectochaeta*.
> The simple stage with prototroch is by-passed in the eggs,
> And each when hatched has three good pairs of parapodial legs.

The circumstances of metamorphosis vary with the species, and, as we shall see, are related to the habits of the adult. Sometimes, as in *Polynoë*, the nectochaetous stage may continue its growth and differentiation until it has formed a small but well-developed juvenile worm, and only then does pelagic life cease. Others retain the form of trochophores externally, but develop the body of the future worm, enclosed within the larval body in an invaginated state. This is seen in the larva of a North Sea species of *Polygordius*, which for some time carries a segmented body enclosed within a cavity that develops by invagination around the anus, but otherwise has something in common with the amniotic cavity of a vertebrate embryo. At a given moment the wall of the trochophore starts to shrink, so that the segmented trunk is evaginated posteriorly. The apical region of the larva is drawn onto the trunk anteriorly, while the equatorial protrochal region shrivels and is lost.

A much more specialized version of this device is seen in the mitraria larva of *Owenia fusiformis* (Fig. 19-3), described in detail by Wilson. In this species a trochophore stage is reached about 2 days after fertilization, but growth in size continues thereafter, associated with a great elaboration of the prototroch, which becomes folded into a large and sinuous band. This is presumably a locomotor adaptation,

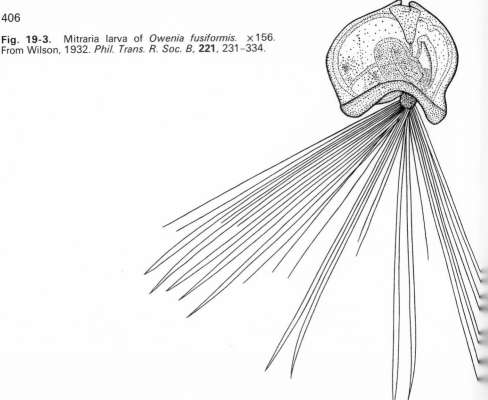

Fig. 19-3. Mitraria larva of *Owenia fusiformis.* ×156. From Wilson, 1932. *Phil. Trans. R. Soc. B,* **221**, 231–334.

correlated with the continued growth and differentiation of the larva. Large provisional larval chaetae, developed from the lower end of the larva, presumably aid in its support, and may also serve to provide some protection from predators. Feeding is carried out, according to Wilson, by the cilia of the metatroch; these sweep food particles into the mouth, a procedure that involves them passing around several folds of the prototroch. The rudiment of the future trunk forms in this larva as an invagination between the anus and the mouth, its growth involving a process of invagination and folding (Fig. 19-4). The most anterior segments, in Wilson's words, are 'turned inside out and drawn back over the succeeding segments much as the top of a stocking can be turned inside out and drawn back over the foot.'

The metamorphosis of this larva is a sudden (cataclysmic) process, which occurs about 4 weeks after fertilization, and which is thought to be initiated by contact with fine sand similar to that in which the tube-dwelling adults live. We shall discuss this aspect of habitat selection further below. The trunk is everted into its correct position, the stomach and oesophagus are pulled into it, and the larval tissues, including the ciliated bands and nephridia, disintegrate, while the larval chaetae drop away. The whole process is extraordinarily rapid. Most of the main changes are completed within 30 seconds of their initiation, and little material is wasted in the process, for the young worm swallows the discarded larval structures at the same time that it begins to secrete its protective tube. The swallowing is completed in about 15 minutes, the tissues being digested intracellularly during the next 2 days. The whole sequence of events in this larval history, as in that of the *Polygordius* species mentioned above,

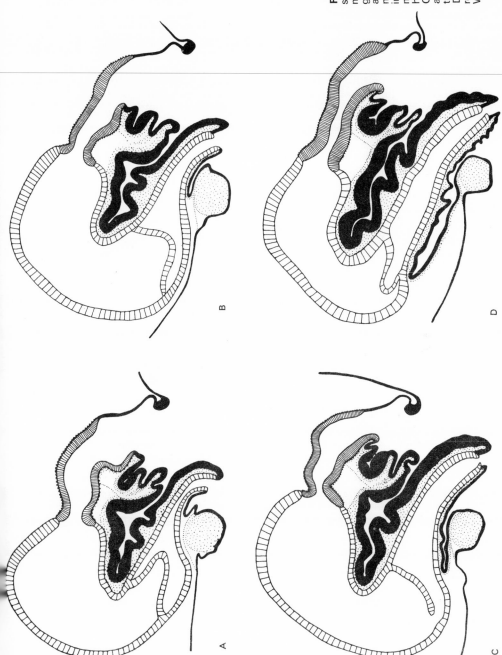

Fig. 19-4. Diagrams of median sagittal sections of the worm rudiment of *Owenia* to illustrate its growth in the later stages. A, from a larva 22 days old, before the mesoderm has surrounded the intestine. B, the same age, but more advanced, the mesoderm having met around the intestine. C, the same age, but still more advanced. The dorsal part of the trunk rudiment is growing rapidly. D, from a larva 27 days old, and ready to metamorphose. From Wilson, 1932. *op. cit.*

is a striking solution of the problem of integrating development and dispersal. No less significant, however, is its demonstration of the way in which the specializations of larval life can diverge from those of the adult. The importance of this will be appreciated later, when we consider the larval organization of the higher Protostomia.

Spiral cleavage occurs only in the polyclads among the platyhelminths, which suggests that the course of their development must be more primitive than that of other members of the phylum. It is significant from this point of view that in polyclads and in the Acoela, unlike the other turbellarians, yolk glands are absent, so that yolk is deposited within the ova, in the primitive fashion, instead of being laid down in separate yolk cells. In most of the acotylean polyclads the development is direct, and there emerges from the egg capsule a small flatworm, but in some, and typically in the Cotylea, there is a larva known as Müller's larva. This has an apical ganglion, overlain by a tuft of sensory cilia, and a typically platyhelminth alimentary tract, with a mouth and a blind intestine. The feature that chiefly relates it to the trochophore is the locomotor mechanism, which consists of a ciliated band lying above the mouth, and corresponding in its position to the prototroch. The characteristic feature of the larva is that this band is situated on the edges of eight posteriorly directed lobes. These disappear after a few days, when a flattening of the body converts the larva into a young worm. The metamorphosis is thus a simple one, and it is easy to see that the larva is essentially an early developmental stage of the flatworm, adapted for a pelagic life by its specialized ciliation.

Development in the nemertines may be either direct or indirect, the latter mode being particularly characteristic of the heteronemertines. The typical larva of these forms is the pilidium larva (Fig. 19–5), so called because of its helmet-like shape (*pilidion*, a small cap). There is an apical plate and tuft (but no other sign of nervous structures), and a mouth that leads into a blind alimentary tract, the organization in this latter respect being platyhelminth-like. As with Müller's larva, locomotion depends upon a lobed ciliated girdle, the cilia in this instance being carried on the edges of a pair of oral lobes that grow down, one on either side of the mouth, giving the larva its characteristic shape. A variant of the pilidium larva is found in the development of *Lineus*. This larva, known as Desor's larva, lacks the apical plate and tuft, and the oral lobes and specialized ciliation, and it remains within the egg membranes. It has been supposed that this is a secondary modification of the more typical indirect development, enabling the whole of the life cycle of this littoral form to be confined to the limits of the shore.

It might be expected that the pilidium larva would undergo a simple and straightforward metamorphosis into the adult form, much as does Müller's larva, but this is not so; a fact that illustrates the plasticity of larval life histories and the consequent difficulty in generalizing from a few examples. Both in the pilidium larva and in Desor's larva metamorphosis is preceded by the development of seven or eight ectodermal invaginations of the larval ectoderm. These separate off to produce a series of sacs with thin outer walls and thick inner ones formed of columnar epithelium. The sacs eventually join together, and the continuous inner wall gives rise to the epidermis of the adult worm. The larval alimentary tract and mesoderm, enclosed by this wall, undergo a good deal of reorganization and differentiation during the metamorphosis, and it is at this stage that the anus develops. At the end of these changes the larval ectoderm and the outer wall of the fused invaginations are shed, together with the apical plate, and the young nemertine emerges from its larval container. The metamorphosis is thus considerably more drastic than might have been expected at this level of organization, and it is not easy to see why this should be so. Functionally, however, as with the mitraria larva, the process provides for laying the foundations of adult structure without interfering with the distributive activity of the larva during its pelagic life. It may well be that these dual requirements, always fundamental to larval life, are here provided for more efficiently than in the simpler developmental history of the polyclads.

Another method of securing this provision is found in the molluscs. As is to be expected in such a large group, there is much variation in the life history, correlated in part with the varied habitats of the adults. Close relationship with the annelids is seen, however, in the occurrence of a trochophore stage in many forms, particularly in the lower gastropods, or archaeogastropods (e.g. *Patella*), and in the lamellibranchs; it is found also in the development of chitons (Amphineura) and *Dentalium* (Scaphopoda). This larva is rapidly transformed into a more complex stage, the

Fig. 19-5. Larval development of the nemertine *Cerebratulus*. A, early pilidium. B, advanced pilidium containing the larva. C–F, development of larva inside the pilidium from embryonic discs. *1*, larval epidermis; *2*, definitive epidermis; *3*, proboscis invagination; *4*, stomodaeum; *5*, mid-gut; *6*, definitive intestinal cells; *7*, apical sensory organ; *8*, dorsal disc; *9*, trunk disc; *10*, disc for cerebral organ; *11*, cephalic disc; *12*, amnion; *13*, larva; *14*, oral lobes. From Hyman, 1951. *The Invertebrata: Platyhelminthes and Rhynchocoela.* McGraw-Hill, New York. Used by permission.

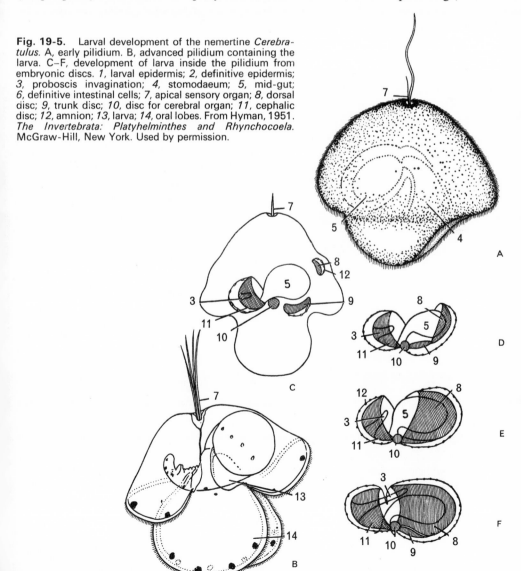

veliger larva (Fig. 19-6), which is particularly characteristic of the gastropods and bivalves. In this the prototroch is drawn out into a pair of ciliated lobes, an arrangement that considerably increases the support given to the larva and makes for a more vigorous and controlled locomotion. The reason for this development is apparent in the advanced state of differentiation reached by the veliger. It has something of the form of a mollusc, with a shell, a mantle cavity, and the beginnings of a foot, the latter sometimes bearing an operculum that can close the opening of the shell. Clearly the improved ciliation is necessary for the support and movement of this heavier and more complex body.

In the early larval life of gastropods there is another complication that is more difficult to explain. This is the process known as torsion, which is a twisting of the viscera through 180° relative to the rest of the body; it brings the originally posterior mantle cavity to the anterior end, and leaves the originally left side of the pallial complex on the right. This transformation, which is effected very quickly—in some species in a few minutes—is brought about through the contraction of an asymmetrically arranged retractor muscle. This runs from the right side of the shell to be inserted on the left side of the head and foot.

We have earlier discussed the torsion of gastropods from the standpoint of adult anatomy, and have seen that its advantages to the adult are by no means clear. Some have argued that it carries positive disadvantages in that it leads to the contamination of the mantle cavity, and they support this view by emphasizing that these effects are eliminated independently in the opisthobranchs and pulmonates.

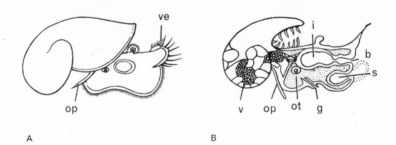

Fig. 19-6. Veliger larva of *Entoconcha*. A, external aspect. B, optical longitudinal section (after Baur). *b*, mouth; *g*, pedal gland; *i*, gut; *op*, operculum; *ot*, otocyst; *s*, sac-like invagination; *v*, residual yolk; *ve*, velum. From Caullery, 1952. *Parasitism and Symbiosis*. Sidgwick and Jackson, London.

Against this Morton has suggested that there may be certain advantages in the anterior position of the gills and osphradium, since it enables the latter to sample the water into which the animal is moving. However this may be, a widely favoured theory of the origin of torsion is one originally put forward by Garstang. He suggested that it arose as a larval adaptation that was carried over into the adult stage, the adults being then compelled, so to say, to make the best of the resulting situation. Garstang's argument was that prior to torsion the protective value of the larval shell is limited because the delicate head and velum cannot be withdrawn into the posterior mantle cavity until the foot has been withdrawn; in effect, it is impossible to give them adequate protection. Torsion, which could conceivably have resulted from a genetic mutation promoting asymmetrical muscular development, facilitates the withdrawal of the head and velum, because the mantle cavity is now in a more favourable position. This would have had sufficient survival value to ensure the persistence of this new feature, and thereby to establish the fundamental distinguishing character of the Class Gastropoda. Again in Garstang's words,

> Predaceous foes, still drifting by in numbers unabated,
> Were baffled now by tactics which their dining plans frustrated.
> Their prey upon alarm collapsed, but promptly turned about,
> With tender morsel safe within and the horny foot without!

It can be argued against this explanation that the advantage gained in protection is of little value against larger predators, such as herring, which indulge in mass consumption of these larvae. Yet Garstang's theory remains a favoured one. Indeed, it has been so widely accepted by British zoologists that their students must often feel that it is the only possible explanation of the origin of gastropod torsion. This, however, is not so. Ghiselin, for example, while accepting that torsion confers a functional advantage upon the larva, considers it to be too complex a transformation to have been evolved in a single step. Basing his argument on an earlier view of Lang, he suggests that torsion arose after exogastric coiling had already been established in the larval stage as a by-product of ontogenetic growth processes. This coiling need not have interfered with larval locomotion, but the movements of the adults (and even of the larvae when they began to settle) might well have been handicapped by the difficulty of balancing the shell. Torsion could then have evolved as an adaptation to overcome this difficulty.

Obviously the problem of the origin of this torsion, like various other phylogenetic problems that we consider elsewhere, may, from its very nature, remain for ever unresolved. It is just for this reason, however, that it is so important to scrutinize carefully the theoretically possible alternatives, and to subject them from time to time to critical evaluation in the light of developing evolutionary theory. In this context, both of the views that we have outlined stand in need of some form of experimental verification, or at least of a more exhaustive analysis of the developmental factors involved.

Garstang's theory is in any case of exceptional interest. It has a significance ranging far beyond the field of molluscan evolution, for it recognizes the immense potential importance of the capacity of larvae for evolving, independently of their adults, in adaptation to their own particular modes of life. Other examples to be mentioned later will show this being carried to a point at which a profound and drastic metamorphosis is needed to bridge the gap between larva and adult—something far in excess of that seen in the mitraria larva. Even more important, we shall be able to consider further the possibility of some of these divergent larval specializations being retained in the adult phase and thereby establishing entirely new types of adult form, much as Garstang's theory visualizes the origin of gastropod form as a result of the retention in the adult of the larval torsion.

19–3 CRUSTACEAN LARVAE

We have seen that the inclusion of the Arthropoda within the Protostomia rests upon inferences drawn from adult anatomy rather than upon any direct evidence obtainable from their pattern of early development. Their larvae are no more informative. The Crustacea have a wide variety of larvae, but these are entirely crustacean in form, and show no relationship at all with the ciliated larvae of annelids. In fact, the almost complete loss of cilia by the phylum extends to their larval stages; these, like the adults, rely upon their limbs for locomotion. Whether there ever was a trochophore stage in the remote ancestry of the marine arthropods is unknown, for, if there was, it has certainly been lost without trace. The larvae now hatch in a relatively advanced stage of development, with at least a few functional appendages present and with the accompanying metameric segmentation. In this there is no new principle; we have seen in the nectochaetous larva an example of a metamerically segmented stage that may be achieved at hatching, and crustacean larvae merely illustrate a further extension of this acceleration of development.

The simplest crustacean larva is the nauplius (Fig. 19-7), a three-segmented organism with three pairs of limbs; the first pair are uniramous antennules, the other two being biramous and representing respectively the antennae and mandibles of the adult. They differ in form, however, from the adult appendages, for they are specialized to meet the locomotor needs of the larva, and because of this it is as meaningless to seek in the nauplius for the characteristics of the ancestral crustacean as it would be to interpret the nectochaetous larva as an ancestral polychaete. The phylogenetic significance of larval forms is as difficult to determine as is that of the different modes of cleavage and gastrulation. We shall refer to this problem again later, but it is well to bear constantly in mind that larvae, too, are developmental stages, specialized for functions that are peculiar to them, and that may be widely different from the activities of the adults.

In the branchiopods the further development of the nauplius involves continuous growth, interrupted by periodical moults, at which additional somites and limbs are added; the adult form is thus achieved without drastic metamorphosis. We may reasonably assume that this simple type of life history was the primitive mode of development of Crustacea. In the other groups with free larvae, however, including the Copepoda, Ostracoda, Cirripedia, and Decapoda, we find one or more stages which include a sharply defined metamorphosis. The most obvious reason for this is when larva and adult have entirely different modes of life, as, to take extreme examples, in the barnacles (Cirripedia) and in the crabs (Brachyura). Yet this cannot be the only explanation, for metamorphosis may occur when the modes of life are not greatly dissimilar, and there may even be a sharp transition from one larval stage

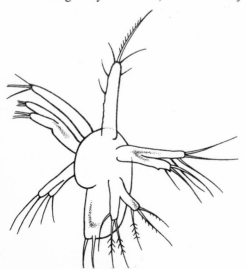

Fig. 19-7. Nauplius larva of a Penaeid (*Sicyonia*). From Gurney, 1942. *Larvae of decapod Crustacea.* Ray Society, London.

to another. Such metamorphoses probably reflect marked changes in level of specialization of the stages concerned, or in the pattern of organization of particular functions; such is to be seen, for example, in the transition, during the development of the Penaeidae (see below), from the antennal propulsion of the nauplius larva to the thoracic propulsion of the zoea larva.

The Copepoda typically begin their free-swimming life with a nauplius larva that subsequently undergoes a clearly marked yet simple metamorphosis. There are six nauplius stages, the last one still having three pairs of limbs, but possessing rudiments of five further pairs. The sixth moult gives rise to the first copepodid stage, with an essentially adult form; two pairs of swimming legs are present, and the future regions of the adult body are defined. Subsequent development may involve five copepodid stages, during which the assumption of the final adult form is progressive and direct, with no further metamorphosis, at least as far as free-living species are concerned. In the highly modified parasitic forms, however, there may be only one copepodid stage, and a considerable measure of metamorphic change.

How the adult mode of life influences larval development is well seen in the Cirripedia, sessile forms that are so profoundly modified that on first inspection they are hardly recognizable as crustaceans at all. They begin their free-swimming phase as a nauplius, characterized in this group by a distinctive pair of anterior lateral horns, and by a posterior forked spine. This larva undergoes a series of moults, and then passes at a single moult into the cypris stage, so called because the body and appendages are enclosed within a bivalved shell in a manner that recalls the appearance of an ostracod. Eventually this larva settles, attaching itself to the substratum by its modified antennules and by a secretion of cement glands that are situated at the bases of these appendages. The shell of the cypris is now discarded, and its place is taken by the valved shell of the adult. The behaviour of the cypris larva at settling has been closely studied, for barnacles play a major part in the fouling of ships' bottoms, so that the assessment of the value of anti-fouling paints demands an understanding of the biology of the larvae. Knight-Jones and Crisp have described how, after alighting, the cyprids 'walk about, pulling themselves forward by each antennule alternately, and changing direction only infrequently. . . . On an unsuitable surface . . . they may swim off almost at once'. We shall be examining later the significance of this and similar behaviour patterns in invertebrate larvae.

In the Decapoda the larvae have become more specialized and the life histories correspondingly more complex. One result of this is that hatching is usually at a later stage, the nauplius being no longer recognizable. Yet we should expect that it must at one time have been a normal stage of the life history of the ancestral malacostracans; that this was so is certainly suggested by the life cycle of the penaeid prawns. These are members of the Natantia, but are distinct from the true prawns and shrimps. *Penaeus*, the Mediterranean prawn, hatches as a nauplius with the typical three pairs of limbs. Thereafter, by growth and moulting, it develops rapidly without any abrupt transition through a series of nauplius stages into a protozoea (Fig. 19–8). This still lacks compound eyes, but the thorax is fully segmented, a small carapace is present (developed as a fold from the maxillary segment), and the telson is forked. The appendages comprise antennules, antennae, and mouth parts, and also the first and second maxillipedes, which are functional biramous limbs; rudiments of the third maxillipedes may also be present. There are altogether three protozoea stages, which

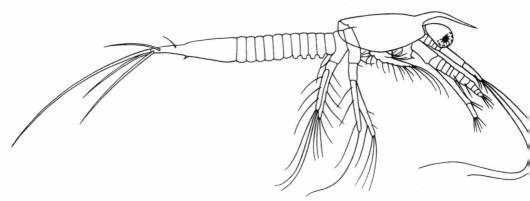

Fig. 19-8. Protozoea 2 of a Penaeid (*Gennadas*). From Gurney, 1942. *op. cit.*

may be regarded as a transitional phase in the life history; the third stage has uropods, together with rudiments of all of the legs.

Gurney has emphasized that the organization of the main developmental stages of the higher Crustacea is primarily determined by their mode of locomotion. The nauplius depends upon antennal propulsion, and so, in general, does the protozoea, as is shown by the large natatory exopodites of its antennae. The appearance of the maxillipedes foreshadows the next stage, which depends upon thoracic propulsion. This is initiated by the transformation of the protozoea into the zoea larva (Fig. 19-9), which itself passes through several stages. Initially it is characterized by the possession of stalked eyes and at least three pairs of biramous thoracic limbs which function as swimming appendages. Further, the carapace, which remains free of the tergites in the protozoea, now begins to fuse with them. The remainder of the thoracic limbs are at first only rudiments; the abdominal segments are defined, but their appendages are not yet developed.

In the later zoea stages the remainder of the thoracic limbs develop; they are all biramous, with large natatory exopodites, so that such larvae are sometimes referred to as the schizopod stage. The abdominal pleopods also appear, but are not yet functional. Finally, with the moult to the post-larval stage, these latter appendages develop setae and become functional swimmerets, while the thoracic limbs lose their exopodites. A curious feature of this stage (which is not quite fully adult) is the temporary loss or reduction of the fourth and fifth thoracic limbs; these reappear later during the course of several moults.

This penaeid life cycle, varying considerably in detail in different species, indicates the primitive form of decapod development. The general trend in other decapods has been towards a shortening of the life cycle, a trend that is probably correlated with the widespread habit of protecting the eggs by carrying them on the body of the parent. Thus the true crabs (Brachyura) hatch as zoea larvae (Fig. 19-10).

Fig. 19-9. Zoea of *Gennadas*. From Gurney, 1942. *op. cit.*

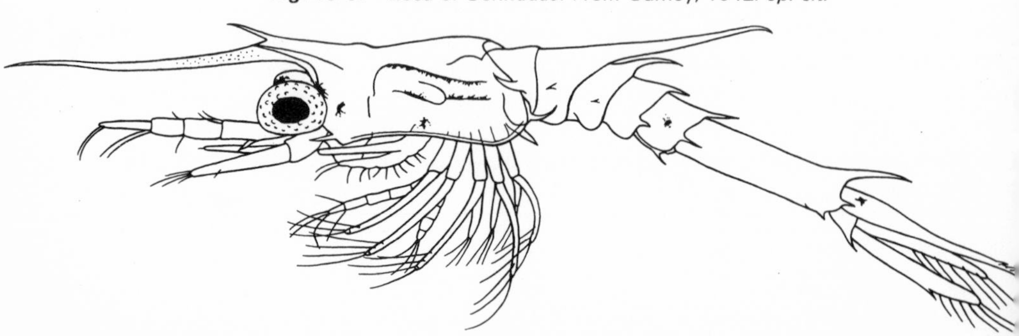

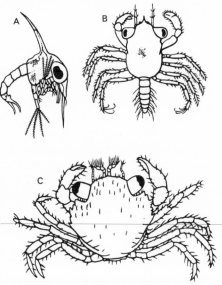

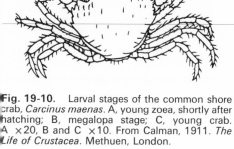

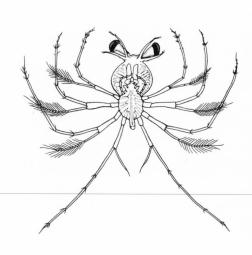

Fig. 19-10. Larval stages of the common shore crab, *Carcinus maenas*. A, young zoea, shortly after hatching; B, megalopa stage; C, young crab. A ×20, B and C ×10. From Calman, 1911. *The Life of Crustacea*. Methuen, London.

Fig. 19-11. Phyllosoma larva of the spiny lobster, *Palinurus vulgaris*. From Calman, 1911. *op. cit.*

These have a forked telson, a curved abdomen, and a helmet-shaped carapace which bears two long spines: a median rostral one, extending forwards, and a median dorsal one. Later the rudiments of the swimmerets and of the remaining thoracic limbs appear, and the larva becomes transformed into another clearly defined stage, the megalopa. This is an essentially crab-like form in which the spines become shorter and all of the appendages are present. At first the abdomen is still extended; the megalopa swims at the surface, using the swimmerets, but later it moults on the sea bottom to become a fully formed crab, with its abdomen folded and the abdominal limbs no longer locomotory. The megalopa, often referred to as a larva, can alternatively be regarded as a first post-larval stage, which marks, with its abdominal propulsion, the transition to the specialized form of the adult crab. The Anomura are significant from this point of view. These animals, which include *Galathea*, *Porcellana*, and the hermit crabs, have partly evolved a crab-like organization. They hatch as zoea larvae, but do not pass through a schizopod stage. Hermit crabs have a glaucothoë stage, with symmetrical abdomen and swimming pleopods; this corresponds to a megalopa. The zoea of the Anomura is distinguishable by its long anterior spine, and the two spines that extend backwards from the posterior angles of the carapace; these spines, particularly the anterior one, are enormously and characteristically elongated in the larva of *Porcellana*.

The larvae of lobsters (Astacura) illustrate another abbreviation of the life cycle, for they hatch in the schizopod stage. All of the thoracic appendages are present, with well-developed exopodites, and with the first three pairs of legs chelate. Abdominal pleopods and uropods are absent at first, but these appear during subsequent moults, so that by the third stage the pleopods have setae. The transition to the adult form is thus a comparatively rapid one and involves no profound transformation.

A remarkable variant of this abbreviated type of life cycle is that of the spiny lobster, *Palinurus*, and its allies. The larva hatches as the phyllosoma larva (Fig. 19–11), which is so modified that it is immediately distinguishable from any other larval type. In some respects it is a modified schizopod stage, with two pairs of large maxillipedes (the first pair being rudimentary) and three pairs of legs, the fourth and fifth pairs of legs being only small buds. The most obvious external characteristics, however, are the flattening of its thorax, and its glassy transparency; features that give it, in the words of Hardy, the appearance of being fashioned from a coverslip. The phyllosoma larva is an extreme example of planktonic adaptation; it is not easily comparable with any other crustacean larva, and illustrates very well the possibilities of independent larval evolution. For all its schizopod appearance, it is protozoea-like in that the carapace is mostly free from the thorax; yet the development of three pairs of legs in its first stage is a degree of precocity unexpected in a protozoea.

Finally, the true shrimps and prawns (e.g. *Crangon*, *Palaemon*, *Hippolyte*) hatch as zoea larvae with three pairs of functional maxillipedes; the remaining legs appear in succession or, sometimes, out of order, with the fifth forming in advance of the third and fourth. These larvae have their own distinguishing characteristics; they lack both the conspicuous median spine of the brachyuran zoea and the backwards-directed ones of the anomuran larva.

19–4   SOME DEUTEROSTOME LARVAE: THE ORIGIN OF VERTEBRATES

The fundamental characteristics of deuterostome larvae are to be seen in the array of larval forms produced by the Phylum Echinodermata (Fig. 19–12). The range of modification found in these larvae, their drastic metamorphoses, and the possible bearing of their own organization upon the problem of the origin of vertebrates have long made them a focus of interest. The phylum is sharply divided into two major groups, the Subphylum Pelmatozoa and the Subphylum Eleutherozoa. The former, now largely extinct, comprises animals that are attached to the substratum directly or by a stalk, either throughout life or at least during the juvenile phase. The region of attachment is aboral, the oral surface being directed upwards and being associated with a ciliary feeding mechanism that we have considered elsewhere. The Subphylum Eleutherozoa comprises free-living forms, with the oral surface directed downwards or to one side. They depend for locomotion upon the water vascular system, which in the Pelmatozoa is primarily associated with feeding. These distinctions are relevant to the development and relationships of the larvae.

The development of the Pelmatozoa, as exemplified in *Antedon*, leads to the hatching of a doliolaria ('little barrel') larva. This swims for a limited period, probably no more than a few days, with the aid of four or five ciliated bands, which are arranged like the hoops of a barrel. At the anterior or apical end is an apical sensory plate with a tuft of cilia; the opposite end, in accordance with the deuterostome plan of structure, marks the site of the blastopore. The larva soon becomes attached by an adhesive pit which is situated mid-ventrally, and towards the anterior pole. Later, the internal organs, which have been differentiating progressively throughout this period, rotate through about 90°; as a result of this the original anterior end of the larva becomes

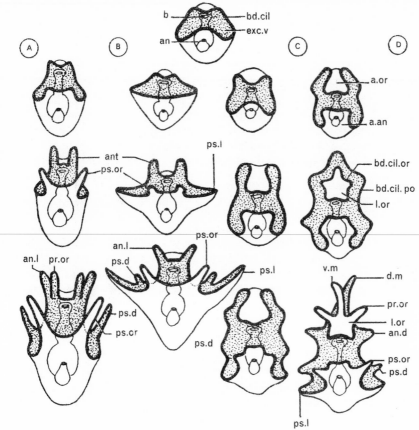

Fig. 19-12. Diagrams illustrating the possible evolution of larvae derived from the dipleurula. Series A represents the transformation of the dipleurula into the echinopluteus, B into the ophiopluteus, C into the auricularia, and D into the bipinnaria. The ciliated band is shown as a thick line. *an,* anus; *a.or, a.an,* preoral and anal areas; *b,* mouth; *bd.cil.or, bd.cil.pr,* preoral and circumoral (postoral) ciliated bands; *exc.v,* ventral depression. Larval arms: *an.d,* antero-dorsal; *an.l* (and *ant*), antero-lateral; *d.m,* dorso-median; *pr.or,* preoral; *ps.d,* postero-dorsal; *ps.l,* postero-lateral; *ps.or,* postero-oral; *v.m,* ventro-median. From Grassé, 1948. *Traité de Zoologie,* vol. 11. Masson, Paris.

the attachment stalk, while the expansion of the free or oral region makes the larva look like a stalked pelmatozoan. This is the cystidean stage, so called because the organism now resembles one of the extinct cystids. At first it cannot feed, for the stomodaeum is closed over to form the vestibule, but within a few days it opens up and feeding then begins. After remaining in this form for some 6 weeks the larva develops arms, and is now referred to as the pentacrinoid larva. Finally, after some further months of sessile life, it breaks away from the stalk and begins the free-swimming life characteristic of *Antedon* and of most living crinoids. Some, the so-called sea-lilies, remain stalked and sessile; this mode of life is thought to be the primitive one in echinoderms (p. 194), but it has been abandoned by present-day forms except in this particular group of species.

The early development of *Antedon* agrees with the basic plan that we have outlined for deuterostomes in so far as cleavage is not spiral, gastrulation is by invagination, and coelomic sacs are cut off from the archenteron. The larva, on the other hand, does not conform to our suggested scheme, a point that we shall return to later. The scheme is, however, evident in the larvae of the Eleutherozoa, which can usually be sharply distinguished from the trochophore type of protostome larva. This is readily apparent in the pluteus larva (Fig. 18–15, p. 398), which is the starting point of the larval development of the Echinoidea and Ophiuroidea. Internally this is distinguishable from the trochophore by the paired coelomic sacs, the absence of protonephridia, and by the posterior blastopore leading into the invaginated archenteron. Externally the young larva possesses the usual apical plate and tuft, but the single ciliary band which develops later is entirely characteristic; this is curved in such a way that at one point it passes between the mouth and anus, thereby differing from a prototroch.

The further development of the pluteus is marked by the improvement of its locomotion and of its suspension in the water. This is a result of the outgrowth of long paired arms which carry the ciliated band with them, and which are supported by a skeletal system of slender calcareous rods. Further improvement results, in some genera, from the specialization of parts of the cilated band between the bases of certain of the arms; these parts, which have specially well-developed cilia, separate from the main band to form structures called epaulettes. The echinoids and ophiuroids differ in the mode of outgrowth of the arms, the resultant larvae being distinguished in consequence as the echinopluteus and the ophiopluteus. The four principal pairs of arms of the echinopluteus (antero-lateral, pre-oral, post-oral, and postero-dorsal) do not correspond exactly with those of the ophiopluteus (antero-lateral, postero-lateral, post-oral, and postero-dorsal), the pre-oral arms of the echinopluteus being absent from the ophiopluteus. The larvae differ, too, in general appearance, the arms being more widely opened out in the ophiopluteus.

These larvae may live for weeks or months in the plankton before undergoing their metamorphosis. This is necessarily a drastic process, so different are the larvae from the adults, yet the metamorphosis of the echinopluteus may be completed within an hour. The speed is made possible by what may be termed careful preliminary preparation, the effect of which is both to prolong the dispersal phase and at the time time to minimise the highly vulnerable phase of transformation. During this preparation the continued elaboration of the coelomic sacs in the echinopluteus leads, among other things, to the development of a hydrocoel which becomes closely apposed to an ectodermal invagination; the latter closes off, and at this stage clearly corresponds with the vestibule of the crinoids, although it is here situated on the left side of the larva. The hydrocoel grows around the gut to form the water-vascular ring, and outgrowths from it establish its pentamerous symmetry.

The pre-oral lobe region, which corresponds to the stalk of the crinoid larva, makes no contribution to the adult echinoids. At the culmination of metamorphosis, which occurs without any fixation, the vestibule and its associated structures (termed the echinus rudiment) form the oral region of the sea-urchin, which thus represents the left side of the larva, while the right side of the larva gives rise to the aboral region. The larval arms are meanwhile absorbed and their skeletal supports discarded. With the hydrocoel and primary podia already established, the young urchin, probably less than 1 mm in diameter, is immediately capable of independent movement.

The metamorphosis of the ophiopluteus is similar in general principle to that of the echinopluteus, the radially symmetrical organization of the adult being laid down within the larva until this sinks to the bottom under the influence of the in-

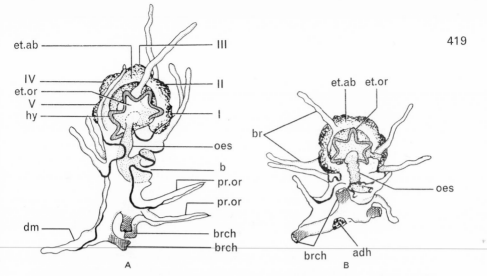

Fig. 19-13. Two stages in the metamorphosis of the brachiolaria of *Asterias pallida*. The attached larva is shown from the left side, so that the oral rudiment of the starfish (*et.or*) is seen in full view. The thick line represents the ciliated bands. I–V, five brachial expansions of the aboral rudiment (*et.ab*); *adh*, adhesive disc; *b*, larval mouth; *br*, larval arms degenerating; *brch*, brachiolar arms; *dm*, dorso-median arms; *oes*, oesophagus; *pr.or*, preoral arms. From Grassé, 1948. *op. cit.*

creasing weight of the developing skeletal material. The arms and their skeleton, together with the anterior end of the larva, are either absorbed or discarded. Among the many differences in detail we need only mention here the fact that the region corresponding to the echinus rudiment develops on the ventral surface of the larva instead of on its left side. Moreover, it does so without the appearance of a vestibule, although there are reasons for interpreting the stomodaeum as a vestige of this.

The characteristic larva of the Asteroidea is the bipinnaria. This is characterized by the growth and folding of the ciliated band to form two ventral loops; a smaller pre-oral one and a larger circumoral one. Of these, the pre-oral loop separates off from the main band to give rise to a separate loop which thus encloses a pre-oral lobe. As with the pluteus larva, the locomotion and support of the growing organism are aided by further extension of the ciliated band into arms, but these are not so long as those of the pluteus; moreover, they lack skeletal supports, and so are much more flexible in use.

The metamorphosis of the asteroid larva (Fig. 19–13) is often, but not always, preceded by temporary fixation. In preparation for this there develop, after some weeks of planktonic life, three brachiolar arms, lying anterior to the pre-oral loop. These arms differ from the others in possessing extensions of the coelom, and in bearing adhesive cells at their tips, while an adhesive glandular area or sucker develops between their bases. The larva is now known as a brachiolaria. It attaches to the substratum, first by the brachiolar arms, and then by the sucker, and begins metamorphosis. During this process the anterior region is absorbed, as in the other examples described above, while the future starfish develops in the posterior region of the brachiolaria. Its formation follows the same general course as that of the young sea-urchin, the left side of the larva becoming the oral part of the disc and the right side the aboral part; there is, however, no vestibule. The metamorphosis may be completed within one day from fixation, the starfish being able by then to pull itself free from the remains of the larva, which Hardy has aptly likened to its perambulator.

A larva closely resembling the early bipinnaria is found in many of the Holothuria, which hatch at around the third day of development as an auricularia larva (*auricula*, a little ear). This has a circumoral ciliated band which is folded in a complex manner, somewhat like that of the bipinnaria, but its subsequent history differs, for it breaks up into sections that become rearranged and extended to form from three to five transverse ciliated bands. This is the doliolaria stage, so called because of its obvious resemblance to the characteristic larva of crinoids. Owing to the elongated and cylindrical form of the holothurian body, the adult stage is attained without such a drastic metamorphosis as is seen in the other Eleutherozoa. Such metamorphosis as does occur recalls to some extent the events of crinoid development; the stomodaeal invagination forms a vestibule which, after almost completely closing over, rotates to establish the oral structures at the anterior end.

Before we attempt to judge the phylogenetic significance and the interrelationships of these several types of echinoderm larvae, it is necessary to appreciate that the pattern of development within each group has been subjected to much secondary modification. This has led to examples of convergence and divergence that are fully comparable to those found in the adult structure of any group of animals. We can here mention only a few examples.

Abbreviation of the larval life history, and even direct development, certainly occurs in echinoderms, although Hyman suggests that the incidence of the latter has probably been exaggerated because stages of this are more easily collected than are stages of indirect development. An example of secondary modification of larval form is seen in the ophiuroid *Ophioderma brevispina*; this lacks a pluteus stage, passing instead through a doliolaria-like larva (here called a vitellaria larva, see below) with four ciliated bands. As in other comparable cases, the appearance of rudimentary skeletal spicules shows that this type of life history must have evolved from a more typical one involving a pluteus stage. Fell ascribes this type of modification to an increase in the yolk content of the egg, which, he suggests, so modifies the course of development that radial symmetry is established relatively early. In some instances a fully direct development may be established, as in *Amphipholis squamata*, where eggs are shed into the bursal sacs and develop within these into young ophiuroids, again with rudimentary larval skeletons. The increase of yolk in these forms modifies development in essentially the same way as in the chordates. Invagination is reduced to a solid inpushing of cells; these differentiate to form the mesoderm and the wall of the enteron, the archenteron and the formation of coelomic sacs having disappeared from the ontogeny.

Such shortening of the larval life history is not restricted to the ophiuroids. In asteroids either the brachiolaria or the bipinnaria stages may be omitted, often in association with the production of large yolky eggs. *Astropecten* omits the brachiolaria, and metamorphoses from the bipinnaria stage without undergoing fixation. In *Solaster endeca*, by contrast, brachiolar arms are formed without the larva passing through a clearly defined bipinnaria stage at all. So also in echinoids, where forms with yolky eggs may have their free-swimming stage restricted to no more than a few days, and where the larvae may be simplified to an oval form and uniform ciliation.

As for the phenomena of convergence and divergence, we may quote one or two examples from Fell's discussion. There has clearly been an independent evolution of cylindrical larvae with ciliated rings (vitellaria larvae) from the yolky eggs of holothurians, crinoids, and ophiuroids, but there are also more specific cases of close resemblances between unrelated species. For example, the larvae of the echinoid genus *Diadema* have an unusual development of the post-oral arms, and a reduction of the others, which gives them a superficial resemblance to an ophiopluteus. As for divergence, this is illustrated in a broad sense in what we have already said of modifications of the life cycles, but it may occur even between closely related forms. Thus the ophiuroid *Ophioderma brevispina* has a vitellaria larva, yet the closely related *Ophiura texturata* has a well-developed and normal ophiopluteus.

Fell has argued that with such plasticity in larval development we cannot attach phylogenetic significance to the various larval forms. This, however, is only true if one attempts to interpret them as a strict recapitulation, in the Haeckelian sense, of phylogenetic history. Such an interpretation cannot possibly be justified. Larvae undergo independent adaptation to their particular modes of life, and to their primary function of ensuring development and dispersal of the species. They cannot, therefore, be precise guides to the organization of adult ancestors; a conclusion that is particularly well demonstrated by the structure of crustacean larvae. This, however, is not a counsel of despair, implying that it is impossible to unravel anything of the history of larval forms. Rather must they be approached as we would approach adult forms, resting our interpretation of their relationships upon a careful differentiation between the primary features of their organization and the secondary modifications that have been imposed upon them.

From this point of view we can see in eleutherozoan larvae certain common features of organization, including bilateral symmetry, an apical plate and tuft, an antero-ventral mouth, a posterior anus derived from the blastopore, a tripartite and paired enterocoel, and a ciliated band curving to run round the mouth and in front of the anus. These we may regard as primary features; they are the foundation of the concept of the Deuterostomia. They have also been used, but less convincingly, as the basis of the concept of the Dipleurula (Fig. 19–12), a hypothetical organism conceived to be the possible ancestral form of echinoderms.

For reasons outlined above, it is unwise to extrapolate from larval organization to adult; yet the drastic character of echinoderm metamorphosis must surely reflect a time in their past history when a bilaterally symmetrical and free-living stage, which may or may not have had the characteristics attributed to the Dipleurula, settled and in due course developed a pentamerous symmetry. To regard the behaviour of contemporary larvae as an exact recapitulation of ancestral history would be wrong. Events that must have been spread over a vast extent of time are here compressed into hours or minutes; moreover, the execution of the transition has been independently modified in the various groups, as may be seen by comparing the metamorphosis of the crinoids with that of asteroids. Yet here again the evidence available need not be completely ignored. Viewing the metamorphic events of all of the echinoderm groups as a whole, we may reasonably infer that the settling of the ancestral stock took place by the anterior end; this became a stalk of fixation, with the left side of the organism becoming the oral surface and the right side the aboral one. This was presumably followed by the development of radial symmetry, by the rotation of the oral surface upwards and of the aboral one downwards, and by the consequent asymmetrical development of the coeloms of the two sides, the anterior structure of the right side undergoing regression.

If we now extend our analysis to a comparison of the several types of eleuthero-zoan larvae, we see that the Holothuria stand somewhat apart from the other three classes in the possession of the doliolaria stage and in the development of a vestibule that subsequently rotates into an anterior position. These features suggest a close relationship between holothurians and crinoids, and, as a corollary, an early separation of the Holothuria from the other Eleutherozoa. The close resemblance between the auricularia of the Holothuria and the early bipinnaria of the Asteroidea suggests a close relationship between these two groups. Similarly, the presence of the pluteus in the Echinoidea and Ophiuroidea suggests a close relationship between these. We are thus led to the surprising conclusion that the asteroids must have diverged early, and that the ophiuroids, for all their superficial similarity to starfish, are more closely related to the sea-urchins. Other considerations support this conclusion. The asteroids are the only Eleutherozoa to retain a stalk at any stage in their life history. These animals are also undoubtedly primitive in retaining open ambulacral grooves—the only example of this in the Eleutherozoa, and a feature that links them closely with the Pelmatozoa.

The crinoids are the most difficult group of echinoderms to interpret from the point of view of larval history, since their larvae correspond neither to the auricularia nor to the pluteus type. Their characteristic doliolaria can, however, be recognized also in the life history of holothurians, in which group it develops from the auricularia stage; thus it is possible that a stage corresponding to the auricularia may have been lost in the crinoids, just as stages have been lost in individual species of Eleutherozoa. Our difficulty here is not confined to developmental stages. The crinoids are an isolated group from any point of view—impossible to regard as direct forerunners of the Eleutherozoa, and difficult to relate to any of the extinct groups of Pelmatozoa. In both development and adult form they must surely reflect a long period of isolated evolutionary history.

The larval history of the other deuterostomes is no less complex than that of the echinoderms. The most straightforward situation is seen in the Phylum Hemichordata, some members of which have an indirect development with the production of a characteristic tornaria larva (Fig. 19–14). This larva, in its mode of origin and in its organization, differs only in points of detail—notably in the presence of a posterior telotroch, which is a ciliated band additional to the main pluteus-like one—from an early pluteus larva. On the assumption that this type of larval organization is fundamental to the echinoderms, and an indication of a common inheritance, we are bound to regard the tornaria as indicating a close relationship between hemichordates and that phylum.

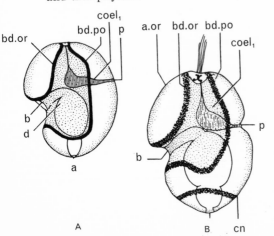

Fig. 19-14.   Two early stages in the development of the tornaria larva. a, anus; a.or, preoral area; b, mouth; bd.or, bd.po, preoral and circumoral ciliated bands; cn, preanal ciliated band; coel, proboscis coelom with pore; d, digestive tract; p, pore. The ventral depression is stippled. From Grassé, 1948, op. cit.

Fig. 19-15. A segmented embryo of the pogonophoran *Oligobrachia dogieli*, at the stage of the first appearance of tentacles, seen from the ventral side. *ms,* mesosoma; *mts,* metasoma; *ps,* protosoma; s^1, groove between protosoma and mesosoma; s^2, groove between the mesosoma and the metasoma; *td,* first tentacle. *ts,* bud of second tentacle. From Ivanov, 1963. *The Pogonophora.* Academic Press, London.

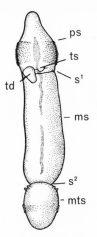

An illuminating feature of the metamorphosis of the tornaria of *Saccoglossus horsti* is the development of a temporary post-anal tail. This is probably a vestige of the attachment stalk of the sessile hemichordates, seen today in *Rhabdopleura* and *Cephalodiscus*. In other respects the metamorphosis of the larva involves little more than simple growth and transformation, without the drastic reorganization that echinoderms undergo. If, then, we accept that hemichordates were derived from the same type of sessile, microphagous ancestor as were the echinoderms, we may infer that they have diverged much less from that ancestral type than have the echinoderms. We may infer, too, that the Enteropneusta have evolved from the Pterobranchia by assuming the limited degree of independent movement involved in their burrowing life. The temporary development of the tail recalls the appearance of the stalk in asteroid metamorphosis. In both instances, although in quite different contexts, the larva carries something of the past with it. The fact that we can confirm our interpretation of the tail of the *Saccoglossus* larva by checking it against the structure of living relatives must surely give us some confidence in our interpretation of the stalk of the asteroid larva.

In some enteropneusts development is direct. As with echinoderms, this is best regarded as a result of secondary loss of the larva, the more so in that an intermediate stage of this is seen in *Saccoglossus horsti*; this has a free-swimming stage of short duration, which does not develop into a tornaria. Undoubtedly the differences in modes of development are to be associated with the yolk content of the egg, as so often in echinoderms. The tornaria is planktotrophic, whereas the larva of *S. horsti* is lecithotrophic, relying entirely upon the yolk laid down in its egg for the whole of its free-swimming activity. This lasts for only 1 or 2 days, at the end of which time the organism is ready to settle and metamorphose. The logical sequel to this is seen in *S. kowalevskii*, which hatches as a worm-like organism, and has no planktonic phase at all.

These facts help us to interpret the developmental history of the Pogonophora, as far as it is yet known. There are sound considerations drawn from adult anatomy that justify the association of these animals with hemichordates. Among them are the tripartite division of the elongated body, the organization and mode of development of the coelom, and the structure of the nervous system. A study of the general course of development is less immediately helpful, for there is no larval stage, but it can be brought into line with the deuterostome pattern if we suppose that, exactly as in the hemichordates, the possession of eggs rich in yolk has led to the secondary loss of a pelagic larva. Pogonophores develop through a stage that closely resembles the early metamorphic stages of enteropneusts, with an elongated body marked off into three main regions (Fig. 19–15); the hindmost of these grows later to form the main bulk of the body, exactly as in enteropneusts. At one stage the embryo possesses bands of cilia, the functional value of which is doubtful, although conceivably they may produce some sort of respiratory current in the tube of the parent, where the whole of the development takes place. Primarily, however, they must surely be regarded as the vestiges of the locomotor ciliation of the free-swimming larva that we have postulated, particularly since there is a posterior ring that could correspond exactly with the telotroch of enteropneusts. These bands, therefore, provide evidence comparable in significance with the vestigial skeletal spicules that develop in those ophiuroids that have lost their free-swimming stage.

With the protochordates (the Urochordata and the Cephalochordata) we pass to larvae that show no obvious relationship with any of those that we have so far considered. This is not to say that these groups lack developmental characters justifying their inclusion in the Deuterostomia. In amphioxus, where these characters are easiest to appreciate, we find total and non-spiral cleavage, gastrulation by invagination, the origin of the anus from the blastopore, and an enterocoelic coelom with indications of a tripartite differentiation. The larvae, however, are of more advanced organization than those of echinoderms and enteropneusts, possessing distinctively chordate features that, in the case of the urochordates, provide the main reason for including the adults within the Phylum Chordata.

We are concerned here with only two main larval types, the ascidian tadpole and the larva of amphioxus, for the larval stages of the pelagic urochordates (Thaliacea) are considered to have been modified or lost in correlation with the pelagic life of these animals. The functions of development, dispersal, and habitat selection are all discernible in the ascidian tadpole, but it is the last of the three that predominates. The larva possesses the embryonic rudiment of the adult alimentary canal, but it does not itself feed, for its free-swimming life is restricted to a matter of hours or perhaps to a few days at the most. Its chordate features are particularly well seen in the dorsal nervous system, and also in the locomotor mechanism, which is, however, confined to the tail. This mechanism, like that of the vertebrates, does not employ the principle of the hydrostatic skeleton, but relies instead upon the association of lateral muscle bands with an axial support, the notochord.

Closely associated functionally with locomotion are the ocelli and statocyst in the cerebral vesicle, at the anterior end of the central nervous system. Ascidian tadpoles are at first positively phototropic, and swim to the surface of the water. This behaviour pattern marks the distributive phase of their activity. Soon, however, they become negatively phototropic and positively geotropic, moving downwards into shaded rock crevices and overhanging surfaces that are suitable for the life of the adults. This is the phase of habitat selection, and its importance can be judged, paradoxically enough, in certain species in which the larval stage has been secondarily lost. This has occurred, for example, in certain molgulids that are adapted for life on submerged sand flats. Because of the uniformity of this habitat, and the ease with which it can be thickly populated, a larval stage is no longer as essential as it is in species that require particular types of rock surface. No doubt this explains why these species have secondarily evolved a direct form of development.

The significance of the tadpole in the ascidian life history is thus apparent; but its phylogenetic relationships are puzzling. The most illuminating interpretation is due to Garstang. One line of analysis led him to the suggestion that the tadpole could have been evolved from a larva like the auricularia of echinoderms as a consequence of the further elaboration of locomotor adaptation. This, Garstang suggested, could have led to the approximation of the loops of the ciliary band in the mid-dorsal line, where, with their associated nerve fibres, they could have given rise to the neural folds. The aboral ciliated band, situated inside the mouth and responsible for maintaining a feeding current, might have been the forerunner of the endostyle. It is difficult to evaluate this argument, for there is no direct evidence for it. Although a possibility, it is certainly not essential for our assessment of urochordate affinities. We can visualize the ascidian tadpole evolving as a special product of the urochordate line without weakening the arguments for associating the group with the Deuterostomia.

Where the larval history of urochordates is of outstanding importance is in connection with the second main line of Garstang's thought, in which he attempted to trace the line of evolution from the protochordates to the vertebrates. This, indeed, is a crucial evolutionary issue. Fundamental to the concept of the deuterostomes is the supposition that they all stem from a sessile and microphagous ancestry, a supposition that leaves us with the difficulty of seeing how vertebrate organization could have evolved from such a background. Garstang's answer was analogous to his explanation of the torsion of gastropods as resulting from the persistence of a larval adaptation in the adult. He suggested that the fundamentals of chordate organization, including the nervous system and notochord, were initially established in ancient larval forms like ascidian tadpoles. In due course their metamorphosis was eliminated, so that their larval organization became that of sexually mature adults. This is the process, well known in urodele Amphibia, that we call neoteny (the retention of larval characters into sexual maturity). In this instance it is visualized as leading to a new type of adult organization, one containing the immense potentialities that flowered in the evolution and diversification of vertebrate animals.

Speculative though this argument may be, it presents fewer difficulties than any other suggested explanation of vertebrate origins. It does not, of course, imply that the vertebrates arose from ascidian tadpoles of the modern type. Indeed, this is rendered virtually impossible by the way in which their free-swimming life has been reduced to a minimum compatible with habitat selection. Garstang's theory demands larvae that have not become specialized in this way, but are rather tending to prolong their independent life. It seems, therefore, that vertebrate origins must be sought in some remote and primitive deuterostome, urochordate-like in fundamental organization, but perhaps not very far from the level of organization of hemichordates, and with a generalized type of tailed larva. Hypothetical though the argument may seem, the contention that new forms of adult organization may arise through neoteny is by no means unsupported by protochordate life histories. It is generally agreed that the Larvacea are neotenous urochordates, preserving their tail into the adult stage, but even more illuminating are conditions within the Cephalochordata.

Amphioxus has a metamerically segmented and planktotrophic larva, highly specialized in its asymmetry; the mouth is relatively enormous, and lies on the left side of the body, probably as an adaptation to the intake of food by a ciliary feeding mechanism (Fig. 19–16). Clearly this larva is much more highly organized for in-

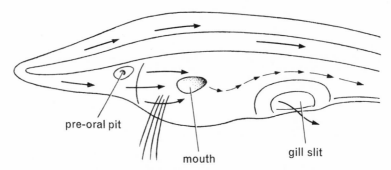

Fig. 19-16. Diagram showing the ciliary currents in the feeding of the young larva of amphioxus. The heavy arrows represent the currents produced by the action of the body cilia; the smaller ones represent the course taken by food particles that have entered the mouth. The mouth is small at this stage, having just pierced; later it rapidly enlarges, and at the same time other gill slits pierce. Adapted from Bone, 1958. *Proc. zool. Soc. Lond.,* **130,** 289–293.

dependent life than is the ascidian tadpole; yet some affinity with the latter is seen in the tendency of young amphioxus larvae to attach themselves temporarily to the bottom of aquaria by the secretion of the club-shaped gland. Moreover, older larvae become temporarily attached by three anterior adhesive papillae, which strikingly recall the attachment papillae of the ascidian tadpole.

What is especially significant, however, is that the larval life of amphioxus lasts for as much as 4–5 months, a striking contrast with that of ascidians, and much more reconcilable with the requirements of Garstang's hypothesis. Such behaviour in the earlier stages of deuterostome evolution might very well have led to the further exploitation of the possibilities of pelagic life by the introduction of some degree of neoteny. This, indeed, seems actually to be happening at the present day in the amphioxides larva, a cephalochordate larva, world-wide in distribution, that differs from the typical larva in the prolongation of its pelagic life. It may, as a result, develop as many as 34 pairs of gill slits, in contrast to the 24 which seem to be the normal maximum reached before metamorphosis. But, and more significantly, the gonads may appear in the amphioxides larva before metamorphosis begins—a clear trend towards neoteny.

As with other problems of larval biology, we must interpret these facts with caution and flexibility. It is not suggested that the vertebrates arose from the amphioxides type of larva, which may well be a specialized product of modern cephalochordates. All that is claimed is that certain processes which operate today may equally well have operated in the remote past, and that, had they done so, they might have led to the origin of the vertebrate line. To this line the Cephalochordata must, on the evidence of their general organization, be closely related. But they have none the less followed a line of evolution that diverges from that of vertebrates. However efficient the exploitation of pelagic life by their larvae, the adult cephalochordates lead a restricted life, sheltered in temporary burrows in sharply defined types of gravelly substrata. It was left for the vertebrates to exploit to the full the possibilities that have always been implicit in the modes of life of pelagic larvae.

20
Larval Lives

20–1 COMPETITION AND COOPERATION

We have been considering the invertebrates largely in terms of individual animals, yet this gives only part of the picture. The origin and establishment of life involved the interaction of different types of organism, as we have seen, and the maintenance of life at the present day is equally dependent upon such interactions. No animal or plant is an island, complete unto itself. But to say this is not merely to refer to the fundamental biological cycles of carbon and nitrogen that link autotrophs and heterotrophs together. At a different level of analysis each individual organism is a member not only of a species, but also of an integrated community which is characteristic of a particular type of habitat and is regulated by processes developed by natural selection. We can here draw an analogy with the evolution of the organization of cells and tissues to form bodies of increasing complexity. This organization depends upon the coordination and integration of the cells; it involves a measure of competition between them for the limited resources that are available for their maintenance; and it involves also the cooperation that allows them an influence far greater than any one cell could exert on its own.

The relationships of organisms with their environment are no less complex, and this is true in their developmental stages as well as when they are fully adult. The environment in the broadest sense of the term comprises inorganic or physical factors, and also the biotic factors that arise from the activities of the organisms themselves. All of these are therefore involved in the 'struggle for existence'. This was clearly perceived by Darwin, who emphasized that the term 'struggle' is used in this context in 'a large and metaphorical sense'. The struggle is partly against the physical conditions of the environment, and partly against predators, parasites, and disease. But it also involves competition for essential requirements that are limited in availability: nutrients for maintenance, space in which to function, and a mate to ensure reproduction. Within this general framework it is possible to analyze some-

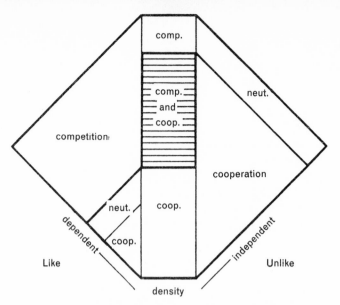

Fig. 20-1. The relations between individuals in respect of needs or activities in which they are alike may in principle be competitive, neutral, or cooperative (left of diagram). In respect of needs of activities in which the individuals are unlike the relation can only be neutral or cooperative (right of diagram). The resultant of two (or more) such characters may give a relation which is wholly competitive, wholly cooperative, or competitive in some respects and cooperative in others (centre of diagram). This last relation is basic to biological organization at all levels and imposes the need for control if the cooperative relation, necessary for the organization at a higher level of complexity, is not to be vitiated by the competition. From Mather, 1961. *Symp. Soc. exp. Biol.,* **15**, 264–281.

thing of the nature of organic interrelationships, but the analysis is by no means simple. This is not only because of the complexity of organization of natural communities; it is also because the precise relationships of any one species are not constant, but vary with such factors as age, season, and population density.

One useful expression of this has been outlined by Mather (Fig. 20-1). If animals are to compete, the individuals concerned must have some similarity in their needs or activities (left side of Fig. 20-1). This is commonly true of members of the same species, although the situation is modified, as we shall see, by polymorphism. The degree of competition will, however, be density-dependent, its intensity in any given population varying with the density of individuals. There will be an upper limit of density beyond which no more individuals can be accommodated, and at this level competition will be maximal. But at lower densities the situation will be otherwise. We may expect that at a certain level, with ample resources, the individuals may be independent of each other, so that their relationships will be neutral. It is also possible to visualize still lower densities, below which the population may be too small to exploit its environment adequately, to deal with the physical stresses that it imposes, or to compete with other species. At this level the relationships between the individuals will be cooperative rather than competitive.

At the other extreme, competition will be minimal or non-existent when the needs or activities of the individuals concerned are entirely unlike. This situation might exist between two quite unrelated species, although requirements for essential nutrients make it perhaps improbable that two species within the same community will be entirely independent of each other in their demands, unless they are very different indeed in their modes of life. If, however, we assume for the sake of argument that competition may be non-existent in certain circumstances (right side of Fig. 20–1), then the relationship between two such species may be one of neutrality or may give rise to some degree of cooperation. More usually, however, the complexity of the requirements of different species will produce the types of relationship seen in the centre of Fig. 20–1. They are unlikely to be neutral, but may rather be expected to be wholly cooperative, wholly competitive, or a combination of both. Mather points out that this interrelationship of competition and cooperation is fundamental at all levels of biological organization, from the cellular upwards. Competition determines the evolution of adaptation under the influence of natural selection, yet the resultant adaptations may eventually be so complex that they depend on cooperation for their maintenance. It is because of this that control systems are needed, to ensure that the required degree of cooperation is not made unattainable by competition. We shall see that colonial life, with its associated polymorphism, provides excellent examples of this principle in operation.

It follows from these considerations that the action of natural selection is itself necessarily complex, and that it is exerted at more than one level. Within any one group or population it may be acting upon the competitive relationships of the individuals. In respect of the relationships of this group with another, however, natural selection may be acting within the group to favour cooperative relationships of its members and hence the efficiency of the group as a whole, relative to other groups. Nor is this all. We have suggested above that relationships between two different species may also develop a degree of cooperation, and we shall later be considering specific examples of this. But it is possible, as Lucas has argued, that the degree of such cooperation may have been greatly underestimated. We have noted the extent to which organisms are dependent upon the nutrient metabolites produced by other organisms, but there is now much evidence that such dependence extends far beyond the limits of nutritional requirements.

For example, the rate of feeding of barnacles is influenced by the abundance of phytoplankton through a metabolite released by the latter. Again, the rate at which oysters pump water is influenced by the abundance in that water of certain carbohydrates that are released by the phytoplankton. It can be argued that in these examples, the efficiency of feeding of microphagous forms has been increased by the evolution of adaptive responses to metabolites released by the organisms upon which they feed. From this point of view the interactions of the phytoplankton and the animals that depend upon it are subtle ones; more than a blind engulfing of the food that happens to be present, but contributing rather to a greater degree of efficiency in the organization of this particular link in the food chain. The relationship is a cooperative one, in the large and metaphorical sense of Darwin, in so far as the phytoplankton is contributing to ensure that it shall be efficiently exploited! At this point, however, it will be well to translate these general considerations into an examination of some specific types of interrelationship.

Examples of the combination of competition with cooperation between members of the same species are well seen in gregarious animals. These are animals that grow so closely crowded together that sometimes, as with the pseudo-colonies of *Phoronis*, they may be superficially indistinguishable from true colonies, although in fact the individuals lack the direct organic continuity that is characteristic of colonial forms (see below). Such close crowding may, no doubt, arise by chance in particular populations of a species that is not normally gregarious. Truly gregarious species, however, are species in which this is a normal and predictable mode of life; it is part of the adaptive organization with which they confront their environment, and it depends upon specialized patterns of structure and behaviour, such as the settling responses of larvae that we have already discussed.

Knight-Jones and Moyse have pointed out how the pseudo-colonies of tubicolous polychaetes can modify and improve their environment. Associations of *Sabellaria alveolata* increase both the mass and the surface areas of the sandy reefs upon which they grow, while the associations of *Filograna implexa*, increasing by fission of the worms, build up structures in which the individual members enjoy mutual support. The competitive aspect of the relationship is seen in the way in which each worm adds to its tube until it is adequately orientated outwards and has room to expand its branchial crown for feeding.

Crowded populations of barnacles are governed by the same principles. They grow in ridges and hummocks, the distribution of which is perhaps determined initially by the presence of prominences on the substratum which place those that settle there in a more favourable position for feeding. However the pattern may be initiated, the result is a cooperative improvement of the environment, for the effect of the irregularities is to increase both water turbulence and the surface area, and thereby to increase the efficiency of feeding. Individuals in the centre of a hummock must be elongated, but, given this growth response, they are as well placed for feeding as are less crowded individuals that have more space to occupy. The only ill-placed ones are probably the small barnacles in the hollows between the humps; their food supply may be insufficient to ensure breeding, but on the other hand they may provide support for the edges of the humps. In this respect we may think of them as subordinated to the benefit of the aggregation as a whole—a phenomenon of much greater importance in the associations that we call colonies, where it involves a high level of adaptive specialization. These associations are considered later; for the moment we are concerned with the role of larvae in animal relationships with each other and with their environment.

20–2 MARINE LARVAE AND HABITAT SELECTION

Larvae are important agents of competition and cooperation. Their life is to be viewed as a compromise (dependent to some extent upon the mode of life of the adult) between the three requirements that we have earlier outlined: development, dispersal, and habitat selection. The first of these is not, of course, dependent upon producing larvae, for it can be adequately met by viviparity and a non-pelagic life history, a mode of development that also carries the advantage of reducing wastage to a minimum. This wastage, which is brought about to a large extent by predation, is often enormous, as may be judged from Thorson's estimate that the females of most marine invertebrate species each produce from several thousands to some millions of ova during a lifetime. Its impact in different species can be estimated by considering their rate of egg production, on the assumption that larger production is correlated with greater wastage. The relevant data show clearly that the higher levels of egg production are found in those species that have planktotrophic larvae with a long pelagic phase. Evidently this method of development is extravagant, but against this drawback can be set two benefits. Firstly, the larva and adult are able to exploit independently of each other, and without intraspecific competition, the resources of two different environments, so that cooperation is a factor here. Secondly, the prolonged larval phase facilitates the wide dispersal of the species.

As with oviparity and viviparity, however, it is by no means easy to demonstrate these advantages by comparing particular species. To quote another example given by Smith, most shore-dwelling polychaetes have a prolonged larval life, yet the larva of *Arenicola* probably remains in the sand, although it is adapted for independent movement. Very likely this is true also of other larvae, which may well be able to survive without leaving the shore, even though they may appear to be structurally equipped for pelagic life. Many nemertean larvae can cling to the substratum, and many polychaete larvae can probably survive by creeping over the substratum or by living in rock pools. Indeed, one can imagine that a pelagic larval phase might lead to unnecessarily wide dispersal, and that this, combined with the very large production of eggs that it requires, might restrict larval freedom in more specialized life histories. Of such possibilities, however, we can say no more than that different species have independently achieved different solutions of the problem, and therefore different equilibria in their life histories.

Irrespective of the length of larval life, habitat selection remains the third important aspect of reproduction for which the larva has to provide, especially in those species that are either sessile in the adult, or that change their position only very little. This is one aspect of metamorphosis, and it is the aspect that is most readily analyzed experimentally since it permits a critical determination of the conditions in which metamorphosis occurs. We might expect these conditions to be most flexible in those species that are the freest to move in the adult and that do not, therefore, depend upon larval mobility alone for ensuring survival in a suitable habitat. Little is known of this, although there is some evidence to support the argument. For example, the youngest stages of freely moving shore forms such as *Carcinus maenas* are not normally found on the shore itself, which suggests that their larvae metamorphose in conditions that allow the adults to establish themselves independently in their preferred habitats. The course of events is quite different, however, in species with less mobile adults. Here, as the studies of Wilson and others have shown, there are remarkable adaptive specializations in the receptor systems and behaviour of larvae, even of those which seem, from the morphological point of view, to be of comparatively simple organization.

Wilson has closely studied the development and behaviour of the larva of the polychaete *Ophelia*. This larva (Fig. 20-2) is a simple type of trochophore, which possesses at first a broad prototroch, a small and incomplete telotroch, and groups of neurotrochal cilia extending ventrally between these main bands. It swims freely in the plankton, growing and forming its first few segments, until at the age of about 6-8 days it has three setigerous segments, and is capable of some muscular wriggling of the trunk region. At this stage it is ready to undergo metamorphosis, a process that involves growth of the body, and the loss of the larval ciliation and of the capacity for swimming. The behaviour of the larva changes, and it is now able to crawl among sand particles on the substratum.

This complex of metamorphic changes does not take place abruptly and regardless of the environment in which the larvae find themselves. As soon as a larva is

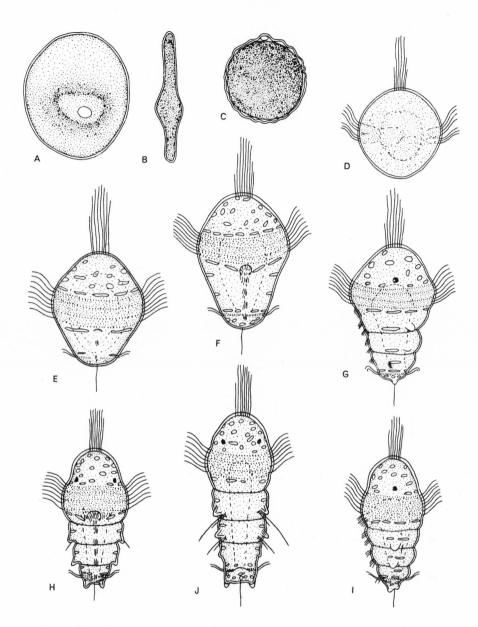

Fig. 20-2. Eggs and larvae of *Ophelia bicornis*. × 225. A, unfertilized egg; B, the same in side view; C, fertilized egg with polar body; D, 1-day-old larva; E, 2-day-old larva, ventral view; F, 3-day-old larva, ventral view; G, 4-day-old larva, view of left side; H, I, 4- to 5-day-old larva, ventral view and view of left side; J, 5-day-old larva,

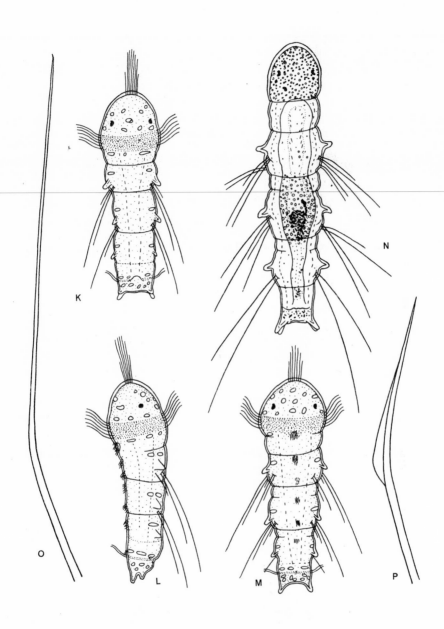

dorsal view; K, L, 7-day-old larva, ventral view and view of left side; M, 11-day-old larva, ventral view; N, young worm, after metamorphosis and 19 days old, dorsal view; O, capillary chaeta; P, winged chaeta. From Wilson, 1948. *J. mar. biol. Ass. U.K.*, **27**, 540–553.

ready for metamorphosis its reactions change in much the same way as those of ascidian larvae. Initially the larvae swim towards the surface and show no reaction to light, but then they become negatively phototropic and positively geotropic, so that they swim towards the sea bottom. At this stage they readily adhere to surfaces, attaching themselves by a secretion, but their subsequent behaviour depends upon the nature of the substratum. They may burrow into it and metamorphose, but if the sand is unsuitable they remain attached for a little time with their body upright, and then swim away. They can repeat this behaviour for several days, so that throughout this period they have the opportunity to test substrata and to reject unsuitable ones. Naturally there is a limit to this, determined by increasing firmness of adhesion and decline in the power of the prototroch. Eventually they must metamorphose or die, but at least their behaviour provides reasonable assurance that some will be able to establish themselves in suitable sand.

What is the nature of the stimuli that determine these responses by such minute organisms? Observations of the settling of larvae on different types of sand show that these types can be classified as attractive, neutral, or repellent. Attractive ones are those on which larvae settle heavily, and then undergo almost immediate metamorphosis. At the opposite extreme are the repellent ones on which few or no larvae settle or metamorphose. The neutral ones are sands on which larvae settle and metamorphose in quite large numbers, if there is no other substratum available. If, however, they are offered a choice by being presented with both an attractive and a neutral substratum in the same vessel, few will select the latter. One factor determining attractiveness seems to be the size and shape of the sand particles, but this is probably of minor importance, for the attractiveness can be removed from the particles by cleaning them with acid, and then washing them thoroughly. Attractiveness can also be removed by heating the sand. This suggests that the stimulus may be an organic one, as does the fact that acid-washed sand grains recover some attractiveness if they are soaked for a long time in filtered sea water.

Extended experimentation along these lines has led to the conclusion that the most important factor in the settling and metamorphosis of *Ophelia* larvae is the presence on the sand grains of bacteria and other micro-organisms. These must be neither too abundant nor too few; dead organic matter is repellent, but so is too heavy a growth of micro-organisms. Probably, then, the relative attractiveness or repellency of substrata depends upon the particular species of micro-organisms that grow on it, and the abundance of the growth. For example, acid-cleaned grains will collect a heavy growth of micro-organisms if they are soaked in sea water containing peptone, but they never become as attractive as do those that are soaked in filtered sea water without peptones or other added nutrients. Presumably the nutrients encourage species of micro-organisms that are not attractive to the larvae, and that do not grow in untreated sea water.

Not the least interesting aspect of these findings is the demonstration of the immense importance of the most obscure micro-organisms in determining the distribution of animal life. It is an example of the closely woven warp and woof of organic communities, and of the importance of chemical communication systems in maintaining their organization. Although our knowledge of these reactions is at present restricted to only a few species, there is no reason to doubt the wide applicability of the principle. Thus the cypris larvae of *Balanus balanoides* can delay metamorphosis for up to two weeks should they not encounter suitable rock surfaces for settling. During their free-swimming period they are positively phototropic, so that they remain in the surface water, brief periods of negatively phototropic movement enabling them to find rocks on and near the shore. Other larvae are strictly limited in the type of material on which they will settle, the larvae of *Phoronis* selecting limestone rocks, while those of *Spirorbis borealis* settle mainly upon fronds of *Fucus serratus*.

For many species the selection of the substratum is not the only function of larvae when they are settling. When we consider colonial life, we shall see something of the importance of sessile individuals being sufficiently spaced to avoid over-crowding and ensure a balanced exploitation of the habitat. The same consideration applies to all forms of animal life, whether it be birds establishing territorial rights or barnacles distributing themselves over rock faces. Here the larvae of sessile marine invertebrates have an important part to play. Thus, larvae of *Spirorbis* explore a *Fucus serratus* frond before finally settling down on it. During this exploratory phase they crawl over the surface and may swim away to another one; the exact behaviour depends upon how long they have previously been swimming, for prolonged activity encourages rapid settling. Contact with another *Spirorbis* induces them to settle, for these animals are highly gregarious, yet at the same time they become spaced out in such a way that they have adequate room for subsequent growth. Here the determining factor is apparently their sensitivity to any raised object that they encounter, which need not necessarily be an individual of their own species. The final spacing depends upon the initial density of the larval population, but even at high densities the larvae do not settle as closely to each other as they would do if these limiting factors were not operating.

In *Spirorbis* the relevant stimuli seem to be mainly tactile ones, but the cypris larvae of barnacles show a more complex behaviour. In principle they behave at settling much like *Spirorbis*, undertaking searching movements followed by a final settling. This is influenced by the presence of other individuals of the same species, for these animals also are highly gregarious. According to the analysis of Knight-Jones and Moyse (Figs. 20–3 and 20–4), there are two factors operating in the settling of barnacles: the response to the species, and the response to protuberances on the surface that is being explored. If both stimuli act together, as when a cypris makes contact with a recently attached member of its own species, the spacing-out reaction follows, and the larva settles at a certain distance from the other individual. If, however, the larva, under experimental conditions, makes contact with the base of an adult that has recently been detached, it will settle upon this base because this does not provide the additional stimulus of a protuberance. Then again, if the larva makes contact with an individual of another genus, *Elminius modestus*, it will settle upon this without any prior spacing response; this is because in this instance it does not receive the other necessary stimulus, the presence of an individual of its own species.

The effect of this behaviour is two-fold. On the one hand it ensures that members of one species, settling gregariously, have adequate room for growth. On the other hand, it makes for acute competition between barnacles of different species, since individuals of one will settle upon those of another, with consequent over-crowding. This may well explain the distribution that is sometimes actually observed upon the shore. As Knight-Jones points out, the barnacle *Chthamalus stellatus* extends well down the shore on the southern coasts of Britain, but on the more northerly ones, where it is approaching the limits of its range, it is restricted much more to the higher levels. The lower levels on the northerly coasts are densely populated by *Balanus balanoides*, which in these regions seems to be the dominating partner in this competition.

The gregarious habit seen in these sessile forms is in one sense an inevitable result of the crowded conditions that develop where marine habitats are highly favourable for growth and reproduction. Yet the crowding must also have a survival value, for otherwise how could mechanisms ensuring gregariousness with optimum spacing have been evolved? The advantages are presumably not different in principle from those that we shall later suggest are gained by colonial organisms. The spacing of the newly settled larvae does not prevent the building-up of crowded populations as the animals grow older. The effect of this is to establish a large surface area for the production of feeding currents, the value of which is evident because crowded barnacles may, given favourable conditions, be as fecund as those that are less crowded. Cross-fertilization is facilitated, and these crowded areas may also be more resistant to wave action, while, by increasing the local turbulence, they may further aid the feeding process. Thus intraspecific cooperation in the exploitation of the environment is possible in solitary species as well as in colonial ones. We shall see later how it may also develop between individuals of more than one species.

Fig. 20-3. Frequency distributions of distances between cyprids of *Balanus balanoides*, just settled upon limestone, and the nearest previously settled barnacle. The cyprids spaced themselves out from their own species, (A), but readily settled alongside other species (B). From Knight-Jones and Moyse, 1961. *Symp. Soc. exp. Biol.,* **15,** 72–95.

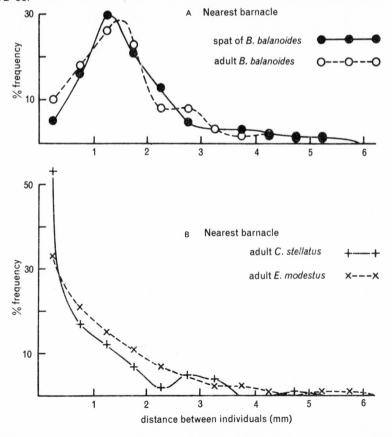

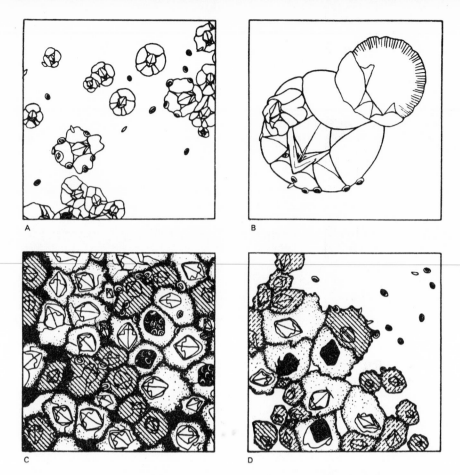

A   B

C   D

Fig. 20-4. Episcope drawings to show typical distributions of recently settled *Balanus balanoides* in relation to older barnacles. They have spaced themselves out from their own species, but many have settled in contact with other species. Unmetamorphosed cyprids are about 1 mm long and are distinguished by their shape, pointed at each end. Each drawing is of an area 25 mm square. A, part of a smooth slate. There are six *Elminius modestus* in this area, recognizable by their four parietal plates and by the cyprids in contact with them. The remaining adults are *Balanus balanoides*. B, a large *Balanus improvisus* on a shell of *Mytilus*, bearing an adult *Balanus balanoides* (left of drawing) and several smaller ones. C, dense mixture of adult *B. balanoides* and *Chthamalus stellatus* (the latter cross-hatched). Spat of *B. balanoides* have settled on the *Chthamalus* but not so readily on their own species (though many have settled inside empty plates). D, a piece of limestone rock, with adult *B. balanoides*, *C. stellatus* (cross-hatched), and *E. modestus* (hatched by interrupted lines). From Knight-Jones and Moyse, 1961. *op. cit.*

20–3 LARVAL LIFE IN FRESH WATER

We have so far considered only marine larvae, because indirect life histories are particularly characteristic of marine organisms. The small groups of fresh-water sponges and Ectoprocta have larvae, and the branchiopod crustaceans hatch as nauplii, but the Cladocera, Ostracoda, and Malacostraca of fresh water all undergo direct development, as also do the fresh-water oligochaetes, leeches, and pulmonate molluscs. The fresh-water mussels incubate the embryos within the gill folds, and eventually liberate the young as the very active glochidium larva, but this is a peculiar secondary adaptation in a highly specialized life history, in which fish serve to distribute the parasitic larva. The only fresh-water mollusc that liberates its young as veliger larvae is *Dreissensia polymorpha*, but this merely reinforces the general argument: this species is a very recent invader of rivers, first recorded from the Volga and the Danube during the eighteenth century.

We have earlier emphasized and discussed the well-known fact that the main animal phyla are far better represented in the sea than in fresh water. Not only are some major groups wholly lacking in fresh-water representatives, but even when they do contain such representatives these are often relatively few and specialized. From this, and from the phylogenetic relationships of the groups mentioned above, we can deduce that much of the fresh-water fauna is of marine origin. The important exceptions to this are the pulmonate molluscs and the insects, together with the fresh-water mites and spiders, all of which must have colonized fresh-water habitats from the land. That terrestrial forms should have lost their primitive indirect life histories is to be expected, so that the absence of larvae from pulmonates is easy to understand. What is less obvious is why the transition from the sea to fresh water should so often have involved the loss of larval stages, yet in fact more than one line of explanation can be suggested.

One aspect that is certainly relevant is the strength and persistence of the currents in rivers and streams, for these endanger the survival of the young by impelling them away from the habitats of the adults. This in itself goes a long way to explain why fragile larval stages have so often been eliminated, and why eggs are often protected by incubation in brood pouches or by deposition in sheltered places. Another factor is the instability of fresh-water habitats, with the recurrent risks of desiccation or freezing. These risks are more prevalent in temperate zones, and this is probably one reason why the number of fresh-water species in any particular group is often found to increase nearer the equator.

But there is another and less obvious consideration that has been emphasized by J. Needham, who has drawn attention to the importance of embryos securing adequate supplies of the various salts that are needed during their growth. Marine invertebrates can readily obtain these from the sea, and the extent to which they draw upon this source of supply is illustrated by data available for the Pacific sand dollar, *Dendraster excentricus*, to take just one example. The total phosphorus content of this organism increases from 760 mg% dry weight at fertilization to 990 mg% at the gastrula stage and 1,230 mg% at the pluteus stage. Some of this phosphorus will have been gained from the combustion of organic material present at the beginning of development, but this accounts for only about 3% of the 62% increase; the remainder must be obtained from the surrounding medium.

Supplies in the sea are certainly adequate for the purpose. In the surface water

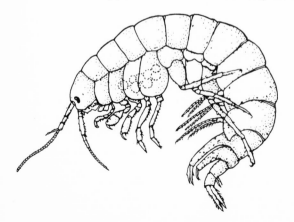

Fig. 20-5. A female *Gammarus*. The position of the eggs in the thoracic brood-pouch, sheltered by the coxal plates, is dotted. From Carpenter, 1928. *Life in Inland Waters*. Sidgwick and Jackson, London.

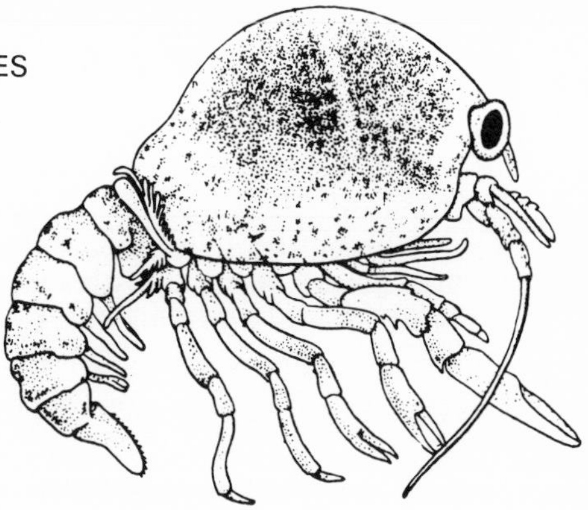

Fig. 20-6. Newly-hatched young of a crayfish (*Astacus fluviatilis*). From Calman, 1911. *op. cit.*

of the English Channel the phosphorus content may range from 0.0162 mg/l at the winter maximum, down to 0.0032 mg/l at the summer minimum. At times, however, the larvae may have to swim energetically to obtain all of their requirements, and Needham suggests that this is one reason for the early hatching and vigorous activity of so many larval types. In fresh water, of course, with its low mineral content, the situation is much less favourable. Here the phosphorus content may range from zero up to perhaps the minimum value quoted above. Thus the young cannot obtain their requirements from external supplies, and they need reserves in the egg. This, then, provides another explanation for the omission of the larval stage. A consequence is that the eggs must be larger, for they must supply all the necessary nutrients, and this in its turn means that far fewer will be produced by fresh-water forms than are produced by marine ones. The common oyster, which is viviparous, spawns 1.8 million eggs at once, while oviparous oysters can produce over 100 million eggs at a spawning. *Anodonta cygnea*, by contrast, spawns about 15,000, although this particular species may sometimes produce as many as 2 million, which is an exceptionally high figure for a fresh-water form. In gastropods the difference is even more noticeable; *Buccinum undatum* may lay 12,000 eggs, and *Nucella lapillus* about 245 capsules that may contain from 400 to 600 eggs apiece, but fresh-water snails lay only 20 to 100, and the fresh-water limpet 5 or 6.

This reduction in number, together with the danger of removal by currents, makes adequate protection of the eggs essential. A need for protection, however, is not peculiar to fresh water, and in fresh-water forms it is frequently met by adaptations similar to those found in marine species. Fresh-water pulmonates fix masses of eggs, coated with jelly, upon stones or vegetation; marine molluscs may also do this. Fresh-water amphipods and isopods protect their eggs within the thoracic brood pouch (Fig. 20–5) formed by their thoracic limbs; so also do their marine peracaridan relatives. The female of the fresh-water crayfish carries her developing eggs attached to the swimmerets, but does not differ in this respect from the lobster and many other crustaceans. It does differ from its marine relatives, however, in that the young do not hatch until they have the form of miniature adults, with a carapace that is globular because of the large food reserves stored within the body (Fig. 20–6). They lack the first pair of swimmerets and the uropods, but have hooked tips to their chelae, so that they are able to cling for some time to the mother. An essentially similar life cycle has been quite independently evolved in the tropical river crabs of the family Potamonidae; in these too the free-swimming zoea has been eliminated and the young hatch as miniature adults.

The disadvantages of fresh-water larval stages are so clear that it may seem surprising that they should be so widely retained in the Branchiopoda, a group that is almost entirely fresh-water in distribution. It should be noted, however, that the Cladocera, in which direct development occurs, are the only branchiopods that live in large ponds, lakes, and streams. The remainder (with the exception of *Artemia*, the brine shrimp, which inhabits salt lakes) are restricted to small areas of water and temporary ponds, where there is little danger of the young being swept away. To this extent, then, the production of nauplius larvae by many branchiopods may well limit their distribution. Moreover, these animals, including the Cladocera, show another important adaptation in their life cycles which doubtless improves their fitness for fresh-water life. This adaptation (found also in the Rotifera, another group that is almost exclusively fresh-water in distribution) is the capacity for producing two types of egg: quickly-developing ones or resting ones. They are sometimes referred to, although less accurately, as summer and winter eggs, respectively. The production of these two types is closely associated with the capacity for parthenogenesis (development of the egg without fertilization); indeed, in some species males are very uncommon, and are possibly not produced at all.

In Cladocera, to take one example, only females are found at certain times of the year. These lay parthenogenetic eggs that develop very rapidly in the brood pouch, which is a cavity, characteristic of the group, lying under the carapace and dorsal to the body. Multiplication takes place rapidly during this phase. Eventually, it leads to the production of males, the appearance of which initiates normal sexual reproduction. Each of the eggs produced at this phase, normally only one from each ovary, is extruded in a protective covering; this is usually an 'ephippium', formed from the modified wall of the brood chamber and shed at a moult. Within this the segmented egg may remain dormant for a long period, and in this way it can survive the winter. The reproductive cycle is not, however, necessarily as simple as this. There may be several phases of sexual reproduction during the year, or reproduction may be entirely parthenogenetic. The former type of cycle is often found in pond-dwelling Cladocera, liable to frequent desiccation, and the latter in planktonic species, which are free of this hazard. There is evidence, then, of some innate correlation of the pattern of the life cycle with the type of environment. It has been thought, however, that the pattern is not wholly determined by genetic factors, but rather by an interaction of these with external ones.

This type of life cycle is found in many other branchiopods, and also in rotifers, with quick-developing thin-shelled eggs and resting thick-shelled ones. An alternation of parthenogenetic and normal sexual development is also common, although either type of egg may be produced in either of these two ways; moreover, the alternation of the two phases may be very flexible. Thick-shelled eggs are also produced in copepods, but less commonly than in the Branchiopoda, although some adult copepods can withstand desiccation by entering into a resting stage with a cyst-like secretion that forms a protective covering around the body.

20–4 INSECT LARVAE

Insects, which are primarily terrestrial forms, have necessarily lost any traces of whatever pelagic larvae may have been possessed by their unknown aquatic ancestors.

Yet they have themselves developed a new type of larval history, one that presents, both in its origins and its functional significance, an instructive comparison with those of aquatic invertebrates. As with so many other aspects of insect biology, however, the immense size and range of diversification within the group makes it impossible to do more than consider these matters in the most general terms.

The growth of an insect, like that of other arthropods, is interrupted by periodical moults or ecdyses, the form of the insect between any two ecdyses being called an instar. The primitive type of life cycle is probably that seen today in the primitively wingless insects such as the *Thysanura* (silver-fish). Here the only major difference between the young stages and the final adult instar is the appearance of the mature reproductive organs in the latter. The change produced at the final moult is therefore so slight that such insects are commonly regarded as undergoing no metamorphosis, and they are termed ametabolous.

In the winged insects the situation is altogether more complex, with two distinct types of life cycle. The more primitive of these is probably that seen, for example, in cockroaches, insects that have apparently persisted from the Carboniferous with very little change. The young stages (nymphs) differ from the adults (imagines) in lacking fully developed wings, although these are growing externally during the nymphal period. Nymphs also lack the sexual armature of the adults, but in other respects they resemble the imagines quite closely; they possess, for example, compound eyes. Thus the metamorphosis, although clearly discernible, is comparatively slight, and these insects are said to be heterometabolous. Alternatively they are known as Exopterygota, because of the external development of their wings.

The more advanced type of life cycle, termed holometabolous, is characterized by the young stages lacking compound eyes, and differing from the adults very markedly in many other respects, including body form, mouth parts, and often mode of life, which may be adapted to a habitat remote in character from that of the imagines. The young stages are now called larvae, and the metamorphosis is a drastic one, so much so that a pupal stage is interposed between the larva and the final adult instar. The pupa, superficially a quiescent phase, is one in which profound reorganization of the tissues take place. In this type of life cycle the wings develop internally, from buds called imaginal discs, and for this reason the holometabolous insects are alternatively known as the Endopterygota.

It seems probable, to judge from the fossil evidence, that the holometabolous type of life cycle evolved later than the heterometabolous, the earliest examples of it being seen in the Coleoptera, which are known from the Upper Permian. Its adaptive value is clear enough. With the adult stages so freely motile, the functions of dispersal and habitat selection have little significance. The value of the holometabolous life history lies rather in the other aspect of larval life that we have discussed earlier: the opportunity that it affords for divergent evolution of young and adult, and the consequent exploitation of two entirely different types of habitat. The diversified specialization of terrestrial larvae is one demonstration of this. It is illustrated also by those insects that have secondarily adopted aquatic habits during their development, a line of evolution that has been followed by heterometabolous forms as well as by holometabolous ones.

The Plecoptera (stoneflies), Ephemeroptera (may-flies), Odonata (dragonflies), and Hemiptera (bugs) provide examples of the establishment of aquatic habits in the nymph. This has been achieved by the secondary invasion of water from the land, with perhaps an intermediate stage of association with the damp earth at the edges of fresh water. Primarily, the young stages have become so adapted, evidently because of the flying habits of the imagines. In the aquatic Hemiptera (including the water-boatmen and pond-skaters), however, the adults are unharmed by immersion, and in these forms flight has become relatively unimportant. It seems probable that the fundamental advantage gained by the nymphs in this type of life cycle is some protection from the extremes of conditions on land, for temperature changes are less drastic in water, and plant food and organic detritus are never lacking. Frequently it is the aquatic nymph that survives the winter. In fact, the adult stage may become of relatively minor importance, as regards its duration; the extreme example of this is seen in the may-flies, where the imago is concerned solely with reproduction, taking no food at all, and often surviving for only a few hours.

No less instructive are the life cycles of holometabolous insects that have taken to the water. Divergence between the habits of larva and adult is here very much more marked, a familiar contrast being between the blood-sucking of the adult mosquito, with its piercing mouth parts, and the microphagy of its aquatic larva, which is dependent upon currents produced by moving its food brushes. In some instances— for example, the Trichoptera (caddis-flies)—the adults are short-lived, just as in some of the Heterometabola. In aquatic beetles, however, the imago may be the predominant phase, but this only emphasizes the importance of water in the life cycle, for in these instances the adult is often aquatic or semi-aquatic in habit. That these highly specialized animals should invade water in this way is a sufficient tribute to its value as a habitat, particularly since many Holometabola with aquatic larvae have had to solve the difficult problem of providing for the escape of the imago from the pupa into the air. Indeed, aquatic life might have played an even more important part in the evolution of insects had it not been for the evolution of flowering plants. The full evolutionary diversification of the Lepidoptera, Hymenoptera, and Diptera broadly coincided with this phase of plant evolution. At the present day the mode of life of the adults of these groups, and the details of their life histories, are closely correlated with the exploitation of the higher plants.

The course of the evolution of insect life histories can only be guessed at, and there is more than one opinion regarding the relationship between the heterometa-bolan and holometabolan type of development. We shall not discuss these here beyond remarking that there is a divergence between two views: one that the larva is a specialized nymph, and the other that it is a new development inserted into the life cycle in advance of the nymph as a result of earlier hatching. On the former view the pupa is a specialized last-stage nymph, whereas on the latter view it represents a fusion of nymphal stages, the larva being essentially an elaboration of an embryonic phase. Whatever the truth may be, the origin of these life histories is rooted in caenogenetic changes. These have brought about alterations in the relative rates of development of juvenile and adult characters, with consequent divergence of the youthful and adult stages. We have seen that the developmental stages of these animals can be maintained in a juvenile state or switched into the adult one by changes in the hormonal balance. It is likely that a vital factor in establishing these complex and highly adaptive life histories must have been the possession by insects of an endocrine system with a far-reaching capacity for precise regulation and coordination.

21
Colonial and
Social Life

21–1 PROTOZOAN COLONIES

We have referred to colonies as a form of intraspecific association in which individuals are subordinated to the interests of the whole aggregation. True colonies can be defined more precisely as associations in which the constituent individuals are not completely separated from each other, but are organically connected together, either by living extensions of their bodies, or by material that they have secreted. This connection, whatever its precise nature, is more than structural. Commonly the members of the colony are physiologically linked and integrated so that each contributes to the life of the whole colony, but there is much variation in the closeness of the relationship and in its structural and physiological consequences. Colonial life, as thus defined, is necessarily restricted to animals that are of comparatively simple organization, and that can reproduce asexually, for it is fundamentally a result of fission products failing to separate. It is found in the Protozoa, and is particularly characteristic of sponges (although there is a problem of definition in this group, as we shall see), coelenterates, and Polyzoa. Instructive examples are also found in the Pterobranchia and Urochordata.

A well-known series of colonial organisms is found in the flagellate Protozoa, in the Order Phytomonadina. Although holophytic forms, they have long attracted zoological speculation, for, as we have mentioned earlier, they have been regarded as one path by which multicellular organisms might, in theory, have evolved from unicellular ones. These colonies arise as the result of the continued association of a group of individuals produced by asexual reproduction. In this way there are formed flat plates of 4 to 16 individuals or zooids (*Gonium*), a sphere of 16 zooids (*Pandorina*), or a layer of 32 (*Eudorina*) or 128 zooids (*Pleodorina*) arranged near the surface of a gelatinous sphere. Typically the members of the colonies are biflagellate, with an organization like that of *Chlamydomonas*, and they are held only loosely together in a common membrane or jelly. There is no direct continuity between them, so that they do not strictly fit the definition of a colony given above; but this definition, like

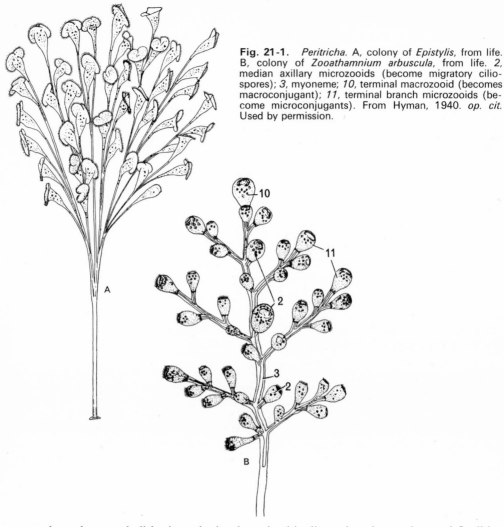

Fig. 21-1. *Peritricha.* A, colony of *Epistylis*, from life. B, colony of *Zooathamnium arbuscula*, from life. *2*, median axillary microzooids (become migratory ciliospores); *3*, myoneme; *10*, terminal macrozooid (becomes macroconjugant); *11*, terminal branch microzooids (become microconjugants). From Hyman, 1940. *op. cit.* Used by permission.

others that we shall be introducing later in this discussion, has to be used flexibly, as is well illustrated by *Volvox*. This forms colonies that are essentially further elaborations of the types already mentioned. They are composed of hundreds or thousands of zooids, which are carried on the surface of a gelatinous sphere, but which in this instance retain direct connection with each other by protoplasmic threads.

Irrespective of such connections, the phytomonodinan colonies exemplify a principle that is of fundamental importance in colonial life: the establishment of an organization that transcends the individuality of the constituent organisms. All the colonies swim with one particular region foremost; they are said, therefore, to be polarized, and to have an anterior pole. In *Pleodorina* and in *Volvox* this functional differentiation is carried further, to a point at which the anterior zooids are unable to reproduce. Thus we arrive at a division of labour between the constituent members of the colony, analogous to the division of labour between the cells of a metazoan body and, similarly, leading to a more efficient deployment of the potentialities of the whole. This is emphasized in other ways. For example, in *Pleodorina* the anterior zooids are smaller than the others, and have larger stigmata, implying some differentiation of sensitivity to light. The reproductive processes are another illustration of this differentiation of activity. In the less highly organized colonies each zooid is capable both of asexual and sexual reproduction. Asexual reproduction is effected by the repeated division (multiple fission) of a zooid, with the formation of a daughter colony that then escapes from the parental one. Sexual reproduction in *Gonium* is effected by the escape of individual zooids, which function as isogamous gametes. In *Volvox*, however, the zooids are differentiated in this respect. Some enlarge without division to form macrogametes, which, as we have already seen, may be compared with ova; others undergo multiple fission to form groups of biflagellate microgametes which are motile, and which may be compared with sperm.

Unquestionably the evolution of colonial life in the Phytomonadina has involved some reduction in the range of activities of the zooids; to some degree they have become subservient to the life of the colony as a whole. Indeed, we may go further: it is precisely this subservience, and the division of labour that goes with it, that is the primary characteristic of colonial life. It is this, rather than purely structural relationships, that defines a colony. Certainly, a colony involves its component members in some loss of individuality, but concurrently a higher order of individuality develops, which is the individuality of the colony as a whole. This, however, remains a highly abstract conception unless we can understand individuality. This understanding eludes us in the phytomonadinan colonies, but we can find a clue in another type of protozoan colony.

We have already encountered the Peritricha as examples of ciliate Protozoa with a specialized arrangement of ciliation. Some of these animals are free-swimming, or are free-moving epizoites, but most of them are attached posteriorly by a disc or stalk, and of these some are solitary and some colonial (Fig. 21-1). An unusual association occurs in *Vaginicola* and *Cothurnia*, which sometimes live in pairs in protective cases, but more typical of colonial life are the associations formed by *Carchesium*, *Epistylis*, or *Zoothamnium*, where a number of *Vorticella*-like zooids are united by their stalks. New colonies are formed from individuals that become free-swimming; they separate from the parent colony, undergoing repeated fission after becoming attached to the substratum. In some genera (e.g. *Carchesium*) the zooids show no differentiation among themselves, yet even so the individuality of the colony is shown by the specificity of its form, which depends upon the precise pattern of branching. In vorticellids in general the contractile myonemes of the stalk are collected into a spiral band, the spasmoneme, the arrangement of which in the colonial genera reflects different degrees of unification of their members (p. 39).

In many colonial peritrichs a new colony may arise from any of the zooids, the one concerned developing a posterior band of cilia and swimming away. Eventually it will attach to the substratum and give rise to a colony by growth and fission. In some species, however, there is a measure of differentiation among the zooids. In *Zoothamnium*, for example, the end of the axis of the colony bears a terminal macrozooid, the only one of these in the colony. The branches each end in a terminal branch microzooid, and bear also median axillary microzooids and ordinary vegetative microzooids. Of these four types of zooid, the median axillary microzooids and the vegetative ones can swim away as migratory ciliospores, which can then grow into new colonies. The sexual process, as in solitary forms like *Vorticella*, involves the fusion of a motile microconjugant with a sessile macroconjugant. But in *Z. alternans* only the terminal macrozooid can become a macroconjugant, while microconjugants can arise either from the terminal branch microzooids or from certain of the vegetative microzooids.

The basis of this differentiation, and of the influence that coordinates it, has been indicated by experiments in which terminal zooids have been cut off from the colony. Removal of either the terminal macrozooid or the terminal branch micro-zooids results in the neighbouring zooids assuming both their form and their repro-ductive functions. Thus the normal fate of a zooid presumably depends in some way upon its position relative to the terminal ones. These perhaps exert some inhibitory influence on the zooids lower down the stem, a supposition supported by the observa-tion that when the terminal macrozooid conjugates, the lateral branches increase their growth; it is as though the influence of the macrozooid is reduced by the physio-logical changes consequent on conjugation. We shall see that a similar effect exists in coelenterates, and that it may indicate some physiological basis for the establish-ment of individuality.

The colonial flagellates and ciliates that we have mentioned demonstrate in two ways the advantages that accrue from this cooperative mode of life. The flagellate forms are holophytic; it is thus unlikely that they gain any nutritional advantage from their association, for their requirements are freely available in the water that bathes them. It is conceivable that their association with a gelatinous ground substance allows the transmission of metabolites, and that the differentiation of reproductive zooids depends upon the transmission of nutrients from the vegetative individuals. Probably the main benefit of this type of association, however, is to be found in the locomotor advantage obtained by combining the flagellar activity of a number of zooids. The spherical form of many of the colonies must be significant from this point of view, since for a given volume a sphere exposes the smallest surface area. For these colonies the resistance of the surrounding water is thus reduced to a minimum, and the beat of their flagella acts to the fullest advantage. The gains by sessile and branched ciliate colonies are necessarily different. Apart from the pro-tective advantage of such group associations, which will be especially pronounced where the colony has a continuous system of spasnomemes, the main advantage probably lies in more efficient exploitation of food supplies, with wasteful competi-tion reduced by the orderly spacing of the individuals.

21–2 SPONGE, COELENTERATE, AND POLYZOAN COLONIES

It is customary to regard sponges as being either solitary or colonial in habit. Solitary forms are those with only one osculum, while colonial forms are those with a number of oscula, each osculum with its associated system of canals being considered as corresponding to one individual. This, admittedly, is a somewhat arbitrary point of view, but the fact is that a discussion of individuality in sponges becomes resolved only too easily into a purely verbal issue. It cannot be denied that the sponge body has an individuality transcending that of its component cells, however limited may be its powers of coordination. This individuality is revealed in the characteristic form and organization of a particular species, which permits the systematist to handle the group, in principle, in the same way as any of the higher groups of animals. It is shown also in the well-known experiments in which sponge bodies have been fragmented by squeezing them through fine gauze, or, more recently, have been dissociated into suspensions of single cells in calcium- and magnesium-free sea water. The resulting groups or suspensions of cells can associate and build up again the basic organization of a sponge body, with dermal epithelium and choanocyte layer, pores and osculum. We have seen that the relationship of oscular opening to pores and canal system is interpretable in hydraulic terms, and is highly adaptive. Presumably the appearance of additional oscula with continued growth of the body is an expression of these same hydraulic factors. To regard the appearance of a new osculum as marking the differentiation of a new individual is therefore to apply an entirely arbitrary meaning to the concept of individuality. Nothing remotely recalling division of labour between individuals occurs in this type of colony, and we can only conclude that if individuality is indeed associated with a single osculum, it exists there at a lower level of differentiation than anywhere else in the animal kingdom.

We can be more certain in analyzing other examples of colonial life. Thus in hydrozoan coelenterates the individuality of the polyps is well defined, as also is their asexual budding; the continued association of their offspring leads to colony formation. The mode of budding varies, establishing characteristic colony patterns in particular species. In fixed forms the colony is attached at its base by strands of living tissue called stolons. In some (e.g. *Hydractinia*) the polyps arise direct from the stolons in an irregular way. More usually a main stem or hydrocaulus grows up from the stolons, and the polyps are borne upon this and upon its branches. The growth of the hydrocaulus largely determines the form of the colony. Growth may, for example, be monopodial; in this a terminal polyp is situated permanently at the end of each branch and of the main stem, and lengthens at a growth zone below the base of each polyp. Alternatively, growth may be sympodial; here the terminal polyp of each branch is temporarily the youngest, and is overgrown by the next one to develop, which arises as a bud at its base. Clearly there is a genetic mechanism, built into each colony, which determines its form, and to which the individual polyps are subordinated.

Other aspects of the hydrozoan colony reveal this subordination. The organization of a polyp shows a marked polarization, extending from the mouth and tentacles at one end to the closed base at the other end. This is a morphological expression of individuality, but experiment has shown that underlying this there is an invisible physiological polarization. In extensive studies, Child has demonstrated that different parts of a polyp vary in their susceptibility to lethal agents, and that this variation follows the pattern of a gradient, with maximum susceptibility at the apical (oral) end. Similar gradients are revealed by other criteria. For example, the rate of carbon dioxide production varies, being maximal at the apical end; the rate of reduction of methylene blue also varies, again being maximal at the apical end. Gradients in electric potential have also been observed, not always uniform, but indicating that the apical end is electronegative to more basal regions.

Child used such observations, derived from many groups of animals, and from many stages of their development, to frame a general theory of the nature of individuality and organization. Essentially, he argued that living material is organized in a spatial pattern, of which the external structure is only one aspect. The pattern is also expressed in differences in the concentration of various substances, and in differences in the rates of their metabolism. The existence of these patterns in the form of gradients of activity is, according to Child's views, an essential element in

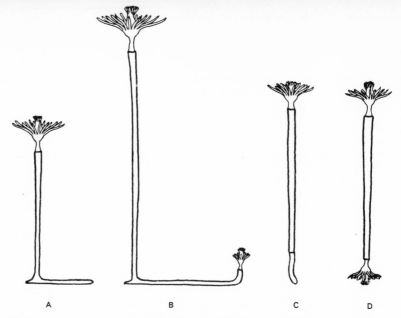

Fig. 21-2. *Tubularia.* A, young individual with developing stolon; B, transformation of stolon tip into hydranth after physiological isolation by increase in distance from dominant hydranth; C, reconstitution of stem piece with hydranth distal and stolon proximal; D, bipolar reconstitution. From Child, 1941. *Patterns and Problems of Development.* University of Chicago Press, Chicago.

the development of the axiate organization of polyps, which results in one end of the gradient, the apical end, being able to dominate the rest of the body. The ability to bud, and the pattern of the associated growth, is determined by the capacity of other parts of the body for escaping from the inhibitory influence of this dominant region.

Consider, as an illustration of this concept, the behaviour of the species of *Tubularia* shown in Fig. 21-2. As the unbranched stem of a young individual lengthens, a bud forms at its base and grows out as a stolon. The stolon represents a new gradient system, which has, so to speak, escaped from the inhibitory effect of the polyp's gradient as it has lengthened. For a time the stolon shows no structural differentiation, but as soon as it reaches a certain length (or, according to this interpretation, a certain further degree of physiological isolation) the stolon starts to grow away from the substratum and to differentiate a new polyp.

We can thus regard differentiation in *Tubularia* as being influenced by the inhibitory action of the dominant end of the polyps. On this interpretation it should be possible to release growth and differentiation by the artificial reduction of the inhibitory influence. This result can, in fact, be achieved, as, for example, in *Bougain-*

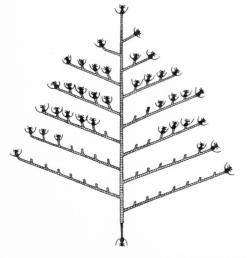

Fig. 21-3. Reconstitution of hydranths in *Pennaria cavolinii*; note that it progresses basipetally in the whole and in each axis. From Child, 1941. *op. cit.*

Fig. 21-4. A young specimen of a siphonophore, *Nanomia cara*. From Mackie, 1963. In *The Lower Metazoa* (Dougherty et al., eds.). University of California.

villea. A colony immersed in an inhibiting agent (M/200 ethyl urethane for 48 hours) shows a disintegration or regression of its polyps and buds, and an outgrowth of stolons. These latter are thought of as the expression of growth gradients, released by the inhibition of the differentiation gradients of the polyps. If the colony is allowed to recover, these growth gradients will themselves become differentiation gradients, and will produce new polyps.

The evidence that hydrozoan polyps are polarized systems is convincing, although interpretation of the action of these gradients remains theoretical, for we can only discuss their nature in general concepts of metabolic activity. Indeed, we cannot be sure whether the gradients are themselves causal factors, or whether they are the expression of other and more subtle features of protoplasmic organization. But at least they give us some descriptive basis for visualizing how the individuality of a colony may come to dominate the individuality of its component members. Gradient patterns are detectable in these colonies, as might be expected from what we have just seen of the growth of a *Tubularia* polyp. This is well shown in *Pennaria cavolinii* (Fig. 21-3), a species that has a regularly graded series of lateral branches. If all the polyps are removed, new ones develop in a regular order, beginning at the apical end of the main stalk and of each of the branches. No morphological differentiation is visible in the branches, so that this pattern would seem to be the expression of some physiological aspect of the organization and individuation of the colony.

An important feature of hydrozoan colonies is polymorphism, which is the existence of the individual members in more than one form, there being division of labour between the several types. Here we see an illustration of the interplay of competition and cooperation, with the competitive element reduced, and with a consequent facilitation of the unified life of the colony. The commonest situation is the differentiation of the colonial polyps into gastrozooids, concerned with feeding, and gonozooids (blastozooids), concerned with reproduction. Typically the gonozooids bud off medusae, which provide for sexual reproduction, and which are themselves another variant of the common ground plan of structure. In addition, the colony may bear individuals called dactylozooids, which serve for pro-

float

nectophore

gastrozooid

palpon

bract

tentacle

tection. These are derived by simplification of the structural plan of the gastrozooid. Mouth, tentacles, and enteron are reduced or lost, so that in its extreme specialization the dactylozooid may have the form of a tentacle, bearing many nematocysts; less highly modified types may still bear terminal tentacles, as do the protective spiral zooids of *Hydractinia*. Extreme examples of polymorphism, combined with subordination of individuals to the life of the colony as a whole, are seen in the Siphonophora, which form floating or swimming colonies of most elaborate constitution (Fig. 21–4). Gastrozooids, dactylozooids, and gonozooids are all present, the gastrozooids being the only feeding individuals. In addition, the medusae are seldom set free; they undergo their own polymorphic modifications, so that they are able to contribute to the variety of form. Besides producing the gonophores which bear the germ cells, they give rise to protective bracts, to muscular nectophores which provide for locomotion of the colony, and to pneumatophores which contain air and serve as floats.

We do not know how polymorphism is regulated in these colonies. Genetic factors must certainly be involved, but, if we may draw an analogy from the polymorphism of social insects (see p. 466), we may reasonably suspect that the expression of these is determined by chemical factors, diffusing, perhaps, from the several types of zooid, and ensuring the maintenance of these in suitable proportions. Braverman and Schrandt have shown that the pattern of growth of a hydroid colony can to some extent be simulated by an electronic computer that has been supplied with a set of simple growth rules. This, they point out, is an illustration of the more general proposition that the complexity of living organisms can, in theory, be shaped by a relatively small amount of genetic coding. Whatever its mode of development, however, there can be no doubt of the success of this type of organization. The spectacle of a Portuguese man-of-war seizing and digesting a fish is an impressive demonstration of the power that can be achieved by simple forms of life through the subordination of competition to cooperation. The biggest impact, however, is made by quite a different type of colony, that of the madreporarian corals. These animals, members of the Anthozoa, and essentially anemones that secrete a calcareous skeleton, form colonies of a structurally simple character, lacking any polymorphism, and reproducing without an intermediate medusoid stage. Yet they have played a major part in the building of coral reefs. In doing this they have so profoundly modified their environment that they have made a unique type of marine habitat available for exploitation by other organisms, including man. We shall see later, however, that the coral polyps do not work unaided, their activities being powerfully assisted by a form of association quite different in character from those that we are at present considering.

The principles exemplified in the colonial life of coelenterates operate elsewhere in the animal kingdom where this habit has been developed, but with sufficient differences in results to make comparisons instructive. The Ectoprocta are a group of coelomate animals that are at a higher level of organization than coelenterates, and it is probably because of this that the zooids retain much more of their independence. Moreover, they are not interconnected by living tissue, the colony being held together in its characteristic form by the external secretions of its members. Even so, some degree of polymorphism and division of labour is found, associated, as in the coelenterates, with feeding, protection, and reproduction.

We have seen that the ectoproctan feeding individual is composed of two parts,

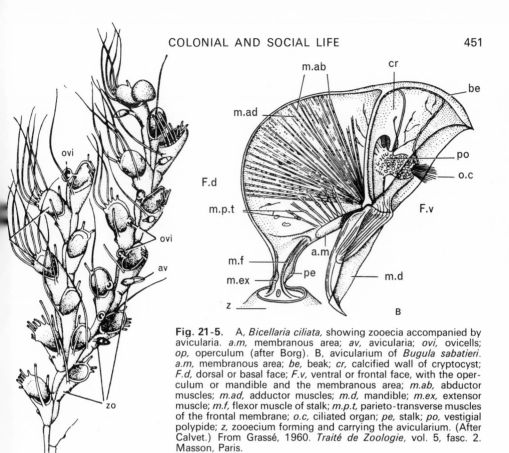

Fig. 21-5. A, *Bicellaria ciliata,* showing zooecia accompanied by avicularia. *a.m,* membranous area; *av,* avicularia; *ovi,* ovicells; *op,* operculum (after Borg). B, avicularium of *Bugula sabatieri. a.m,* membranous area; *be,* beak; *cr,* calcified wall of cryptocyst; *F.d,* dorsal or basal face; *F.v,* ventral or frontal face, with the operculum or mandible and the membranous area; *m.ab,* abductor muscles; *m.ad,* adductor muscles; *m.d,* mandible; *m.ex,* extensor muscle; *m.f,* flexor muscle of stalk; *m.p.t,* parieto-transverse muscles of the frontal membrane; *o.c,* ciliated organ; *pe,* stalk; *po,* vestigial polypide; *z,* zooecium forming and carrying the avicularium. (After Calvet.) From Grassé, 1960. *Traité de Zoologie,* vol. 5, fasc. 2. Masson, Paris.

the zooecium, or protective body wall, and the polypide, which includes the mouth, tentacles, and alimentary tract. Protective individuals arise by reduction of the polypide, this process giving rise (in *Bicellaria* and *Bugula,* for example, Fig. 21-5) to the remarkable individuals called avicularia. These resemble nothing so much as the heads of birds; each has a movable beak derived from the operculum that closes over the opening of the zooecium in unmodified individuals of many genera. Primitive ectoproctans indicate how this result has come about, for in these the avicularium may still possess a polypide; it then occupies in the colony the normal position of an individual. With further evolution the polypide is lost, and the avicularium becomes merely the appendage of a normal zooecium situated near its opening. An even more extreme modification is seen in the vibracula, which are like mobile bristles. These make sweeping movements that keep the colony free of unwanted material, while the avicularia seize animals and other objects that they encounter.

Polymorphism associated with reproduction, structurally simple but with some physiological complexity, is seen in the Order Cyclostomata of the Ectoprocta. In these forms the fertilized egg begins its development as a primary embryo within a modified individual called the ovicell, being nourished from a placenta-like association with nutritive tissue. This nutritional adaptation is probably correlated with the fact that the primary embryo does not itself give rise directly to a new individual, but instead buds off groups of cells that form secondary embryos; these eventually develop into motile larvae.

21–3   ASEXUAL REPRODUCTION AND COLONIAL LIFE IN UROCHORDATES

Finally, and to pass to a very different group, the Urochordata are animals in which colony formation is often an important feature, associated here with a widespread capacity for asexual reproduction and with the secretion of the characteristic tunic. The distinction between aggregated solitary forms and true colonial species is not very sharp in this group; colonies arise when the daughter zooids, produced by budding, remain in organic association and enclosed within a common tunic. Because of this, and because of the high level of structural differentiation, polymorphism and division of labour are commonly absent.

Many ascidians show a regular alternation of asexual and sexual reproduction, corresponding more or less with the sequence of seasons. The sexual phase takes place during the summer months, and the asexual phase during the winter, unless growth ceases during the coldest part of the year. Whether this alternation is a primitive feature of the group is not clear, although it is often assumed to be. This would mean that in the Cionidae and Ascidiidae, families in which the adults are solitary and reproduce entirely by sexual means, a primitive capacity for budding has been lost. It is possible that the botryllids have secondarily redeveloped the budding habit, for they have a peculiar form of budding from the body wall, unlike that of other ascidians in not making use of a stolon.

However, the modes of budding in the urochordates are, in fact, so varied that it is difficult to trace out the history of the habit with complete assurance (Fig. 21-6). A good measure of order can, however, be introduced into this complex field if we follow Berrill's analysis of asexual reproduction in ascidians. The bud may be thought of as essentially a fragment that has become isolated from the control of the parent organism, and which can then grow and differentiate independently. Berrill sees the epidermis as the active agent in urochordates, cutting through the other tissues to form the bud. This contains fragments of one or more tissues, often with nutritive reserves contained in cells called trophocytes, the formation of which may well be a consequence of regression of the parent tissues. This marked tendency of urochordates to regress has probably been a major factor in the evolution of budding within the group, another factor being the remarkable plasticity of the tissues, which makes it possible for a complete organism to be regenerated from only a limited selection of tissue rudiments. Fundamentally, then, we can view budding in ascidians as an adaptation that dissociates the competing nutritive demands of growth and sexual reproduction, and that takes account also of the marked seasonal fluctuations in the food supplies of ciliary feeders. Presumably the process has been elaborated into colony formation because this mode of life confers increased powers of resistance to stress and capacity for exploitation of the environment, as mentioned earlier. In some species the members of the colony are so closely associated that they form a structural and functional unit. In *Botryllus*, for example, the zooids share a common atrium and atrial aperture, and this may perhaps increase hydraulic efficiency. To the extent that the individuals are then interdependent, and are subordinated to the life of the whole assemblage, they may be said to form a true colony. In other instances the association is much looser; often the only connection between the individuals may be that they are embedded in a common tunic, so that there is little to distinguish them from an aggregation of separate individuals.

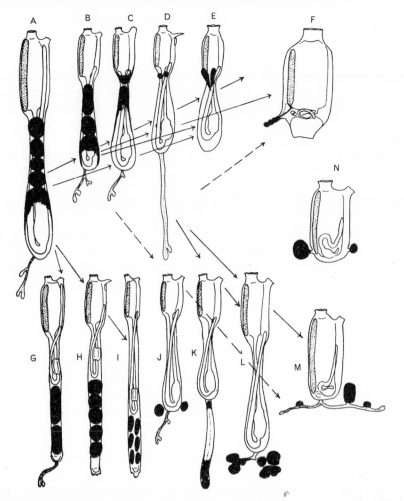

Fig. 21-6. Diagram to show mutual relations of the various methods of budding among the Urochordata. The types represent: A, *Diazona*; B, *Archidistoma*; C, *Eudistoma*; D, *Distaplia*; E, *Diplosoma*; F, a thaliacean; G, *Tylobranchion*; H, *Morchellium* or *Aplidium*; I, *Euherdmania*; J, *Pycnoclavella*; K, *Colella*; L, *Clavelina*; M, *Ecteinascidia* or *Perophora*; N, a Polystelid or Botryllid. The arrows show the probable directions of specialization in the course of evolution, the discontinuous lines possible relationships. From Berrill, 1935. *Phil. Trans. R. Soc. B,* **225**, 327–379.

As regards the evolutionary history of the ascidian colony, there is reason to believe that *Diazona*, which forms large colonies in several fathoms of water, is a very primitive ascidian, and that its mode of budding is also primitive (Fig. 21-7). It provides a good illustration of the epidermis as a primary agent of the process, for at the end of the sexual season, this tissue constricts the posterior part of the body into separate buds, while the anterior end is regressing and disappearing. In due course the buds develop into adults by what is essentially a process of regeneration. Here too is a very close correlation with the seasons; asexual reproduction sets in during autumn and early winter, while the regenerative development of the buds, with their contained masses of trophocytes, takes place during late winter.

Clavelina (Fig. 21-8) forms colonies in which the individuals may be more or less free, or may be embedded in a common tunic. It has a cycle very similar to that of *Diazona*, except that asexual reproduction, accompanying the rapid growth of the

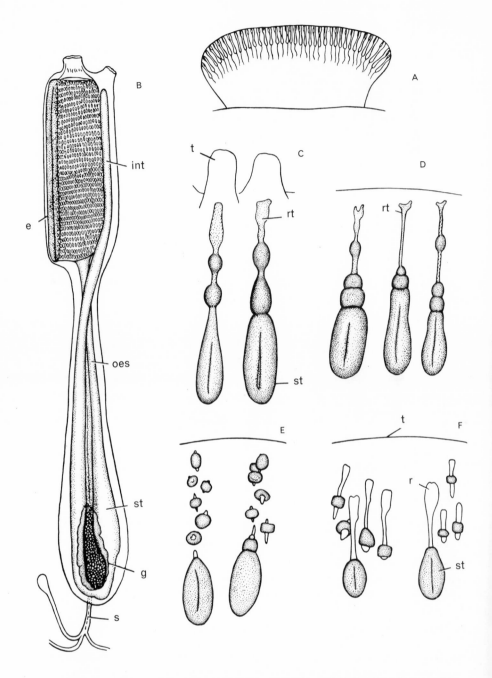

Fig. 21-7. *Diazona violacea.* A, section of whole colony; B, isolated zooid; C, zooids typical of colony taken on November 20; D, zooids of colony taken on January 1, showing regression and constriction; E, F, from colonies taken on January 30 and March 5 respectively, showing isolation and regeneration. *e,* endostyle; *g,* gonads; *int,* intestine; *oes,* oesophagus; *r,* regenerating thorax; *s,* vascular septum; *st,* stomach; *r.t,* regressing thorax; *t,* test at surface of colony. From Berrill, 1935. *op. cit.*

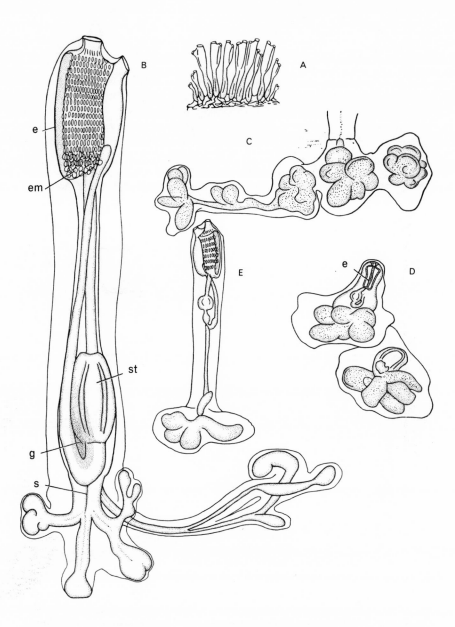

Fig. 21-8. *Clavelina lepadiformis*. A, colony; B, mature zooid showing hypertrophied ventral vessel; C, constriction of ventral vessel following degeneration of zooids to form bud masses; D, development of new zooids from single lobe of each of two isolated parts of ventral vessel; E, later development of bud. *e,* endostyle; *em,* embryos; *g,* gonads; *st,* stomach; *s,* septum of vascular stolon. From Berrill, 1935. *op. cit.*

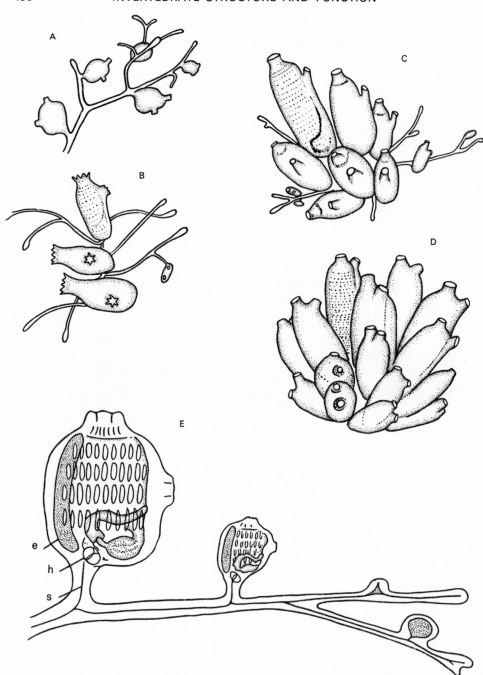

Fig. 21-9. Budding in the Perophoridae. A, small part of colony of *Perophora bermudensis*; B, part of colony of *Ecteinascidia conklini minuta*; C, small colony of *E. conklini typica*; D, part of colony of *E. turbinata*, showing length of ventral stolonic vessels and influence on appearance of colony; E, *Perophora*, showing relation of buds to parent zooid, stolonic vessel, and vascular septum. *e*, endostyle; *h*, heart; *s*, septum of vascular stolon. From Berrill, 1935. *op. cit.*

newly formed zooids, may also take place during the summer, while the parent zooids are sexually mature. This genus exemplifies the use of a ventral budding stolon, which is here an epidermal outgrowth containing a mesenchymal septum that permits an outflow and return of blood. Trophocytes accumulate in swellings of the stolonic vessel, but these swellings seem unable to develop into active buds while the vessels remain in functional continuity with the parent zooids. When, however, they become separated, or when the parents regress, active development ensues; the ectoderm of the stolon gives rise to the ectoderm of the new zooid, while the vascular septum forms all the remaining tissues.

The interplay of parent and bud in *Clavelina* reminds us of the physiological control regulating asexual reproduction in the coelenterates. Another and somewhat contrasted example is provided by *Perophora* (Fig. 21-9). This also forms stolons with vascular septa, the formation of buds being here initiated by a bulging of the epidermis and an associated proliferation of the septum. No trophocytes accumulate, apparently because the circulation is adequate for the provision of nutrition, and perhaps also because asexual reproduction takes place throughout the period of sexual activity, before there is any regression of the parent forms. In contrast to the stolons of *Clavelina*, those of *Perophora* and *Ecteinascidia*, both members of the Perophoridae, can differentiate new zooids while they are still in organic connection with the adults. The end result is said to depend upon environmental conditions. If circumstances are adverse the daughter zooid may grow at the expense of the parent, whereas in other conditions the parent dominates the situation and may re-absorb the bud. This type of budding can produce true colonies, in which each individual remains in organic connection with the remainder.

The situation in the Thaliacea is very much more complex than that in the Ascidiacea, largely because of their varied adaptations to a pelagic life. All of them bud by means of stolons, but these differ from the stolons of ascidians in the variety of tissues that they contain (Fig. 21-10). These arise from the pharynx, the atrial chambers, and the pericardium—regions of the body that are well situated to contribute to the stolon contents. In principle, budding is brought about by the constricting activity of the epidermis, as with ascidians, but the relationship between the ascidian and thaliacean type of stolon has been a matter for disagreement. Garstang took the view that the complex stolon of thaliaceans was primitive. Berrill prefers to regard it as a specialization resulting from the increased importance of asexual reproduction in the life histories of these forms; the elaboration of these life histories can be interpreted as correlated with the requirements of pelagic life, which is generally agreed to be a secondary development in thaliaceans.

In the free-swimming colonies of *Pyrosoma* the discharge of the excurrent stream through a single posterior atrial opening, narrowed by a diaphragm, provides for

Fig. 21-10. Diagram to illustrate the relations of the budding stolon of the Thaliacea, e.g. *Salpa*. *e*, endostyle; *ep*, epidermis; *g*, gonadial strand; *pc*, pericardium; *ph*, pharyngeal diverticulum. From Berrill, 1935. *op. cit.*

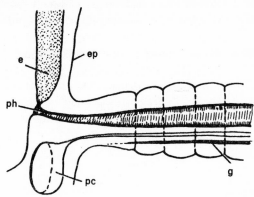

efficient and continuous jet-propulsion. Thus the zooids are here truly subordinated to the life of the colony as a whole. A much more extreme example of this, however, is seen in the life cycle of *Doliolum*, where a remarkable level of polymorphism is achieved during the reproduction of the free-swimming asexual individual called the oozoid. Numerous buds are given off from a stolon, and are moved backwards and upwards onto a dorsal process through the agency of wandering cells, the phorocytes. Those buds that come to lie along the two lateral edges of the process develop into gastrozooids with an enormously enlarged pharynx. They provide for the nutrition of what is now a colony, the parent oozoid losing its own alimentary function and becoming devoted solely to asexual reproduction, so that it is now termed the nurse. Wandering buds also settle along the middle line of the dorsal process; these develop into another type of individual, the phorozooid. Each of these is at first attached by a stalk, on which settles another bud. This elongates, and gives rise to a series of buds which remain attached to the phorozooid as a group of developing individuals. The phorozooid eventually breaks free, and leads an independent free-swimming life until the buds that it is carrying have developed into hermaphrodite sexual individuals. These, the gonozooids, are then set free individuâlly to carry out the sexual phase of the life cycle. Unfortunately, the fragility of doliolids, and their oceanic habit, has so far made it impossible to unravel any of the factors that determine the course of this bizarre and intricate product of the colonial habit.

21–4   SOCIAL LIFE IN INSECTS

The term 'colony' is often applied to the complex societies that are formed by certain species of insects. Since the animals concerned are very highly organized, and retain their individual freedom of movement, the phenomenon clearly does not fall within the strict definition of colonial life that we have so far been using. Yet the term is not inappropriate, for the members of these societies are certainly subordinated to the life of the community as a whole, and they are bound together by mechanisms that are none the less real because they are chemical and physiological rather than structural. In illustration of this we may first review briefly the life of the honey bee, *Apis mellifera*—a species that was known in its domesticated form to the early Egyptians, and that has been carried by man throughout the world.

The bee colony is polymorphic, comprising three varieties or castes. One of these, the queens, consists of fertile females; the other two, workers and drones, are respectively sterile females and fertile males. The queen copulates once only, at the beginning of her reproductive life, when as a virgin queen she is followed out of the hive by a swarm of drones in the nuptial flight. Thereafter she is concerned solely with laying eggs in the cells prepared by the workers; she achieves, in the spring, a maximum rate of about one egg per minute. During the discharge of an egg she is able to release or to withold sperm, thereby determining whether or not the egg is fertilized; in doing so she effects the primary caste distinction between males and females, for Hymenoptera have a peculiar mode of sex determination in which males can only arise from unfertilized eggs and females from fertilized ones. The factor that determines her action seems to be the size of the cell, for drones are larger than workers and their cells are correspondingly bigger.

A larva hatches from the egg three days after it has been laid, and it has then to be nursed within its cell by workers, which have two important contributions to make in this connection. First, they have to maintain a constant temperature of 95°F. This they do in cold weather by crowding together and imparting their collective heat of metabolism to the hive, while in warm weather they set up a current of air by fanning with their wings. The cooling effect of this current is supplemented by its evaporation of the water which other workers bring into the hive and distribute over the combs. The second function of the workers at this stage is the feeding of the larvae. This completes the determination of the castes, for nutrition is the factor that determines whether the females develop into queens or workers.

During the first three days of life all the larvae are fed upon royal jelly, which is a secretion of the pharyngeal glands of the workers. After the third day the royal jelly fed to the larvae in normal cells is diluted with honey and pollen from the crops of the workers, and the total amount of food is rationed. These larvae receive, therefore, a restricted diet, and in consequence of this the female ones become workers. The future queens are treated differently. They develop in special cells, large in size and irregular in shape, and are fed exclusively upon royal jelly, which they receive in substantial amounts. The diets of queens and workers is thus markedly different, and the determining influence of this is shown by the fact that larvae transferred from worker cells to queen cells will develop at least some of the characters of queens, forming what are called intercastes. The precise nature of the dietary difference remains uncertain. According to one view, royal jelly is rich in nutrients (it contains a large proportion of B vitamins, including pantothenic acid and biotin), and it is supposed that the large supplies of these promote queen development. According to another view, the virtue of royal jelly resides in some specific factor, either ingested as a vitamin-like substance by the workers and stored in their pharyngeal glands, or else actually secreted by them.

The production of a sterile worker caste is an example of intraspecific control and cooperation exerted through polymorphism. It solves a problem that is crucial for the maintenance of social organization, in bees as in men: the control of reproduction so that the community remains of manageable size and does not over-exploit its food supply by insensate intragroup competition. The queen is of central importance in this control, as is shown by the behaviour that results if she is removed from the hive. Soon after her disappearance the workers change some of the normal cells, containing young larvae, into emergency queen cells, while the ovaries of these workers, which are normally atrophied, start to develop towards a functional condition. The presence or absence of the queen thus determines both the behaviour and the sexual development of the workers, the loss of the queen leading to changes that tend to increase the production of sexually active females. This control is exerted through the release from the queen of a secretion called queen substance, which has now been obtained as a crystalline material. Analysis and synthesis have shown it to be 9-oxodec-2-enoic acid ($CH_3.CO.CH_{25}.CH:CH.COOH$), closely related chemically to 10-hydroxydec-2-enoic acid, which is present in royal jelly. The queen substance inhibits the sexual development of the workers that ingest it, and also regulates their building activities. Since, however, the workers can only obtain this substance by licking it from the queen's body, her influence depends upon direct contact with them, and it is eliminated if they are separated from her by a double wire screen. The functioning of the bee community thus depends upon linking queen and workers

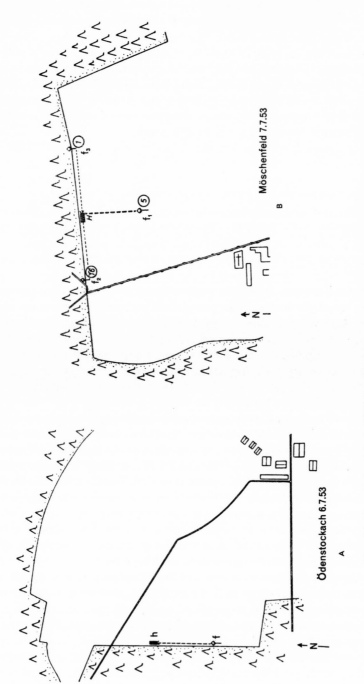

Fig. 21-11. A: On July 6, 1953, in the *afternoon*, a group of bees was trained to the south, along the edge of a forest. B: In the next *morning* the bees saw a similar forest, but this time the edge of the forest ran E–W, i.e. at right angles to the training situation. Sixteen bees were led to the west by the forest's edge; only 5 bees flew south. (The encircled numbers indicate the number of bees recorded at the feeding places.) From Lindauer, 1960. *Cold Spring Harb. Symp. quant. Biol.,* **25,** 371–377.

Ödenstockach 6.7.53

A

Möschenfeld 7.7.53

B

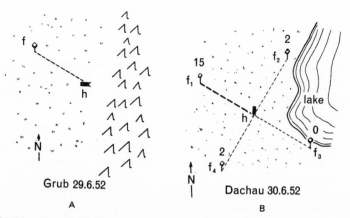

Fig. 21-12. A: A beehive (*H*) was placed in an unknown region, and a group of bees was fed *in the afternoon* on a feeding table (*F*) 180 m NW. B: During the night the hive was translocated to another area and, *in the morning*, the bees had to choose one of four feeding tables (F_1–F_4) 180 m NE, NW, SE, and SW. The new landscape did not offer any familiar landmarks; the sun stood at another angle relative to the training line as compared with the previous afternoon. Nevertheless, most bees (encircled numbers) came to the NW table, i.e. the bees had calculated the sun's movement. From Lindauer, 1960. *op. cit.*

through a chemical, an example of the ectohormones (or sociohormones) to which we refer elsewhere. To this extent the description of the community as a colony, with the implication by definition of some organic link between its members, is not inappropriate.

In theory the bee community can perpetuate itself indefinitely, but for this to be possible an aging queen must from time to time be replaced by a new one, as each queen can only reproduce for four or five years. A single additional queen cell, or at most a very few of them, would be needed for this. In practice, however, the community must do more, for it must propagate itself to compensate for the risk of its destruction by some environmental hazard; this is provided for by the process known as swarming. A number of queen cells are constructed, and eventually the old queen leaves the hive accompanied by many of the older workers. Soon thereafter a new queen emerges from her cell, and within a week or two she flies from the hive on the nuptial flight, accompanied by drones. On her return the remaining workers kill the other young queens, unless, as sometimes happens, the new queen herself leads a swarm of workers from the hive; in this case a second new queen will survive as the reproductive centre of the community. Any remaining drones are eventually discarded, and the hive is then ready for its normal working activity.

We have mentioned that this elaborate control of reproduction is needed to regulate the exploitation of food supplies. Yet this control is not in itself enough, for the individual workers must be able to exploit their environment successfully, not only in their own interests but in those of the community as a whole. This result is achieved by a development of genetic and neural mechanisms similar to those found in independently living animals, and remarkable for their precise and complex integration.

One aspect of this is the highly specialized life history of the worker bee. Although it may only live for five to six weeks, it is able to carry out during this time all of the essential requirements of the community life, taking these up one by one in a rigidly predetermined order. For the first three days of its life the young worker cleans the brood cells and keeps them warm. Next it becomes a nurse, feeding the older larvae from the third to the sixth day of its life, and the younger larvae and the queen from the sixth to the fourteenth. From the fourteenth to the eighteenth day it is a builder, secreting wax and constructing combs, from the eighteenth to the twentieth day it guards the entrance of the hive, and finally, up to about the fortieth day, it journeys out from the hive to obtain nectar and pollen.

This sequence of behaviour is in part genetically controlled, bringing particular neural and effector systems into action in a predetermined sequence. But the worker bee is more than an inflexible machine. We have seen something of the elaboration of the nervous system and receptor equipment of arthropods. With this as a basis, the worker bee can familiarize itself with the surroundings of its hive, and learn to find its way back to it, memorizing for this purpose the colours, positions, and relative distances of landmarks (Fig. 21-11), and the odours produced by the scent glands of the other bees. Further, bees are able to orientate themselves by the sun, using it as a compass to establish their position, and having also a sense of time which enables them to allow for the movement of the sun during their absence from the hive (Fig. 21-12). This is a well-authenticated example of the internal clock mechanisms that we have referred to elsewhere. Finally, their eyes are sensitive to the vibrations of polarized light, so that they can orientate themselves by a patch of blue sky, even if the sun itself is concealed. This enables them to make the fullest use of the compound eye; only a small area of this may be directed towards the sun at any one moment, but the remainder of it can nevertheless be functioning as a navigational aid.

These capacities, together with sensitivity to the colour and scent of flowers, ensure success for the individual worker in its round of foraging duties, but they do nothing to ensure the efficient integration of the activities of the foragers as a whole. To provide for this a system of communication has evolved, which has been brilliantly deciphered by von Frisch. It works in this way (Fig. 21-13). When a forager returns to the hive it regurgitates its honey as droplets that are taken up by other workers and distributed to other members of the colony or to the storage cells of the combs. If the source of the honey was near to the hive the forager embarks upon a whirling 'round dance', in which she dances clockwise and anticlockwise in rapid succession. Other workers join in the dance, and, stimulated by the excitement, eventually leave the hive themselves to secure more of the honey. They are aided in their search by their detection of the specific flower scent which the first worker will have brought back with the honey, a good illustration of the close mutual adaptation of bees and the flowers that they frequent.

This, however, is by no means all that is required to organize the foraging activities. It is important that the workers shall not waste their energies on flying after supplies of nectar that are poor in quality or in quantity. This is ensured by variation in the vigour of the dancing; a limited supply or a low sugar content results in a feebler dance, or in no dance at all, and this will determine how many, if any, workers will search for it: the weaker the dance, the less they are stimulated to fly.

The foragers also need some indication of the distance that they have to fly. This information is given by a second type of dance, the 'tail-wagging dance', in which the bee runs along semicircles, alternately left and right, ending each turn with a straight run back to her starting point. During the straight run she performs a rapid wagging movement of her abdomen. This dance has an effect different from that of the 'round dance', for it indicates that the nectar is at a more distant source. It also signals the distance that must be travelled in order to reach the nectar, for with increasing distance the dance becomes slower, and the time taken to travel along the straight run becomes correspondingly longer. Thus von Frisch found that the straight run was traversed nine to ten times in $\frac{1}{4}$ minute if the food source was 100 metres away, but only twice if it was 5,000 metres away. These figures remain remarkably constant, not only within the same colony at different times of the year, but even in different colonies; evidently the workers have an accurate computer, which seems to depend either on the time that they take to travel a particular distance, or on the energy that they expend in so doing.

Finally, and to complete this very brief survey of truly astonishing adaptations,

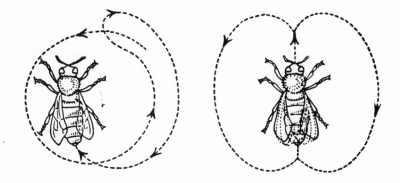

Fig. 21-13. Dances of the honey bee. *Left,* round dance; *right,* tail-wagging dance. From Richards, 1953. *The Social Insects.* Macdonald, London.

the 'tail-wagging dance' also indicates the direction of the food supply. In this instance the signal depends upon the bees' use of the sun as a compass, and of polarized light if the sun is obscured. If the 'tail-wagging dance' is on the horizontal platform of the hive, the angle between the axis of the dance and the direction of the sun's rays is the same as the angle between the correct direction of flight and the rays. If, as is more usual, the dance takes place on the vertical comb, the angle of flight is indicated by the angle between the straight wagging run and the vertical. Further, if the wagging run is carried out in an upward direction the feeding place is situated towards the sun, while if it is carried out downwards the feeding place is situated away from the sun. As with all phases of this communication system, remarkable demands are made upon the interpretative powers of the recipients of the information, as well as upon the computing capacity of the successful foragers. The vertical dance takes place in the darkness of the hive, yet the bees are able to translate patterns of vertical orientation into horizontal characteristics of the illuminated world outside. Information relating to sources of pollen is also imparted in the same way, by round and tail-wagging dances, the essential difference lying in the characteristic scent of the pollen, which the bees are well able to detect.

The essential features of social life in the honey bee, distinguishing it from a merely gregarious habit, are the abandonment of the uninhibited predatory and reproductive life of the individual, the establishment of division of labour, and the integration of the colony by means of a communication system. Probably the first step in its evolution was the establishment of some degree of maternal care as a result of an association between the mother and her developing young. An often-quoted example of such a situation is the behaviour of the female earwig, which lays her eggs in a hole in the ground and then remains with them, turning them over and licking them. When the young hatch they remain with the parent, but only for a few days.

More directly relevant to the evolution of the social habit of bees, however, are the varied types of life history found in many members of this group. Some of these are solitary, each fertilized female hibernating and then raising a brood of males and females by placing eggs and food in holes which she prepares. There is here no community life; the mothers never see their young and the males die after they have mated, while the new generation of females hibernates in isolation. In other species the female lives longer, and is still in the nest when her offspring are emerging, much like the earwig; it is this relationship that contains the potentialities of social life. True social organization, although at a very simple level, is seen in certain species of *Halictus* in which a further important step has been taken: some females work on behalf of the others, without themselves reproducing. The spring females, working alone or in groups of up to three individuals, build a simple nest and produce in it offspring that are all female. These offspring are essentially workers, for their ovaries remain imperfectly developed, the founder females being queens that continue to lay eggs and also guard the nest. It is said (and this is in accordance with the habits of honey bees) that where several founder females are initially associated, only one survives as a queen for the rest of the season. Later in the year males and females arise, mating takes place between them, and the young females hibernate.

Whatever its precise mode of evolution, social life has certainly developed independently along several different lines in insects. In the Hymenoptera it is found among wasps and ants, as well as in bees, and it occurs also in the quite unrelated group of termites (Order Isoptera). Not surprisingly, having regard to the complexity of the adaptations demanded by a fully organized social community, only a relatively small number of species has achieved it. According to Richards, of the 20,200 species of insects in the British fauna, about 88 are social, 37 of these being ants, 44 bees, and 7 wasps.

The characteristic of the hymenopteran colonies is that they are dominated by females, presumably because of the peculiar method of sex determination found in this group, allowing the fertile female direct control over the sex ratio. The mode of origin of the wasp colony can be gauged from the diverse habits of solitary wasps. Some lay their eggs in cells in a nest, and practise what is called mass-provisioning, placing with the egg sufficient food (in the form of paralyzed grubs) to serve the young throughout their development. Others employ progressive provisioning, adding more food to the cell after the larva has emerged; this may have been a crucial factor in the origin of the social habit. The colony of the common wasp *Vespula* differs from that of the hive bee in that it is strictly an annual one. During the summer the nest will contain a queen and some thousands of workers, but when colder weather arrives in the autumn the workers and males die, the young queens being left to hibernate and to found new colonies in the spring.

Remarkable as are the specializations of wasps and bees, it is the ants that have most fully explored the possiblities of social life. The group, which comprises over

10,000 species, all of which are social, has exploited terrestrial habitats in every part of the world except the arctic region. We see in ants, more strikingly, perhaps, than in any other insects, the extraordinary potentialities of arthropodization, which in these animals permits the application of social techniques to solve comprehensively a wide range of ecological problems. Elsewhere in the animal kingdom (except in the human species), these problems are dealt with in only a fragmentary way, by species that are specialized for the execution of only a limited range of activities. The comparison of ants with men has often been made. We shall not pursue it here beyond pointing out that one fundamental difference lies in the rigidity of individual behaviour within the hymenopteran colony. The flexible and exploratory behaviour of man, together with his delayed maturation and consequent educability, has made it possible to develop human societies without dependence upon structural and physiological polymorphism. The division of labour is there, however, and so are communication systems; thus comparisons between the human lot and that of the ant are not unprofitable, once the essential differences between the two modes of social organization have been grasped. The comparisons are the more worth while because, as Richards has pointed out, man has probably been social for less than 1 million years, and it is still early to judge his future course. Ants, by contrast, have been organized in societies for much longer even than bees and wasps, certainly for at least 30 to 40 million years, for they are found preserved in Baltic amber.

It is significant, having regard to the success of ants, that they display more flexibility than other social Hymenoptera. Their nests, built in the soil or out of plant materials, are readily modified and extended, while the animals are less rigidly committed to particular types of food. Moreover, there is within the group as a whole a wide diversification of habit, doubtless reflecting their long evolutionary history.

As regards feeding habits, comparisons can be made with the hunting, food gathering, and cultivation practised by human societies. Some species obtain their food by killing small animals and conveying them to the nest, where they are shared among the members. Others, comparable with human food gatherers, collect seeds or nectar, and some of these grade into agriculturists. Thus leaf-cutting ants carry pieces of leaves in procession, 'like Sunday-school children carrying banners', to form in their nests a compost for the growth of the fungus on which they feed. Another illustration, suggestive of an analogy with human agricultural practice, is the association between ants and aphids and scale insects. This association, which we shall discuss later, provides the ants with an important source of carbohydrate in the form of the liquid excreta (honey dew) of the other insects.

Division of labour and control of reproduction proceeds in principle much as in other hymenopteran colonies. Commonly a colony is founded by a new queen on her return from her nuptial flight, at which time her spermathecae contain enormous numbers of sperm, over 300 million in *Atta sexdens*, according to one estimate. Not surprisingly, some of these queens are believed to survive for as long as 15 years. The workers, which are wingless, and have a small thorax, are variable in form. Sometimes the variation is only a matter of size, but this caste may also be markedly polymorphic, consisting then of smaller workers and larger soldiers, the latter having relatively large heads. The sexual forms, which are winged males and females, are found for only a short season, the males serving merely for the insemination of the new generation of queens. The primary determination of sex depends, as in other

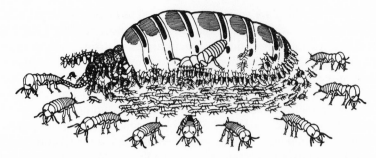

Fig. 21-14. Scene in the royal chamber of the African termite, *Termes bellicosus*, showing the king, queen, and attendant soldiers and workers. After Escherich, from Richards, 1953. *op. cit.*

Hymenoptera, on whether or not the eggs are fertilized, but apart from this we know little of the basis of caste differentiation, and we cannot assume that the details are necessarily uniform in such a highly diversified group. There is evidence (in *Myrmica rubra*) that the young larvae are plastic, and that their fate depends upon their food supply. It has been suggested that the course of events can be interpreted as a competitive relationship between different sets of organs, with gonads and wing buds developing late, so that sexual females can only arise from larvae that are provided with enough food to enable these organs to complete their development.

Information regarding the modes of integration of ant colonies is no less inadequate, but chemical communication systems are certainly widely exploited. In fact, most of the social behaviour is probably controlled in this way, the agents being exocrine glands discharging a variety of specific secretions which then release innate and stereotyped responses. Odour trails are one illustration of this. They may be exploratory trails, laid by the foraging columns of legionary ants, or the recruitment trails that are laid in many species by workers returning to their nests after discovering food. It seems from studies of the fire ant, *Solenopsis saevissima*, that the strongly attractant qualities of the trail secretion can release all the required behaviour of the followers. The procedure is, in principle, a very simple one, apparently less complex than that of bees. The better the quality and quantity of the food, the more will it be visited. The amount of attractant in the trail will be correspondingly greater, and this will attract still more workers to forage in the same direction.

Other examples of chemical communication are the attractants produced by queens, which stimulate workers to tend her and to transport her eggs away. The removal of dead bodies from the nest is stimulated by decomposition products of the corpses, a reaction that may well illustrate, in its use of by-products of metabolism, the way in which some chemical communication systems originated. Chemical control of reproduction, so well authenticated in the hive bee, is probably operative also in ants, although the situation is less clear. Certainly there are cases on record in which the presence or the removal of queens influences the fate of the larvae; in *Myrmica*, for example, the presence of a queen is said to result in smaller pupal size and a reduced rate of production of other queens. The effect is not confined to the production of sexual forms. There is evidence that, where the worker caste is polymorphic, the presence of soldiers has an inhibitory effect on the production of other soldiers. Hypotheses based on the supposed distribution of inhibitory ectohormones undoubtedly provide the simplest explanation of such phenomena, but not the only one, for it is conceivable that individuals may be influenced by tactile or visual signals (in those species, of course, in which eyes are well developed), or there may be more subtle group effects, dependent upon the composition of the colony and influenced also by external factors. It has been well said of ants that we know in a general way what many species do, yet we do not know how they do it; it is, of course, a comment that is by no means applicable only to this group of animals.

The evolution of social life in the Hymenoptera has clearly been favoured by the peculiar method of sex determination of these animals, and by the high general level of their organization, but there is no reason in principle why it should not also have evolved in other insects. This has, in fact, happened in the termites, the Order Isoptera. If we compare these with the Hymenoptera, we find similar biological results being achieved in very different ways along very different paths of evolution.

We can trace the distinguishing features of termite social organization to two fundamental characteristics of the group. First, their mode of sex determination is of the type more normal in animals—males and females both arise from fertilized eggs, the two sexes differing in the balance between the sex chromosomes and the remaining chromosomes. Probably because of this, both sexes are present in all of the castes, the queen being associated with a king (forming the 'royal couple') instead of relying upon a single act of insemination (Fig. 21–14). The abdomen of the queen becomes enormously enlarged, and she becomes an immensely efficient egg-laying machine, capable sometimes of laying at the rate of 36,000 eggs in 24 hours.

The second important characteristic is that termites, being heterometabolous insects, have a gradual and progressive development through a series of nymphal instars (Fig. 21–15), instead of beginning life as helpless larvae. Thus each member of the colony can soon be useful, while both its form and its function can be modified during its development. This makes for a caste system that is at the same time more flexible and more complex than that of hymenopteran colonies. One caste comprises the soldiers, typically without any sign of wing pads, and to this extent representing an early stage of development. They may be of two different sizes, and they may also be of two distinct types (Fig. 21–16) which do not, however, occur in the same species. One of these types has large mandibles, while the head of the other (the nasute) is produced into a snout from which can be discharged a secretion that is used for attack on other insects. The soldiers do not feed, nor do they carry out the basic work

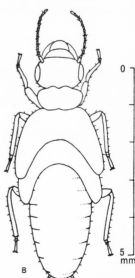

Fig. 21-15. Nymphal stages of *Odontotermes latericius*. A, undifferentiated second-stage nymph; B, fifth-stage nymph with developing wing pads. From Harris, 1961. *Termites: their Recognition and Control.* Longmans, London.

A

B

0

5
mm

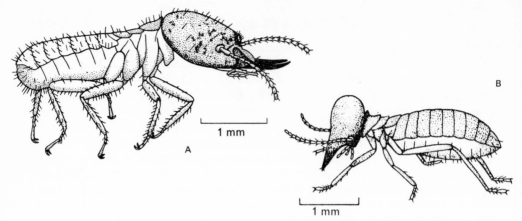

Fig. 21-16. A, soldier of *Coptotermes niger*. B, side-view of soldier of *Nasutitermes infuscatus*. From Harris, 1961. *op. cit.*

of the community, their function being probably a defensive one. The basic work is performed either by the developing nymphs (in the less specialized colonies) or by a worker caste (in the more specialized ones). The distinguishing feature of a true worker caste is that its individuals are incapable of further growth or development. They, like soldiers, have no wing pads, and may be of two different sizes.

Normally, new termite colonies are formed after the flight of winged sexual forms, which appear in large numbers during a very limited season. The flexibility of the system, however, is shown by the fact that if the royal couple is removed, or dies, certain developing nymphs become capable of reproduction, although they cannot fly, and do not leave the nest. These forms are called substitute sexual forms. Presumably some inhibitory influence exerted by the royal couple normally prevents their development. This effect is well illustrated in some species in which the nest may be enlarged until it spreads far underground. In such conditions the peripheral parts of the nest may be budded off as independent colonies, with substitute sexual forms taking the place of royal couples. This effect suggests that the inhibitory influence of the original royal couple can operate only over a limited distance, a curious parallel with the control of individuality that we have discussed in connection with coelenterate organization.

This is not the only example that can be given of the adaptive regulation of the composition of the termite colony. There is the case of the young colony in which only one nymph normally becomes a soldier; if this is removed, another nymph transforms to take its place, while, on the contrary, the differentiation of the first one can be suppressed if a soldier is introduced into the colony from outside. Then again, if fourth-stage nymphs of *Calotermes* are reared in isolated pairs, both members of the pair will become sexually mature if they are of opposite sex, but only one of the pair if they are of the same sex. Finally, it has been recorded that when 545 nymphs of *Prorhinotermes* were placed in an artificial nest they gave rise to 103 large workers, 37 soldiers, and 82 substitute sexual forms, while 323 died or remained as nymphs. The complexity of this transformation can be appreciated when it is realized that some of these nymphs had regressed (the workers and soldiers had lost the wing pads), while the heads of the soldiers and the gonads of the reproductive forms showed progressive development.

We do not know how this developmental integration is effected. It may partly depend upon genetic differences influencing the growth and behaviour of individuals. Other factors might be the signalling of information that influences metabolism, and the direct transmission of inhibitory chemicals, acting as ectohormones (socio-hormones) like the queen substance of the hive bee. Experimental evidence indicative of the complexity of the situation has been obtained from *Calotermes flavicollis*. If a colony is divided into two by a double gauze screen, so that one portion contains the royal couple, the other portion then develops substitute sexual forms, all but one pair of these being destroyed. If, however, the gauze screen is single instead of double, substitute sexual forms are again developed, but in this instance they are all destroyed. It is suggested that when there is a single screen the presence of the royal couple is indicated by some signal, perhaps by antennal contact. A chemical inhibitor, which would normally prevent the differentiation of substitute sexual forms, cannot, however, pass, because the gauze acts as a barrier, perhaps by preventing licking. The double gauze partition would prevent direct sensory contact, so that in this circumstance the complete destruction of the substitutes does not occur. The existence of a chemical inhibitor is further indicated by experiments in which a queen is attached to the screen so that her abdomen belongs to one portion of the colony and her head to the other. Only in the group possessing the abdomen is there complete inhibition of the development of substitute sexual forms; this suggests that an inhibitory ectohormone is being released from the abdomen.

22

Interspecific Associations

22–1 TYPES OF ASSOCIATION

We have seen that the members of natural communities are linked by systems of relationships, partly cooperative and partly competitive, that operate in subtle ways to ensure the efficient exploitation of the environment. Among these relationships there are certain interspecific partnerships that are characteristic of particular species, and that are marked by their intimacy, by being obligatory for at least one of the partners, and by the high degree of specialization that they involve. These relationships have often been described as though they were isolated phenomena, and partly because of this they have sometimes been interpreted in over-imaginative and sentimental terms. In fact, however, they are no more than specialized types of ecological relationship in which the two partners have come to form a functional unit, with its own means of perpetuation, and subject to the action of natural selection.

These intimate interspecific associations are so varied in their nature and in their biological significance that some scheme of nomenclature and classification is needed to describe them. The framing of the appropriate definitions, however, is difficult; these associations present a continuous spectrum of relationships, so that any classification of them must be somewhat artificial. Because of this difficulty, the terms employed do not always carry the same meanings; for our present purpose, however, we shall use them in the following ways, always remembering that they are terms of convenience, and that particular examples will not always conform neatly with them.

Commensalism (*cum*, with; *mensa*, table) is a regular and close association between individuals of two different species, in which one partner gains some benefit, while the other gains no benefit at all, but at the same time suffers no serious disadvantage. Of the two partners, the former is often called the commensal and the latter the host. The requirement that the host shall not suffer seriously from the association has to be interpreted flexibly; it may well be, for example, that the commensal robs it of some of its food, so that to this extent the host does incur some

470

disadvantage; but the implication is that this is minor in character, and that it does not impede survival or reproduction.

Inquilinism (*inquilinus*, tenant) is a regular and close association in which one partner lives within a host, obtaining shelter thereby, and perhaps also appropriating some of the host's food. It will be obvious that on this definition the only distinction between inquilinism and commensalism is that in the former association one partner is within the other; inquilinism can therefore be considered as a particular form of commensalism.

Mutualism (*mutuus*, exchanged) is a regular and close association from which both partners benefit, and from which neither derives any disadvantage.

Symbiosis (*symbioun*, to live together) is also an association from which both partners benefit, so that it is difficult to differentiate it from mutualism. In fact, the two terms are often used as being interchangeable. Yet some writers do make a distinction, although not a clear-cut one, by regarding symbiosis as (in Caullery's words) the extreme form of mutualism. From this point of view symbiosis is an association so close that the two partners may be thought of as living a common life, permanent in its character, and satisfying certain of their metabolic requirements.

Parasitism is an association in which one partner (the parasite) lives on or in the body of the other partner (the host), nourishing itself at the expense of the host, but without destroying it. This proviso is intended to distinguish the relationship from that existing between a predator and its prey, but it is not always applicable, for some parasitic associations certainly lead to the death of the host. This difficulty of definition can, however, be overcome by regarding those parasites that kill their hosts as imperfectly adapted; such, for example, is certainly true of the trypanosomes that infect man. A further difficulty is that the distinction between commensalism and parasitism may not always be easy to define. Essentially, however, parasitism involves nutritional exploitation of the host, whereas a commensal operates within its host's margin of reserves, so that from the physiological point of view its presence may, so to say, pass unnoticed.

22–2 COMMENSALISM AND MUTUALISM

We can easily visualize some possible origins of commensal relationships. They would be an inevitable consequence of the crowded conditions of life in many environments, particularly in the littoral zone, and of the way in which the habits and life histories of some animals bring them into the closest contact with members of other species. The attachment of a sessile animal to the surface of a free-moving one would thus appear a type of association that could very readily be formed, perhaps as a result of the accidental settling of larvae upon the host. However, life is unlikely to be as simple as this. It must be remembered, for example, that larvae are highly selective in their choice of substrates, and that the secretions of free-moving animals may often be toxic, and may be specialized to keep the body surface clear of precisely such entanglements. We must certainly expect, therefore, that the maintenance of commensal associations of this kind (whatever their origin may have been) will often involve considerable specialization on the part of one or both partners.

Thus some of the sessile vorticellids that are common on the surface of aquatic crustaceans have come to depend for their survival upon the movement of the host.

If they are allowed to become attached to pieces of chitin in artificial conditions they will only continue to live if the fragments are kept in continuous movement. Whether the initial growth of the vorticellid on the host depends upon some specific attraction is not known, but it is clear that the association is far from being simple and unspecialized. This is a case of physiological specialization. The vorticellid *Ellobiophrya donacis* (Fig. 22–1) provides an example of morphological specialization in its attachment to the gills of the bivalve, *Donax vittatus*. The benefits obtained by the protozoan are presumably protection within the shell, and a supply of food from the feeding currents that pass over it. At this level of analysis the association would seem to be a very simple form of commensalism, yet the vorticellid is highly specialized to maintain it, the attachment stalk being bifurcated in a unique way so that it can be virtually padlocked to the meshwork of the gill.

No less specialized are the two-tentacled commensal hydroids that live as colonies upon the tubes of sedentary sabellid polychaetes, and that are sometimes referred to as 'Lar', from the name first given to them by Gosse (Fig. 22–2). Three species of these animals have been described, all belonging to the genus *Proboscidactyla*, and all occupying very similar habitats, for they live respectively on the tubes of *Potamilla torelli*, *P. myriops*, and *Pseudopotamilla ocellata*.

The feeding of *Potamilla* is similar to that of *Sabella* (p. 179), depending upon collection and rejection currents upon the tentacular crown, palps, and lips. To these currents the commensals are closely adapted. The colony consists of gastrozooids, orientated around the opening of the worm's tube, and of mouthless gonozooids, situated lower down, along the sides of the tube. The positions are themselves of obvious adaptive significance, and this is emphasized by the behaviour of the gastrozooids. These are in continuous movement, their actions giving them the ludicrously human appearance from which Gosse derived their name (*lar*, household deity). By leaning back they secure food from the incoming current of water, while by leaning

Fig. 22-1. *Ellobiophrya donacis* attached to the gill-grid of its host. Upper left, an individual with a bud that has resulted from a longitudinal fission, showing the posterior circle of cilia. From Baer, 1951. *Ecology of Animal Parasites.* University of Illinois.

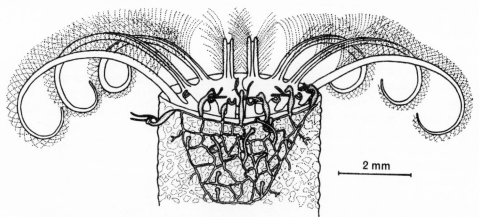

Fig. 22-2. A colony of *Proboscidactyla* sp. in place upon a tube of sabellid, *Pseudo-potamilla ocellata*. Several of the worm's tentacles have been cut away, and the number of tentacles shown on it is reduced from the natural condition. From Hand and Hendrickson, 1950. *Biol. Bull. mar. biol. Lab., Woods Hole,* **99**, 74–93.

forwards, among the tentacles or into the opening of the tube, they can remove particles carried in the ciliary currents. 'The head lobe moved to and fro on the neck' wrote Gosse when he first described them; 'the body swayed from side to side . . . while the long arms were widely expanded . . . and then waved downwards, as if to mimic the actions of the most tumultuous human passion'.

Hand and Hendrickson point out that the two-tentacled condition of the gastro-zooids is well suited for this commensal life. The tentacles are unusually active, and they can be greatly extended to explore much of the host's feeding currents. More tentacles might easily be a disadvantage, for they would tend to become entangled with the branchial crown; their peculiar origin, from a single common area below the mouth, probably helps in avoiding this entanglement. *Pseudopotamilla* repro-duces by free-swimming medusae. How these become associated with new hosts for the asexual phase is unknown; we may assume that this involves some response no less specialized than the behaviour of the gastrozooid, for Hand and Hendrickson remark that the species studied by them was never found associated with any animal other than *Pseudopotamilla ocellata*. This aspect of animal relationships we shall return to later. In the meantime, we may accept 'Lar' as an example of specialized commensalism, with the benefit accruing solely to the epizoitic coelenterate, as far as we know at present.

Another example of commensalism associated with extensive morphological specialization is seen in the Temnocephalida. These are platyhelminths that are be-lieved to be related to rhabdocoels. They live mainly on the body surface or within the branchial chamber of fresh-water crustaceans, and are distinguished from other rhabdocoels by this habit. They are distinguished also by possessing anterior tentacles and a posterior attachment disc which are used for carrying out leech-like movements. It is difficult to believe that this association gives sufficient advantage to the temno-cephalids to account for their high level of structural adaptation, particularly since they can feed on diatoms and small animals, and can live for months without their hosts. It seems more likely, especially in view of our earlier discussion of the role of chemical regulation in the organization of animal and plant communities, that many commensal relationships involve some form of chemical dependence, operating at a level of subtlety that has not yet been explored. Such situations could hardly have arisen ready made. In the case of temnocephalids it is conceivable that in the earlier stages of their evolution some slight advantage in the supply of nutrients, or of oxygen, in the respiratory streams of the hosts, would have provided a foundation upon which a more intimate dependence was later evolved.

Some of the commensalism that we observe today may still involve little adaptive modification of the partners. One example is the association between the coelenterate *Hydractinia echinata* and the hermit crab *Pagurus* (*Eupagurus*) *bernhardus*. Experimental study has shown that the crab has no marked preference for shells that are covered by the coelenterate. *Hydractinia* is equally independent in habit; it feeds mainly on living plankton, and, although it may share the food of the crab, it does

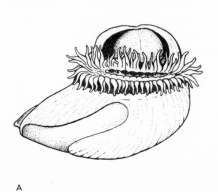

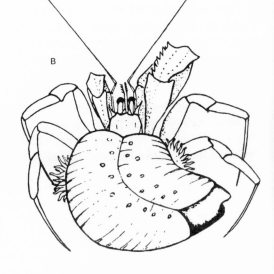

Fig. 22-3. A, shell of *Scaphander*, enveloped by *Adamsia palliata*, seen from below. B, *Pagarus* (*Eupagurus*) *prideauxi* in a shell of *Scaphander* which is enveloped by *Adamsia palliata*. From Faurot, 1910. *Archs Zool. exp. gén., 5 sér,* **5,** 421–486.

not rely upon this for its regular supply of nutriment. It possesses a form of zooid, called the spiralzooid, that is defensive in function as far as the colony is concerned, but there is no evidence that this zooid is of any value to the crab. In particular, it is not especially developed around the opening of the shell in which the crab lives, where any defensive value would show to the greatest advantage.

There is, however, a significant difference in the distribution of the two partners, and this suggests a possible explanation of the association. *Hydractinia* can live in colder conditions than can *Pagurus*, which is one reason why it is found growing on empty shells in the complete absence of the crab. On the other hand, its freedom for reproduction is limited because its eggs sink to the bottom; thus it cannot reproduce successfully in regions where the substratum is too soft or too poorly aerated to permit survival. Its association with the hermit crab enables it to invade and exploit such regions, to an extent that would be impossible without the support of its host. Consequently, *Hydractinia* is found almost exclusively on hermit crabs in regions where the substratum itself is unsuitable for it. It lives abundantly as independent colonies, however, where suitable rocks and piles are readily available.

A more specialized association of this type has developed between the anemone *Adamsia palliata* and the hermit crab *Pagurus prideauxi* (Fig. 22-3), first described in detail by Gosse. In this association, unlike the previous one, the specializations both of the crab and of the anemone are very evident, involving as they do both structural and behavioural features. Indeed, so intimate is the association that neither partner can survive without the other, once they have grown beyond an early juvenile stage. The crab can recognize the anemone by touch, being aided, perhaps, by chemical stimulation, and it can transfer it from the substratum to its shell. Thereafter the anemone grows in a highly specialized way to enclose the shell, maintaining its mouth immediately below that of the crab so that it is placed in the best position to make use of the feeding processes of the host. As for the crab, it is very active in movement, because of its elongated appendages and because it habitually lives in a shell that is too small to enclose it completely. This is possible because the pedal disc of the anemone secretes a horny membrane that extends over the opening of the shell, and so increases the shelter afforded to the host. No doubt the crab also obtains some protection from the anemone's nematocysts, which are borne on particularly long acontia. Such is the intimacy of this relationship that if the crab is removed from its shell the anemone drops off and soon dies. Here, then, is surely a true symbiosis, in the sense of the definition given earlier.

One feature of this association that has attracted particular attention is the mode of transference of the anemone when the crab moves out of one shell to occupy a larger one. This was closely studied by Gosse, who initially formed the impression that the anemone was an active participant in the removal, and that the crab's behaviour was attuned to that of the coelenterate. During his earlier observations he unfortunately absented himself from his aquarium during the vital hour when the transfer was effected. He concluded from the position of the anemone when he returned that it must have attached itself to the crab and relinquished its hold on the original shell. This drew from him an enthusiastic if incautious paen:

> But what a series of instincts does this series of facts open to us! The knowledge by a crab of the qualities of the new shell; the delay of his own satisfaction till his associate is ready; the power of communicating the fact to her; the power in her of apprehending the communication; her immediate obedience to the intimation; her relinquishment of her wonted hold . . . all these are wonderful to contemplate, wonderful considered singly, far more wonderful in their cumulation!

Later, however, when he removed an anemone from a shell, he observed that the crab replaced it with its chelipeds; this cast some doubt on his earlier interpretation, and somewhat quenched his wonder, for it suggested to him 'a suspicion that the claws of the crab may have been employed in the transference of the cloaklet from shell to shell'.

This suspicion was well founded; the crab does indeed remove the anemone, as happens also in another well-known association: that between the anemone *Calliactis parasitica* and hermit crabs of the species *Pagurus bernhardus*, *P. striatus*, and *P. arrosor*. The involvement of more than one species of host is an indication of a less extreme specialization. So also is the ability of *Calliactis* to live independently of its host, and the occasional presence upon one shell of a number of anemones which show no regular orientation with reference to the mouth of the host. *Calliactis*, like *Adamsia*, has very long acontia with nematocysts, and the protrusion of these through lateral openings in the body wall doubtless contributes to the defence of the crab as well as to that of the anemone itself. Since the anemones are probably aided in feeding, both by the movement provided by the crab and by the possibility of securing some of its food, the association can be regarded as an example of mutualism, but one that is not as intimately symbiotic as that of *Adamsia* and *Pagurus prideauxi*.

The degree of specialization involved in the *Calliactis* type of relationship should not, however, be underestimated. Indeed, it has been clearly demonstrated in Cowles's study of *Pagurus deformis*. This crab, which lives in the shells of *Dolium*, carries two different kinds of anemone, a large greyish one that is usually situated on the sides of the shell, and a smaller and almost colourless one that is attached on the underside below the protruding head of the crab. One shell may bear as many as eight of the former and four of the latter. Cowles observed that after a crab had transferred itself to a new shell it removed the anemones from the old one by clawing, pinching, and pulling them. Its movements were clumsy, and the anemones sometimes slipped off, with the result that the crab temporarily ceased to give them its attention; eventually, however, they became attached, guided into position by the crab's limbs. Two features of this performance illustrate the specialized character of the behaviour of both partners. Firstly, the anemones appear to separate from the old shell more readily and with less disturbance than under the hands of an experimenter. Secondly, the crab's behaviour appears to involve a chain of reflexes that the animal may be unable to complete if it is disturbed. Thus in one instance a crab made no attempt to transfer its anemones when it was removed with them to a new aquarium immediately after it had secured possession of a new shell. Presumably the normal sequence of the behaviour pattern had been interrupted.

We might expect a comparative study of these relationships to reveal various degrees of specialization, and *Calliactis* does, in fact, provide good examples of this. It is associated not only with *Pagurus striatus* and *P. arossor* but also with *P. bernhardus*, and Ross has shown that in this last instance the hermit crab seems to be indifferent to the presence of the anemone, and does not participate actively in establishing the association. The necessary stimulus is given when the anemone comes into contact with a suitable shell, to which it adheres by its tentacles as a result of discharging their nematocysts. Probably some chemical stimulus is derived from the organic deposits on the shell, while the physical features of the latter doubtless play some part also. The situation, in fact, is strongly reminiscent of the relationships between the larvae of *Ophelia* and the characteristics of their preferred sand grains. That the threshold of discharge of the nematocysts can be controlled in some way is shown by the fact that an anemone already attached to one shell will not adhere to another shell when this is presented to it.

This, then, is a commensal relationship, with the anemone as the active partner; we may suppose, therefore, that it was the anemone that initially derived selective advantage from it, presumably in connection with the securing of food. The associations between *Calliactis* and *P. striatus* and *P. arrosor* are more specialized. In both associations the anemone requires some preliminary stimulation before it will climb onto the shell, while with *P. arrosor* it requires further assistance before it can become firmly attached. As Ross points out, the three relationships are suggestive of an evolving ecological situation, in which there is a shift in emphasis from the anemone to the crab, accompanied by changes in behaviour pattern and presumably in the balance of selective advantages.

The demonstration that associations between some hermit crabs and anemones depend upon the latter being seized by their host allows us to relate these situations to other examples of crab behaviour, and thus to see them as part of a wider spectrum of adaptations. Certain crabs, of which *Maia* and *Hyas* are familiar examples, rely upon a variety of objects for camouflage and concealment. The surface of their bodies is frequently decorated with algae, sponges, and hydroids in a manner that provides effective disguise in the crowded conditions of the littoral zone. Some at least of these objects are seized by the crabs and placed upon their dorsal surfaces, where they are held in position by hooked setae. In aquaria the animals have been observed to make use of coloured rags; they select appropriate colours, and move on to backgrounds

Fig. 22-4. *Melia tessellata* from the Hawaiian Islands, bearing an expanded actinian in each claw. When food is placed on the disc of the actinian, the first ambulatory limbs of the crab reach over and abstract it and pass it to the crab's mouth. From Duerden, 1905. *Proc. zool. Soc. Lond.,* **2,** 494–511.

that match their disguise. There is no evidence of such a practice among hermit crabs, but some such behaviour may well have played a part in the evolution of their associations with coelenterates. This is the more likely in view of the remarkable way in which anemones are handled by *Melia*, a crab that is unrelated to those so far mentioned, and that is found on coral reefs.

It is the habit of *Melia* (Fig. 22-4) to carry a small anemone in each of its two chelae, and to brandish these towards a threatening agressor. Observations have shown that this depends upon the crab coming into contact with the anemones during its wanderings. If a crab that has been deprived of its anemones is placed with them in an aquarium it shows no sign of recognizing them until it actually touches them; once it has done this, however, it picks them up by inserting the tip of its first walking leg under the base of the anemone and prising it away from the substratum. The behaviour of the crab is clearly specialized to facilitate the grasping of the anemones, and so also is the structure and use of its appendages. The chelipeds are so slender that they are unsuited for defence or predation, but just because of this they are well adapted for holding the polyps around the middle of their bodies. They do this without injuring the anemones, which soon expand after seizure and maintain their tentacles in full extension. The chelipeds themselves cannot, of course, be used for feeding as they are in other crabs. Instead, the animal relies upon the walking limbs for seizing material from the substratum, the first pair of legs being the most active in this respect. But the most striking adaptation is the way in which the crab exploits the feeding activity of its anemones. If an observer places meat upon the oral disc of one of them, the crab quickly becomes aware of this. Presumably it receives some chemical stimulus from the food, although the possibility of it being sensitive to particular patterns of movement of the anemone is not excluded. Whatever the explanation, however, the crab moves one of its anterior legs forward to the oral disc and removes the food from it, transferring it to its mouth. Should the actinian have begun to swallow the food, the crab declines to be cheated. If necessary it inserts its limb into the stomodaeum and withdraws the food from it.

The remarkable specializations of the crab are not paralleled in the anemone. Both *Sagartia* and *Bunodeopsis* are carried in the chelipeds, and the crab shows no preference for one or the other. Neither seems to be modified for the association, and, although observers of *Melia* have failed to find free-living specimens of the anemones in the same habitat, there seems no reason why they should not live independently. The balance of adaptive advantage is thus the converse of that existing between *Calliactis* and *Pagurus bernhardus*. Even more is this so in a similar association between another crab, *Polydectus cupilifera*, and small specimens of the anemone *Phellia*. Despite the establishment of this association, free-living specimens of the anemone are common around the Hawaiian Islands where the crab is found. Moreover, on Atlantic coasts where *Melia* is absent there are free-living specimens of *Bunodeopsis* that are anatomically indistinguishable from the specimens carried by the crab in other localities. It would appear, then, that this association is not essential to maintain the life of the anemone. Through being carried by the crab it may encounter more food than it otherwise would, but against this must be set its risk of losing this food to its host.

By contrast, the crab probably derives marked benefit from the association, and its adaptations seem to make it actually dependent upon the anemone. The presence of the latter in a cheliped aids both in securing food and warding off enemies; indeed, the chelipeds are of limited value without this aid, for they have little power of grasping food or other objects when these are presented to the animal. The maxillipeds and walking limbs are equally limited in these functions, owing to their lack of chelae. Whether the crabs always carry the anemones is not certain, for they have sometimes been found without them, but this may be only a temporary loss, either from accident or as a result of moulting. The evidence as a whole suggests that the association is a common one, characteristic of the species, and one for which it has become closely adapted. We may regard it as mutualism of a rather one-sided character.

22–3 BEHAVIOURAL ASPECTS

These examples show how far we have now moved from the sentimental and anthropomorphic interpretations of the nineteenth-century naturalists. This does not, of course, imply that we fully understand these associations, but at least we can see that they sometimes depend upon structural and behavioural adaptations paralleling those that fit free-living animals to particular niches in their habitat. We must now probe a little more deeply into the nature of some of the adaptations that contribute to these associations.

A crucial problem is to determine how the two partners are brought together. We have already suggested that initially the association must have been an accidental one, promoted, perhaps, by some similarity or complementary feature in the habits of the two species. Such could have been the origin of the associations of anemones and crabs. In some other instances one partner may have provided a suitable settling point for the larvae or juvenile stages of the other—as, for example, in the association between the sipunculid *Aspidosiphon* and the polyp *Heteropsammia*. The latter grows over a gastropod shell in which the sipunculid lives; as a result, the polyp secures some mobility, while the sipunculid is well protected by it, to the point of being almost completely enclosed. In this instance the association is initiated by the larva of the polyp settling on the shell. To what extent this is a selective settling is not known, but even if it is selective rather than a chance distribution there is evidently nothing here that cannot be paralleled in the normal course of larval life histories.

We have seen that the settling of larvae may be profoundly influenced by the physical and chemical properties of the substratum, and similar factors presumably operate in commensalism. An example of this, although demonstrated on adults and not on larvae, is the behaviour of mites that are commensal within the mantle cavities and gills of *Anodonta*. Mites of the species *Unionicola ypsilophorus*, when washed free of any contaminating factor derived from its host, *Anodonta cataracta*, are positively phototactic. If they are placed in an aquarium containing a chemical factor from the host they immediately become negatively phototactic, a reaction that will normally lead them to enter between the lamellibranch's valves. In principle this is similar to the change in the phototactic response of the ascidian tadpole, except that this latter change is initiated within the larva at a particular stage of its free-swimming life. The response of the mites, incidentally, is a highly specific one. Welsh studied three species which were each specifically commensal with three different species of mussels; he showed that reversal of phototaxis occurred in each species, but that it could be produced only by a chemical factor from the particular species of mussel with which the mite was normally associated.

In view of the importance of chemical communication in animal organization, we might expect that the type of response shown by these ticks would be widely distributed in commensal relationships. Some convincing evidence for this has been obtained by Davenport in his studies of the responses of polynoid worms. An example is provided by the genus *Arctonoë*, three species of which constitute a commensal complex in the littoral zone of Puget Sound. The principle of Davenport's experiments was to place a worm in a Y-shaped choice tube, the two arms of which were connected to two aquaria (Fig. 22-5). In these were placed various echinoderms. Water from the aquaria was passed through one or other of the two arms, and the worm was then observed in order to see which stream of water it preferred, or, in other words, which arm of the Y it entered.

The species *Arctonoë fragilis* is commensal on the inter-tidal starfish *Evasterias troschelii*; in one type of test this worm distinguished readily between untreated sea water and sea water coming from the aquarium in which a host was contained. Similarly, another species of worm, *A.* (*pulchra-vittata?*), was attracted by sea water coming from its own particular host, the holothurian *Stichopus californicus*. The specificity of these responses was demonstrated by two further types of test. In one of these it was shown that *A. fragilis* is not attracted to sea water coming from the starfish *Pisaster*, which is not its host; similarly, *A.* (*pulchra-vittata?*) was not attracted to *Cucumaria*, which again is not a host for this species. The other type of test involved cross experiments in which *A. fragilis* (from *Evasterias*) was tested against *Stichopus*, and *A.* (*pulchra-vittata?*) (from *Stichopus*) was tested against *Evasterias*.

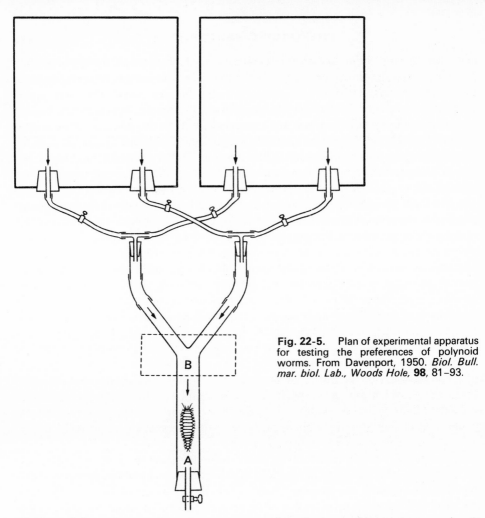

Fig. 22-5. Plan of experimental apparatus for testing the preferences of polynoid worms. From Davenport, 1950. *Biol. Bull. mar. biol. Lab., Woods Hole,* **98**, 81–93.

Neither of the commensal worms was attracted to the host of its partner species. It may thus be concluded that these polynoids are able to react specifically to a substance or substances released from their own particular host species.

The nature of these chemical attractants is not known; attempts to extract them have proved unsuccessful, possibly because they are very unstable, or because their action is easily obscured by contaminants from the tissues. There is no reason, however, why they should not be common metabolites, just as the respiratory centre of vertebrates is influenced by that commonest of metabolites, carbon dioxide. In fact, this principle may account for the responses of another polynoid, *Harmothoë*, which is commensal both with a terebellid worm, *Amphitrite gracilis*, and with a eunicid worm, *Lysidice ninetta*. It responds positively to both hosts, but gives no response at all, or at best a very weak one, to other terebellids which are not its host. If we are correct in assuming that the response is the result of the worm recognizing some simple chemical product, we could assume either that it is adapted to respond to two different substances from the two hosts, or that both hosts are producing one and the same substance. Davenport considers that the latter is more likely, and that the double association results from the chance production by two species of a similar metabolite.

Undoubtedly the responses of commensal species need much further investigation before we can reason with any assurance about their nature. Nevertheless, the general principle of chemical recognition seems to be well established. Davenport mentions other examples in which this appears to be the means by which two species are associated; among these are the commensalism of *Hesperonoë* (*Harmothoë*) *adventor* and *Urechis caupo*, to which we have earlier referred. But we cannot suppose that chemical factors are the only means of communication involved. Lees has shown that in finding its host the sheep tick *Ixodes ricinus* depends upon sensitivity to contact, light, gravity, moisture, temperature, and vibration, as well as chemosensitivity. All the sensory perceptions help in finding the host, on which the survival of the ticks depends, and a similarly wide range of perceptions is probably involved in many forms of interspecific relationship.

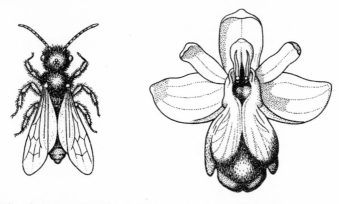

Fig. 22-6. *Left*, the andrenid bee, *Andrena trimmerana. Right*, a flower of the orchid *Ophrys fusca*, on the libellum of which the bee will make copulation attempts. From Davenport, 1955. *Q. Rev. Biol.*, **30**, 29–46.

This must evidently be so in those associations that depend upon sequences of complex behaviour patterns, such as are involved in the relationships of anemones and crabs. In analyzing these we can employ the concept that responses are evoked by specific sign stimuli, or releasers. This principle, to which we have already made some reference, was initially formulated by Lorenz to account for the maintenance of intraspecific associations. It operates, for example, in reproductive physiology, where the association of the two sexes, and the initiation of mating behaviour, is evoked by sexual recognition signals displayed by one sex to stimulate the other. An illustration is the enlarged chela of the male fiddler crab. The manipulation of this organ serves as a signal to the female; it is highly specific, and constitutes a barrier to interspecific mating.

Such a system, providing for animal communication between the members of the same species, could equally well provide for communication between members of two different species. As Baerends points out, the mutual development in two species of a releasing stimulus in the one and a releasing mechanism in the other can only occur if the situation is of benefit to both species, since only then will natural selection favour the necessary adaptation in both of them. There must be many examples of mutual associations in which this condition is met. One particularly striking one, mentioned by Baerends, is the interrelated adaptations of orchids and Hymenoptera that result in pseudo-copulation and sexual exploitation (Fig. 22-6). Certain of these plants are always visited by the male, which fertilizes the flowers while it copulates. The flowers, and particularly the libellum, closely resemble the insect, and this resemblance serves as a sign stimulus that releases the copulation response in the male. It is doubtful whether the insect obtains any benefit from the association, since these flowers do not produce food for it. The flower, on the other hand, is certainly dependent upon the insect, and may be said in a sense to be parasitic upon a clearly defined and essential reflex act of the latter.

23
Further Interspecific Associations

23–1 SYMBIOSIS AND DIGESTION

Symbiosis in the sense defined earlier is such a delicately balanced relationship that it is far from easy to demonstrate it convincingly even when the association is an intimate one and the host is modified to make it possible. Consider, for example, the mycetocytes of insects. Mycetocytes are large cells, probably highly polyploid, that may be scattered in the fat-body, or concentrated into groups, or may associate to form multicellular or syncytial structures called mycetomes. These cells harbour yeast-like or bacterium-like bodies, that have been interpreted as symbiotic micro-organisms which supposedly invade the cells when these become embryonically differentiated. The identification of the intracellular bodies as living micro-organisms is, however, far from easy. Some have been successfully cultivated outside the host, and can be accepted unequivocally as true micro-organisms, but in other instances this has not been possible. On the one hand, therefore, it has been suggested that some of the non-cultivable bodies are cell inclusions (mitochondria, for example), while at the other extreme it has been argued that they may actually be symbiotic organisms, but so specialized that they are no longer capable of independent life.

The so-called bacteroids of cockroaches illustrate the problem. These bodies, which are found within mycetocytes, are certainly not mitochondria, for they can be distinguished from these by selective staining. Moreover, they can be eliminated by treatment of the host with antibiotics, which suggests that they are micro-organisms, although it has been difficult to confirm this by cultivating them outside the host. Here it is necessary to rely largely upon indirect evidence. During the development of the insect the bacteroids are passed into the oocytes and are eventually distributed only to the mycetocytes, which certainly suggests that they have a specialized role within the body. In short, the evidence is suggestive of a biologically adapted relationship between micro-organisms and specialized cells, but it is not completely convincing.

An important element in the analysis of all such relationships is to determine whether or not the mutual benefits are actually obtained by the two partners. No

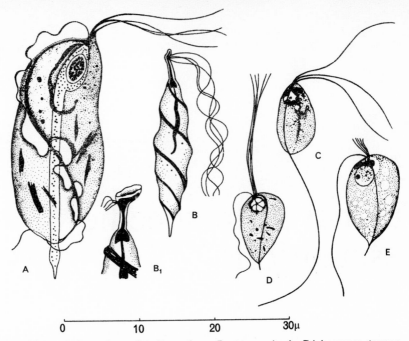

Fig. 23-1. Polymastigote flagellates from *Zootermopsis*. A, *Trichomonas termopsidis*; B, *Streblomastix strix*, and B$_1$, diagram to show the anterior end of the same; C, *Tricercomitus termopsidis*; D, *Hexamastix termopsidis*; E, *H. laticeps*. From MacKinnon and Hawes, 1961. *An Introduction to the Study of Protozoa.* Clarendon Press, Oxford.

doubt bacteria would derive nutritive benefits from the association, and it is now well established that some species of insects derive benefit from their bacteria-like symbiotes. *Rhodnius*, for example, contains a micro-organism, *Nocardia*, living in its gut but not enclosed within cells. There is no specialized arrangement for the harbouring of this organism, yet if the organisms are removed the host's development is adversely affected, and it only rarely metamorphoses to the adult stage. In other instances, in *Stegobium*, for example, studies with artificial diets have shown that removal of the symbiotes increases the nutritional demands of the host, and that the symbiotes probably supply it with B vitamins and sterols. Other conclusions have been drawn for other species, based partly upon similar experimental studies and partly upon inferences from the history of the symbiotes within the host. When they degenerate in the adult phase it has been supposed that they may supply nutritional growth factors, while when they persist in the adult it has been suggested that they facilitate in some way the reproductive processes. Other ideas are that they may cooperate in some special aspect of metabolism, decomposing uric acid, for example, or making use of the ammonia produced in protein metabolism. Underlying all of these suppositions is the belief that these micro-organisms (when they truly are micro-organisms) make some contribution to the metabolic processes of the host. Advances in our knowledge of the subtle chemical relationships that may exist between organisms, and of the complexity of their nutritional requirements, are a warning against expecting the benefits of the relationships to be immediately obvious, or readily open to experimental demonstration. Conceivably the symbiotes may be of value as a source of metabolites, not because the host is unable to manufacture them for itself, but because at certain periods of its life cycle, or under particular stresses, they are needed in greater amounts or in different proportions. This, in theory, could

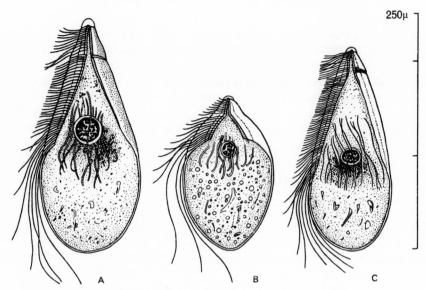

250μ

Fig. 23-2.   *Trichonympha* from *Zootermopsis angusticollis.* Diagram to show typical forms and average sizes.   ×250. A, *Trichonympha collaris*; B, *T. sphaerica*; C, *T. campanula.* From MacKinnon and Hawes, 1961. *op. cit.*

explain why the beetle *Rhyzopertha dominica* suffers no apparent ill effects from the removal of its symbiotes, although it has evolved a mycetome in which to contain them. At least it is evident that associations between insects and micro-organisms must have arisen independently on many occasions. Fortunately the resulting symbiotes have not always been yeast-like and bacteria-like enigmas. In some instances they are undeniably Protozoa, and the analysis of the function of these in aiding termites to digest cellulose provides a well-documented illustration of a truly symbiotic relationship.

The cellulose of plants is a valuable store of energy, but one to which few animals have been able to obtain physiological access. Exceptions include the wood-boring mollusc *Teredo*, the wood-boring isopod *Limnoria lignorum*, and the silver-fish *Cteno-*

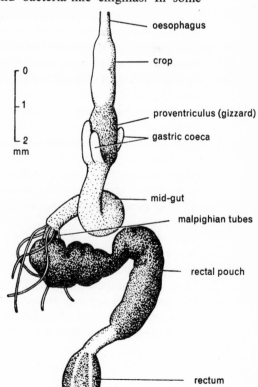

oesophagus

crop

proventriculus (gizzard)

gastric coeca

mid-gut

malpighian tubes

rectal pouch

rectum

0

1

2

mm

Fig. 23-3.   Alimentary canal of *Zootermopsis* worker, a damp-wood termite, with cellulose-digesting protozoa (cf. Figs. 23-1, 23-2). From Harris, 1961. *op. cit.*

lepisma lineata, which lives on the bark of Eucalyptus trees. These species are able to digest cellulose by their own secretions, but in general animals have been unable to evolve the cellulase and β-glucosidase that are needed for its hydrolysis, despite the virtually universal distribution of the corresponding enzoymes, amylase and maltase, that are used in the hydrolysis of starch. Termites, nevertheless, feed largely upon cellulose obtained from wood, and do so in such numbers and with such vigour that in warmer countries they are a serious menace to timber. The means by which many of them contrive to do this are still unknown. Some feed upon broken-down plant material in the soil. Others rely upon fungi which they cultivate within their nests, growing them upon masses of chewed wood, and using them in their diet to provide protein and, perhaps, vitamins. The more primitive termites, however, feed directly upon the timber within which they excavate their nests. It is the relatively few species of these with which we are here concerned, for the finely fragmented wood particles which they swallow are digested by symbiotic zooflagellates. These (Figs. 23–1 and 23–2) live in enormous numbers in their hind-guts (Fig. 23–3), forming, in the words of one observer, 'a tangled mass of writhing protoplasmic bodies, the movements and appearances of which defy description'. In the nymph of *Zootermopsis* this formidable microfauna has been estimated to make up from one-third to one-seventh of the total weight of the animal.

Included among these symbionts are polymastigine flagellates such as *Trichomonas termopsidis*, related species of which are common in the alimentary canal of many vertebrates. This is a comparatively simple form, with few flagella, one of which trails and has an undulating membrane. Other members of the fauna are species of the hypermastigine genus *Trichonympha*. These are exceedingly complex, with a large number of flagella and many parabasal bodies and axostylar filaments. Cleveland originally demonstrated the role of these Protozoa in the digestion of the wood eaten by their hosts, and later studies have supported his interpretation. Much of the evidence derives from the discovery that these termites can be defaunated (i.e. deprived of their symbionts) by subjecting them to high temperatures or to high oxygen concentrations. Termites treated in this way die within a few weeks if they are supplied with no more than their normal diet of partially decayed wood, but this is not because they have themselves been injured: their lives can be prolonged if they are given cellulose that has been predigested by fungi. Further evidence is that some of the flagellates ingest particles of wood, while a cellulase is present in extracts prepared from cultures of *Trichomonas termopsidis*.

The toxic effect of oxygen on the flagellates results from them being obligate anaerobes, for they cannot release energy by oxidation processes, but must rely instead upon fermentation. The carbohydrates of the wood serve as the substrate for this, the products being carbon dioxide and organic acids, with acetic acid as the main component of the latter. These fermentation products are absorbed by the host, and are oxidized by it. Their value is indicated by calculations showing that the oxygen requirements of the termites are about equal to the amount necessary to bring about complete oxidation of the fermentation products of the Protozoa. Since little, if any, of these products are actually excreted, it follows that the insects depend for their energy supplies almost entirely upon the fermentation of cellulose by their symbionts. It might be thought that they would also digest the symbionts and make use of them as a source of nitrogen, but this seems not to be so. More probably they obtain their nitrogen from fungi in their food; these, of course, will have obtained their own nitrogen supply from the wood in which they grow.

There is thus no doubt of the dependence of wood-eating termites upon their microfauna, which is present in all of the wood-feeding members of a colony. Where a worker caste is present, the workers feed the old reproductive members; these do not, therefore, have to feed themselves on wood, and it is significant that they do not possess symbionts. The importance of the association is further shown by the speed with which larvae acquire the Protozoa; although they do not possess them on hatching, they secure them within 24 hours, apparently by taking them up from the anus of older members. The Protozoa, however, are equally dependent upon the termites, upon which they rely for their own nutrition. This is readily seen if the insects are starved, for this results in most of the larger Protozoa and many of the smaller ones dying long before the insects do.

The association seems, then, to be a particularly well-balanced symbiosis, with the maximum of mutual benefit and the minimum of exploitation. One reservation must, however, be made in this interpretation. It has been suggested that the symbionts, like most other animals, may not actually produce the cellulase used in their digestive processes, but that they rely upon the production of the enzyme by bacteria living within their bodies. This contention is difficult either to prove or to disprove, and the issue cannot be regarded as entirely settled. Even if this view is well founded, however, it does not effect our general interpretation of the relationship. What it does do is to increase its complexity, for it means that this is an example of hypersymbiosis, in which one symbiotic partner is itself in symbiotic relationship with a third partner of the complex, in this instance the supposed cellulolytic bacteria.

There is a singular and instructive parallel between the digestive processes of termites and those of ruminating mammals, which have also found a way of exploiting cellulose as a source of food. The rumen of these animals, constituting the first, and by far the largest, division of their stomach, contains a rich population of bacteria and ciliate Protozoa. At least thirty species of protozoans have been identified, making up in numbers of individuals as many as 1 million per gramme of contents. Included among them are *Isotricha* and *Dasytricha* (Order Holotricha) and *Entodinium*, *Diplodinium*, and *Ophryoscolex* (Order Oligotricha). These vary in their digestive physiology. The holotrichs feed on soluble carbohydrates and starch, but *Diplodinium* actually ingests cellulose fibres and hydrolyzes them; its dependence upon this material is shown by the fact that when it is cultured *in vitro* it is essential to add cellulose to the medium if it is to grow, whereas this is unnecessary for the two holotrichs.

The relation between the mammalian host, the bacteria, and the protozoans is a complex one, and by no means fully understood, although there seems to be some degree of mutual benefit. It is certain that fermentation is important in the functioning of the rumen, and that the resulting fatty acids are absorbed by the host and used as a source of energy. To this extent the system is similar in principle to that of the termite's hind gut; as with the latter, indeed, hypersymbiosis may be a factor, and the apparent cellulolytic activity of *Diplodinium* may actually be due to the presence of intracellular bacteria. From the point of view of the symbionts, as Barnett and Reid remark, the rumen provides a factory of immense capacity, amounting to 50 pints in a sheep and 40 gallons in a cow. In it the symbionts find controlled pH and temperature, mechanical equipment for their use (in the form of churning and rumination), and a very well-developed blood system which functions as a conveyor belt for the removal of their metabolic products. In their absence this specialized vascularization would have little function, so that the organization of the host has been adapted to the needs of the association. There is, however, one difference in comparison with the termites. Unlike the latter, the mammalian host digests its micro-organisms as they pass backwards through the other chambers of the stomach into the abomasum, and it is estimated to obtain as much as 20% of its nitrogen from them. It is arguable, then, that the system is not so neatly balanced as that of the termites, since the latter are thought not to use their symbionts as a primary source of nitrogen. Probably we cannot distinguish sharply between the two associations, but at least the difference indicates how narrow is the boundary between an ideally balanced system and the exploitation of one of the members of it.

23–2   ZOOXANTHELLAE

Certain supposedly symbiotic relationships between animals and plants have long attracted attention, for they are readily observed and in some instances they lend themselves well to experimental study. The cosmopolitan green hydra, *Chlorohydra viridissima*, owes its colour to the presence within its endoderm cells of organisms called zoochlorellae, which are transmitted in the egg. These are, in fact, algae belonging to the genus *Chlorella*, so that they are related to forms that are normally free-living. This is probably a true symbiosis, the alga obtaining an environment which is protected and which also provides it with the nutrient excreta (carbon dioxide, nitrates, phosphates) of the host, while the host derives oxygen and metabolic products from the algal photosynthesis. For this view there is both observational and experimental justification. The zoochlorellae survive when *Chlorohydra* is kept in the dark, and they may even increase in numbers, apparently because they can live chemotrophically on the metabolites produced by the host. Conversely, the host, providing that it is kept in the light, withstands reduced feeding or starvation better than do individuals lacking the algae; in this instance it is being aided in some way by metabolites from the algae. What these metabolites are is unknown, but, bearing in mind what has been said above regarding symbiosis in insects, they may well be vitamins or their precursors.

It is very difficult to deprive *Chlorohydra* of its zoochlorellae, and this, together with the widespread and normal occurrence of the association, indicates that the relationship is a specific adaptation. How it arose is unknown, but the origin can hardly have been a consequence of the algae being ingested by the host, for, as we have seen, hydroids are specialized carnivores. Some observations made on other species suggest that it may have resulted from infection. It is said that algal infection is unknown in *Hydra circumcincta*, but that it sometimes occurs spontaneously in *H. vulgaris*, preceded by enfeeblement of the host, and accompanied by pathological symptoms. The infection can be induced artificially in this species, but is only maintainable for a brief period; in *H. attenuata* it is easier to produce, and the algae are more difficult to dislodge.

The relationship of *Chlorohydra* and *Chlorella*, however it may have arisen, can reasonably be regarded as a balanced symbiosis. So also, probably, is the similar situation found in many rhabdocoel platyhelminths, such as *Dalyellia*, where large numbers of zoochlorellae (probably *Chlorella*) are present in the mesenchyme. The young animals acquire these by ingesting them with their food, and in this instance the relationship may well have originated in that way. It has been remarked that species of *Dalyellia* possessing symbionts are larger than those without them, and it is supposed that one service rendered by the algae is the utilization of waste products. The oxygen produced by them during photosynthesis may also be of value to species living in stagnant waters, or otherwise subject to oxygen deprivation. The acoelan *Amphiscolops langerhansi* can survive confinement in small bottles of sea water provided that it is kept in the light, but it rapidly succumbs in the dark.

At best, however, symbiotic relationships like these are balanced on a knife-edge, and it is easy for one partner to begin exploiting the other. *Dalyellia* is said to digest senile algal cells, and the boundary between this and the eating of active algae is clearly a very fine one. The acoelan *Convoluta roscoffensis*, as described by Keeble and Gamble, has long provided a classical example of this. The animal obtains algae (probably a chlamydomonad, *Carteria*, which is abundant in the environment) from its egg case when it hatches. At first it feeds holozoically, and at this stage the relationship can be interpreted as a balanced symbiosis. Later, however, the alimentary canal degenerates, and the animal cannot digest external supplies of food; it now eats its algae, and eventually dies of starvation after laying its eggs, the supplies of symbionts being by then exhausted. Here there is frank exploitation, which from one point of view is tending towards the parasitism that we shall be considering later. It might also be argued, however, that the animal is, in effect, cultivating plant food within its own body, essentially as certain ants tend fungi within their colony. An element of cultivation is suggested by the way in which *Convoluta* comes to the surface of the sand at low tide, appearing there in numbers so enormous that large areas of the shore are coloured green.

However we interpret the relationship of *Convoluta* with its algae, a clear and remarkable example of exploitation is presented by the Tridacnidae, lamellibranchs that are uniquely modified for what we can justly describe as the farming of zooxanthellae. *Tridacna*, the giant clam, which reaches a length of $4\frac{1}{2}$ ft and a weight of 4 cwt, lives among the corals of the Great Barrier Reef. Here it rests in a highly unusual position, with the umbo of the shell downwards, but with the visceral mass inverted with reference to the shell, so that the pedal opening is also downwards. This allows the inner lobes of the mantle edges to extend over the free edges of the valves of the shell and to be exposed to the light (Fig. 23–4). The significance of this arrangement is that in these areas there are abundant zooxanthellae, which in this instance are deep-brown, spherical bodies carried in amoeboid blood cells in the blood sinuses of the mantle tissue. Like other zooxanthellae, they contain food reserves, which here are in the form of starch and oil-droplets. In effect, their host is deliberately exposing them to light, where they can best carry out photosynthesis, and the adaptive significance of this is accentuated by the presence in the upwardly directed mantle surface of many conical protuberances. These contain hyaline structures formed of transparent cells surrounded by a connective tissue capsule. The algae are particularly abundant around these structures, which, according to Yonge's interpretation, seem to concentrate light and thereby facilitate the metabolism of the symbionts.

Confinement of *Tridacna* in sealed containers in light and in darkness has shown

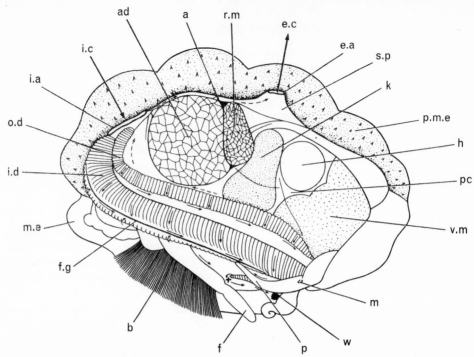

Fig. 23-4. *Tridacna crocea*, drawn from life, to show an individual lying on the left shell valve, right mantle lobe removed. *a*, anus; *ad*, adductor muscle; *b*, byssus; *e.a*, exhalent aperture; *e.c*, exhalent current (represented by arrow); *f*, foot; *f.g*, food-groove on inner demibranch; *h*, heart; *i.a*, inhalent aperture; *i.c*, inhalent current (represented by arrow); *i.d*, inner demibranch of gill; *k*, kidney; *m*, position of mouth; *m.e*, mantle edge, unpigmented, bordering the pedal gap on the underside; *o.d*, outer demibranch; *p*, labial palps; *p.c*, pericardium; *p.m.e*, pigmented mantle edge of upper, exposed side; *r.m*, retractor muscle of foot; *s.p*, siphonal process of exhalent aperture; *v.m*, visceral mass; *w*, accumulation of waste matter rejected by palps. Small complete arrows show direction of food-collecting currents on the gills; broken arrows show currents in the exhalent chamber. From Yonge, 1931. *Gt. Barrier Reef Exped. Sci. Rep*, **1**, 283–321. Used by courtesy of The Trustees, British Museum (Natural History).

no significant differences in the oxygen content and pH of the surrounding water in these two conditions. It follows, then, that the output of oxygen and the removal of carbon dioxide by the zooxanthellae is insufficient to affect the metabolism of the clam. The water, however, is completely depleted of phosphorus, whereas if *Spondylus*, a mollusc without zooxanthellae, is confined in similar conditions the phosphorus content of the water increases owing to the excretory output of the animal. Undoubtedly, then, the zooxanthellae utilize this excretory material in their own synthetic activities, as we have earlier postulated for the symbionts of *Chlorohydra* and the Acoela.

This, however, is by no means the whole story. Not only is *Tridacna* adapted for 'farming' its zooxanthellae by aiding their photosynthesis; it is also adapted for exploiting them as a source of food. They are carried from the mantle in phagocytes, which accumulate in large numbers around the digestive diverticula, where they contain zooxanthellae in all stages of digestion. These are apparently used as food, the indigestible remains being carried to the excretory organs, which are much enlarged in order to deal with this material. Unlike *Convoluta roscoffensis*, the giant clam has not carried this relationship to the point of losing its own capacity for securing external food supplies. Nevertheless, its alimentary system is certainly modified.

The selective mechanisms on the gills and palps are highly developed, while the mouth is small, there are no sorting mechanisms in the stomach, and the digestive diverticula are reduced in number. In Yonge's picturesque phrase, *Tridacna* is specialized to exploit imprisoned phytoplankton as a source of food. Probably this accounts for its great size, for, as we have earlier seen, unaided ciliary feeding mechanisms must limit the size of the animals relying upon them.

Whether the zooxanthellae can be said to derive any advantage from the situation is a matter of opinion and definition. Their perpetuation is guaranteed by the clam, and the fate of the individual algal cell is no worse than it would be in the outside world. Yet the relationship is essentially one of exploitation by one partner. If it does not fit our formal definition of symbiosis, this is because our definitions have artificial boundaries. How this particular relationship arose is not easy to see. Unlike coelenterates, the lamellibranchs are not specialized carnivores, so that an essential preliminary must have been the ability of the invading organisms to resist digestion. It is conceivable that they first entered the mollusc tissues from coelenterate planulae (see below), already able to withstand digestion by a host.

23–3 CORALS AND SYMBIOSIS

Coral reefs extend over an area of some 68 million square miles in tropical and subtropical seas. Best developed where the mean annual temperature of the water lies within the range of 23° to 25°C, they do not develop to any significant extent in regions where temperatures fall below 18°C, nor are they found in waters that contain continental sediments. An adequate oxygen supply is important, but this, as we have learned, is not normally a limiting condition for animal life in the sea. Much more important factors for coral reefs are the intensity of surface illumination and radiant energy. This may seem surprising since animals rather than plants are important in constructing reefs, but we shall see that it is a direct consequence of the animals' symbiotic relationships.

A reef, as described by J. W. Wells, mainly consists of the skeletons of reef-building (hermatypic) coelenterates, or corals, and of calcareous red algae. These form an interlocking framework, upon which are deposited sediments derived from the breakdown of the skeletal materials and of the organisms that have secreted them. Thus are provided a range of ecological niches, occupied in part by the commensals, symbionts, and parasites of the primary organisms, and in part by an assemblage of free-moving organisms that are unique in their beauty and variety. This remarkable biological phenomenon is a dramatic demonstration of the dominating results that can flow from the colonial association of lowly animals, fortified in their metabolic activity by the presence within their tissues of symbiotic micro-organisms.

We can conveniently distinguish four types of coral reef (Fig. 23–5): atolls, barrier reefs, fringing reefs, and platform reefs. Atolls are usually oceanic, and without association with land. They consist of low reefs, rising no more than 30 ft above the level of the sea, and enclosing a central area of water called the lagoon. Externally to the reef lies the seaward slope, composed of débris derived from the degradation of the reef, while internally to it are the lagoon slope and floor, of similar origin. Barrier reefs are also low reefs, but they differ from atolls in being associated with land. Between them and the mainland lies a narrow strip of sea, perhaps up to 180 ft

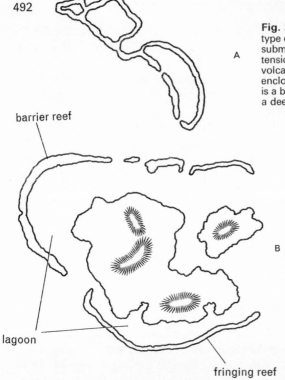

barrier reef

lagoon

fringing reef

Fig. 23-5. A, atoll, encircling a lagoon. This type of structure is thought to be formed by the submergence of an island and the upward extension of its original fringing reef. B, two volcanic islands. To the south is a fringing reef, enclosing a shallow lagoon. To the north-west is a barrier reef, lying farther out, and enclosing a deeper lagoon. After Darwin.

deep, which is not much less than the greatest depth attained by lagoons. The Great Barrier Reef of Australia is the best-known example of such a structure, reaching a length of at least 1,200 miles. Fringing reefs are similar in principle to barrier reefs, but differ from them in lying much closer to the mainland; this may be either an island or a stretch of continental coastline, but in either case the intervening water constitutes only a narrow channel. Finally, the platform (table) reefs are, as their names imply, flat structures without lagoons. They rest on the shallower parts of continental shelves; they may appear in the water between the coast and a barrier reef, for example, or they may be associated with atolls.

The recognition of these four categories is a matter of descriptive convenience. From the biological point of view they are essentially similar, arising from the interaction of environmental conditions with the habits of the reef-building organisms, and providing a basis for the establishment of biological communities that are very constant in composition. Nevertheless, the differences in the form of the reefs reflect differences in their modes of origin.

Current views on this derive from a theory originally put forward by Darwin, and based by him not only upon direct study of coral reefs, of which his experience, as Yonge points out, was very limited, but also upon the requirements which are known to limit the activity of the coral polyps. These include, as we have mentioned, a dependence upon tropical water temperatures, and also a requirement for light, the polyps being unable to flourish at greater depths than between twenty and thirty fathoms, and rarely below fifteen fathoms (90 ft). These limitations create no problem as far as fringing reefs are concerned for they can readily be established on a sloping shore at points where the depth is suitable. Barrier reefs and atolls present an altogether different situation, for these drop sharply down to great depths where it is out of the question for reef construction to take place.

Darwin's solution of the problem of their origin was based upon a comparison of the distribution of reefs with the distribution of areas of present-day or recent volcanic activity. This showed that active volcanoes were associated with the areas in which fringing reefs were distributed, but that areas containing atolls and barrier reefs were free of volcanic activity. He thus suggested that conditions for the development of the latter two types were provided by subsidence, which led to the submergence of peaks of land. Corals would then grow on these when they had sunk to the appropriate depth. Fringing reefs, by contrast, developed in areas where the land surface was either stationary, or was rising with associated outbursts of volcanic activity. It was an explanation which, as Darwin rightly claimed, offered 'a grand and harmonious picture of the movements which the crust of the earth has undergone within a late period'.

This theory, supported by the observations of Dana, and therefore known as the Darwin–Dana theory, has been widely accepted. An additional possibility is that the growth of modern reefs may have been influenced by the locking away of water in the polar ice caps during the ice age. It is argued that the older, Tertiary, reefs would have been cut down during the resulting exposure, and that new growths could then have become established on the margins of the exposed platforms as they were submerged by the later release of the water. This modification of the original theory has the advantage of accounting for the depths of lagoons and lagoon channels being largely constant from reef to reef, for this depth can be explained as determined by the amount of water released when the ice melted. However this may be, it is certain that with Darwin's views as a foundation, we can account for much of the known distribution of coral reefs.

It has long been recognized that this theory could be tested by examining the foundations of reefs, and it has, in fact, been supported by a deep boring made at the Eniwetok atoll by the United States Atomic Energy Commission. Previous attempts at boring, by the Royal Society in 1904, had led to inconclusive results, but the latest one has shown that the coral sediments extend to a depth of 4/5 mile, where they rest upon the summit of a volcano rising some 2 miles above the sea bottom. Here, then, there must have been prolonged subsidence, the growth of the reef having extended, it is thought, from Eocene times, over a period of some 60 million years. It would be going too far to suggest that this is the only mode of origin of barrier reefs and atolls. Yet little support can now be found for the alternative theory put forward by Murray, according to which these reefs were founded upon the tops of submarine volcanoes after these had been raised to suitable levels by the deposit of sediments.

The complex structure of coral reefs, and their isolation in the sea, make them attractive material for the analysis of the forces that have determined their growth and that permit their continued existence. As we see them today, they are a balance of constructive and destructive agencies. The construction of the reef, and compensation for its continuous erosion, depends upon the continued secretion of the calcareous skeletons of the reef-building algae and coelenterates, and the addition to these of sediments that become cemented by precipitated calcium carbonate. The destructive agencies are in part biological, comprising organisms such as algae, molluscs, echinoids, and fish, that in one way or another erode away the reef material

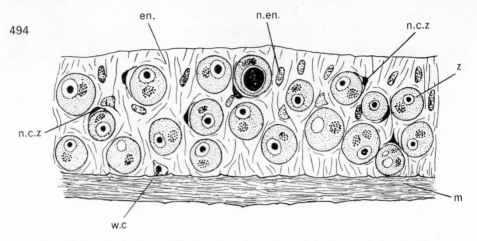

Fig. 23-6. *Goniastrea* sp. Section through endoderm of coenosarc, showing zooxanthellae enclosed within tissue cells. *en*, endoderm; *n.c.z*, nucleus of cell containing zooxanthellae; *n.en*, nucleus of endoderm cell; *m*, mesogloea; *z*, zooxanthella. From Yonge and Nicholls, 1931. *Gt. Barrier Reef Exped. Sci. Rep.*, **1**, 135–176. Used by courtesy of The Trustees, British Museum (Natural History).

by dissolving it, boring through it, or biting it. No less destructive is the wave action of the surrounding water, which breaks away and redistributes fragments of the reef, and undermines its edge.

This balanced system is founded on the organic productivity of the reef-building organisms, which can be expressed in terms of the production and consumption of oxygen from selected areas of the reef. Such measurements have shown that reefs are more productive than are the open seas around them, and they have shown also that this productivity is not directly related to the abundance of the available plankton. This may be plentiful in lagoons, for example, but much scarcer in the water outside the reefs, yet productivity is no less on the outward slopes than it is on the inner sides. This wide distribution of productivity may be partly a consequence of the large amounts of green algae present on the reefs, but it is certainly to be attributed also to the symbiotic relationships in which the hermatypic coelenterates are involved, and which account for the dependence of these animals upon radiant energy.

All reef-building corals contain zooxanthellae, which are present in the endoderm (Fig. 23-6) in wandering carrier cells, and which are distributed to the next generation in the planula larvae. They are found in the hermatypic Madreporaria, but not in the non-reef-building (ahermatypic) corals such as *Dendrophyllia*. They occur also in the hydrozoan *Millepora*, and the octocorallines *Tubipora* and *Heliopora*, all of which secrete skeletons that contribute to reef structure. They are found, too, in many other coelenterates, including hydrozoans, scyphozoans, and anthozoans, which may live in reef communities without contributing calcareous skeletal material to them. The absence of zooxanthellae from ahermatypic corals is thus all the more significant.

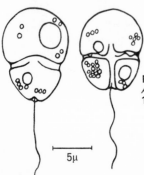

Fig. 23-7. *Gymnodinium* sp., dinoflagellate stage of zooxanthellae from *Acropora corymbosa*. After Kawaguti, from Yonge, 1963. *Adv. Mar. Biol.*, **1**, 209–260.

5µ

Artificial culture methods have conclusively shown that in certain instances the zooxanthellae are the vegetative resting stages of dinoflagellates (Fig. 23–7), *Gymnodinium* and *Symbiodinium* having been mentioned as generic names. We cannot say whether this is true of all coelenterate zooxanthellae, but it probably is, having regard to their general uniformity of appearance. As with the association of *Chlorohydra* with *Chlorella*, then, we are dealing with a relationship between an animal and an autotrophic micro-organism, and in this case one that has lent itself particularly well to experimental analysis.

The foundations of our knowledge were laid by Yonge and his colleagues during the Great Barrier Reef Expedition of 1928–29. By keeping corals in sealed glass jars of sea water, it was shown that after 9 hours exposure to light there was a negligible increase of acidity in the medium surrounding a hermatypic coral, amounting to a fall in pH of 0.001. By contrast, the pH fell by 0.219 during the same period of darkness. The inference is that during daylight the zooxanthellae are utilizing the metabolic carbon dioxide output of the animal tissues, but are unable to do so in the dark. This

Fig. 23-8.   Graph showing exchange of phosphorus between corals and surrounding sea-water. A′, A″, A, *Dendrophyllia*; B, *Fungia*; C, *Psammocora*; D, *Favia*; E, *Porites*; K, control. From Yonge and Nicholls, 1931. *op. cit.* Used by courtesy of The Trustees, British Museum (Natural History).

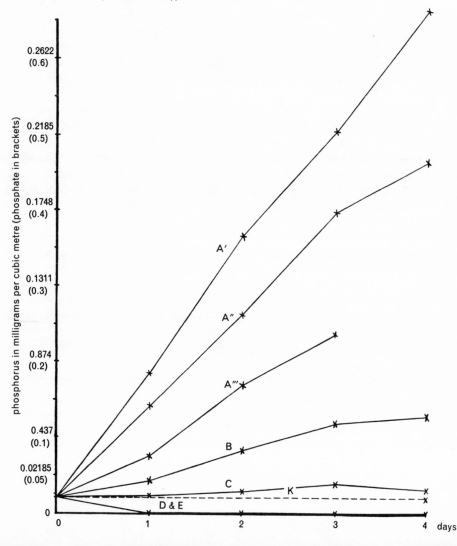

inference was confirmed by the observation that no such difference was seen in the water around an ahermatypic coral (*Dendrophyllia*). Here the medium fell in pH by 0.103 and 0.10 during 9 hours of light and of darkness respectively; the similarity can be attributed to the absence of zooxanthellae, as a result of which CO_2 produced during daylight could not be removed.

Measurements of the phosphorus content of the enclosed sea water gave comparable evidence of the anabolic activity of the zooxanthellae (Fig. 23-8). Using the hermatypic *Favia*, the phosphorus content fell to zero during the first day, in a glass jar that was open to the air, and remained at zero for four days afterwards. With the hermatypic *Psammocera* and *Fungia* there was some increase, but this was very slight for the former. Using *Dendrophyllia*, there was a marked contrast, for the phosphorus content showed a substantial and continuous increase during the same period. Evidently the zooxanthellae of *Favia* and the other hermatypic species were taking up all or most of the phosphorus excreted by the host. This conclusion was confirmed by the demonstration that the accumulated phosphorus in the *Dendrophyllia* jar was taken up in 24 hours when a specimen of *Favia* was placed in the water. Indeed, as much as 2,036 mg of phosphate were removed from the water in 5 days.

These observations provide important clues in the understanding of the advantage obtained by the symbionts. As in *Tridacna*, they may be thought of as 'imprisoned phytoplankton', gaining from their coral hosts protection, carbon dioxide, and materials for protein synthesis. Not only phosphates, but also nitrogen is needed, and it has now been shown that hermatypic corals do, in fact, remove ammonia from the surrounding water. Zooxanthellae can also utilize a variety of amino acids, together with guanine, adenine, and uric acid. The metabolic advantages of their situation cannot, therefore, be doubted.

The advantage of the association to the animal is not so immediately obvious, but is none the less striking when the situation is critically analyzed. We have earlier noted examples of hosts that eat their zooxanthellae, and it has been argued that corals may do the same. This possibility, however, has been rejected by Yonge, who has emphasized that these animals are specialized carnivores; they are believed to feed exclusively on animal prey through the agency of their tentacles, nematocysts, and cilia. The crucial evidence here is the sequence of events that ensues when corals are starved, and when they are kept in the dark. Starvation results not in the digestion of the zooxanthellae but in their extrusion, and many of the extruded organisms, although not all, are dead. So also with the anemone *Anemonia sulcata*, which also contains zooxanthellae. These are gradually ejected if the host is starved in light, while if it is starved in darkness they are all ejected within 2 months. This does not damage the anemone in any way; on the contrary, it continues to live healthily for at least 16 weeks. The same is true of corals. Zooxanthellae cannot flourish in these in the dark, yet a specimen of *Fungia*, fed in the dark, has remained healthy for 164 days; during this time large numbers of its zooxanthellae were extruded, so that its tissues were left almost colourless.

The extruded zooxanthellae pass out through the mesenteric filaments, at the extreme edge of the absorptive zone, and it is this that has particularly led to the suggestion that they are being eaten. Yet there is no good evidence of this at all. The region concerned is also the point where foreign material, such as carmine granules, is excreted; it seems clear, therefore, that the symbionts are simply being extruded

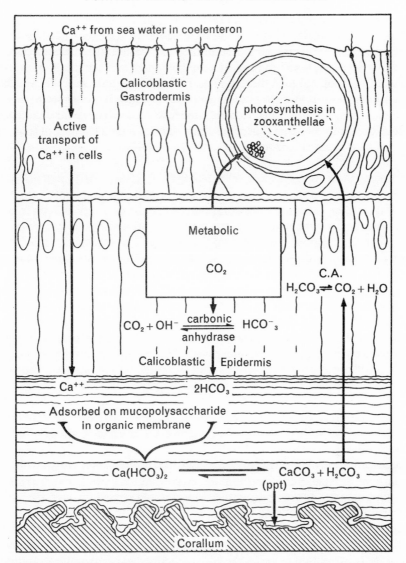

Fig. 23-9. Diagram (after Goreau) showing possible pathways of calcium and carbonate during calcification in a reef-building coral. A diagrammatic cross-section of the calicoblastic body wall at the base of the polyp is shown but the parts are not drawn to scale. The coelenteron and the flagellated gastrodermis containing a zooxanthella are shown at the top of the figure, the calicoblastic epidermis is in the middle, and the organic membrane with crystals of calcareous matter is at the bottom. The direction of growth is upward, i.e. calcium deposition is in a downward direction. From Yonge, 1963. *op. cit.*

from an animal that is no longer able to harbour them, presumably because the experimental conditions have set up some state of metabolic disharmony. It follows, then, that if the zooxanthellae are indeed of advantage to their host, the benefit must lie in some metabolic contribution that they are able to make while they are alive. We cannot, however, generalize from this to include all coelenterates that contain zooxanthellae, as is shown by the instructive example of the Xeniidae, a group of tropical Alcyonacea common on coral reefs. These, too, contain zooxanthellae, but, in contrast to corals, their digestive (ventral) mesenteric filaments are reduced. More-over, it is said that these animals, despite their possession of tentacles armed with nematocysts, do not respond to food. If xeniid colonies are kept in the dark, even in the presence of zooplankton, they soon begin to disintegrate and die, yet rapidly regain a normal condition if they are returned to daylight. It would seem, then, that in these animals, again in contrast to corals, the host has become so far adapted to the presence of the symbionts that it depends upon them as a direct supply of food, much as does the giant clam, or the mature *Convoluta roscoffensis*.

Corals are unlikely to benefit from the oxygen produced by their zooxanthellae, for experiment shows that they are well adapted to the levels of oxygen tension found in the sea. More probably, the zooxanthellae make an important contribution to the growth and secretory activity of the coral polyps. Yonge has emphasized the advant-age that these gain by the removal of their nitrogenous and phosphate waste, parti-cularly under the crowded conditions of the colonial and reef-dwelling habit; later studies by Goreau have revealed more subtle possibilities of the same kind. Using radioactive calcium (^{45}Ca) growth rates have been precisely measured in terms of calcium deposition. Comparison of normal corals (*Mancinia areolata*) with those from which zooxanthellae have been removed by keeping them in darkness shows convinc-ingly that the presence of the symbionts greatly increases calcium deposition. Growth is reduced in the dark, although zooxanthellae may still be present; even a cloudy day will reduce calcification by as much as 50%. One interesting point, suggesting that there is still much to be learned about this situation, is that the rate of calcification in darkness in the presence of the symbionts is greater than it is in light in their absence. In other words, they seem to assist the process even when they are unable to photosynthesize. This could mean, as Goreau suggests, that they contribute some growth factor to the animal, an aspect of symbiosis that we have already mentioned in another context.

The contribution of the algae to the calcification process apparently involves their fixing carbon dioxide and bicarbonate. According to Goreau's interpretation (Fig. 23-9), calcium is taken up from the sea water and passed through the tissues to be absorbed on an extracellular organic matrix. There it is incorporated first into bicarbonate and then into carbonate, the efficiency of the reactions depending on the removal of H_2CO_3 and its breakdown by carbonic anhydrase to CO_2 and water. Part at least of the contribution made by the zooxanthellae can be attributed, on this view, to their known capacity for absorbing CO_2 and bicarbonate. A general scheme for this phase of coral metabolism is shown in Fig. 23-9. It well illustrates the potential complexity of this symbiotic relationship, even when we confine our attention to only one aspect of metabolism. In so doing it indicates also at what a superficial level so much of our analysis of animal and plant interrelationships has been conducted in the past.

23–4   HOST–PARASITE RELATIONSHIPS

The definition of parasitism as living at the expense of other organisms leads to the reflection that it is a fundamental and universal feature of organic communities. The chemical phase of evolution may be said to have culminated in the establishment of organized exploitation. Animals live at the expense of plants, larger animals at the expense of smaller ones, and carnivores at the expense of herbivores. This is not, of course, the whole of the definition. The association of parasite and host is an intimate one, with the former living on or in the body of the latter, yet the implication that we have suggested is not entirely a verbal one. It emphasizes that parasitism is not a mode of life *sui generis*, unrelated to other types of association, and mainly of significance to us as a source of disease in man and his domestic stock. Like the other types of association that we have been considering, it is one of the main ways in which communities of plants and animals are bound together and regulated, and it needs approaching in part as an aspect of ecological relationships.

But the issues involved are not solely ecological, as becomes apparent when we consider the varying degrees of specificity that are found in the host–parasite relationship. Sometimes there is a very high specificity—that is, the parasite can only live successfully in a single host species, or at best in a small range of related forms. This situation, which reflects a delicate balance of mutual adaptation between parasite and host, is commonly held to show that the relationship is an ancient one, and that the specificity has a phylogenetic significance. The advancing specialization of the host is supposed to have been accompanied by a comparable advance in the specialization of the parasite, while, if the host has become specifically diversified as a result of adaptive radiation, the parasite will show a corresponding diversification. In such cases a taxonomic analysis of the parasitic group may prove to illuminate the taxonomy of the host.

Alternatively, a host-parasite relationship may show only a low degree of specificity—that is, the parasite can flourish in a range of host species. In these circumstances the specificity in the relationship may be determined primarily by the overlapping of the ecological distribution of the two partners. This situation is held to be characteristic of more recently evolved parasitic infections. But ecological relationships are important in even the most extreme examples of high specificity, for they permit the maintenance of the relationships, and must necessarily have contributed also to their origin. No parasitic association could have become established in the first instance had the two partners not been brought together by some common feature of their mode of life.

The ecological importance of the host–parasite relationships is not confined to the analysis of the past history of the relationship; equally significant in its ecological implications is the effect of the parasite upon the host. Many parasites seem to have no obvious ill effect upon their hosts. Some do kill them, but these parasites are often regarded as imperfectly adapted forms, since the death of the host must militate against the building-up of large populations of the parasite. Yet to speak of parasites as harmless may well be an over-simplification, for there is obvious difficulty in determining whether or not a wild host is being placed at some disadvantage as a consequence of harbouring other organisms. The presence of these must often create physiological demands arising from the nourishment that they remove from the host, but presumably there is a margin of safety here, and the demands can be met by the ingestion of more food. There are, however, other possibilities. Conceivably a parasite may produce some decrease in the vigour or in the speed of response of its host—effects that may be difficult to overcome, and that may leave the host population more exposed to attack by predators, and less able to achieve a high density of numbers. Parasites can thus be important in regulating the balance of communities. The situation evidently involves a complex and closely integrated adaptation of the host and parasite with each other and with their environment.

As an illustration of this, one of the important biological agents controlling the size of oyster populations is a tissue parasite, *Dermocystidium*. This organism cannot flourish in waters of low salinity, which is one reason why oysters of the southern United States achieve a high density of population in such waters. The oyster, if it were an independent organism, free of parasites, could flourish in waters of high salinity, and could build up there populations of greater density than are actually maintained in lower salinities. That it does not succeed in this is a measure of the important part played by its parasites in determining its survival in particular types of habitat. The effect is seen in the differences in distribution of the oyster along different parts of the Atlantic Coast of North America. In the more northerly waters there are larger oyster populations in more saline conditions, because the lower temperatures favour the oyster more than they do its parasites and predators. Farther south the balance of advantage changes, and there the larger oyster populations live in less saline conditions.

Another illustration of the ecological influence of parasites is seen in the history of the eelgrass, *Zostera marina*. *Zostera* beds were at one time the foundation of characteristic communities in areas of high salinity along the Atlantic coast, some of the organisms of these communities being so well suited to the existing conditions that they lived in densities unequalled elsewhere. During the early 1930s the eelgrass disappeared from all high-salinity waters, and it is believed that one factor in this was a protozoon parasite *Labyrinthula*. As with the oyster, the precise balance between parasite and host is influenced by salinity. The eelgrass, like the oyster, can tolerate lower salinities than can the parasite, and so it survived in the regions of low salinity, and has to some extent recovered elsewhere. One of the ecological and economic effects of the reduction of the *Zostera* beds was the elimination of the United States scallop fishery in those regions, for the bay scallop was an important member of the eelgrass community. Its disappearance, which was presumably a consequence of changes in its biological circumstances rather than in the physical conditions of its environment, meant that some areas of Virginia lost what was formerly a considerable scallop industry. Yet the activity of *Labyrinthula* was not entirely without benefit: some of the flats that were originally populated by the *Zostera* community became occupied by oysters.

The problem of the relationship of parasitism to the other types of association that we have considered raises a number of issues. There is, for example, the question whether it has developed from one or other of those types, or as a direct consequence of the invasion of one organism by another. Then again there are problems relating to the factors that determine the host–parasite relationship; to the degree of mutual adaptation of the two partners; and to the nature of the benefits received by the parasite and the extent to which these are disadvantageous to the host.

As regards origins, we have seen from the beginning of our survey of invertebrate life how wide is the scope for the independent and convergent achievement of similar results in unrelated groups. We must suppose, therefore, that however superficially similar the end results of parasitism may be, the association is likely to have been achieved in many different ways. We have seen that this is in part an ecological issue, for parasitism, like other associations, can only have been evolved when the habits and distribution of the invading organism brought it into frequent contact with its host. Yet the process could certainly have been aided by some preadaptation to facilitate the initial stages of mutual accommodation. Unfortunately, the intense specialization of parasites often conceals their evolutionary history, yet some light can be shed on this if we study non-parasitic members of the same group, while comparative studies of host–parasite relationships can also be very revealing.

Free-living Protozoa are clearly pre-adapted for parasitism by virtue of their habit of forming protective cysts which could readily be ingested by potential hosts. As Baer points out, the Foraminifera, with their alternation of sexual and asexual generations, show that Protozoa, even when free-living, have the potentiality for evolving the complex life cycles that are such an important and characteristic feature of their parasitic adaptations. These factors enable us to visualize something of the mode of origin of the sporozoan life cycles that we have earlier reviewed.

Gregarines, for example, are parasites of the alimentary tract, body cavities, and excretory and reproductive systems of annelids, arthropods, and occasionally urochordates. This, together with their simple life cycle, which usually lacks schizogony, and which depends for its completion upon one host ingesting cysts liberated by another, suggests that these particular parasites first became established in the intestine of invertebrate hosts through chance ingestion of this kind. Gregarines remain typically parasites of the various cavities within their hosts, but they show a tendency to invade cells. This tendency, which is apparent in the behaviour of the sporozoites of *Monocystis*, probably led on to the characteristically intracellular habit of the coccidians. Equally important, however, has been the introduction of a multiplicative phase, as, for example, in *Ophryocystis* (from the Malpighian tubules of *Tenebrio*), which has a life cycle complicated by schizogony.

This multiplication has an obvious adaptive value, for it increases the chances of successful infection of a new host. Thus it may well have been important in the evolution of the Haemosporidia, the blood-dwelling Sporozoa to which belong the malaria parasites. An illustration of the possible course of events is seen in *Schellackia*, a parasite of lizards, which undergoes schizogony and sexual reproduction (gamogony) in the cells of the wall of the alimentary tract. From here the spores pass into the red blood corpuscles and are ingested by mites, the cycle being completed when these are in turn eaten by lizards. The metabolic role of erythrocytes makes them also an ideal home for parasites. Strong selection pressure could thus have promoted the further evolution of this type of cycle into the form that is typical of the Haemosporidia, with multiplication taking place in the reticulo-endothelial system, and sexual reproduction in the blood-sucking arthropod vector.

Comparison of the Haemosporidia with the zoomastigine Trypanosomidae suggests that exploitation of the vertebrate blood stream by these two groups has been achieved not only independently but in two quite distinct ways. Trypanosomes, most of which are harmless commensals, are polymorphic, occurring in four main types, the leptomonad, leishmanial, crithidial, and trypanosome stages (Fig. 23–10). The leptomonad stage, with its nucleus lying centrally and the kinetoplast at the anterior end, is probably the primitive stage. From this the crithidial stage can be derived by backward movement of the kinetoplast to a position near the nucleus, and by the development of an undulating membrane. Both stages are common in the intestine of invertebrates, particularly insects, and in some instances they represent species in which the life cycle is confined to the one invertebrate host. Thus *Leptomonas jaculum*, which occurs in the water scorpion, *Nepa cinerea*, has a leptomonad stage abundant in the mid-gut, and a leishmanial stage, rounded and lacking the flagellum, in the rectum. Distribution is direct, by the swallowing of cysts.

Leptomonad stages occur only in invertebrates, but all the other three may occur either in these hosts or in vertebrates. Familiar examples are *Trypanosoma gambiense* and *T. rhodesiense*, highly pathogenic species which cause African sleeping sickness in man. These two species are morphologically indistinguishable from each other, and

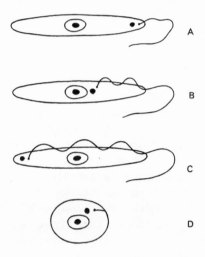

Fig. 23-10. The four basic morphological types of haemoflagellate. A, leptomonad; B, crithidial; C, trypanosome; D, leishmanial.

also from *T. brucei*, which is a non-pathogenic parasite of African wild game. Crithidial stages of these organisms develop in the alimentary tract of the invertebrate vector, the tsetse fly, *T. gambiense* and *T. rhodesiense* being distributed by different species of *Glossina* under natural conditions. It is upon such physiological differences that the independent status of the three species is founded. Indeed, we can regard them as biological races of the same species, adapted to different hosts.

It is commonly supposed that trypanosomes are recent invaders of man, having passed to him from wild animals, and that their longer association with the latter has allowed time for the establishment of a non-pathogenic relationship; the pathogenic relationship with man is thus seen as a less perfect adjustment. This implies that these parasites are readily able to invade fresh hosts, and that they do not achieve a specialized stability of host–parasite relationship such as we commonly find elsewhere. Other aspects of their biology support this view, for they can be readily inoculated into many different hosts under laboratory conditions, and lend themselves well to *in vitro* cultivation. This instability makes it easier to visualize the probable course of their earlier history. Their abundance in insects, and the occurrence in these hosts of leptomonad forms with direct transmission, make it reasonably certain that this was the origin of their parasitic habit, and that they have secondarily invaded the plants and vertebrates with which their invertebrate hosts developed close ecological relationships.

Trypanosoma cruzi, the cause of Chagas' disease in Central and South America (and perhaps, as some believe, of Darwin's chronic ill health), probably shows a primitive pattern of transmission of a trypanosome infection from the invertebrate to the vertebrate host. The parasites are taken up from the human blood stream by bugs. Infective stages, which develop in the hind gut of the insects, are deposited on to human skin when the insects defaecate in the course of their meal; these stages are then readily rubbed into the wound as the victim reacts to the irritation. Other mammalian hosts may also become infected by swallowing the bugs, or perhaps by eating other infected hosts. Transmission by inoculation with the saliva through the mouth parts, such as is found in *Trypanosoma gambiense*, is likely to have evolved as a later specialization; it clearly affords greater certainty of successful infection.

In the groups so far considered there is an absence of close relatives that are also free-living. In many other groups these are still surviving, and our understanding of the host–parasite relationship is correspondingly enlarged. This is notably true of the Nematoda, of which Baer has said that no other single group is so perfectly pre-adapted to becoming parasitic. We have already noted this aspect of nematode organization. The free-living species of this group, which greatly outnumber the parasitic ones, are animals of peculiar yet generalized structure that are particularly well able, both in the adult stage and during development, to resist environmental stress. In consequence, they have successfully exploited an enormous range of habitats, from polar seas to hot springs, from arid deserts to the ocean depths. Add to this their saprophagous habits and their enormous reproductive potential, and it would be surprising indeed if they had not given rise to successful parasitic forms. The same considerations suggest that this will have happened along many independent lines, and this must surely account for the great variety of relationship between nematode parasites and their hosts, and in the details of their life cycles and modes of transmission. This variety precludes further discussion here, beyond remarking that life in the tissues or body cavities of invertebrates may have been the earliest form of parasitism among these animals. It is significant from this point of view that the parasitic status of their relationships is often inferred, and is unsupported by clear evidence. In some instances the nematodes remain within the host after its death and then feed upon its decomposing tissues. In these circumstances it is difficult to distinguish them from predators, and it is likely that their habit of active searching for such food sources was important in the establishment of their parasitism.

Another group in which free-living and parasitic forms can readily be compared is the Platyhelminthes. The extensive development of parasitism in this group indicates that here also there must have been much pre-adaptation to this mode of life. Creeping progression and powers of adhesion, which are ecologically important in free-living forms, and notably in the littoral zone, would have contributed to this. So also would the complex and hermaphrodite reproductive system, facilitating the propagation of isolated individuals, and making possible the production of large numbers of resistant eggs. Here, as in the nematodes, the parasitic forms have evolved along more than one line, but in this instance their history is easier to analyze.

In the Class Trematoda the Monogenea are characterized by being mostly ectoparasities with a complicated posterior attachment disc, and with a direct life cycle; the eggs give rise to a larva that metamorphoses on a new host, so that no vector is required. A few species parasitize amphibians and turtles, but as many as 95% are found on fish, particularly upon their gills; of these species the majority are parasites

504

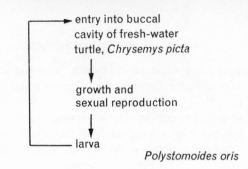

entry into buccal
cavity of fresh-water
turtle, *Chrysemys picta*

↓

growth and
sexual reproduction

↓

larva

Polystomoides oris

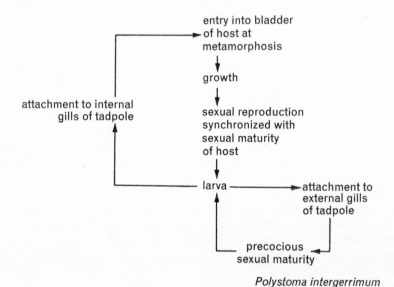

entry into bladder
of host at
metamorphosis

↓

growth

↓

attachment to internal
gills of tadpole

sexual reproduction
synchronized with
sexual maturity
of host

↓

larva ⟶ attachment to
external gills
of tadpole

precocious
sexual maturity

Polystoma intergerrimum

Fig. 23-11. Patterns of life cycles in the Monogenea. In *Polystoma intergerrimum* the normal cycle is shortened by the development of precocious sexual maturity (neoteny) if the larva attaches to external gills instead of to internal ones.

of elasmobranchs, showing a very high degree of host-specificity. It would appear, therefore, that the Monogenea are ancient parasites that have remained confined to the lower vertebrates. Probably they arose from rhabdocoel-like forms that exploited the skin of early fish, and then, finding protection on the gills, became dependent on blood sucking for their nutrition.

Particularly interesting from this point of view is *Polystoma integerrimum* (parasitic in the bladder of frogs), for this species, and its polystomid relatives, are the only Monogenea (Fig. 23-11) that have successfully exploited hosts other than fish. This they have done by moving into internal cavities such as the mouth, nostrils, and bladder; never, however, into the digestive regions of the alimentary tract, although the young *Polystoma* passes down the gut of the metamorphosing tadpole to reach the bladder. This limitation is a reminder that a transition from ecto-parasitism to endoparasitism, or, in more general terms, from an ectozoic to an entozoic habit, may be attractively plausible in theory, but has not always been easily achieved in practice. In particular, the stresses experienced in the alimentary tract are such that animals must always have found it difficult to establish themselves there unless they possessed from the beginning strongly developed powers of resist-ance to peristaltic movement and to enzyme action; the Monogenea have perhaps been lacking in these, although there are isolated records of species occurring in the oesophagus or intestine of fish. As we shall see, these may support the possibility of cestodes having evolved from early monogeneans.

The Digenea (which include the liver flukes) differ substantially from the Monogenea. Some authorities have nevertheless supposed that they originated from monogeneans, but even if this is so it seems likely that the two groups must have diverged from a rhabdocoel-like ancestry at a very early stage. This follows from the differences in their host relationships. Most digeneans are endoparasites of the vertebrate alimentary tract and its outgrowths, where they exploit the exceptionally rich food resources of these organs. They have a complex and indirect life history, with several developmental stages in which multiplication may occur. Particularly significant is the fact that, although more than one intermediate host may be involved, the first is invariably a mollusc, usually a gastropod but sometimes a lamellibranch or a scaphopod; this is so, irrespective of whether the final host is marine, fresh-water, or terrestrial. When, however, there is a second intermediate host, this may be a member of almost any group of animals. No less significant is the high degree of specificity that digeneans show towards their molluscan hosts, and the low degree that they sometimes show towards their definitive vertebrate ones. This implies that they were first associated with molluscs, and began to parasitize vertebrates at a later stage. (See Fig. 23–12.)

Fig. 23-12. Patterns of life cycles in the Digenea. In the hypothetical ancestral stage there would have been only one host, a mollusc. Later this becomes the first intermediate host. A second intermediate host may (*Bucephalopsis*) or may not (*Fasciola*) be involved.

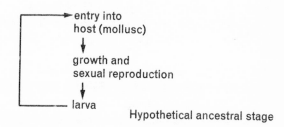

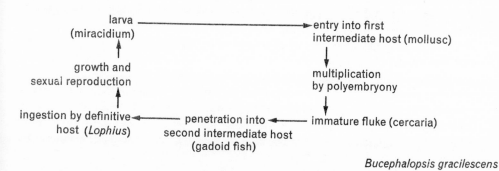

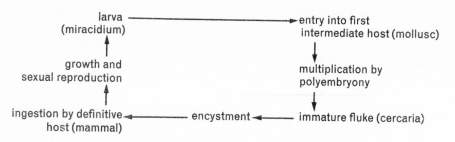

Thus we can plausibly visualize the Digenea as being derived from rhabdocoel-like ancestors that invaded molluscs, perhaps as a result of ingestion, the invasive stage being the free-swimming larva that is represented today by the miracidium. Whether the worm would have matured within the host is not clear, although it is probably significant that rhabdocoels now occur in molluscs and echinoderms. In any case, we may suppose that extension of the life history into a vertebrate host occurred later, when encysted cercariae were ingested by vertebrates and proved able to mature within their alimentary tract. Once this had happened, the group became closely adapted to the ecology of a wide range of vertebrate hosts; this has made possible the proliferation of digenean habits that we find today.

To give only a few examples, *Schistosoma mansoni*, one of the devastating blood flukes of man, is transferred from its molluscan vector to its primary host by the cercaria directly penetrating the skin of human beings that enter the water. *Fasciola hepatica* takes advantage of the amphibious habits of the snail, *Lymnaea truncatula*; the motile cercariae encyst on vegetation as metacercariae, and are eaten by sheep and cattle. *Dicrocoelium dendriticum* enters the bile ducts of as many as 40 different mammalian hosts (including sheep and cattle) by a more elaborate procedure. Groups of the cercariae are enclosed in slime balls, secreted partly by the larvae and partly by the terrestrial snail host, and are then ingested by ants; within the body cavity of this second intermediate host they form metacercariae, and are eventually swallowed by the mammalian host.

Alternative routes into terrestrial vertebrates are seen in *Haematoloechus spp.* and *Lecithodendrium chilostomum*. The former is parasitic in the lungs of amphibians, arriving there by a life cycle that passes first (Fig. 23–13) through molluscan hosts (*Lymnaea spp.*) and then through the nymph of the dragon fly, in which metacercariae are formed; these are then ingested by the primary host when it eats the imago. The life cycle of *Lecithodendrium*, a parasite of bats, depends in a similar way upon the formation of metacercariae in the haemocoel of the larva of a caddis fly.

Exceptionally there may be no motile cercaria stage, as in the life cycle of *Ptychogonimus megastoma*, a parasite of sharks that is elegantly adapted to the habits of two intermediate hosts. The first of these hosts is a scaphopod, from which the cercariae escape still enclosed within the rediae. The latter wriggle slowly on the sea bottom, thereby attracting the attention of crabs, which proceed to eat them. The cercariae escape from the rediae within the crab, encyst in its body cavity, and are readily transmitted to the sharks that prey upon the crabs.

The third major group of platyhelminth parasites is the Cestoda. One view of cestode origins is that these animals are the product of a monophyletic history, leading from monogeneans through digeneans. This view now receives little support in its original form; apart from what has been said above regarding the relationships of the latter two groups, many other considerations argue against it. The organs of attachment in trematodes and cestodes are very different, and there are important differences also in the reproductive system, particularly as regards the uterus; in trematodes this opens into a genital atrium with the male duct, but it is entirely independent of the atrium in the cestodes. However, Llewellyn has suggested that these differences do not necessarily preclude a derivation of cestodes from early monogeneans.

Cestodes are further characterized by the loss of the alimentary canal, while the eucestodes typically produce a tape-like chain of proglottids; these features limit the

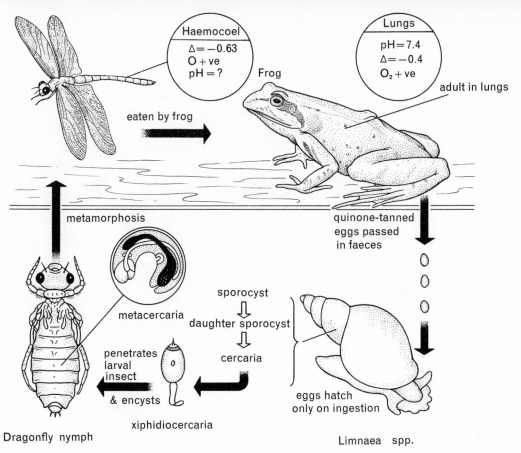

Fig. 23-13. *Haematoloechus variegatus:* the life cycle and some physiological factors relating to it. The eggs are probably embryonated when laid. The details of the cycle are very imperfectly known. From Smyth, 1962. *Introduction to Animal Parasitology.* English Universities Press, London.

adults, with few exceptions, to the alimentary tracts of vertebrate hosts, although their larvae use a diversity of intermediate hosts. Following the arguments of Baer, we may suppose that cestode parasitism, like that of the Digenea, began with the ingestion of rhabdocoel-like organisms. Alternatively, monogeneans may have succeeded in invading the alimentary tract of their hosts, if Llewellyn's arguments are accepted. In any case, the first hosts must have been fish; to this day the more primitive tapeworms survive in the alimentary tract of fish, using other aquatic animals as intermediate hosts.

Subsequently the eucestodes clearly evolved in parallel with the vertebrates, for they are unusually host-specific, with each vertebrate group having its characteristic genera and species. Thus the Orders Tetraphyllidea and Trypanorhyncha are exclusively parasites of elasmobranchs, whereas the Order Pseudophyllidea chiefly parasitizes teleosts, birds, and mammals. In this last group of cestodes the transition to land-dwelling hosts has depended upon the fish-eating habits of the latter. An example is *Diphyllobothrium dendriticum*, parasitic in gulls, with a life history (Fig. 23–14) involving copepods as the first intermediate host and fish as the second. *D. latum*, a parasite of man, has a similar cycle. In these instances the parasites have succeeded in exploiting the higher vertebrates by extending their own life cycles.

A more complete adaptation to terrestrial hosts is seen in the order Cyclo-

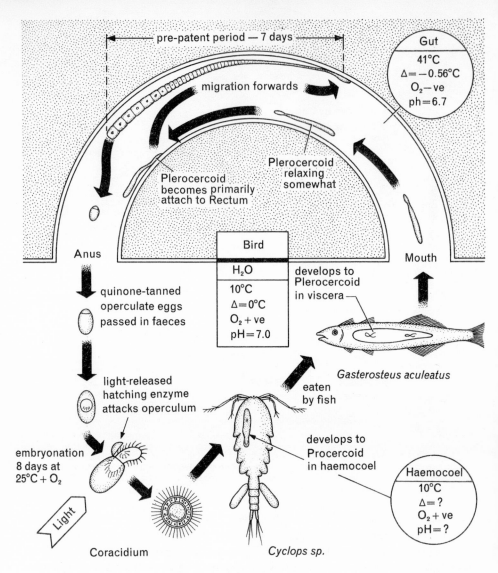

Fig. 23-14. *Diphyllobothrium dendriticum:* the life cycle and some physiological factors relating to it. From Smyth, 1962. *op. cit.*

phyllidea (Taenioidea), which are mainly parasites of birds and mammals, although found also in reptiles and amphibians. The majority of species are found in birds, a peculiarity that has been attributed to the diversified and almost explosive radiation of that group, as compared with the slower rate of mammalian evolution. In these cestodes the life cycle has come to depend entirely on terrestrial hosts. Examples are *Hymenolepis diminuta* of rodents, transmitted by insects, and *Taenia saginata* of man, distributed by cattle and other mammalian intermediate hosts. The ultimate limit of success along this line of evolution has been attained by *Hymenolepis nana nana*, the dwarf tapeworm of man, which can be transmitted directly through the faecal contamination of food; no intermediate host is now required, although arthropod hosts can be employed. (See Fig. 23–15.)

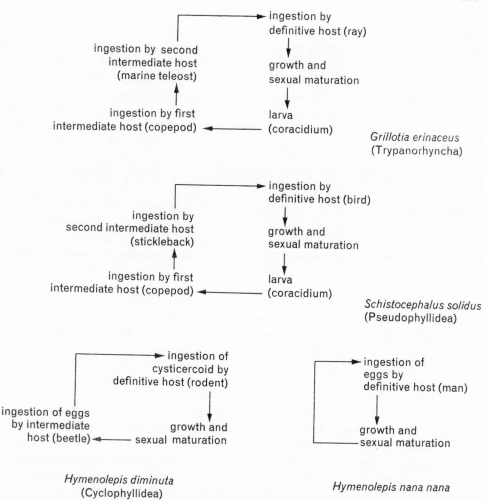

Fig. 23-15. Patterns of life cycles in the Eucestoda. The life cycle of *Diphyllobothrium* (Fig. 23-14) is similar in principle to that of *Schistocephalus.*

The descriptive terms in which we have so far considered the development of host-parasite relationships are, of course, only one aspect of parasitic adaptation. The specificity of these relationships must surely depend also on physiological adaptations, although there is no reason to expect these to differ in principle from those that regulate the relationships and life histories of free-living forms. The precision and delicacy of parasitic adaptations is emphasized by Baer, who points out that the miracidium of the trematode *Opisthorchis felineus* is attracted to a prosobranch snail, *Bithynia leachi*, but not to the closely related *B. tentaculata*, although this occurs in the same habitat and may even be more abundant there. As with the symbiotic relationships discussed earlier, little is known of the basis of these attractions. We may assume that they often involve chemoreception of characteristic secretory products of the host, although these need not be essential features of parasitic life cycles. Thus it is said that the cercariae of *Schistosoma mansoni* locate the skin of their human host by chance; their entrance depends upon the secretion of enzymes, known to include hyaluronidase, with which they are able to break down the epidermis so efficiently that they can enter the lymphatics within 20 minutes.

Once an association has been established between a parasite and a host its further evolution will depend upon the reactions of both organisms. Indeed, the initial establishment depends upon an over-riding of the normal tendency of animals to react to invasions with responses that immobilize or destroy the invader. Such a response is the origin of natural oriental pearls, which usually contain a plerocercoid larva of a tetraphyllidean cestode that parasitizes elasmobranchs. The rarity of pearls suggest that this is a chance infection of the oyster, perhaps a result of it ingesting an infected planktonic crustacean that is acting as the first intermediate host. The life history of the dog tapeworm suggests how such a barrier can be overcome. Flea larvae become infected with the onchospheres, but these do not develop further in the larva because they become enclosed by phagocytes; at pupation, however, these cells leave the onchospheres, which can then develop into cystercoid larvae. Thus the adult flea is fully infective. Here the reactions of the intermediate host are nicely attuned to the requirements of the parasite, providing a balance that is as necessary for successful parasitism as we have seen it to be for symbiosis.

A similar degree of balance is seen in the life history of *Trypanosoma lewisi*, a parasite of wild rats, the blood of which may contain as many as 600,000 parasites per cubic millimetre. This organism is non-pathogenic, because its host is able to control it by establishing an immunity to it. This is effected through the production of an antibody, called ablastin, which may act specifically against enzymes concerned in the nutrition of the parasites. Whatever the precise nature of the reaction, the effect of it is that an infected rat is completely cleared of trypanosomes within at most a few months of the start of the infection, yet during that period the parasites are able to establish and propagate themselves. The contrast with the pathogenic effects of *Trypanosoma gambiense* and *T. rhodesiense* has been ascribed, as we have earlier indicated, to their parasitic relationship with man having been more recently established, so that it is less well adapted to the needs of both partners.

The reactions of the parasite to its host are determined by the fact that the chief benefits that it obtains are protection and a ready source of nutrition; the latter is so richly provided that it permits the impressive fecundity that is such a feature of parasitic life. Thus the reproductive system tends to predominate in the organization of the

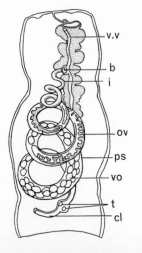

Fig. 23-16. *Entoconcha mirabilis* (after Baur) and its relationships with its host, *Synapta. b*, mouth, fixed to the ventral vessel, *v.v.* of the host's intestine; *cl*, ciliated canal; *i*, intestine; *ov*, ovary; *ps*, pseudopallium; *t*, testes; *vo*, masses of developing eggs. From Caullery, 1952. *Parasitism and Symbiosis*. Sidgwick and Jackson, London.

Classification

The classification of the animal kingdom is under continuous review, so that the treatment of particular groups is liable to be modified from time to time. The scheme shown below is a simplified and conservative outline, designed to enable the reader to place in an acceptable context the main groups referred to in the text. For more detailed classification, and for alternative treatments of certain groups, the following should be consulted:

Barnes, R. D., 1963. *Invertebrate Zoology*. Saunders, Philadelphia.
Honigberg, B. M., *et al.*, 1964. A revised classification of the Phylum Protozoa. *J. Protozool.*, **11**, 7–20.
Rothschild, Lord, 1961. *A Classification of Living Animals*. Longmans, London.

Some of the multi-volume treatises and other general works listed in the Bibliography contain detailed classifications of individual groups.

Phylum Protozoa

    Class Mastigophora (= Flagellata)
      Subclass Phytomastigina (= Phytoflagellata)
      Subclass Zoomastigina (= Zooflagellata)
    Class Rhizopoda (= Sarcodina)
      Order Rhizomastigina
      Order Amoebina
      Order Testacea
      Order Foraminifera
    Class Actinopoda
      Order Radiolaria
      Order Heliozoa
    Class Ciliata (= Ciliophora)
    Class Sporozoa (= Telosporidia)
      Subclass Gregarinomorpha
      Subclass Coccidiomorpha
    Class Cnidosporidia

Phylum Porifera (= Parazoa)
    Class Calcarea
    Class Hexactinellida
    Class Demospongiae

Phylum Coelenterata (= Cnidaria)
  Class Hydrozoa
  Class Scyphozoa
  Class Anthozoa (= Actinozoa)
    Subclass Ceriantipatharia
    Subclass Octocorallia
    Subclass Zoantharia

Phylum Ctenophora

Phylum Platyhelminthes
  Class Turbellaria
    Order Acoela
    Order Rhabdocoela
    Order Alloeocoela
    Order Tricladida
    Order Polycladida
    Order Temnocephalida
  Class Trematoda
    Order Monogenea (= Heterocotylea)
    Order Aspidogastrea (= Aspidocotylea)
    Order Digenea (= Malacocotylea)
  Class Cestoda
    Order Cestodaria
    Order Eucestoda

Phylum Mesozoa

Phylum Nemertina (= Nemertea)

Phylum Aschelminthes
  Class Nematoda (= Nemathelminthes in part)
  Class Nematomorpha (= Gordiacea; Nemathelminthes in part)
  Class Rotifera
  Class Gastrotricha
  Class Echinoderida (= Kinorhyncha)

Phylum Priapulida

Phylum Acanthocephala

Phylum Entoprocta (= Polyzoa Endoprocta)

Phylum Sipunculoidea

Phylum Echiuroidea

Phylum Annelida
  Class Polychaeta
  Class Myzostomaria
  Class Oligochaeta
  Class Hirudinea
  Class Archiannelida

Phylum Arthropoda
  Class Trilobita
  Class Merostomata (= Chelicerata in part)
    Subclass Eurypterida
    Subclass Xiphosura
  Class Arachnida (= Chelicerata in part)
  Class Pycnogonida (= Chelicerata in part)
  Class Pentastomida
  Class Tardigrada
  Class Crustacea
    Subclass Branchiopoda
    Subclass Ostracoda
    Subclass Copepoda
    Subclass Mystacocarida
    Subclass Branchiura
    Subclass Cirripedia
    Subclass Malacostraca
      Series Leptostraca
        Superorder Phyllocarida
          Order Nebaliacea
      Series Eumalacostraca
        Superorder Syncarida
          Order Anaspidacea
        Superorder Hoplocarida
          Order Stomatopoda
        Superorder Peracarida
          Order Mysidacea
          Order Cumacea
          Order Tanaidacea
          Order Isopoda
          Order Amphipoda
        Superorder Eucarida
          Order Euphausiacea
          Order Decapoda
            Suborder Natantia
            Suborder Reptantia
  Class Diplopoda (millipedes; = myriapods in part)
  Class Chilopoda (centipedes, = myriapods in part)
  Class Symphyla (= myriapods in part)
  Class Pauropoda (= myriapods in part)
  Class Insecta
    Subclass Apterygota
    Subclass Pterygota
      Division Palaeoptera (= Exopterygota in part)
      Division Neoptera
        Section Polyneoptera (= Exopterygota in part)
        Section Paraneoptera (= Exopterygota in part)
        Section Oligoneoptera (= Endopterygota, Holometabola)

Phylum Mollusca
  Class Monoplacophora
  Class Amphineura
    Subclass Aplacophora
    Subclass Polyplacophora

Class Gastropoda
    Subclass Prosobranchia (= Streptoneura)
        Order Archaeogastropoda
        Order Mesogastropoda
        Order Neogastropoda
    Subclass Opisthobranchia
    Subclass Pulmonata
Class Scaphopoda
Class Lamellibranchia (= Pelycypoda, Bivalvia)
    Subclass Protobranchia
    Subclass Filibranchia
    Subclass Eulamellibranchia
    Subclass Septibranchia
Class Cephalopoda
    Subclass Nautiloidea
    Subclass Ammonoidea
    Subclass Coleoidea
        Order Decapoda
        Order Octopoda
        Order Vampyromorpha

Phylum Ectoprocta (= Polyzoa Ectoprocta)
    Class Phylactolaemata
    Class Gymnolaemata

Phylum Brachiopoda

Phylum Phoronida

Phylum Chaetognatha

Phylum Echinodermata
    Subphylum Pelmatozoa
        Class Crinoidea
    Subphylum Eleutherozoa
        Class Holothuroidea
        Class Echinoidea
        Class Asteroidea
        Class Ophiuroidea

Phylum Pogonophora

Phylum Hemichordata
    Class Pterobranchia
    Class Enteropneusta

Phylum Chordata
    Subphylum Urochordata (= Tunicata)
        Class Ascidiacea
        Class Thaliacea
        Class Larvacea
    Subphylum Cephalochordata
    Subphylum Vertebrata (= Craniata)

Selected Bibliography

GENERAL

Multi-volume treatises on Zoology

Grassé, P.-P. (ed.), 1948 onwards. *Traité de Zoologie*. Masson et Cie, Paris.
Harmer, S. F. and A. E. Shipley (eds.), 1895–1909. *The Cambridge Natural History*. Macmillan, London.
Hyman, L. H., 1940 onwards. *The Invertebrates*. McGraw-Hill, New York.
Kükenthal, W. and T. Krumbach (eds.), 1923 onwards. *Handbuch der Zoologie*. de Gruyter, Berlin and Leipzig.
Lankester, E. Ray (ed.), 1900 onwards. *A Treatise on Zoology*. Black, London.
Sedgwick, A., 1898–1908; 2nd ed. of vol. 1 in 1927. *A Student's Textbook of Zoology*. Sonnenschein, London.

Other general works

Certain multi-author volumes that are cited below in full are referred to elsewhere in a shortened form (e.g., In Bourne, **1**, 265–335).

Baldwin, E., 1963. *Dynamic Aspects of Biochemistry* (4th ed.). Cambridge University Press, London.
Baldwin, E., 1964. *An Introduction to Comparative Biochemistry* (4th ed.). Cambridge University Press, London.
Bourne, G. H. (ed.), 1960. *The Structure and Function of Muscle*, vols. 1–3. Academic Press, New York.
Brachet, J. and A. E. Mirsky, 1959–64. *The Cell*, vols. 1–6. Academic Press, New York.
Calkins, G. N. and F. M. Summers (eds.), 1941. *Protozoa in Biological Research*. Columbia University Press, New York.
Carter, G. S., 1961. *A General Zoology of the Invertebrates*. Sidgwick and Jackson, London.
Davson, H., 1964. *A Textbook of General Physiology* (3rd ed.). Churchill, London.
Florkin, M. and H. S. Mason, 1960–64. *Comparative Biochemistry*, vols. 1–7. Academic Press, New York.
Fruton, J. S. and S. Simmonds, 1958. *General Biochemistry* (2nd ed.). Wiley, New York.

Hall, R. P., 1953. *Protozoology*. Prentice-Hall, New Jersey.

Harrison, K., 1965. *A Guide-book to Biochemistry* (2nd ed.). Cambridge University Press, London.

Hoar, W. S., 1966. *General and Comparative Physiology*. Prentice-Hall, New Jersey.

Hutner, S. H. (ed.), 1965. *Biochemistry and Physiology of Protozoa*, vol. 3. Academic Press, New York.

Hutner, S. H. and A. Lwoff (eds.), 1955. *Biochemistry and Physiology of Protozoa*, vol. 2. Academic Press, New York.

Karlson, P., 1963. *Introduction to Modern Biochemistry*. Academic Press, New York.

Kudo, R. R., 1954. *Protozoology* (4th ed.). Thomas, Springfield, Illinois.

Lenhoff, H. M. and W. F. Loomis (eds.), 1961. *The Biology of Hydra*. University of Miami Press, Coral Gables, Florida.

Lwoff, A. (ed.), 1951. *Biochemistry and Physiology of Protozoa*, vol. 1. Academic Press, New York.

MacGinitie, G. E. and N. MacGinitie, 1949. *Natural History of Marine Animals*. McGraw-Hill, New York.

Nicol, J. A. C., 1960. *The Biology of Marine Animals*. Pitman, London.

Pringle, J. W. S. (ed.), 1965. *Essays on Physiological Evolution*. Pergamon, Oxford.

Ramsay, J. A., 1951. *A Physiological Approach to the Lower Animals*. Cambridge University Press, London.

Rees, W. J. (ed.), 1966. *The Cnidaria and their Evolution*. Symp. zool. Soc. Lond., no. 16.

Rockstein, M., 1964. *The Physiology of Insecta*, vols. 1 and 3. Academic Press, New York.

Roeder, K. D. (ed.), 1953. *Insect Physiology*. Wiley, New York.

Scheer, B. T. (ed.), 1957. *Recent Advances in Invertebrate Physiology*. University of Oregon Publications, Eugene, Oregon.

Scheer, B. T., 1963. *Animal Physiology*. Wiley, New York.

Stephenson, J., 1930. *The Oligochaeta*. Clarendon Press, Oxford.

Waterman, T. H. (ed.), 1960–61. *The Physiology of Crustacea*, vols. 1 and 2. Academic Press, New York.

Wigglesworth, V. B., 1961. *The Principles of Insect Physiology* (5th ed.). Methuen, London.

Wilbur, K. M. and C. M. Yonge, 1964–66. *Physiology of Mollusca*, vols. 1 and 2. Academic Press, New York.

CHAPTER 1

Many citations are relevant to more than one chapter, but they are usually not repeated.

Arnon, D. I., 1960. The role of light in photosynthesis. *Scient. Am.*, **203** (5), 105–118.

Bernal, J. D., 1954. The origin of life. *New Biol.*, **16**, 28–40.

Blum, H. F., 1962. *Time's Arrow and Evolution* (2nd ed.). Harper and Row, New York.

Calvin, M., 1962. Evolution of photosynthetic mechanisms. *Perspect. Biol. Med.*, **5**, 147–172.

Calvin, M., 1956. Chemical evolution and origin of life. *Am. Scient.*, **44**, 248–263.

Crick, F. H. C., 1962. The genetic code. *Scient. Am.*, **207** (4), 66–74.

Echelin, P. and I. Morris, 1965. The relationship between blue-green algae and bacteria. *Biol. Rev.*, **40**, 143–187.

Florkin, M., 1960. *Unity and Diversity in Biochemistry*. Pergamon, Oxford.

Fox, S. W., 1960. How did life begin? *Science, N.Y.*, **132**, 200–208.

Gaffron, H., 1960. The origin of life. In *Evolution after Darwin* (S. Tax, ed.), **1**, 39–84. University of Chicago Press.

Glaessner, M. F., 1962. Pre-Cambrian fossils. *Biol. Rev.*, **37**, 467–494.

Haldane, J. B. S., 1954. The origins of life. *New Biol.*, **16**, 12–27.

Hardy, Sir Alister, 1965. *The Living Stream: Evolution and Man*. Collins, London.
Jevons, F. R., 1964. *The Biochemical Approach to Life*. Allen and Unwin, London.
Keosian, J., 1964. *The Origin of Life*. Chapman and Hall, London.
McCrea, W. H., 1966. Cosmical physics. *Advmt. Sci., Lond.*, **23**, 379–397.
Miller, S. L., 1953. A production of amino acids under possible primitive earth conditions. *Science, N.Y.*, **117**, 528–529.
Needham, A. E., 1959. Origination of life. *Q. Rev. Biol.*, **34**, 189–209.
Needham, A. E., 1965. *The Uniqueness of Biological Materials*. Pergamon, Oxford.
Nirenberg, M. W., 1963. The genetic code, II. *Scient. Am.*, **208** (3), 80–94.
Nursall, J. R., 1962. On the origins of the major groups of animals. *Evolution*, **16**, 118–123.
Oparin, A. I., 1961. *Life: Its Nature, Origin, and Development*. Oliver and Boyd, Edinburgh.
Poonamperuma, C., R. Mariner, and C. Sagan, 1963. Formation of adenosine by ultra-violet irradiation of a solution of adenine and ribose. *Nature, Lond.*, **198**, 1199–1200.
Popper, K. R., 1965. *The Logic of Scientific Discovery*. Hutchinson, London.
Reines, F., 1966. Neutrino Astronomy. *Sci. Journ.*, **2**, 84–89.
Urey, H. C., 1952. *The Planets, their Origin and Development*. Yale University Press.
Wald, G., 1963. Phylogeny and ontogeny at the molecular level. In *Evolutionary Biochemistry* (A. I. Oparin, ed.), 12–51. Pergamon, Oxford.
Whitrow, G. J., 1961. *The Structures and Evolution of the Universe*. Hutchinson, London.

CHAPTER 2

Anfinsen, C. B., 1959. *The Molecular Basis of Evolution*. Wiley, New York.
Baker, J. R., 1948. The Cell-theory: a restatement, history, and critique. *Q. Jl microsc. Sci.*, **89**, 103–125; **90**, 87–108, 331; **93**, 157–190.
Belâr, K., 1926. Die Formwechsel der Protistenkerne: ein vergleichend-morphologische Studie. *Ergebn. Fortschr. Zool.*, **6**, 235–654.
Boyden, A., 1957. Are there any 'acellular animals'? *Science, N.Y.*, **125**, 155–156, 990.
Butler, J. A. V., 1959. *Inside the Living Cell*. Allen and Unwin, London.
Corliss, J. O., 1957. Concerning the 'Cellularity' or Acellularity of the Protozoa. *Science, N.Y.*, **125**, 988.
Davson, H. and J. F. Danielli, 1952. *The Permeability of Natural Membranes* (2nd ed.). Cambridge University Press, London.
Dillon, L. S., 1962. Comparative cytology and the evolution of life. *Evolution*, **16**, 102–117.
Dobell, C. C., 1911. The principles of protistology. *Arch. Protistenk.*, **23**, 269–310.
Gray, J., 1961. Quoted by Ramsay, J. A. in *The Cell and the Organism* (Ramsay, J. A. and V. B. Wigglesworth, eds.), p. 158. Cambridge University Press, London.
Grimstone, A. V., 1959. Cytology, homology, and phylogeny—a note on 'organic design'. *Am. Nat.*, **93**, 273–282.
Grimstone, A. V., 1961. Fine structure and morphogensis in Protozoa. *Biol. Rev.*, **36**, 97–150.
Hutner, S. H. and L. Provasoli, 1957. Concerning the 'Cellularity' or Acellularity of the Protozoa. *Science, N.Y.*, **125**, 989.
Minchin, E. A., 1915. The evolution of the cell. *Rep. Br. Ass. Advmt. Sci.*, **85**, 437–464.
Needham, J., 1934. *A History of Embryology*. Cambridge University Press, London.
Pantin, C. F. A., 1951. Organic design. *Advmt. Sci., Lond.*, **8**, 138–150.
Picken, L. E. R., 1960. *The Organization of Cells and other Organisms*. Clarendon Press, Oxford.

Russell, E. S., 1916. *Form and Function*. John Murray, London.
Waterman, T. H., 1961. Comparative physiology. In Waterman, **2**, 521–593.
Woodger, J. H., 1929. *Biological Principles, a Critical Study*. Kegan Paul, London.

CHAPTER 3

Allen, R. D., 1962. Amoeboid movement. In Brachet and Mirsky, **2**, 135–216.
Allen, R. D., 1962. Amoeboid movement. *Scient. Am.*, **206** (2), 112–122.
Bailey, K., 1956. Muscle proteins. *Br. med. Bull.*, **12**, 183–187.
Bovee, E. C., 1964. Morphological differences among pseudopodia of various small Amoebae and their functional significance. In *Primitive Motile Systems in Cell Biology* (Allen and Kamiya, eds.), 189–219. Academic Press, New York.
Bradfield, J. R. G., 1955. Fibre patterns in animal flagella and cilia. *Symp. Soc. exp. Biol.*, **9**, 306–334.
de Bruyn, P. P. H., 1947. Theories of amoeboid movement. *Q. Rev. Biol.*, **22**, 1–24.
Fawcett, D., 1961. Cilia and flagella. In Brachet and Mirsky, **2**, 212–297.
Gray, J., 1928. *Ciliary Movement*. Cambridge University Press, London.
Hanson, J. and J. Lowy, 1960. Structure and function of the contractile apparatus in the muscles of invertebrate animals. In Bourne, **1**, 265–335.
Huxley, H. E., 1956. Muscular contraction. *Endeavour*, **15**, 177–188.
Huxley, H. E., 1958. The contraction of muscle. *Scient. Am.*, **199** (5), 66–86.
Jahn, T. L. and E. C. Bovee, 1965. Protoplasmic movements and locomotion of Protozoa. In *Biochemistry and Physiology of Protozoa* (Hutner, S. H., ed.), **3**, 62–129.
Lowndes, A. G., 1943. The swimming of unicellular flagellate organisms. *Proc. zool. Soc. Lond. A*, **113**, 99–107.
Mast, S. O., 1926. Structure, movement, locomotion, and stimulation in *Amoeba*. *J. Morph.*, **41**, 347–425.
Mercer, E. H., 1959. An electron microscope study of *Amoeba proteus*. *Proc. R. Soc. B*, **150**, 216–232.
Noland, L. E., 1957. Protoplasmic streaming: a perennial puzzle. *J. Protozool.*, **4**, 1–6.
Pantin, C. F. A., 1923. On the physiology of amoeboid movement. *J. mar. biol. Ass. U.K.*, **13**, 24–69.
Pantin, C. F. A., 1956. Comparative physiology of muscle. *Br. med. Bull.*, **12**, 199–202.
Perry, S. V., 1960. Muscular contraction. In Florkin and Mason, **2**, 245–340.
Satir, P., 1961. Cilia. *Scient. Am.*, **204** (2), 108–116.
Sleigh, M. A., 1962. *The Biology of Cilia and Flagella*. Pergamon, Oxford.
Sleigh, M. A., 1964. Flagellar movements of the sessile flagellates *Actinomonas, Codonosiga, Monas,* and *Poteriodendron*. *Q. Jl microsc. Sci.*, **105**, 405–414.
Wichterman, R., 1953. *The Biology of Paramecium*. McGraw-Hill, New York.
Willmer, E. N., 1960. *Cytology and Evolution*. Academic Press, New York.
Wolpert, L., C. M. Thompson, and C. H. O'Neill, 1964. Studies on the isolated membrane and cytoplasm of *Amoeba proteus* in relation to Amoeboid movement. In *Primitive Motile Systems in Cell Biology* (Allen and Kamiya, eds.), 143–171. Academic Press, New York.

CHAPTER 4

Batham, E. J. and C. F. A. Pantin, 1950. Muscular and hydrostatic action in the sea-anemone *Metridium senile* (L.). *J. exp. Biol.*, **27**, 264–288.
Batham, E. J. and C. F. A. Pantin, 1951. The organization of the muscular system of *Metridium senile*. *Q. Jl microsc. Sci.*, **92**, 27–54.
Carlisle, D. B., 1961. Locomotory powers of adult ascidians. *Proc. zool. Soc. Lond.*, **136**, 141–146.

Chapman, G., 1953. Studies of the mesogloea of coelenterates 1. Histology and chemical properties. *Q. Jl microsc. Sci.*, **94**, 155–176.

Chapman, G., 1958. The hydrostatic skeleton in the invertebrates. *Biol. Rev.*, **33**, 338–371.

Chapman, D. M., C. F. A. Pantin, and E. A. Robson, 1962. Muscle in coelenterates. *Revue can. Biol.*, **21**, 267–278.

Clark, R. B., 1964. *Dynamics in Metazoan Evolution*. Clarendon Press, Oxford.

Harris, J. E. and H. D. Crofton, 1957. Structure and function in the nematodes: internal pressure and cuticular structure in *Ascaris*. *J. exp. Biol.*, **34**, 116–130.

Pantin, C. F. A., 1960. Diploblastic animals. *Proc. Linn. Soc. Lond.*, **171**, 1–14.

Robson, E. A., 1957. The structure and hydromechanics of the musculo-epithelium in *Metridium*. *Q. Jl microsc. Sci.*, **98**, 265–278.

CHAPTER 5

Barrington, E. J. W., 1965. *The Biology of Hemichordata and Protochordata*. Oliver and Boyd, Edinburgh.

Goodrich, E. S., 1945. The study of nephridia and genital ducts since 1895. *Q. Jl microsc. Sci.*, **86**, 113–392.

Harmer, S. F., 1930. Polyzoa. *Proc. Linn. Soc. London.*, *141st session*, 68–118.

Lemche, H. and K. G. Wingstrand, 1959. The anatomy of *Neopilina galatheae* Lemche, 1957. *Galathea Rep.*, *vol. 3*. Danish Science Press Ltd., Copenhagen.

Lissman, H. W., 1946. The mechanism of locomotion in gastropod molluscs, II. Kinetics. *J. exp. Biol.*, **22**, 37–50.

Morton, J. E., 1958. *Molluscs*. Hutchinson, London.

Smith, J. E., 1947. The mechanics and innervation of the starfish tube foot-ampulla system. *Phil. Trans. R. Soc. B*, **232**, 279–310.

CHAPTER 6

Chapman, G., 1950. Of the movement of worms. *J. exp. Biol.*, **27**, 29–39.

Gray, J., 1939. Studies in animal locomotion, VIII. The kinetics of locomotion of *Nereis diversicolor*. *J. exp. Biol.*, **16**, 9–17.

Gray, J. and H. W. Lissman, 1938. Studies in animal locomotion, VII. Locomotory reflexes in the earthworm. *J. exp. Biol.*, **15**, 506–517.

Smith, J. E., 1957. The nervous anatomy of the body segments of nereid polychaetes. *Phil. Trans. R. Soc. B*, **240**, 135–196.

Trueman, E. R., 1966. *Observations on the burrowing of Arenicola marina* (L.). *J. exp. Biol.*, **44**, 93–118.

Wells, G. P., 1950. Spontaneous activity cycles in polychaete worms. *Symp. Soc. exp. Biol.*, **4**, 127–142.

Wells, G. P., 1954. The mechanism of proboscis movement in *Arenicola*. *Q. Jl microsc. Sci.*, **95**, 251–270.

CHAPTER 7

Beament, J. W. L., 1954. Water transport in insects. *Symp. Soc. exp. Biol.*, **8**, 94–117.

Boettiger, E. G., 1957. The machinery of insect flight. In Scheer, 117–142.

Boettiger, E. G. and E. Furshpan, 1952. The mechanics of flight movements in Diptera. *Biol. Bull. mar. biol. Lab.*, *Woods Hole*, **102**, 200–211.

Chadwick, L. E., 1953. The motion of the wings. In Roeder, 577–614.

Chadwick, L. E., 1953. Aerodynamics and flight metabolism. *ibid.*, 615–636.

Chadwick, L. E., 1953. The flight muscles and their control. *ibid.*, 637–655.

Cloudsley-Thompson, J. L., 1958. *Spiders, Scorpions, Centipedes, and Mites*. Pergamon, Oxford.

Dennell, R., 1960. Integument and Exoskeleton. In Waterman, **1**, 449–472.

Evans, H. E., 1959. Some comments on the evolution of the Arthropoda. *Evolution*, **13**, 147–149.

Gilmour, D., 1961. *The Biochemistry of Insects*. Academic Press, New York.

Manton, S. M., 1950. The evolution of arthropodan locomotory appendages. Part 1: The locomotion of *Peripatus. J. Linn. Soc. (Zool.)*, **41**, 529–570.

Manton, S. M., 1952. Part 2: General introduction to the locomotory mechanisms of the Arthropoda. *ibid.*, **42**, 93–117.

Manton, S. M., 1952. Part 3: The locomotion of the Chilopoda and Pauropoda. *ibid.*, **42**, 118–167.

Manton, S. M., 1954. Part 4: The structure, habits, and evolution of the Diplopoda. *ibid.*, **42**, 299–368.

Manton, S. M., 1956. Part 5: The structure, habits, and evolution of the Pselaphognatha (Diplopoda). *ibid.*, **43**, 153–187.

Manton, S. M., 1958a. Part 6: Habits and evolution of the Lysiopetaloidea (Diplopoda), some principles of the leg design in Diplopoda and Chilopoda, and limb structure in Diplopoda. *ibid.*, **43**, 487–556.

Manton, S. M., 1958b. Habits of life and evolution of body design in Arthropoda. *ibid.*, **44**, 58–72.

Manton, S. M., 1960. Concerning head development in the arthropods. *Biol. Rev.*, **35**, 265–282.

Manton, S. M., 1961. Part 7: Functional requirements and body design in Colobognatha (Diplopoda), together with a comparative account of diplopod burrowing techniques, trunk musculature, and segmentation. *J. Linn. Soc. (Zool.)*, **44**, 383–461.

Manton, S. M., 1964. Mandibular mechanisms and the evolution of arthropods. *Phil. Trans. R. Soc. B*, **247**, 1–183.

Pringle, J. W. S., 1948. The gyroscopic mechanism of the halteres of Diptera. *Phil. Trans. R. Soc. B*, **233**, 347–384.

Pryor, M. G. M., 1962. Sclerotization. In Florkin and Mason, **IVB**, 371–396.

Richards, A. G., 1951. *The Integument of Arthropods*. University of Minnesota Press, Minneapolis.

Sharov, A. G., 1966. *Basic Arthropodan Stock*. Pergamon, Oxford.

Snodgrass, R. E., 1952. *A Textbook of Arthropod Anatomy*. Cornell University Press, Ithaca, New York.

Tiegs, O. W. and S. M. Manton, 1958. The evolution of the Arthropoda. *Biol. Rev.*, **33**, 255–337.

CHAPTER 8

Barrington, E. J. W., 1962. Digestive enzymes. In *Adv. Comp. Physiol. Biochem.* (Lowenstein, O., ed.), **1**, 1–65.

Chen, Y. T., 1950. Investigations of the biology of *Peranema trichophorum* (Euglenineae). *Q. Jl microsc. Sci.*, **91**, 279–308.

Corliss, J. O., 1959. Comments on the phylogeny and systematics of the Protozoa. *Syst. Zool.*, **8**, 169–190.

de Duve, C., 1963. The lysosome. *Scient. Am.*, **208** (5), 64–72.

Holter, H., 1959. Pinocytosis. *Int. Rev. Cytol.*, **8**, 481–504.

MacKinnon, D. M. and R. G. J. Hawes, 1961. *An Introduction to the Study of Protozoa*. Clarendon Press, Oxford.

Mast, S. O., 1942. The hydrogen ion concentrations of the contents of the food vacuoles and the cytoplasm in *Amoeba* and other phenomena concerning the food vacuoles. *Biol. Bull. mar. biol. Lab., Woods Hole*, **83**, 173–204.

Mast, S. O., 1947. The food vacuole in *Paramecium. ibid.*, **92**, 31–72.

Mercer, E. H., 1959. An electron microscope study of *Amoeba proteus. Proc. R. Soc. B*, **150**, 216–232.

CHAPTER 9

Bidder, G. P., 1923. The relation of the form of a sponge to its currents. *Q. Jl microsc. Sci.*, **67**, 293–323.

Hardy, Sir Alister, 1958. *The Open Sea: The World of Plankton.* Collins, London.

Jennings, J. B., 1957. Studies on feeding, digestion, and food storage in free-living flatworms. *Biol. Bull. mar. biol. Lab., Woods Hole*, **112**, 63–80.

Jennings, J. B., 1960. Observations on the nutrition of the Rhynchocoelan *Lineus ruber. ibid.*, **119**, 189–196.

Jennings, J. B., 1962. Further studies on feeding and digestion in triclad Turbellaria. *ibid.*, **123**, 571–581.

Pantin, C. F. A., 1942. The excitation of nematocysts. *J. exp. Biol.*, **19**, 294–310.

Picken, L. E. R. and R. J. Skaer, 1966. A review of researches on nematocysts. In Rees, 19–50.

Southward, A. J., 1955. Observations on the ciliary currents of the jelly-fish *Aurelia aurita* L. *J. mar. biol. Ass. U.K.*, **34**, 201–216.

van Weel, P. B., 1949. On the physiology of the tropical fresh-water sponge *Spongilla proliferens* Annand. 1: Ingestion, digestion, and excretion. *Physiologia comp. Oecol.*, **1**, 110–126.

Yonge, C. M., 1937. Evolution and adaptation in the digestive system of the Metazoa. *Biol. Rev.*, **12**, 87–115.

CHAPTER 10

Barrington, E. J. W., 1965. *The Biology of Hemichordata and Protochordata.* Oliver and Boyd, Edinburgh.

Bidder, A., 1950. Digestive mechanisms of European squids. *Q. Jl microsc. Sci.*, **91**, 1–43.

Cannon, H. G., 1933. On the feeding mechanism of the Branchiopoda. *Phil. Trans. R. Soc. B*, **222**, 267–352.

Dales, R. P., 1955. Feeding and digestion in terebellid polychaetes. *J. mar. biol. Ass. U.K.*, **34**, 55–79.

Graham, A., 1949. The molluscan stomach. *Trans. R. Soc. Edinb.*, **61**, 737–778.

Jørgensen, C. B., 1955. Quantitative aspects of filter feeding in invertebrates. *Biol. Rev.*, **30**, 391–454.

Jørgensen, C. B., 1966. *Biology of Suspension Feeding.* Pergamon, Oxford.

MacGinitie, C. E., 1939. The method of feeding of *Chaetopterus. Biol. Bull. mar. biol. Lab., Woods Hole*, **77**, 115–118.

Marshall, S. M. and A. P. Orr, 1955. *The Biology of a Marine Copepod.* Oliver and Boyd, Edinburgh.

Morton, J. E., 1960. The functions of the gut in ciliary feeders. *Biol. Rev.*, **35**, 92–140.

Nicol, E. A. T., 1930. The feeding mechanism, formation of the tube, and physiology of digestion in *Sabella pavonina. Trans. R. Soc. Edinb.*, **56**, 537–598.

Sutton, M. F., 1957. The feeding mechanism, functional morphology, and histology of the alimentary canal of *Terebella lapidaria. Proc. zool. Soc. Lond.*, **129**, 487–523.

Thomas, J. G., 1940. *Pomatoceros, Sabella, and Amphitrite. L. M. B. C. Mem. typ. Br. mar. Pl. Anim.*, **33**.

Yonge, C. M., 1926. Structure and physiology of the organs of feeding and digestion in *Ostrea edulis. J. mar. biol. Ass. U.K.*, **14**, 295–386.

Yonge, C. M., 1928. Feeding mechanisms in the invertebrates. *Biol. Rev.*, **3**, 21–76.

Yonge, C. M., 1932. The crystalline style of the Mollusca. *Sci. Prog., Lond.*, **26**, 643–653.

Yonge, C. M., 1937. Evolution and adaptation in the digestive system of the Metazoa. *Biol. Rev.*, **12**, 87–115.

Yonge, C. M., 1939. The protobranchiate Mollusca: a functional interpretation of their structure and evolution. *Phil. Trans. R. Soc. B*, **230**, 79–147.

CHAPTER 11

Fox, H. M., 1949. Blood pigments. *Endeavour*, **8**, 43–47.

Fox, H. M. and G. Vevers, 1960. *The Nature of Animal Colours.* Sidgwick and Jackson, London.

Gratzer, W. B. and A. C. Allison, 1960. Multiple haemoglobins. *Biol. Rev.*, **35**, 459–506.

Krogh, A., 1941. *Comparative Physiology of Respiratory Mechanisms.* Pennsylvania University Press, Philadelphia.

Manwell, C., 1960. Comparative physiology: blood pigments. *A. Rev. Physiol.*, **22**, 191–244.

Miller, P. L., 1960. Respiration in the desert locust. 1. The control of ventilation. *J. exp. Biol.*, **37**, 224–236.

Morton, J. E. and C. M. Yonge, 1964. Classification and structure of the Mollusca. In Wilbur and Yonge, **1**, 1–58.

Redfield, A. C., 1934. The haemocyanins. *Biol. Rev.*, **9**, 175–212.

Wells, G. P., 1950. Spontaneous activity cycles in polychaete worms. *Symp. Soc. exp. Biol.*, **4**, 127–142.

Wigglesworth, V. B., 1930. A theory of tracheal respiration in insects. *Proc. R. Soc. B*, **106**, 229–250.

Wigglesworth, V. B., 1935. The regulation of respiration in the flea, *Xenopsylla cheopsis Roths.* (Pulicidae). *ibid.*, **118**, 397–419.

Yonge, C. M., 1947. The pallial organs in the aspidobranch Gastropoda and their evolution throughout the Mollusca. *Phil. Trans. R. Soc. B*, **232**, 443–518.

CHAPTER 12

Bahl, K. N., 1947. Excretion in the Oligochaeta. *Biol. Rev.*, **22**, 109–147.

Bairati, A. and F. E. Lehmann, 1956. Structural and chemical properties of the contractile vacuole of *Amoeba proteus*. *Protoplasma*, **45**, 525–539.

Cohen, P. P. and G. W. Brown, 1960. Ammonia metabolism and urea biosynthesis. In Florkin and Mason, **2**, 161–244.

Delaunay, H., 1931. L'excrétion azotée des invertébrées. *Biol. Rev.*, **6**, 265–301.

Edney, E. B., 1954. Woodlice and the land habitat. *ibid.*, **29**, 185–219.

Edney, E. B., 1957. *The Water Relations of Terrestrial Arthropods.* Cambridge University Press, London.

Edney, E. B., 1960. Terrestrial adaptation. In Waterman, **1**, 367–393.

Goodrich, E. S., 1945. The study of nephridia and genital ducts since 1895. *Q. Jl microsc. Sci.*, **86**, 113–393.

Jepps, M., 1947. Contribution to the study of the sponges. *Proc. R. Soc. B*, **134**, 408–417.

Kitching, J. A., 1938. Contractile vacuoles. *Biol. Rev.*, **13**, 403–444.

Kitching, J. A., 1952. Contractile vacuoles. *Symp. Soc. exp. Biol.*, **6**, 145–165.

Laverack, M. S., 1963. *The Physiology of Earthworms.* Pergamon, Oxford.

Manton, S. M., 1937. Studies on the Onychophora. II: The feeding, digestion, excretion, and food storage of *Peripatopsis*. *Phil. Trans. R. Soc. B*, **227**, 411–464.

Martin, A. W., 1957. Recent advances in knowledge of invertebrate renal function. In Scheer, 247–276.

Martin, A. W., 1958. Comparative physiology (Excretion). *A. Rev. Physiol.*, **20**, 225–242.

Needham, J., 1938. Contributions of chemical physiology to the problem of reversibility in evolution. *Biol. Rev.*, **13**, 225–251.

Pantin, C. F. A., 1947. The nephridia of *Geonemertes dendyi*. *Q. Jl microsc. Sci.*, **88**, 15–25.

Parry, G., 1960. Excretion. In Waterman, **1**, 341–366.

Pitelka, D., 1963. *Electron-microscopic Structure of Protozoa.* Pergamon, Oxford.

Ramsay, J. A., 1961. The comparative physiology of renal function in invertebrates. In *The Cell and the Organism* (Ramsay, J. A. and V. B. Wigglesworth, eds.), 158–174. Cambridge University Press, London.

Wigglesworth, V. B., 1931. The physiology of excretion in a blood-sucking insect *Rhodnius prolixus* (Hemipter, Reduviidae). *J. exp. Biol.*, **8**, 411–451.

CHAPTER 13

A number of the references given in Chapter 12 are also relevant to this chapter.

Beadle, L. C., 1957. Osmotic and ionic regulation in aquatic animals. *A. Rev. Physiol.*, **19**, 329–358.

Kitching, J. A., 1954. Osmoregulation and ionic regulation in animals without kidneys. *Symp. Soc. exp. Biol.*, **8**, 63–75.

Krogh, A., 1939. *Osmotic Regulation in Aquatic Animals.* Cambridge University Press, London.

Lockwood, A. P. M., 1962. The osmoregulation of Crustacea. *Biol. Rev.*, **37**, 257–306.

Potts, W. T. W. and G. Parry, 1964. *Osmotic and Ionic Regulation in Animals.* Pergamon, Oxford.

Ramsay, J. A., 1949. The osmotic relations of the earthworm. *J. exp. Biol.*, **26**, 46–56, 65–75.

Ramsay, J. A., 1954. Movements of water and electrolytes in invertebrates. *Symp. Soc. exp. Biol.*, **8**, 1–15.

Robertson, J. D., 1957. Osmotic and ionic regulation in aquatic invertebrates. In Scheer, 229–246.

Robertson, J. D., 1960. Studies of the chemical composition of muscle tissue. *J. exp. Biol.*, **37**, 879–888.

Robertson, J. D., 1960. Osmotic and ionic regulation. In Waterman, **1**, 317–339.

Wigglesworth, V. B., 1933. The effect of salts on the anal gills of the mosquito larva. *J. exp. Biol.*, **10**, 1–15.

Wigglesworth, V. B., 1933. The function of the anal gills of the mosquito larva. *ibid.*, 16–26.

Wigglesworth, V. B., 1933. The adaptation of mosquito larvae to salt water. *ibid.*, 27–37.

Wigglesworth, V. B., 1938. The regulation of osmotic pressure and chloride concentration in the haemolymph of mosquito larvae. *J. exp. Biol.*, **15**, 235–247.

CHAPTER 14

Amoore, J. E., J. R. Johnstone, and M. Rubin, 1964. A stereochemical theory of odor. *Scient. Am.*, **210** (2), 42–49.

Bishop, G. H., 1956. The natural history of the nerve impulse. *Physiol. Rev.*, **36**, 376–399.

Bodian, D., 1962. The generalized vertebrate neurone. *Science, N.Y.*, **137**, 323–326.

Cohen, M. J. and S. Dijkgraaf, 1961. Mechanoreception. In Waterman, **2**, 65–108.

Davies, J. T., 1962. The mechanism of olfaction. *Symp. Soc. exp. Biol.*, **16**, 170–179.

Dethier, V. G., 1953. Chemoreception. In Roeder, 544–576.

Dethier, V. G., 1955. The physiology and the histology of the contact chemoreceptors of the blowfly. *Q. Rev. Biol.*, **30**, 348–371.

Dethier, V. G., 1962. Chemoreceptor mechanisms in insects. *Symp. Soc. exp. Biol.*, **16**, 180–196.

Dethier, V. G., 1963. *The Physiology of Insect Senses.* Methuen, London.

Hartline, H. K., H. G. Wagner, and E. F. MacNichol, 1952. The peripheral origin of nervous activity in the visual system. *Cold Spring Harb. Symp. quant. Biol.*, **17**, 125–141.

Lowenstein, O., 1962. Frontiers of knowledge in the study of sensory function. *Advmt. Sci., Lond.*, **19**, 222–235.

Waterman, T. H., 1961. Light, sensitivity, and vision. In Waterman, **2**, 1–64.

Wells, M. J., 1961. What the octopus makes of it; our world from another point of view. *Advmt. Sci., Lond.*, **17**, 461–471.

Wigglesworth, V. B., 1961. *The Principles of Insect Physiology* (5th ed.). Methuen, London.

Wulff, V. J., 1956. Physiology of the compound eye. *Physiol. Rev.*, **36**, 145–163.

Young, J. Z., 1960. The statocysts of *Octopus vulgaris*. *Proc. R. Soc. B*, **152**, 3–29.

Young, J. Z., 1961. Learning and discrimination in the octopus. *Biol. Rev.*, **36**, 32–96.

CHAPTER 15

Carthy, J. D., 1958. *An Introduction to the Behaviour of Invertebrates*. Allen and Unwin, London.

Evans, F. G. C., 1951. An analysis of the behaviour of *Lepidochitona cinereus* in response to certain physical features of the environment. *J. Anim. Ecol.*, **20**, 1–10.

Horridge, G. A., 1954. Observations on the nerve fibres of *Aurellia aurita*. *Q. Jl microsc. Sci.*, **95**, 85–92.

Horridge, G. A., 1956. The nervous system of the ephyra larva of *Aurellia aurita*. *ibid.*, **97**, 59–74.

Jones, W. Clifford, 1962. Is there a nervous system in sponges? *Biol. Rev.*, **37**, 1–50.

Knight-Jones, E. W., 1952. On the nervous system of *Saccoglossus cambrensis* (Enteropneusta). *Phil. Trans. R. Soc. B*, **236**, 315–354.

Pantin, C. F. A., 1950. Behaviour patterns in lower invertebrates. *Symp. Soc. exp. Biol.*, **4**, 175–195.

Pantin, C. F. A., 1952. The elementary nervous system. *Proc. R. Soc. B*, **140**, 147–168.

Parker, G. H., 1919. *The Elementary Nervous System*. Lippincott, Philadelphia.

Ross, D. M., 1960. The association between the hermit crab *Eupagurus bernhardhus* (L.) and the sea anemone *Calliactis parasitica* (Couch). *Proc. zool. Soc. Lond.*, **134**, 43–57.

Smith, J. E., 1937. On the nervous system of the starfish *Marthasterias glacialis* (L.). *Phil. Trans. R. Soc. B*, **227**, 111–173.

Smith, J. E., 1945. The role of the nervous system in some activities of starfishes. *Biol. Rev.*, **20**, 29–43.

Smith, J. E., 1946. The mechanics and innervation of the starfish tube foot-ampulla system. *Phil. Trans. R. Soc. B*, **232**, 279–310.

Smith, J. E., 1950. Some observations on the nervous mechanisms underlying the behaviour of starfishes. *Symp. Soc. exp. Biol.*, **4**, 196–220.

CHAPTER 16

Barnes, G. E., 1955. The behaviour of *Anodonta cygnea* L., and its neurophysiological basis. *J. exp. Biol.*, **32**, 158–174.

Boycott, B. B. and J. Z. Young, 1950. The comparative study of learning. *Symp. Soc. exp. Biol.*, **4**, 432–453.

Dethier, V. G., 1964. Microscopic brains. *Science, N.Y.*, **143**, 1138–1145.

Dorsett, D. A., 1964. The sensory and motor innervation of *Nereis*. *Proc. R. Soc. B*, **159**, 652–667.

Gray, J. and H. W. Lissman, 1938. Studies in animal locomotion. VII: Locomotory reflexes in the earthworm. *J. exp. Biol.*, **15**, 506–517.

Harker, J., 1960. Endocrine and nervous factors in insect circadian rhythm. *Cold Spring Harb. Symp. quant. Biol.*, **25**, 279–287.

Harker, J., 1964. *The Physiology of Diurnal Rhythms*. Cambridge University Press, London.

Jennings, H. S., 1923. *The Behaviour of Lower Organisms*. Columbia University Press, New York.

Mittelstaedt, H., 1957. Prey capture in mantids. In Scheer, 51–71.

Nicol, J. A. C., 1948. The giant axons of annelids. *Q. Rev. Biol.*, **23**, 291–323.

Smith, J. E., 1957. The nervous anatomy of the body segments of nereid polychaetes. *Phil. Trans. R. Soc. B*, **240**, 135–196.

Thorpe, W. H., 1963. *Learning and Instinct in Animals* (2nd ed.). Methuen, London.

Tinbergen, N., 1951. *The Study of Instinct*. Clarendon Press, Oxford.

Wells, M. J., 1962. *Brain and Behaviour in Cephalopods*. Heinemann, London.

Wiersma, C. A. G., 1961. Reflexes and the central nervous system. In Waterman, **2**, 241–279.

Young, J. Z., 1961. Learning and discrimination in the octopus. *Biol. Rev.*, **36**, 32–96.

Young, J. Z., 1964. *A Model of the Brain*. Clarendon Press, Oxford.

CHAPTER 17

Barrington, E. J. W., 1963. *An Introduction to General and Comparative Endocrinology*. Clarendon Press, Oxford.

Butler, C. G., 1954. *The World of the Honeybee*. Collins, London.

Carlisle, D. B. and F. G. W. Knowles, 1959. *Endocrine Control in Crustacea*. Cambridge University Press, London.

Charniaux-Cotton, H. and L. Kleinholz, 1964. Hormones in invertebrates other than insects. In *The Hormones* (Pincus et al., eds.), **4**, 135–198.

Clark, R., 1961. The origin and formation of the heteronereis. *Biol. Rev.*, **36**, 199–236.

Clark, R., 1965. Endocrinology and the reproductive biology of polychaetes. *Oceanogr. Mar. Biol. Ann. Rev.* (H. Barnes, ed.), **3**, 211–255. Allen and Unwin, London.

Galtsoff, P. S., 1961. Physiology of reproduction in molluscs. *Am. Zool.*, **1**, 273–289.

Gilbert, L. I., 1963. Hormones controlling reproduction and moulting in invertebrates. In *Comparative Endocrinology* (von Euler and Heller, eds.), **2**, 1–46.

Hauenschild, C., 1966. Der hormonale Einfluss des Gehirns auf die sexuelle Entwicklung bei dem Polychaeten *Platynereis dumerilii*. *Gen. Comp. Endocr.*, **6**, 26–73.

Jacobson, M. and M. Beroza, 1964. Insect attractants. *Scient. Am.*, **211** (2), 20–27.

Kleinholz, L. H., 1961. Pigmentary effectors. In Waterman, **2**, 133–169.

Knowles, F. G. W., 1963. The structure of neurosecretory systems in invertebrates. In *Comparative Endocrinology* (von Euler and Heller, eds.), **2**, 47–62.

Lucas, C. E., 1949. External metabolites and ecological adaptation. *Symp. Soc. exp. Biol.*, **3**, 336–356.

Treherne, J. and D. S. Smith, 1965. The metabolism of acetylcholine in the intact central nervous system of an insect (*Periplaneta americana* L.). *J. ex. Biol.*, **43**, 441–454.

Wells, M. J., 1960. Optic glands and the ovary of *Octopus*. *Symp. zool. Soc. Lond.*, **2**, 87–107.

Wells, M. J. and J. Wells, 1959. Hormonal control of sexual maturity in *Octopus*. *J. exp. Biol.*, **36**, 1–33.

Welsh, J. H., 1957. Neurohormones or transmitter agents. In Scheer, 161–171.

Welsh, J. H., 1961. Neurohumors and neurosecretion. In Waterman, **2**, 281–311.

Wigglesworth, V. B., 1936. The function of the corpus allatum in the growth and reproduction of *Rhodnius prolixus* (Hemiptera). *Q. Jl microsc. Sci.*, **79**, 91–121.

Wigglesworth, V. B., 1951. Hormones and the metamorphosis of insects. *Endeavour*, **10**, 22–26.

Wigglesworth, V. B., 1954. *The Physiology of Insect Metamorphosis*. Cambridge University Press, London.

Wigglesworth, V. B., 1964. The hormonal regulation of growth and reproduction in insects. *Adv. Insect Physiol.*, **2**, 247–336.

Williams, C. M., 1961. Insect Metamorphosis: an approach to the study of growth. In *Growth in Living Systems* (Zarrow, M. X., ed.), 313–320. Basic Books, New York.

Williams, C. M., 1952. The physiology of insect diapause. *Biol. Bull. mar. biol. Lab., Woods Hole*, **103**, 120–138.

CHAPTER 18

Beale, G. H., 1954. *The Genetics of Paramecium aurelia*. Cambridge University Press, London.

Berrill, N. J., 1928. Regeneration in the polychaete *Chaetopterus variopedatus*. *J. mar. biol. Ass. U.K.*, **15**, 151–158.

Carter, G. S., 1954. On Hadži's interpretations of phylogeny. *Syst. Zool.*, **4**, 163–167, 173.

Dalcq, A. M., 1938. *Form and Causality in Early Development*. Cambridge University Press, London.

Hadži, J., 1963. *The Evolution of the Metazoa*. Pergamon, Oxford.

Hand, Cadet, 1959. On the origin and phylogeny of the Coelenterates. *Syst. Zool.*, **8**, 191–202.

Hanson, E. D., 1958. On the origin of the Eumetazoa. *ibid.*, **7**, 16–47.

Hardy, A. C., 1953. On the origin of the Metazoa. *Q. Jl microsc. Sci.*, **94**, 441–443.

Harvey, L. A., 1961. Speculations on ancestry and evolution. *Sci. Prog., Lond.*, **49**, 111–121.

Jägersten, G., 1955. On the early phylogeny of the Metazoa. The bilaterogastrea theory. *Zool. Bidr. Upps.*, **30**, 321–354.

Jägersten, G., 1959. Further remarks on the early phylogeny of the Metazoa. *ibid.*, **33**, 79–108.

Mackinnon, D. L. and R. S. J. Hawes, 1961. *An Introduction to the Study of Protozoa*. Clarendon Press, Oxford.

Marcus, E., 1958. On the evolution of the animal phyla. *Q. Rev. Biol.*, **33**, 24–58.

Needham, A. E., 1964. *The Growth Process in Animals*. Pitman, London.

Pantin, C. F. A., 1960. Diploblastic animals. *Proc. Linn. Soc. Lond.*, **171**, 1–14.

Rees, W. J., 1966. The evolution of the hydrozoa. In Rees, 199–222.

Remane, A., 1963. The evolution of the Metazoa from colonial flagellates *vs.* plasmodial ciliates. In *The Lower Metazoa, Comparative Biology and Phylogeny* (Dougherty, E. C. et al., eds.), 78–90. University of California Press, Berkeley.

Russell, E. S., 1930. *The Interpretation of Development and Heredity: A Study in Biological Method*. Clarendon Press, Oxford.

Sonneborn, T. M., 1957. Breeding systems, reproductive methods, and species problems in Protozoa. In *The Species Problem* (E. Mayer, ed.), 155–324. A.A.A.S. Pub., Washington, D.C.

Wilson, E. B., 1892. Cell lineage of *Nereis*. *J. Morph.*, **6**, 361–480.

Waddington, C. H., 1956. *Principles of Embryology*. Allen and Unwin, London.

CHAPTER 19

Crofts, D. R., 1955. Muscle morphogenesis in primitive molluscs and its relation to torsion. *Proc. zool. Soc. Lond.*, **125**, 711–750.

Fell, H. B., 1948. Echinoderm embryology and the origin of chordates. *Biol. Rev.*, **23**, 81–107.

Garstang, W., 1928. Origin and evolution of larval forms. *Rep. Br. Ass. Advmt. Sci.*, *section D*, p. 77.

Garstang, W., 1929. The morphology of the Tunicata, and its bearings on the phylogeny of the chordata. *Q. Jl microsc. Sci.*, **72**, 51–187.

Garstang, W., 1951. *Larval Forms, and Other Zoological Verses*. Blackwell, Oxford.

Ghiselin, M. T., 1966. The adaptive significance of gastropod torsion. *Evolution*, **20**, 337–348.

Gurney, R., 1942. *Larvae of Decapod Crustacea*. Ray Society, London.

Hardy, Sir Alister, 1956. *The Open Sea: its Natural History*. **1**: *The World of Plankton*. Collins, London.

Knight-Jones, E. W. and D. J. Crisp, 1953. Gregariousness in barnacles in relation to the fouling of ships and to anti-fouling research. *Nature, Lond.*, **171**, 1109–1110.

Smith, J. E., 1953. The maintenance and spread of sea-shore faunas. *Advmt. Sci., Lond.*, **10**, 145–156.

Thorsen, G., 1946. *Reproduction and Larval Development of Danish Marine Bottom Invertebrates*. C. A. Reitzels Forlag, Copenhagen.

Wilson, D. P., 1932. On the mitraria larva of *Owenia fusiformis* Delle Chiaje. *Phil. Trans. R. Soc. B*, **221**, 231–334.

CHAPTER 20

Carpenter, K. E., 1928. *Life in Inland Waters*. Sidgwick and Jackson, London.

Knight-Jones, E. W., 1953. Laboratory experiments on gregariousness during settling in *Balanus balanoides* and other barnacles. *J. exp. Biol.*, **30**, 584–598.

Knight-Jones, E. W. and J. Moyse, 1961. Intraspecific competition in sedentary marine animals. *Symp. Soc. exp. Biol.*, **15**, 72–95.

Lucas, C. E., 1961. On the significance of external metabolites in ecology. *ibid.*, 190–206.

Mather, K., 1961. Competition and cooperation. *ibid.*, 264–281.

Needham, J., 1930. On the penetration of marine organisms into fresh water. *Biol. Zbl.*, **50**, 504–509.

Wilson, D. P., 1948a. The larval development of *Ophelia bicornis* Savigny. *J. mar. biol. Ass. U.K.*, **27**, 540–553.

Wilson, D. P., 1948b. The relation of the substratum to the metamorphosis of *Ophelia* larvae. *ibid.*, **27**, 723–760.

Wilson, D. P., 1952. On the influence of the nature of the substratum on the metamorphosis of the larvae of marine animals, especially the larvae of *Ophelia bicornis* Savigny. *Annls. Inst. océanogr., Monaco*, **27**, 49–156.

CHAPTER 21

Berrill, N. J., 1935. Studies in Tunicate development. Part IV: Asexual reproduction. *Phil. Trans. R. Soc. B*, **225**, 327–379.

Braverman, M. H. and R. G. Schrandt, 1966. Colony development of a polymorphic hydroid as a problem in pattern formation. In Rees, 169–198.

Butler, C. G., 1954. *The World of the Honeybee*. Collins, London.

Butler, C. G., R. K. Callow, and N. C. Johnston, 1962. The isolation and synthesis of queen substance, 9-oxydec-*trans*-2-enoic acid, a honeybee pheromone. *Proc. R. Soc. B*, **155**, 417–432.

Child, C. M., 1941. *Patterns and Problems of Development*. University of Chicago Press.

Harris, W. V., 1961. *Termites: Their Recognition and Control*. Longmans, London.

Lindauer, M., 1961. *Communication among Social Bees*. Harvard University Press, Cambridge, Mass.

Richards, O. W., 1953. *The Social Insects*. Macdonald, London.

von Frisch, K., 1950. *Bees—Their Vision, Chemical Senses, and Language*. Cornell University Press, Ithaca, New York.

von Frisch, K., 1954. *The Dancing Bees*. Collins, London.
von Frisch, K., 1962. Dialectics in the language of the bees. *Scient. Am.*, **207** (2), 79–87.

CHAPTER 22

Baer, J. G., 1951. *Ecology of Animal Parasites*. University of Illinois Press, Urbana.
Baerends, G. P., 1950. Specializations in organs and movements with a releasing function. *Symp. Soc. exp. Biol.*, **4**, 337–360.
Caullery, M., 1952. *Parasitism and Symbiosis*. Sidgwick and Jackson, London.
Dales, R. P., 1957. Commensalism. *Mem. geol. Soc. Am. 67*, vol. 1, 391–412.
Davenport, D., 1955. Specificity and behaviour in symbioses. *Q. Rev. Biol.*, **30**, 29–46.
Faurot, L., 1910. Étude sur les associations entre les Pagures et les Actinies: *Eupagurus prideauxi* Heller et *Adamsia palliata* Forbes, *Pagurus striatus* Latreille et *Sagartia parasitica* Gosse. *Archs Zool. ex. gen.*, Ser. 5, **5**, 421–486.
Faurot, L., 1932. Actinies et Pagures. Études de psychologie animale. *ibid.*, **74**, 139–154.
Gosse, P. H., 1857. On a new form of corynoid polypes. *Trans. Linn. Soc. Lond.*, **22**, 113–116.
Gosse, P. H., 1860. *A History of the British Sea-anemones and Corals*. Van Voorst, London.
Hand, C. and J. R. Hendrickson, 1950. A two-tentacled, commensal hydroid from California (Limnomedusae, Proboscidactyla). *Biol. Bull. mar. biol. Lab., Woods Hole*, **99**, 74–93.
Lees, A. D., 1948. The sensory physiology of the sheep tick, *Ixodes ricinus* L. *J. exp. Biol.*, **25**, 145–207.
Ross, D. M. and L. Sutton, 1961. The response of the sea-anemone *Calliactis parasitica* to shells of the hermit crab, *Pagurus bernhardus*. *Proc. R. Soc. B*, **155**, 266–281.
Welsh, J. H., 1930. Reversal of phototropism in a parasitic water mite. *Biol. Bull. mar. biol. Lab., Woods Hole*, **61**, 165–169.
Welsh, J. H., 1931. Specific influence of the host on the light responses of parasitic water mites. *ibid.*, **61**, 497–499.

CHAPTER 23

Barnett, A. J. G. and R. L. Reid, 1961. *Reactions in the Rumen*. Arnold, London.
Cleveland, L. R., 1926. Symbiosis among animals with special reference to termites and their intestinal flagellates. *Q. Rev. Biol.*, **1**, 51–60.
Darwin, C., 1851. *The Structure and Distribution of Coral Reefs* (2nd ed.). Smith Elder, London.
Goodey, T., 1951. *Soil and Fresh-water Nematodes*. Wiley, London.
Hopkins, S. H., 1957. Parasitism. *Mem. geol. Soc. Am. 67*, vol. 1, 413–428.
Keeble, F., 1910. *Plant-Animals, A Study in Symbiosis*. University of Cambridge Press, London.
Koestler, A., 1959. *The Sleepwalkers*. Hutchinson, London.
Llewellyn, J., 1965. The evolution of parasitic platyhelminths. In *Evolution of Parasites* (Third Symposium of the British Society for Parasitology), 47–78. Blackweil, Oxford.
Noble, E. R. and G. A. Noble, 1964. *Parasitology: The Biology of Animal Parasites* (2nd ed.). Lea and Febiger, Philadelphia.
Smyth, J. D., 1962. *Introduction to Animal Parasitology*. English Universities Press, London.
Wells, J. W., 1957. Coral reefs. *Mem. geol. Soc. Am. 67*, vol. 1, 609–631.

Yonge, C. M., 1936. Mode of life, feeding, digestion, and symbiosis with xooxan-thellae in the Tridacnidae. *Gt. Barrier Reef Exped. Sci. Rep.*, **1**, 283–321.

Yonge, C. M., 1944. Experimental analysis of the association between invertebrates and unicellular algae. *Biol. Rev.*, **19**, 68–80.

Yonge, C. M., 1951. The form of coral reefs. *Endeavour*, **10**, 136–144.

Yonge, C. M., 1958a. Darwin and coral reefs. In *A Century of Darwin* (Barnett, S.A., ed.), 245–266. Heinemann, London.

Yonge, C. M., 1958b. Ecology and physiology of reef-building corals. In *Perspectives in Marine Biology* (Buzzati-Traverso, A.A., ed.), 117–135. University of California Press, Berkeley.

Yonge, C. M., 1963. The biology of coral reefs. *Adv. mar. Biol.*, **1**, 209–260.

Index